D0329354

Fundamental Techniques in Virology

Contributors

SAMUEL BARON
J. MICHAEL BISHOP
ALFRED T. H. BURNESS
DAVID H. CARVER
LIONEL V. CRAWFORD
R. L. ERIKSON
KEI FUJINAGA
LANELLE G. GAFFORD
HAROLD S. GINSBERG
MARY C. GLICK
MAURICE GREEN
HANNA GREENBERG
KARL HABEL
JACOB C. HOLPER
M. S. HORWITZ
A. F. HOWATSON
KAZUTO KAJIWARA
ALBERT S. KAPLAN
EDWIN D. KILBOURNE
GEBHARD KOCH
HENRYK KUBINSKI
W. G. LAVER
IAN MACPHERSON
JACOB V. MAIZEL, JR.
PHILIP I. MARCUS
THOMAS C. MERIGAN
BERNARD MOSS
GERALD C. MUELLER
JOSEPH S. PAGANO
SHELDON PENMAN
ROBERT P. PERRY
E. R. PFEFFERKORN
LENNART PHILIPSON
MAGDALENA PIÑA
CHARLES C. RANDALL
ELLIOTT ROBBINS
LEON ROSEN
N. P. SALZMAN
M. D. SCHARFF
KLAUS SCHERRER
NATHALIE J. SCHMIDT
EDWIN D. SEBRING
AARON J. SHATKIN
GEORGE J. TODARO
PETER K. VOGT
LEONARD WARREN
MARGHERITA WILLEMS

Fundamental Techniques in Virology

Edited by

KARL HABEL
Department of Experimental Pathology
Scripps Clinic and Research Foundation
La Jolla, California

NORMAN P. SALZMAN
Chief of Laboratory for Biology of Viruses
National Institute of Allergy
and Infectious Diseases
Bethesda, Maryland

ACADEMIC PRESS New York and London 1969

ACADEMIC PRESS, INC.
111 Fifth Avenue, New York, New York 10003

United Kingdom Edition published by
ACADEMIC PRESS, INC. (LONDON) LTD.
Berkeley Square House, London W.1

LIBRARY OF CONGRESS CATALOG CARD NUMBER: 69-18338

PRINTED IN THE UNITED STATES OF AMERICA

List of Contributors

Numbers in parentheses indicate the pages on which the authors' contributions begin.

SAMUEL BARON (399), U. S. Department of Health, Education and Welfare, National Institutes of Health, Laboratory of Viral Diseases, Bethesda, Maryland

J. MICHAEL BISHOP* (131, 433), Laboratory of Biology of Viruses, National Institute of Allergy and Infectious Diseases, National Institutes of Health, Bethesda, Maryland

ALFRED T. H. BURNESS (94), Virus Research Unit, Medical Research Council Laboratories, Woodmansterne Road, Carshalton, Surrey, England

DAVID H. CARVER† (161), Department of Microbiology and Immunology, Albert Einstein College of Medicine, Bronx, New York

LIONEL V. CRAWFORD (75), Imperial Cancer Research Fund, Lincoln's Inn Fields, London, England

R. L. ERIKSON (451, 460), Department of Pathology, University of Colorado Medical School, Denver; Colorado

KEI FUJINAGA (467), Institute for Molecular Virology, Saint Louis University School of Medicine, Saint Louis, Missouri

LANELLE G. GAFFORD (483), Department of Microbiology, University of Mississippi School of Medicine, Jackson, Mississippi

HAROLD S. GINSBERG (390), Department of Microbiology, School of Medicine, University of Pennsylvania, Philadelphia, Pennsylvania

*Present address: Department of Microbiology, University of California, School of Medicine, San Francisco, California.

†Present address: Department of Pediatrics, Johns Hopkins School of Medicine, Baltimore, Maryland.

MARY C. GLICK (66), Department of Therapeutic Research, School of Medicine, University of Pennsylvania, Philadelphia, Pennsylvania

MAURICE GREEN (467), Institute for Molecular Virology, Saint Louis University School of Medicine, Saint Louis, Missouri

HANNA GREENBERG* (49), Massachusetts Institute of Technology, Cambridge, Massachusetts

KARL HABEL (288), Department of Experimental Pathology, Scripps Clinic and Research Foundation, La Jolla, California

JACOB C. HOLPER (3), Courtland Scientific Products Division, Abbott Laboratories, Los Angeles, California

M. S. HORWITZ(253, 297), Department of Cell Biology, Albert Einstein College of Medicine, Bronx, New York

A. F. HOWATSON (505), The Ontario Cancer Institute, Toronto, Canada

KAZUTO KAJIWARA (21), McArdle Laboratory for Cancer Research, University of Wisconsin, Madison, Wisconsin

ALBERT S. KAPLAN (487), Department of Microbiology, Research Laboratories, Albert Einstein Medical Center, Philadelphia, Pennsylvania

EDWIN D. KILBOURNE (146), Department of Microbiology, Mount Sinai School of Medicine of The City University of New York, New York, New York

GEBHARD KOCH† (131, 433), Heinrich Pette-Institut, Hamburg, Germany

HENRYK KUBINSKI (433), Department of Neurosurgery, University of Wisconsin, Madison, Wisconsin

W. G. LAVER (82, 371, 379), Department of Microbiology, John Curtin School of Medical Research, Australian National University, Canberra, Australia

IAN MACPHERSON (17, 212, 214), Imperial Cancer Research Fund, Lincoln's Inn Fields, London, England

*Present address: Sudbury Valley School, Framingham, Massachusetts.

†Present address: Institut für Mikrobiologie, Medizinische Hochschule Hannover, Hannover, Germany.

JACOB V. MAIZEL, JR. (334), Department of Cell Biology, Albert Einstein College of Medicine, Bronx, New York

PHILIP I. MARCUS* (161), Department of Microbiology and Immunology, Albert Einstein College of Medicine, Bronx, New York

THOMAS C. MERIGAN (363), Division of Infectious Diseases, Department of Medicine, Stanford University, Stanford, California

BERNARD MOSS (327), Laboratory of Biology of Viruses, National Institute of Allergy and Infectious Diseases, National Institutes of Health, Bethesda, Maryland

GERALD C. MUELLER (21), McArdle Laboratory for Cancer Research, University of Wisconsin, Madison, Wisconsin

JOSEPH S. PAGANO (184), Departments of Medicine and Bacteriology, University of North Carolina School of Medicine, Chapel Hill, North Carolina

SHELDON PENMAN (35, 49), Massachusetts Institute of Technology, Cambridge, Massachusetts

ROBERT P. PERRY (242), The Institute for Cancer Research, Philadelphia, Pennsylvania

E. R. PFEFFERKORN (87), Microbiology Department, Dartmouth Medical School, Hanover, New Hampshire

LENNART PHILIPSON (109), Department of Cell Biology, The Wallenberg Laboratory, University of Uppsala, Uppsala, Sweden

MAGDALENA PIÑA (467), Institute for Molecular Virology, Saint Louis University School of Medicine, Saint Louis, Missouri

CHARLES C. RANDALL (483), Department of Microbiology, University of Mississippi School of Medicine, Jackson, Mississippi

ELLIOTT ROBBINS (28), Department of Cell Biology, Albert Einstein College of Medicine, Bronx, New York

LEON ROSEN (276), Pacific Research Section, National Institute of Allergy and Infectious Diseases, National Institutes of Health, Honolulu, Hawaii

*Address after September 1969: Microbiology Section, University of Connecticut, Storrs, Connecticut.

N. P. SALZMAN (59, 327), Laboratory of Biology of Viruses, National Institute of Allergy and Infectious Diseases, National Institutes of Health, Bethesda, Maryland

M. D. SCHARFF (253, 297), Departments of Cell Biology and Medicine, Albert Einstein College of Medicine, Bronx, New York

KLAUS SCHERRER (413), Swiss Institute for Experimental Cancer Research, 1005 Lausanne, Switzerland

NATHALIE J. SCHMIDT (263), Viral and Rickettsial Disease Laboratory, California State Department of Public Health, Berkeley, California

EDWIN D. SEBRING (464), Laboratory of Biology of Viruses, National Institute of Allergy and Infectious Diseases, National Institutes of Health, Bethesda, Maryland

AARON J. SHATKIN* (231, 238, 496), Laboratory of Biology of Viruses, National Institute of Allergy and Infectious Diseases, National Institutes of Health, Bethesda, Maryland

GEORGE J. TODARO (220), Viral Carcinogenesis Branch, National Cancer Institute, National Institutes of Health, Public Health Service, Department of Health, Education, and Welfare, Bethesda, Maryland

PETER K. VOGT (198, 316), Department of Microbiology, University of Washington Medical School, Seattle, Washington

LEONARD WARREN (66), Department of Therapeutic Research, School of Medicine, University of Pennsylvania, Philadelphia, Pennsylvania

MARGHERITA WILLEMS† (49), Massachusetts Institute of Technology, Cambridge, Massachusetts

*Present address: Roche Institute of Molecular Biology, Nutley, New Jersey.

†Present address: Massachusetts General Hospital, Boston, Massachusetts.

Preface

Everyone in research repeatedly finds himself in a situation where in order to properly pursue his current work he is required to use a technique with which he has had no experience. The usual procedure is to search the literature or to impose on colleagues to get the details of what one hopes is the best method. To find a description of a technique published in a form in which each step can be followed is frequently difficult. In other cases, the researcher is faced with a number of descriptions for one procedure, each differing in some way from the others, making it impossible to evaluate which details are important and which method to try first.

To help overcome these difficulties in the field of basic virology, we have planned this volume in which scientists who are using a technique in their own laboratories will describe their currently used methods. We have asked the individual authors to describe each method in the way they might draw up a standard operating procedure for daily use at the laboratory bench, supplemented with some discussion of special problems at specific steps, the interpretation of results, the scope of the method, and the important alternative procedures. The aim has been not a complete treatise on a subject, but a practically oriented description and discussion of the method a particular researcher uses, presented in such a way that another scientist could follow it with a reasonable chance of success on the first try. The fact that in some sections several methods for the same procedure are presented with no preference indicated is evidence that there is no "best" technique.

Obviously it is not possible to include in a single volume all known techniques in such a broad area as basic virology, yet we felt a single volume was important if it was to be used at the bench. Therefore, we have tried to select the more significant, the more frequently used, perhaps the more recently developed techniques, and have omitted others. In certain areas of basic virology we have selected only a few procedures from the many possible ones as in electron microscopy and tissue culture. We have no description of virological methods in the avian embryo or in animals. Broadly based textbooks are available for these disciplines. References have been held to a minimum and, in general, include only key publications.

Finally, we recognize that any book on methods in biology published at this time is bound to need frequent revision as old techniques are improved and new ones developed. However, we have tried to include those which are most fundamental and, therefore, likely to be of continuing importance.

May, 1969

KARL HABEL
NORMAN P. SALZMAN

Contents

PART II
PREPARATION OF SUBCELLULAR FRACTIONS

PART III
CONCENTRATION AND PURIFICATION OF VIRUSES

PART IV
QUANTITATIVE ASSAY PROCEDURES FOR VIRUS INFECTIVITY

14. Plaque Assay for Poliovirus and Poliovirus Specific RNAs

J. MICHAEL BISHOP AND GEBHARD KOCH

15. Plaque Formation by Influenza Viruses

EDWIN D. KILBOURNE

16. Hemadsorption-Negative Plaque Test for Viruses Inducing Intrinsic Interference

PHILIP I. MARCUS AND DAVID H. CARVER

17. Assay of Infectious DNA

JOSEPH S. PAGANO

18. Focus Assay of Rous Sarcoma Virus

PETER K. VOGT

19. Clonal Analysis of Virus-Induced Cell Transformation

IAN MACPHERSON

20. Agar Suspension Culture for Quantitation of Transformed Cells

IAN MACPHERSON

21. Transformation Assay Using Cell Line 3T3

GEORGE J. TODARO

PART V

QUANTITATIVE PROCEDURES FOR ASSAY OF RNA, DNA, AND PROTEIN

22. Colorimetric Reactions for DNA, RNA, and Protein Determinations

AARON J. SHATKIN

23. Estimation of RNA, DNA, and Protein by the Use of Isotopic Precursors Followed by Chemical Fractionation

AARON J. SHATKIN

24. Autoradiography of Cultured Cells

ROBERT P. PERRY

PART VI
PROTEIN ANALYSIS

25. The Production of Antiserum Against Viral Antigens

M. S. HORWITZ AND M. D. SCHARFF

26. Complement Fixation Technique for Assay of Viral Antigens and Antibodies

NATHALIE J. SCHMIDT

27. Hemagglutination with Animal Viruses

LEON ROSEN

28. Virus Neutralization Test

KARL HABEL

34. Peptide Mapping of Viral Proteins

W. G. LAVER

35. N-Terminal Amino Acid Analysis of Viral Proteins

W. G. LAVER

36. Adsorption Chromatography for Isolation of Viral Proteins: The Use of Substituted Celluloses and Calcium Phosphate

HAROLD S. GINSBERG

37. Interferon: Production, Assay, and Characterization

SAMUEL BARON

PART VII
RNA ANALYSES

38. Isolation and Sucrose Gradient Analysis of RNA

KLAUS SCHERRER

PART VIII
DNA ANALYSES

44. Extraction of High Molecular Weight Viral DNA

CHARLES C. RANDALL AND LANELLE G. GAFFORD

45. Isopycnic Banding of Viral DNA in Cesium Chloride

ALBERT S. KAPLAN

46. Base Composition Analysis of DNA

AARON J. SHATKIN

PART IX
ELECTRON MICROSCOPIC PROCEDURES

47. Electron Microscopic Producres in Virology

A. F. HOWATSON

Fundamental Techniques in Virology

I. Tissue Culture Procedures

1. Monolayer and Suspension Cell Cultures

Jacob C. Holper

Courtland Scientific Products Division
Abbott Laboratories
Los Angeles, California

I. Introduction

The utilization of cells cultivated *in vitro* has rapidly evolved as a common modality for study of animal viruses. This change, from the use of a whole animal or embryonate chicken eggs, has been due to simplification of tissue culture techniques, availability of commercially prepared media and cells, broadness of cell types, and resultant broad spectrum of virus susceptibility.

This report will include a review of current tissue culture methods in our laboratories. Very thorough reviews of general tissue culture techniques can be found in several excellent publications (Melnick, 1956; Merchant, 1960; Parker, 1961; Paul, 1965; Penso and Balducci, 1963; Schmidt, 1964).

II. Primary Cells

A. Source of Tissue

The methods used to obtain tissue free from microorganisms can be separated into (a) isolation of animals before use and (b) maintenance of sterile procedures during handling of the tissue. Isolation of individual animals is recommended for a period of no less than 3 to 6 months prior to use where feasible. Only those animals remaining in good health during the quarantine period should be used. During this time, the animals may be tested for mycoplasma, salmonella, leucosis viruses, and tuberculosis, as well as other viruses or bacteria endogenous to the specific host (Public Health Service Regulations, 1967). Serological tests are sometimes used to detect simian agents such as SV5 and SV40 (Stiles *et al.*, 1966). These workers report a good correlation between positive serology to SV5 and SV40 and the presence of these agents in subsequently cultured cells from the test animals. Bacteriological and parasitological tests should be carried out on the isolated tissue (Culbertson *et al.*, 1958; Jahnes *et al.*, 1957; Lundholm *et al.*, 1959; Prier and LeBeau, 1958). These precautionary measures are especially important when cell cultures are a source of viral vaccines.

Embryonic or very young animals are usually the best source of cells for culture because of greater success in culturing and minimal risk of endogenous agents in younger tissue. Marcus (1965) reported that young dogs provided a higher percentage of positive cell cultures than older animals. In over 5 years experience in culturing very young bovine kidney tissues in our laboratories, we have isolated only two agents that appeared to be from the tissue and have never had a failure in culturing cells.

B. Collection of Tissue

Maintenance of aseptic techniques and control of contaminants from the environment must be practiced in all phases of tissue culture work. The tissue to be cultured is aseptically removed from the animal and should be used only if free of any macroscopic lesions. Normal tissue is placed in a sterile container containing a medium composed of 0.5% lactalbumin enzymatic hydrolysate (LH), 4 or 5% heated fetal calf serum, and the antibiotics neomycin (140 μ/ml), polymyxin B (100 μ/ml), mycostatin (100 μ/ml), erythromycin (100 μ/ml), and tetracycline (15 μg/ml) in Hank's salt solution. Eagle's basal medium (EBME) and 10% heated fetal calf serum may be substituted for the LH and serum portion of the above medium.

C. Processing of Tissue

The tissue must be cleansed of fat, blood, connective, and other unwanted tissue (such as the capsule that surrounds the kidney). The tissue is then minced and washed again before dispersing the cells with trypsin (Dulbecco and Vogt, 1954). For cell extraction and dispersion, a variety of containers may be used (Melnick *et al.*, 1955; Youngner, 1954). One example is the fluted Erlenmeyer flask, which is relatively simple and inexpensive. We have used the following cell-to-container size relationship with bovine kidney: one kidney to 400 ml Erlenmeyer, 2 kidneys to 750 ml Erlenmeyer, and 3-6 kidneys to 2000 ml Erlenmeyer. Both the overnight and repeated extraction processes are used in our laboratories with good results.

1. Repeated Extraction Process

In this procedure, the minced tissue is first washed to remove as much unwanted tissue as possible before extraction with trypsin. A measured amount of tissue is placed in the dispersing flask, covered with a wash medium such as phosphate-buffered saline (PBS), stirred with a magnetic device, and extracted 6-12 times until the supernate fluids are free of blood, fat, etc. Warmed 0.25% trypsin is added, stirred, and the remaining, unwanted tissue removed by decantation. The normal tissue is then ready for enzymatic dispersion. Trypsin (0.25%) is then added (2-3 parts trypsin to 1 part tissue; e.g., to 100 gm of tissue, add 200-300 ml of trypsin) and stirred at 37°C for about 1 hour. After the tissue has settled, the supernatant is strained through several layers of cheesecloth into a sterile collecting flask. The strained cells are centrifuged at 600 rpm for 10 minutes and resuspended in an appropriate growth medium. The extraction steps are repeated on undigested tissue clumps until digestion is complete. The centrifuged cells are pooled and spun at 600 rpm for 5 minutes in calibrated centrifuge tubes.

2. Overnight Trypsinization

For overnight processing (Bodian, 1956) the fragmented tissue is briefly washed in cold PBS- trypsin solution to remove fat and waste before stirring at 4°C overnight in trypsin solution. The dispersed cells are then filtered through cheesecloth (to remove clump and connective tissue) into growth medium, washed by centrifugation at low speed, and diluted on the basis of packed cell volume (PCV) in growth medium for planting.

After removal from an animal, tissue may be held up to 4 days before processing if the fragments are kept at 28°C under rapid, constant agitation in a medium containing 0.5% LH and 2% calf serum and antibiotics. Following these periods of holding, cells can be readily extracted with trypsin at 35°C.

Approximately one to 1.5 ml of PCV may be obtained from an average size monkey kidney by overnight or repeated extraction process.

Yields of bovine kidney cells range from 25 to 35 ml of PCV per kidney or 50 ml of PCV per 100 gm of cortical tissue (Patty, 1965).

3. *Processing Avian Tissue*

Chicken or duck embryo tissue is processed by methods generally similar to the continuous extraction procedures described above, except that a briefer period of extraction is used because of the more rapid cell dispersion that occurs with avian tissue. Decapitated embryos are macerated through a 20–50 ml syringe into a trypsinizing flask. After washing the cells with phosphate-buffered saline and removing unwanted connective tissue and debris, the cells are extracted with trypsin and dispersed cells collected by centrifugation as in the continuous process until the embryo tissue is completely digested. Direct cell counts are usually made on extracted duck embryo or chick embryo cells and planted in growth medium at levels of 300,000 and 500,000 cells/ml, respectively. Monolayers in tubes or bottles should be obtained within 48 to 72 hours at 37°C.

D. Cell Planting

Following extraction of cells from the specific organ or whole embryo, the cells are diluted to a specified concentration in growth medium (GM). The number of viable cells may be determined by direct counting in a hemocytometer or electronic counter, or estimated on basis of nuclei count. In addition, cell count may be estimated on the basis of packed cell volume. In the latter procedure, the dispersed cells are centrifuged at a constant gravitational force in a graduated container. A ratio of cell count to packed cell volume can be developed or planting efficiency determined on the basis of experimental determinations at various dilutions of PCV. Primary cells are usually diluted to a PCV of 1:200 to 1:600 for planting. In general, these dilutions represent a final concentration of approximately 400,000-800,000 cells/ml.

E. Containers Used for Monolayer Cultures

The containers generally used for planting primary cells are made of glass or plastic. The costly and difficult problems of glassware washing have been eliminated or minimized by the use of disposable glass tubes and bottles. However, if Pyrex or other permanent glassware is to be used, it must be thoroughly washed and carefully rinsed before use.

Various sizes and shapes of glass and plastic containers are used in tissue culture laboratories depending on specific needs. The containers, after planting, may be incubated in a stationary position or on a roller or rocker apparatus. Closed systems normally employ a bicarbonate buffer system, whereas open systems utilize an incubator flooded with 5% CO_2 in air.

We have recently introduced an apparatus for mass cultivation of monolayer cultures (Weiss and Schleicher, 1968; Schleicher and Weiss, 1968). This equipment employs a multiple tier structure in a closed system. The evolution of this equipment was originally based on the simple observation that the amount of virus produced in a cell culture was a function of the amount of cells in the container. The basic structure of this multisurface mass scale tissue culture propagator is shown in Fig. 1. Units ranging in size up to 200 liters consist of an enclosed vessel containing a multiplicity of separated glass plates or discs upon which the cells attach and proliferate. Means for mixing and aeration of the medium are provided. Sample ports facilitate the addition of cultures and media, withdrawal of samples, washing of cell monolayers, and harvesting of cells and cell products. Various types of cells have been grown in the mass propagator including calf kidney, HDCS-WI-38, neonate human foreskin, BHK 21, and mouse liver, CCL 1. The primary advantages of this system over the bottle method are decreased bacterial and pleuropneumonia-like organism (PPLO) contamination rates, less chance for cross contamination of cells, simplicity of handling, and resultant cost advantages.

F. Media

Media used for growth of tissue cells may be divided into growth medium and maintenance medium (MM). The GM for primary cultures usually contains an animal serum. Calf or fetal calf serum is used extensively in concentrations varying from 2 to 20%, depending on the cell system and other media components employed. Horse, monkey, sheep, and rabbit sera have also been used. Various tissue extracts (Enders *et al.*, 1949; Enders and Peebles, 1954) have been replaced by synthetic media such as 199 of Morgan *et al.* (1950) or Eagle (1959) in a balanced salt solution (Hanks and Wallace, 1949; Earle, 1943) using sodium bicarbonate to provide a CO_2 buffer system. Natural products such as lactalbumin hydrolysate are used extensively (Melnick, 1955) as a substitute for defined media.

Dried, blended media were found by Swim and Parker (1958), Greene *et al.* (1965), and Hayflick *et al.* (1964) to have advantages of

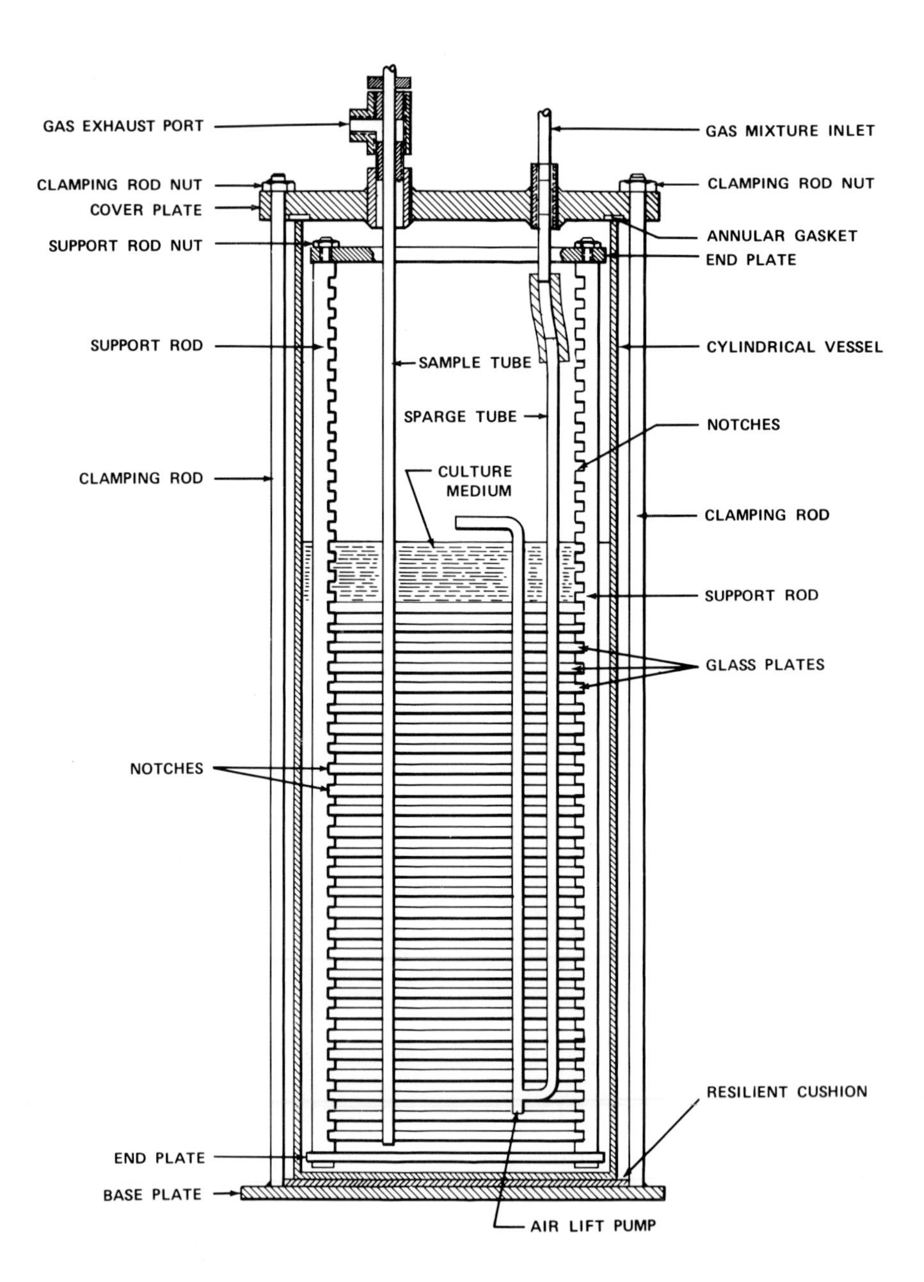

FIG. 1. Diagram of multisurface mass scale tissue culture propagator.

reproducibility, stability, and reduced cost over preparations of liquid media, since larger batches of the dried media can be prepared and held for long periods of time before use.

Maintenance medium most frequently used for primary cultures are 199 or EBME or combinations of the above, usually without sera. However, sera may be necessary for maintenance of certain cells for long periods of time. Antibiotics are generally added to both GM and MM just prior to use.

Media sterilization is generally accomplished by autoclaving stable constituents and filtering unstable substances. Filtration through asbestos filters should be avoided owing to release of toxic components from the filter (House, 1964). Cellulose filters have been generally acceptable. Ethylene oxide has been reported useful for sterilization of media (Brown and Fuerst, 1963).

III. Diploid Cell Cultures

A. Source of Cells

Tissues from animals and man have been reported as good sources of diploid cells. Puck *et al.* (1957, 1958) and Swim and Parker (1957) were the first to report that animal and human cells could be maintained in the laboratory without alteration of morphological or cultural characteristics. Fresh tissue has proved to be the best source of cells, but good results have been obtained from tissue removed from the whole animal and held for hours at low temperatures (Hayflick and Moorhead, 1961). Adult (Puck *et al.* 1957, 1958) and embryonic tissue (Hayflick and Moorhead, 1961), as well as malignant tissues (Ferguson and Wansbrough, 1962), have yielded diploid cells. Human diploid cell strains (HDCS) have been derived from lung, skin, kidney, heart (Hayflick and Moorhead, 1961; Miles, 1964), and thyroid tissue (Miles, 1964). Human amnion has not been a good source of HDCS (Miles, 1964), and Zitcer and Dunnebacke (1957) indicated that chromosomal changes appear fairly frequently in cells cultivated continuously from human amnion. Kalk and Hetrick (1965) have isolated diploid cell strains with normal characteristics from bovine lymph nodes.

B. Cell Planting

Both fragments and trypsin dispersed cells have been used successfully for originating diploid cell growth. The size of the container used for planting the original tissue is usually determined by the amount of tissue available. For example, Hayflick and Moorhead (1961) reported that they have usually dispersed lung fragments from one 3-month-old human fetus into four Blake bottles. Growth medium is added, and incubation is at 37°C until visible growth is evident. Cells are then fed and reincubated until a confluent sheet is formed. This requires about 10 days. The cells may then be removed from the glass surface with trypsin, aspirated, split 2:1 in fresh GM and subcultured in new bottles. Four-to-one splits are also used in some laboratories.

The multiplying cells show contact inhibition, and, therefore, a monolayer will be obtained under routine conditions. Kruse and Miedema (1965), however, report that the contact inhibition can be overcome by regular perfusion of growing cells, and as many as 17 layers of cells have been produced in their special perfusion apparatus.

Perhaps the most critical facets of handling HDCS relate to the need for subculturing on a regular basis following each 3–4 day incubation (Hayflick and Moorhead, 1961; Chagnon and Pavilanis, 1965) and thorough aspiration to break up clumps of cells. Under such conditions, the HDCS are considered useful for virus vaccine production through the first 30 passages (Minutes of Meeting, 1966; Holper *et al.*, 1963). The normal life span of HDCS is generally reported (Hayflick and Moorhead, 1961) to be approximately 50 passages, although other investigators report a much more limited growth potential of HDCS (Miles, 1964). Prior to the time the cells begin to lose their capacity to multiply, they will generally sheet out within 3 to 4 days following a 2:1 split. In subsequent passages, the cells multiply more slowly and, therefore, are not ready for splitting until some time later.

Although Hayflick and Moorhead (1961) reported the HDCS to be generally free of PPLO, we have found many lots of WI-38 cells contaminated with such organisms. Occasionally, we have been able to eliminate PPLO by repeated treatment of cultures with combinations of antibiotics, including erythromycin, tylosin, tetracycline, and chloramphenicol. However, no one specific treatment appears to be effective in curing infected cells. Once free of PPLO, constant care must be taken to keep these organisms from recontaminating the cultures. We have found that elimination of mouth pipetting, and the use of sterile face, head, and body coverings have aided in decreasing the incidence of reinfection of WI-38 cells with PPLO.

Cell stocks of HDCS may be frozen at any time during the rapid growth phase and held indefinitely in liquid nitrogen. Addition of 1.5 to 2.0×10^6 cells to 10% glycerine in GM, followed by slow freezing, has generally been a satisfactory procedure (Hayflick and Moorhead,

1961). The cells are rapidly thawed when they are to be used. The cells retain their normality in terms of chromosome analysis, morphology, virus spectrum, etc.

C. Media

Eagle's basal medium (Eagle, 1959) with 10% unheated calf serum has been used almost exclusively for growth of WI-38 cells (Hayflick and Moorhead, 1961; Holper *et al.*, 1963). Hozinski *et al.*, (1964) have isolated a HDCS from human lung with a medium containing EBME with 0.5% LH. Jacobs (1966) has found that only the amino acids L-cystine and L-glutamine were essential to growth of WI-38 cells, exclusive of other amino acids. In addition, galactose could be substituted for glucose to produce a more stable pH control in the absence of a CO_2 buffer system. Ferguson and Wansbrough (1962) have used 199 with 5% fetal calf serum with good results. Rappaport *et al.* (1965) reported success in culturing diploid cells with a medium composed of EBME 1X, LH 30%, 10% cow serum in Hank's salt solution.

IV. Continuous Cell Lines

A. Monolayer Cultures

Whereas the diploid cell strains have a finite life span, cell lines can be cultured indefinitely. The basic techniques, however, for passage of cell strains and cell types are similar. No significant differences in nutritional requirements between diploid cell strains and cell types have been reported (Eagle, 1963). However, cell types can usually be grown in suspension, but this has not been accomplished with cell strains.

Cell lines commonly in use today include HeLa, KB, kidney, and amnion cells originally derived from man (Gey *et al.*, 1952; Eagle, 1955; Chang, 1954), monkey kidney lines from African green monkeys (Hopps *et al.*, 1963), rhesus monkeys (Hull *et al.*, 1962; Chapin and Dubes, 1964), and bovine kidney cells (Madin and Darby, 1958). These cells readily multiply with growth media such as EBME (Eagle, 1959) supplemented with 10% fetal calf serum to form confluent monolayers on glass surfaces. Satisfactory growth of most continuous cell lines can be achieved with complete synthetic media (Evans *et al.*, 1964). For splitting cultures, the cells may be removed from glass with 0.25% trypsin, divided from 4:1 to 10:1 in growth media and subcultured. The most critical step in processing cell lines is the uniform suspension of cells after they are removed from the glass surface. Equable suspension may be obtained by repeated pipette aspiration.

B. Suspension Cultures

Growth in suspension can be readily achieved with most continuous cell lines (Moore and Ulrich, 1965). Various containers are used for suspension cultures including spinners (Cherry and Hull, 1956; McLimans *et al.*, 1957), rotary shakers (Earle *et al.*, 1956), fermentors (McLimans *et al.*, 1957; Ziegler *et al.*, 1958; Giardinello *et al.*, 1958), cytostats (Bjorklund *et al.*, 1961), chemostats (Cohen and Eagle, 1961), vibromixers (Ulrich and Moore, 1965), and cytogenerators (Graff and McCarty, 1957). In all cases, the cells are kept in suspension by some form of agitation. Cohen and Eagle (1961) and Cooper *et al.* (1959), using a continuous flow apparatus (chemostat), noted that with a continuous slow addition of fresh medium, static growth could be maintained. A nondialyzable substance sometimes appeared in the medium which inhibited cell growth. Thus, the limiting factor in growth of this type of suspended cell culture was not a lack of cell nutrients. Cells may require a lag period on initial transfer from monolayer growth on glass to suspension culture. However, they then (usually) rapidly adapt to suspended growth and do not show a lag phase when continuously grown in suspension. The morphologic characteristics of cell growth vary with the specific cell, ranging from single cells to aggregates of cells (Bryant *et al.*, 1958).

Growth has been reported in stainless steel containers (Ziegler *et al.*, 1958). The use of antifoam agents (Giardinello *et al.*, 1958) may improve growth rates of some cells. Automatic, constant pH control aids in production of optimal cell growth (Ziegler *et al.*, 1958). For L cells, the maximum population densities were obtained in a pH range of 6.8-7.5 (Pirt and Callow, 1964). Phosphate buffers have been used to replace CO_2 buffer systems with L and HeLa cells (Ziegler *et al.*, 1958). Baby hamster kidney cells, strain 21/135, grown in a simple continuously stirred apparatus, planted at cell concentration of 2×10^5 cells/ml, reached maximum growth of 2×10^6 cells/ml in approximately 4 days.

Cells grown in suspension can usually be grown in monolayers on glass. Many laboratories, therefore, use a suspended culture technique for maintenance of cells and draw off cells as needed for bottles or tubes.

At time of maximum growth one-half to two-thirds of the suspension is harvested and replaced by GM.

V. Cell Cloning

Cell cloning procedures currently in use generally rely on plating of the specific cell at limiting dilutions. These techniques have recently seen renewed interest because of a more rapid proliferation of transformed cells than occurs with normal cells (MacPherson and Montagnier, 1964; Trager and Rubin, 1966).

An excellent review of earlier cloning techniques can be found in the article by Sanford *et al.* (1961). Sanford *et al.* (1961) also described an improved capillary tube method for cloning. The cells are suspended and clumps broken up by aspiration. Although most workers use trypsin for suspension, Sanford feels that this enzyme should be avoided because of its damaging effect on cells. Individual dispersed cells are taken up into a capillary tube through which they may be checked microscopically. Areas in which individual cells are found can be broken off and placed in an appropriate medium for growth. In this procedure, there can be little doubt that the evolving cells were derived from an individual cell.

Improvements in tissue culture technology, such as standardized growth medium (Ham, 1965) and methods of cleaning glassware, have also permitted the growth of individual cells by simple limiting dilution procedures. For example, Puck *et al.* (1956) used very dilute suspensions of HeLa cells and merely let the cells remain undisturbed until colonies formed. Puck *et al.* (1955) also introduced the feeder–layer procedure, employing a layer of X-irradiated cells onto which is planted a diluted suspension of cells to be cloned. With both the capillary procedure and the dilution-plating (on glass) method, the cells are allowed to grow into a colony and then transferred to another container for further growth. The transfer may be accomplished by placing a cylinder (previously coated with silicone) over the colony to separate the colony from others in the dish, adding trypsin to release the cells, and transferring the cells to another dish with appropriate GM. Freeman *et al.* (1964) and Martin and Tuan (1966) used the dilution-plating procedure but plated the cells into a petri dish containing cover slips. Cover slips with individual colonies could then be readily removed to another container for further subculturing.

Microscopic observation is the only way to insure that clones are derived from individual cells. This can be readily accomplished only with the capillary method. With all methods, care must be taken in handling the cells because of their fragility. Cloning efficiency varies considerably depending on the type of cell and the investigator. In general, the percentage of subcultured cells successfully cloned under ideal conditions has varied from 5 to 75% (Sanford *et al.* 1961; Ham, 1965; Puck *et al.* 1956). Plating efficiency of primary cultured cells is much less than with passaged cells or cell lines (Pious *et al.*, 1964).

REFERENCES

Björklund, B., Björklund, V., and Paulsson, J. E. (1961). *Proc. Soc. Exptl. Biol. Med.* **108**, 385.

Bodian, D. (1956). *Virology* **2**, 575.

Brown, B. L., and Fuerst, R. (1963). *Science* **142**, 1654.

Bryant, J. C., Schilling, E. L., and Earle, W. R. (1958). *J. Natl. Cancer Inst.* **21**, 331.

Chagnon, A., and Pavilanis, V. (1965). *Rev. Can. Biol.* **24**, 35.

Chang, R. S. (1954). *Proc. Soc. Exptl. Biol. Med.* **87**, 440.

Chapin, M., and Dubes, G. R. (1964). *Proc. Soc. Exptl. Biol. Med.* **115**, 965.

Cherry, W. R., and Hull, R. N. (1956). *Abst. Tissue Culture Assoc. Meeting, Milwaukee, Wisconsin.*

Cohen, E. P., and Eagle, H. (1961). *Proc. Soc. Exptl. Biol. Med.* **113**, 467.

Cooper, P. D., Wilson, J. N., and Burt, A. M. (1959). *J. Gen. Microbiol.* **21**, 702.

Culbertson, G. G., Smith, J. W., and Minner, R. (1958). *Science* **127**, 1506.

Dulbecco, R., and Vogt, M. (1954). *J. Exptl. Med.* **99**, 167.

Eagle, H. (1955). *Proc. Soc. Exptl. Biol. Med.* **89**, 362.

Eagle, H. (1959). *Science* **130**, 432.

Eagle, H. (1963). *Proc. Symp. Characterization Uses Human Diploid Cell Strains, Opatija, 1962* p. 143. Inst. Immunol, Zagreb.

Earle, W. R. (1943). *J. Natl. Cancer Inst.* **4**, 165.

Earle, W. R., Bryant, J. C., Schilling, E. L., and Evans, V. J. (1956). *Ann. N.Y. Acad. Sci.* **63**, 666.

Enders, J. F., and Peebles, T. C. (1954). *Proc. Soc. Exptl. Biol. Med.* **86**, 277.

Enders, J. F., Weller, T. H., and Robbins, F. C. (1949). *Science* **109**, 85.

Evans, V. J., Bryant, J. C., Kerr, H. A., and Schilling, E. L. (1964). *Exptl. Cell Res.* **36**, 439.

Ferguson, A., and Wansbrough, A. (1962). *Cancer Res.* **22**, 556.

Freeman, A. E., Ward, T. G., and Wolford, R. G. (1964). *Proc. Soc. Exptl. Biol. Med.* **116**, 339.

Gey, G. O., Coffman, W. D., and Kubicek, M. T. (1952). *Cancer Res.* **12**, 264.

Giardinello, F. E., McLimans, W. F., and Rake, C. W. (1958). *Appl. Microbiol.* **6**, 306.

Graff, S., and McCarty, K. S. (1957). *Exptl. Cell Res.* **13**, 348.

Greene, A. E., Silver, R. K., Krug, M. D., and Coriell, L. L. (1965). *Proc. Soc. Exptl. Biol. Med.* **118**, 122.

Ham, R. G. (1965). *Proc. Natl. Acad. Sci. U.S.* **53**, 288.

Hanks, J. H., and Wallace, R. E. (1949). *Proc. Soc. Exptl. Biol. Med.* **71**, 196.
Hayflick, L., and Moorhead, P. S. (1961). *Exptl. Cell Res.* **25**, 585.
Hayflick, L., Jacobs, P., and Perkins, F. (1964). *Nature* **204**, 146.
Holper, J. C., Fenters, J. D., and Marquis, G. S., Jr. (1963). *Proc. Symp. Characterization Uses Human Diploid Cell Strains, Opatija, 1962* p. 291. Inst. Immunol., Zagreb.
Hopps, H. E., Bernheim, B. C., Nisalak, A., Tjio, J. H., and Smadel, J. E. (1963). *J. Immunol.* **91**, 416.
House, W. (1964). *Nature* **201**, 1242.
Hozinski, V. I., Seybil, V. B., Tsypkin, L. B., Pan teleeva, N. S., and Mazurova, S. M. (1964). *Acta Virol. (Prague)* **8**, 454.
Hull, R. N., Cherry, W. R., and Tritch, O. J. (1962). *J. Exptl. Med.* **115**, 903.
Jacobs, J. P. (1966). *Nature* **210**, 100.
Jahnes, W. G., Fullmer, H. M., and Li, C. P. (1957). *Proc. Soc. Exptl. Biol. Med.* **96**, 484.
Kalk, C., and Hetrick, F. (1965). *Am. J. Vet. Res.* **26**, 865.
Kruse, P. F., Jr., and Miedema, E. (1965). *J. Cell Biol.* **27**, 273.
Lundholm, B. D., Storz, J., and McKercher, D. G. (1959). *Virology* **8**, 394.
McLimans, W. F., Davis, E. V., Glover, F. L., and Rake, G. W. (1957). *J. Immunol.* **79**, 428.
McLimans, W. F., Giardinella, F. E., Davis, E. V., Kucera, C. J., and Rake, G. W. (1957). *J. Bacteriol.* **74**, 768.
MacPherson, I., and Montagnier, L. (1964). *Virology* **23**, 291.
Madin, S. H., and Darby, N. B., Jr. (1958). *Proc. Soc. Exptl. Biol. Med.* **98**, 574.
Marcus, I. (1965). *Zent. Veterinaermed.* **B12**, 204.
Martin, G., and Tuan, A. (1966). *Proc. Soc. Exptl. Biol. Med.* **123**, 138.
Melnick, J. L. (1955). *Ann. N.Y. Acad. Sci.* **61**, 754.
Melnick, J. L. (1956). *In* "Diagnostic Procedures for Viral and Rickettsial Diseases" (T. J. Francis, Jr., ed.), 2nd ed., p. 97. Am. Public Health Assoc., New York.
Melnick, J. L., Rappaport, C., Banker, D. D., and Bhett, P. N. (1955). *Proc. Soc. Exptl. Biol. Med.* **88**, 676.
Merchant, D. J., Kahn, R. H., and Murphy, W. H., Jr. (1960). "Handbook of Cell and Organ Culture." Burgess, Minneapolis, Minnesota.
Miles, C. P. (1964). *Cancer Res.* **24**, 1070.
Minutes of the Third Meeting of the Committee on Cell Cultures of the Permanent Section of Microbiological Standardization of the International Association of Microbiological Societies. (1966). Wistar Inst., Philadelphia, Pennsylvania.
Moore, G. E., and Ulrich, K. (1965). *J. Surg. Res.* **5**, 270.
Morgan, J. F., Morton, H. J., and Parker, R. C. (1950). *Proc. Soc. Exptl. Biol. Med.* **73**, 1.
Parker, R. C. (1961). "Methods of Tissue Culture," 3rd ed. Harper (Hoeber), New York.
Patty, R. E. (1965). *Am. J. Vet. Res.* **26**, 787.
Paul, J. (1965). "Cell and Tissue Culture," 3rd ed. Williams & Wilkins, Baltimore, Maryland.
Penso, G., and Balducci, D. (1963). "Tissue Cultures in Biological Research." Elsevier, Amsterdam.
Pious, D. A., Hamburger, R. N., and Mills, S. E. (1964). *Exptl. Cell Res.* **33**, 495.
Pirt, S. J., and Callow, O. S. (1964). *Exptl. Cell Res.* **33**, 413.
Prier, J. E., and LeBeau, R. W. (1958). *J. Am. Vet. Med. Assoc.* **133**, 125.
Public Health Service Regulations (1967). "Biological Products," Title 42, Part 73, Publ. No. 437. Public Health Service, Bethesda, Maryland.
Puck, T. T., and Marcus, P. I. (1955). *Proc. Natl. Acad. Sci. U.S.* **41**, 432.
Puck, T. T., Marcus, P. I., and Ciecura, S. J. (1956). *J. Exptl. Med.* **103** , 273.

Puck, T. T., Ciecura, S. J., and Fisher, H. W. (1957). *J. Exptl. Med.* **106**, 145.
Puck, T. T., Ciecura, S. J., and Robinson, A. (1958). *J. Exptl. Med.* **108**, 945.
Rappaport, R. I., Kokovikhina, K. I., Varshaver, W. B., Ermakova, M. N., Koleson, I. M., and Rozina, N. E. (1965). *Vopr. Virusol.* **10**, 187.
Sanford, K. K., Covalesky, A. B., Dupref, L. T., and Earle, W. R. (1961). *Exptl. Cell Res.* **23**, 361.
Schleicher, J. B., and Weiss, R. E. (1968). *Biotechnol. Bioeng.*, **10**, 617.
Schmidt, N. J. (1964). *In* "Diagnostic Procedures for Viral and Rickettsial Diseases" (D. H. Lennette and N. J. Schmidt, eds.), 3rd ed., p. 78. Am. Public Health Assoc., New York.
Stiles, G. E., Vasington, P. J., Bittle, J. L., and Cabasso, V. J. (1966). *Bacteriol. Proc.* p. 137.
Swim, H. E., and Parker, R. F. (1957). *Am. J. Hyg.* **66**, 235.
Swim, H. E., and Parker, R. F. (1958). *J. Lab. Clin. Med.* **52**, 309.
Trager, G., and Rubin, H. (1966). *Virology* **30**, 266.
Ulrich, K., and Moore, G. E. (1965). *Biotechnol. Bioeng.* **7**, 507.
Weiss, R. E., and Schleicher, J. B. (1968). *Biotechnol. Bioeng.* **10**, 601.
Youngner, J. S. (1954). *Proc. Soc. Exptl. Biol. Med.* **85**, 202.
Ziegler, D. W., Davis, E. V., Thomas, W. J., and McLimans, W. F. (1958). *Appl. Microbiol.* **6**, 305.
Zitcer, E. M., and Dunnebacke, T. H. (1957). *Cancer Res.* **17**, 1047.

2. Cell Cloning in Microdrops

Ian Macpherson

Imperial Cancer Research Fund
Lincoln's Inn Fields
London, England

I. Introduction

A clone is commonly taken to mean the phenotypically uniform progeny of a single cell. Isolated colonies cultured from well-dispersed cell suspensions have a high probability of being derived from single cells and are adequate for most types of clonal analysis. However, a definitive production of clonal populations requires the isolation of single cells by micromanipulation. Micromanipulative methods are only feasible with cells possessing a high degree of autonomy *in vitro*. The cloning efficiency using these methods corresponds approximately to the colony-forming efficiency of the cells when they are plated at low concentration (100–200 cells) in petri dishes. Thus it would not be practical to attempt cloning by single cell isolation with cells having colony-forming efficiencies of less than 0.1%. Plating, followed by colony isolations, should be used for such cells. Several methods have been used for single cell isolation.

The first cell clone grown in tissue culture was derived from a single cell isolated in a fine capillary glass tube. The original technique has been modified and made more effective (Sanford *et al.*, 1961). Single cells may also be isolated following their attachment and extension on a petri dish by enclosing them in a small cylinder attached to the dish with silicone grease. Another method is to seed petri dishes containing cover glass fragments with small numbers of cells and then remove fragments bearing one extended cell for cultivation in isolation (see also Schenck and Moskowitz, 1958; Freeman *et al.*, 1964; Martin and Tuan, 1966).

The method described here is based on that described by Lwoff *et al.* (1955) and Wildy and Stoker (1958). Single cells are collected from free suspension with finely drawn pipettes and isolated in small drops of medium under liquid paraffin, where they grow into colonies.

II. Materials

(a) A plate or inverted microscope with a total magnification of about 50–100×.

(b) Nonsterile "liquid paraffin" (B.P. grade). This is a mineral oil of medium viscosity.

(c) Plastic petri dishes 5 or 9 cm in diameter. The dishes need not be tissue culture grade.

(d) Small sterile microscope cover glasses about 1 cm in diameter or 1 cm square. These should be washed as for tissue culture glassware and polished with tissue paper before being sterilized in a hot air oven.

(e) The cell suspension should be derived from a rapidly growing culture by trypsinization and contain approximately 10^4 cells/ml in medium. It is advisable to use a medium which gives the highest colony-forming efficiency with the cell line to be cloned (e.g., with BHK 21 cells a medium consisting of Eagle's medium plus 25% fetal calf serum gives the best results). For other cell lines it may be advantageous to include nonessential amino acids (L-alanine, L-asparagine, L-aspartic acid, L-glutamic acid, L-proline, L-serine, and glycine) at 0.1 m*M* and sodium pyruvate at 1m*M*.

(f) Micropipettes are made in two stages from clean, sterile, plugged soft glass tubing (see Fig. 1a–c). In stage one the tubing is pulled into two fine pipettes with an external diameter tapering to about 1 mm. When cool these are softened again at the edge of a Bunsen flame or over the pilot light of a Bunsen burner. Pipettes of fine bore are made by rapid pulling of the softened glass immediately after it has been removed from the flame. The most suitable pipette bore can be found by trial and error. Generally speaking the finer they can be drawn the better. An internal diameter of about 50–100 μ or about 5–10 cell diameters is suitable. The pipettes are used with rubber tubing (50cm) and a glass mouthpiece.

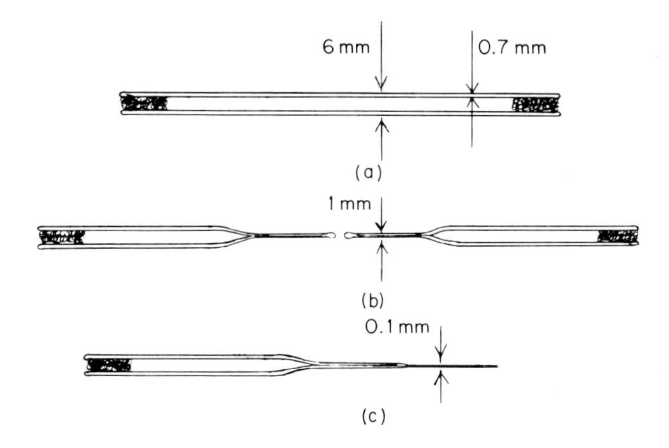

FIG. 1. Preparation of micropipettes: (a) sterile, plugged glass tube about 12 cm long; (b) first stage, in which tube is drawn to about 1 mm; and (c) second stage, in which pipette is drawn out again to fine bore and then broken off.

III. Method

(a) Mark the bases of the petri dishes with grease pencil into numbered sectors. Make six sectors on a 5 cm petri dish and 12 on a 9 cm dish. Place one sterile cover glass in each sector and one in the center of the dish.

(b) Pipette 8 ml of liquid paraffin into 5 cm dishes and 15 ml into 9 cm dishes. It is not necessary to sterilize the paraffin, indeed autoclaving may cause cloudiness in the oil by dispersing a fine suspension of water droplets. It is also unnecessary to "equilibrate" the oil with tissue culture medium before use. (*N.B.* Liquid paraffin creates havoc in conventional glassware washing operations! All glassware that has been in contact with the paraffin should be discarded or retained for use only with paraffin. It is convenient to keep a 10 ml pipette in the paraffin bottle. If the tip of the pipette is broken off the viscous paraffin can be pipetted rapidly. The bottle and pipette should be covered when not in use.)

(c) Insert a finely drawn pipette through the paraffin and place small drops of medium (about 3–4 mm in diameter) on each of the peripheral cover glasses. With another pipette place a drop of cell suspension on the central cover glass. Keep this pipette aside in a sterile test tube and use it exclusively for delivering the central cell pool drop.

(d) Place the petri dish on the microscope stage and focus on the cells in the central drop. Attach a finely drawn pipette to the rubber tubing of the mouthpiece and *partly fill the pipette with medium*. It is necessary to have medium in the pipette since a dry pipette placed in the cell pool would immediately take up medium and cells.

(e) Bring the tip of the pipette into focus near a cell and suck it into the pipette. This operation can be carried out with good control if the pipette has a fine bore. The resistance to medium movement through the pipette is considerable and fairly strong sucking or blowing is required to create flow.

(f) Move the dish to bring the upper surface of a peripheral cover glass into focus within the drop of medium. This is achieved by focusing on the cover glass-medium-paraffin junction. With the tip of the pipette in focus and touching the cover glass slowly discharge the single cell. Small droplets of paraffin may occasionally be carried into the drop on the pipette and be confused with a cell. They are however more refractile than cells and do not have their diffuse granularity.

The process of transferring cells is repeated until each drop has received a single cell. With practice 4 or 5 cells may be taken from the pool at one time and placed in the drops sequentially.

(g) The dishes are incubated at 37°C in a humidified incubator in an atmosphere of 5–10% carbon dioxide in air. After 7–10 days any colonies that have developed may be transferred. The cover glasses are removed from the paraffin with a sterile scalpel and transferred to separate 5 cm petri dishes containing 4 ml medium. When the colony has grown well the medium is discarded and the cells dispersed in the dish with a small amount of trypsin solution. Fresh medium is added to the dish and this is then reincubated.

REFERENCES

Freeman, A. E., Ward, T. G., and Wolford, R. G. (1964). *Proc. Soc. Exptl. Biol. Med.* **116**, 339.

Lwoff, A., Dulbecco, R., Vogt., M., and Lwoff, M. (1955). *Virology* **1**, 128.

Martin, G. M., and Tuan, A. (1966). *Proc. Soc. Exptl. Biol. Med.* **123**, 138.

Sanford, K. K., Covalesky, H. B., Dupree, L. T., and Earle, W. R. (1961). *Exptl. Cell Res.* **23**, 361.

Schenck, D. M., and Moskowitz, M. (1958). *Proc. Soc. Exptl. Biol. Med.* **99**, 30.

Wildy, P., and Stoker, M. (1958). *Nature* **181**, 1407.

3. Synchronization of Cells for DNA Synthesis

Gerald C. Mueller and Kazuto Kajiwara

McArdle Laboratory for Cancer Research
University of Wisconsin
Madison, Wisconsin

I. Introduction

Individual animal cells growing logarithmically in culture are progressing clockwise around a cell replication cycle which appears to be a tightly programmed sequence of genetic expressions (Fig. 1). Intervals of this cycle are concerned with DNA synthesis and chromosomal replication (S period), preparation for mitosis, condensation and segregation of the chromosomes (mitosis), cell division, and interphase growth (G_1) leading to the triggering of nuclei for another round of replication. Studies with metabolic antagonists have shown that the timely synthesis of both RNA and protein is required for a cell to progress from one point in the cycle to the next.

To study either cell- or virus-directed biochemical processes in a particular phase of the cycle, it is necessary to synchronize the population of cells. This can be accomplished either by selective harvesting of metaphase cells or by the use of metabolic inhibitors to accumulate cells behind a blockade of DNA synthesis or mitosis. Amethopterin (Rueckert and Mueller, 1960; Mueller *et al.*, 1962), 5-fluorodeoxyuridine (Rueckert and Mueller, 1960), hydroxyurea (Sinclair, 1965; Pfeiffer and Tolmach, 1967), thymidine (Xeros, 1962; Bootsma *et al.*, 1964), deoxyadenosine, and deoxyguanosine (Xeros, 1962; Mueller and Kajiwara, 1965) have proved useful for synchronizing cells for DNA synthesis, whereas colcemid (Stubblefield *et al.*, 1967) and vinblastine (Kim and Stambuk, 1966) have been effective agents for syn-

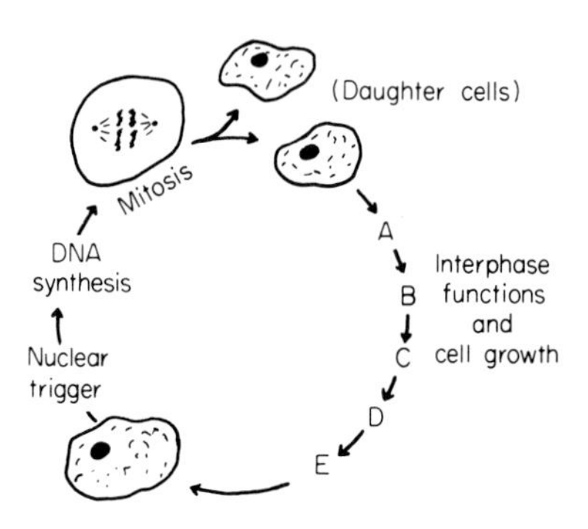

FIG. 1. The cell cycle.

chronizing cells entering mitosis. A description of the procedures currently used in our laboratory for the synchronization of cells for DNA synthesis is now presented.

II. Materials

A. MEDIA AND HANDLING OF STOCK CULTURES

Stock cultures of HeLa cells are grown in siliconized 1 liter spinner flasks using Eagle's HeLa medium with the following modifications. Calcium and magnesium are omitted whereas 10^{-4} *M* glycine, 10^{-4} *M* serine, 10^{-5} *M* inositol, 0.1% pluronic F-68 (Wyandette Chemical Co.), and 10% bovine serum are included (Mueller *et al.*, 1962). Logarithmic growth of the stock cultures is maintained by adding an equivalent volume of fresh medium (prewarmed to 37°C) each day. Under usual operating conditions, the cell concentration doubles in a 24 hour period, rising from an initial 2.0×10^5 cells/ml to 4.0×10^5 cells/ml. The cell concentration of stock spinner cultures can be raised to 5.0×10^5 cells/ml and the total volume of cell suspension in 1 liter flask increased to 700 ml without any noticeable difficulties. Even though siliconized bottles are used, with time the cells begin to clump and stick to the walls of the bottles. Therefore the cells in the stock spinner cultures are trypsinized and transferred to new bottles every 2 weeks.

B. REAGENTS

The following stock solutions are prepared in distilled water, saline, or medium and adjusted to pH 7.4. They are sterilized by filtration and stored in heavy duty glass bottles at −20°C. All solutions can be frozen and thawed repeatedly without noticeable loss of activity.

(a) Amethopterin (Methotrexate), (Lederle): a 10^{-3} *M* solution in distilled water, adjusted to pH 7.4 with KOH.
(b) 5-Fluorodeoxyuridine (FUdr) (Hoffman-LaRoche): a 10^{-3} *M* solution in distilled water.
(c) Thymidine (Tdr) (Calbiochem): a 2×10^{-1} *M* solution in distilled water.
(d) Deoxyadenosine (Adr) (Calbiochem): a 10^{-1} *M* solution in distilled water.
(e) Deoxyguanosine (Gdr) (Calbiochem): a 2×10^{-2} *M* solution in distilled water.
(f) Adenosine and adenine (Calbiochem): a 10^{-2} *M* solution in distilled water.
(g) Hydroxyurea (Nutritional Biochemical Corp.): 10^{-1} *M* solution in distilled water.
(h) Trypsin (Nutritional Biochemical Corp.): a 0.05% stock solution is prepared in saline A* (Puck *et al.*, 1957).

III. Methods

A. Preparation of Monolayer Cultures for Synchronization

The required number of spinner culture cells is harvested by centrifugation at the time of feeding and is resuspended in a 0.05% solution of trypsin. After 5 minutes at 37°C the cells are sedimented and resuspended in Eagle's medium supplemented with 10^{-4} *M* glycine, 10^{-4} *M* serine, 10^{-5} *M* inositol, and 10% bovine serum. Aliquots (10 ml) containing 0.5×10^5 cells/ml are inoculated into 3 ounce pharmacy bottles for monolayer cultures. These cultures are incubated at 37°C for 30 hours prior to initiation of the synchronization step.

B. Preparation of Suspension Cultures for Synchronization

The required number of logarithmically growing cells are harvested from the stock cultures and trypsinized. They are resuspended in fresh spinner medium at a concentration of 1.0×10^5 cells/ml and incu-

*0.002% phenol red, 0.8% NaCl, 0.04% KCl, 0.1% glucose, and 0.035% $NaHCO_3$ in distilled water.

bated either in a spinner flask or in shake flasks on a New Brunswick rotary shaker (200 rpm) for 30 hours prior to the synchronization step. By this time the cells are growing logarithmically again after a brief lag associated with the planting experience.

C. Synchronization of Cells for DNA Synthesis

To synchronize cells with agents or conditions which selectively block DNA synthesis, it is necessary to apply the block for an interval approximating the duration of the G_1 period. In the presence of the blocking agent the cells continue to synthesize the RNA, protein, lipids, and structural units which lead to a normal triggering of the nuclei for replication. Since DNA synthesis is selectively blocked the population of cells is gathered in a state of readiness for this process. Reversal of the block is attended by a synchronous wave of DNA synthesis and the initiation of other coupled processes leading to nuclear replication and cell division (Fig. 2).

1. *Amethopterin System*

Cultures are treated with 10^{-6} *M* amethopterin and 5×10^{-5} *M* adenosine for 16 hours. Amethopterin, acting as an antifolate, blocks the

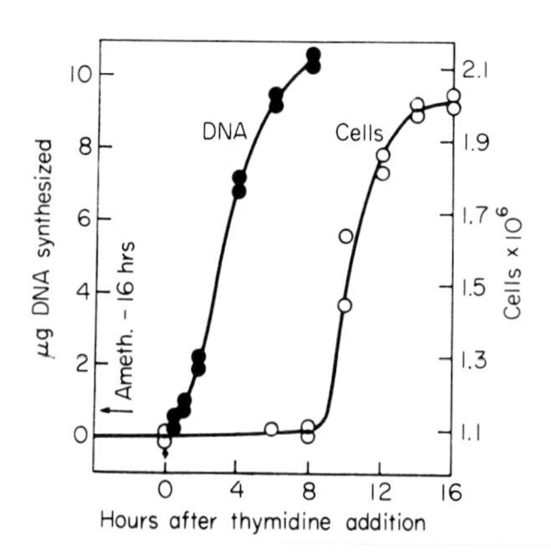

FIG. 2. The accumulation of DNA and cells in monolayer cultures following thymidine rescue. Cultures were prepared as described in text and treated with amethopterin for 16 hours prior to the addition of 10 μg of thymidine-2-^{14}C per culture. DNA synthesis was measured from the amount of thymidine-2-^{14}C incorporated into DNA. Cell numbers were determined by counting in a Coulter counter after treatment with trypsin (Mueller *et al.*, 1962).

synthesis of thymidylic acid, purine nucleotides, and certain amino acids and their metabolites (Cohen and Barner, 1954; Hakala and Taylor, 1959). By supplementing the medium with adenosine, glycine, and serine, the deficiency is confined to thymidine and its nucleotides. The induced thymidine nucleotide deficiency is reversed by the addition of 4×10^{-6} *M* thymidine to the culture medium.

2. *Fluorodeoxyuridine System*

Cultures are treated for 16 hours with 10^{-6} *M* FUdr. This agent blocks the synthesis of thymidylic acid through inhibition of thymidylic synthetase (Bessman, 1963). The induced thymidine deficiency is reversed by the addition of 4×10^{-6} *M* Tdr to the cultures.

3. *Hydroxyurea System*

DNA synthesis is prevented for a period of 16 hours by the addition of $0.5\text{-}1.0 \times 10^{-3}$ *M* hydroxyurea. This agent is a very effective and selective blocker of DNA synthesis, but its mechanism of action is unclear. While hydroxyurea can inhibit reduction of ribosides to deoxyribosides in isolated enzyme systems, its action in whole cells cannot be overcome by providing deoxyribosides (Young *et al.*, 1967). Reversal of the block is achieved by replacement of the medium with fresh medium omitting hydroxyurea.

4. *Thymidine System*

DNA synthesis is prevented for 16 hours by the addition of 2 or 3×10^{-3} *M* thymidine to the culture medium. High levels of Tdr interfere in most cells with the synthesis of other deoxynucleotides (Galavazi and Bootsma, 1966). Reversal of the blocked state is achieved by replacing the medium with fresh medium containing 10^{-5} *M* levels of Adr, Cdr (deoxycytidine), and Gdr.

5. *Deoxyguanosine System*

DNA synthesis is prevented for 16 hours by the addition of 2×10^{-4} *M* Gdr. High levels of Gdr interfere with the synthesis of other deoxynucleotides as well as some unknown adenine requiring process in nuclear replication (Mueller, 1963). Reversal is achieved by the addition of 10^{-5} *M* adenosine or 3×10^{-6} *M* adenine. Depending on cell type it may be necessary to raise the concentration of Gdr to 10^{-3} *M* to block DNA synthesis. In this case reversal is achieved by replacing the medium with fresh medium containing 10^{-5} *M* adenosine or 3×10^{-6} *M* adenine.

6. Deoxyadenosine System

DNA synthesis is blocked for the 16 hour interval with 10^{-3} *M* Adr. High levels of Adr inhibit the synthesis of other deoxynucleotides and compete with ATP in certain other cellular processes (Klenow, 1962). Reversal is achieved by replacement of this medium with fresh medium omitting Adr.

IV. Comments

A. Characteristics of the Synchrony

The use of inhibitors of DNA synthesis to synchronize cultures for this process is most successful with cells that have a generation time of about 24 hours. Under the conditions described above, approximately 70% of the cells in the cultures are synchronized with respect to the initiation of DNA synthesis. Another 20–30% is partially out of phase with respect to the majority of the cells in the culture because the cells of this fraction were in the process of DNA synthesis at the time the block was applied, and when the block was removed, this impeded synthesis of DNA was resumed. Since DNA synthesis in most mammalian cells requires approximately 6 hours, the use of cells with generation times of less than 24 hours results in blocking a larger fraction of the population in the process of DNA synthesis. Using cells with longer generation times requires extended exposure to the blocking agent and may result in unbalanced growth leading to a loss of viability. It should be kept in mind that only those events in the cell which are tightly coupled with chromosomal replication are synchronized by agents which interfere with DNA synthesis. The cytoplasmic synthesis of many proteins, lipids, carbohydrates, and organelles proceeds in the presence of the block and may result in considerable disproportion of the nucleocytoplasmic relationship.

B. The Use of Sequential Blocks for Synchronization

The synchrony of a culture can be improved significantly by using two cycles of synchronization. For this purpose, 10^{-3} *M* thymidine appears to be least toxic, while 10^{-3} *M* hydroxyurea may also be used with certain strains of cells. In practice, the cells are blocked for 16 hours with Tdr or hydroxyurea, reversed for 8 hours by a medium change, and then blocked again for 16 hours with Tdr or hydroxyurea.

The second reversal of the block by medium change may achieve 90% synchrony with respect to the initiation of DNA synthesis.

A similar degree of synchrony may also be achieved in a single cycle by starting with mitotic cells which have been shaken free from logarithmically growing monolayer cultures. The yield of cells in this case is quite low. However, colcemid or vinblastine can be used to collect cells in metaphase thereby providing a higher yield of presynchronized cells.

REFERENCES

Bessman, M. J. (1963). *In* "Molecular Genetics" (J. H. Taylor, ed.), Part 1, pp. 1-64. Academic Press, New York.

Bootsma, D., Budke, L., and Vos, O. (1964). *Exptl. Cell Res.* **33**, 301.

Cohen, S. S., and Barner, H. D. (1954). *Proc. Natl. Acad. Sci. U.S.* **40**, 885.

Galavazi, G., and Bootsma, D. (1966). *Exptl. Cell Res.* **41**, 438.

Hakala, M., and Taylor, E. (1959). *J. Biol. Chem.* **234**, 126.

Kim, J. H., and Stambuk, B. K. (1966). *Exptl. Cell Res.* **44**, 631.

Klenow, H. (1962). *Biochim. Biophys. Acta* **61**, 885.

Mueller, G. C. (1963). *Exptl. Cell Res.* Suppl. 9, 144.

Mueller, G. C., and Kajiwara, K. (1965). *In* "Developmental and Metabolic Control Mechanisms and Neoplasia," pp. 452-474. Williams & Wilkins, Baltimore, Maryland.

Mueller, G. C., Kajiwara, K., Stubblefield, E., and Rueckert, R. R. (1962). *Cancer Res.* **22**, 1084.

Pfeiffer, S. E., and Tolmach, L. J. (1967). *Cancer Res.* **27**, 124.

Puck, T. T., Cieciara, S. J., and Fisher, H. W. (1957). *J. Exptl. Med.* **106**, 145.

Rueckert, R. R., and Mueller, G. C. (1960). *Cancer Res.* **20**, 1584.

Sinclair, W. K. (1965). *Science* **150**, 1729.

Stubblefield, E., Klevecz, R., and Olaven, L. (1967). *J. Cellular Physiol.* **69**, 345.

Xeros, N. (1962). *Nature* **194**, 682.

Young, C. W., Schochetman, G., Hodas, S., and Balis, M. E. (1967). *Cancer Res.* **27**, 535.

4. Synchronization of Mitotic Cells by Selective Detachment from Monolayers

Elliott Robbins

Department of Cell Biology
Albert Einstein College of Medicine
Bronx, New York

I. Introduction

Biochemical characterization of the mitotic cell and especially subcellular constituents requires workable quantities and the exclusion of interphase contaminants. Chemical synchronization by temporary blockage of DNA synthesis provides cell populations which at best show less than a 25% peak mitotic index and thus the only presently available method for obtaining pure populations of dividing mammalian cells entails the selective detachment of those in mitosis from monolayer culture (Terasima and Tolmach, 1963; Robbins and Marcus, 1964).

The methods routinely used in our laboratory are based on two long known facts of cell monolayer behavior: (1) the tenacity of cell attachment to substrate is Ca^{++} dependent, and (2) the typical mammalian cell rounds up when it enters mitosis relinquishing much of its substrate attachment. By maintaining monolayer cultures in medium containing no Ca^{++} other than that normally present in the serum supplement, those entering mitosis become so tenuously attached that relatively gentle shearing forces are sufficient to detach them preferentially.

II. Selective Detachment

Monodisperse suspensions obtained from continuous suspension cultures or by enzymatic detachment of monolayer cultures are planted on Blake (or any flat, large surface) bottles 1–2 days prior to synchronization. The medium used for HeLa cells is that described for suspension cultures (Eagle, 1959) supplemented with 7% fetal calf serum plus nonessential amino acids and is commercially available from any medium supply house. While this medium contains only the calcium in the serum, all cells on which we have used it attach to glass and propagate with a normal generation time; this includes HeLa, Chinese hamster lung, KB, and various diploid cell lines. Optimum cell number per bottle varies with different cell types, but it is generally desirable to have only a partially confluent culture at synchronization.

Before collecting synchronized cells, the bottles are shaken vigorously to detach loosely adherent cells and debris. After rinsing the monolayer, 30 ml of fresh medium are added to each bottle to cover the cell sheet. Thirty to sixty minutes later mitotic cells are harvested by serial transfer of the collecting medium as follows: Medium from bottle No. 1 is carefully decanted to avoid disturbance of the monolayer and 30 ml of fresh medium are added; the bottle is rocked 20 times in the horizontal plane with the medium flowing back and forth over the cell sheet. Bottle No. 2 is then decanted, and the medium containing the harvested cells is transferred to this bottle which is then shaken as described. Bottle No. 3 is treated similarly, and so on. In this manner, two workers can collect mitotic cells from 40 bottles in about 15 minutes with an average yield of 3×10^5 cells per bottle.

Microscopic examination of collected cells from a single bottle reveals that about 50% are in metaphase, 40% are in anaphase or telophase, and the remainder are either in early G_1 or are interphase contaminants at an unknown stage of the life cycle (Fig. 1). When several dozen bottles are collected, many of the first cells shaken off will obviously progress through mitosis while the collection is in progress so that the final population will contain many cells in anaphase and G_1 with relatively fewer in metaphase. A few simple manipulations can improve the percent of cells in metaphase if this particular stage is the desired one. The most obvious is harvesting the cells at low temperature, either in a conventional walk-in cold room or by keeping the bottles in a shallow ice bath, with the former being the only practical way when large numbers of bottles are involved. A second, perhaps more

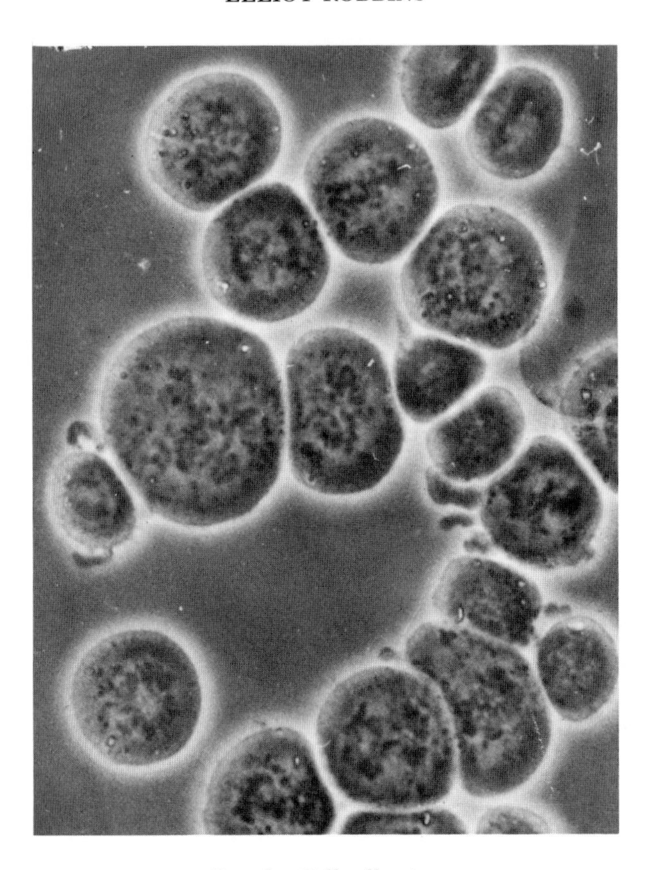

FIG. 1. Cell collection.

physiological method simply requires shortening the length of time between when the cell monolayers are rinsed free of debris and when the mitotic cells are harvested. The initial rinse removes all mitotic cells – metaphase, anaphase, and telophase inclusive. It is clear that if mitotic cells are harvested within 30 minutes of this initial rinse they must be largely in metaphase. This follows from the fact that metaphase is about 30 minutes long; therefore, an interval of 30 minutes between rinsing and harvesting is generally not sufficient for the new crop of metaphase cells appearing subsequent to the rinse to get through this stage. Since prophase cells are not detached by the collection procedure the preparation is largely metaphase. In any case, however, if chilling the cells is not consistent with experimental design, speed still is of the essence in obtaining a metaphase rich population, especially if a large number of bottles are involved.

III. DNA Inhibitors with Selective Detachment

The milligram yield of synchronized mitotic cells can be greatly increased by combining DNA inhibitors with the selective detachment technique. Thymidine (2 m*M*) arrests cells in the S phase of the growth cycle and is immediately reversible without any pronounced residual effects (Bootsma *et al.*, 1964; Xeros, 1962). When monolayers are exposed for 15 hours, (100 m*M* thymidine diluted 1:50 in medium), decanted, and fresh thymidine-free medium added for 7–10 hours before collecting, the yield of synchronized cells is increased tenfold. These cells complete mitosis in the usual time and clone with a normal plating efficiency.

IV. Spindle Inhibitors with Selective Detachment

Selective detachment, combined with the use of spindle inhibitors, such as colchicine or vinblastine, is also an extremely useful tool for biochemical characterization of cells specifically in metaphase since the cells cannot progress into anaphase. By treating monolayer cultures with colchicine (0.1 μg/ml) and then preferentially detaching the mitotic cells as already described, it is possible to acquire pure populations of metaphase-arrested cells which have been exposed to the drug for an hour or even less and which remain metabolically active for 8–10 hours. This is in contrast to a generation time in colchicine required by a random culture to arrive at a point where the population is predominantly metaphase. Perhaps more important than the self-evident advantages of the short drug exposure is the fact that the metaphase-arrested population may be compared with interphase cells incubated with the drug for the same short length of time thus providing a reasonable control on the effects of the treatment per se.

REFERENCES

Bootsma, D., Budke, L., and Vos, O. (1964). *Exptl. Cell Res.* **33**, 497.
Eagle, H. (1959). *Science* **130**, 423.
Robbins, E., and Marcus, P. I. (1964). *Science* **44**, 1153.
Terasima, T., and Tolmach, L. J. (1963). *Exptl. Cell Res.* **30**, 344.
Xeros, N. (1962). *Nature* **194**, 682.

II. Preparation of Subcellular Fractions

5. Preparation of Purified Nuclei and Nucleoli from Mammalian Cells*

Sheldon Penman†

Massachusetts Institute of Technology
Cambridge, Massachusetts

Many methods of preparing separated nuclear and cytoplasmic fractions of mammalian cells are described in the literature. It is reasonable to ask why still another method of separating nuclei from cytoplasm is described here. A partial answer lies in the reproducibility of the method and in the extensive characterization available in the literature, both biochemical and morphological. The method is, in addition, easy and rapid and can be used to process many samples without excessive effort.

Many methods will yield fairly good separation of nuclei from cytoplasm. It is, however, difficult to ascertain, in any preparation, the degree of separation achieved without extensive and laborious morphological examination of the fraction. Part of this uncertainty arises from the existence of the perinuclear or outer nuclear membrane. It is apparently studded with ribosomes and can be considered part of the cytoplasm although most nuclear preparation techniques leave the outer nuclear membrane with the nuclear fraction. In the techniques described here, the outer nuclear membrane is quantitatively removed from the nuclei and is combined with the cytoplasmic fraction. Whether or not this separation reflects physiological compartmentalization, it permits an excellent operational definition of nucleus. It has been found in many laboratories using various cell types, that

*This work has been supported by grants from both the National Institutes of Health and the National Science Foundation, most recently under Grant CA-08416-02 from the former and Grant GB-5809 from the latter.

†Recipient of a Career Development Award from the National Institutes of Health, GM 16127-01.

once the outer nuclear membrane is removed, the remaining nucleus has no mature ribosomes (Penman, 1966; Holtzman *et al.*, 1966). Thus, a very convenient operational definition becomes possible. A nucleus, which contains most of the DNA and other apparatus of nuclear function, but which contains no mature ribosomes, can be considered purified or free of cytoplasmic contamination.

There are several ways to establish the absence of mature ribosomes from nuclei lacking the outer nuclear membrane. The most straightforward is to extract and examine the RNA from the nuclear preparation. It is found that, depending on the cell type, there are different amounts of 45 S ribosomal precursor and 32 S and 28 S RNA precursor to mature cytoplasmic ribosomes, but nearly a complete absence of 18 S RNA. Thus, while approximately 5% of the cell's RNA is found in the nucleus, as precursor to ribosomes, little mature 18 S RNA is found, thus excluding the possibility of many functioning ribosomes being associated with the purified nuclei. When high resolution techniques are used, a small amount of 18 S RNA is found associated with the nucleus, and in particular, with the nucleolus (Weinberg *et al.*, 1967). This 18 S RNA corresponds to less than 0.05% of the 18 S RNA of the cell and can only be observed with very high resolution techniques such as acrylamide gel electrophoresis. When examined kinetically, it is found that this 18 S RNA is not stably associated with the nucleus but represents a transition state between the time the 18 S RNA is cleaved from the 45 S precursor and before it is exported to the cytoplasm.

The methods described have been developed for use with HeLa cells, and are probably useful without major alteration for many cells of human origin. Our experience has now been extended to include L cells, 3T3, which are mouse fibroblastic cells growing in monolayer, and sea urchin embryos. It is found that the general principles of the method apply to these types of cells, but minor adjustments in buffer ionic strength must be made.

The first step is to remove as much of the cytoplasm from cell nuclei as possible. For HeLa cells, from 1 to 4×10^7 cells are first collected by centrifugation and then washed in Earle's saline solution (Earle, 1943) at least once. It is convenient to resuspend the cells in a few milliliters of Earle's saline and transfer them to a 15 ml conical centrifuge tube and deposit the cells by centrifugation at 2000 rpm for 2 minutes in the International PR-2 or equivalent swinging bucket rotor. The Earle's saline is decanted and 2 ml of hypotonic buffer is added. The hypotonic buffer in the case of HeLa cells is reticulocyte standard buffer (RSB) (composed of 0.01 *M* NaCl, 0.01 *M* tris HCl pH 7.4, and

0.0015 *M* $MgCl_2$). Cells are allowed to swell in the hypotonic buffer for 5 minutes and then are transferred to a Dounce-type ball homogenizer. The tight-fitting pestle on the glass Dounce homogenizers will serve. We have preferred to use a stainless steel homogenizer which is precision machined and which avoids the variations that occur from one glass homogenizer to another. Nearly any machine shop can make a stainless steel ball homogenizer. We have used a three-eighth inch ball bearing for the pestle, and the barrel is bored to a clearance of 0.002 inch diameter.

Between 5 and 10 strokes with the pestle of the Dounce homogenizer will serve to rupture nearly all the cells. When first trying the procedure, it is useful to look at the cells in a phase microscope at this point to be sure that there are not many unbroken cells. After experience with the method is obtained, it will be found that microscopic examination is not routinely necessary.

The cell homogenate is transferred to 15 ml conical tubes and centrifuged for 2 minutes at 2000 rpm in the International PR-2 or equivalent centrifuge. The cytoplasm is removed with a Pasteur pipette. At this point it is useful, although not absolutely necessary, to resuspend the crude nuclei in RSB buffer (2 ml) and centrifuge them again. This serves to remove some cytoplasm trapped in the nuclear pellet. Supernatant from the second centrifugation is added to the cytoplasm obtained from the first centrifugation of the cell homogenate.

At this point the nuclei are free of that portion of the cytoplasm which can be removed by mechanical means. It remains to use the double detergent procedure to strip the remaining cytoplasm and the outer nuclear membrane. The nuclei are resuspended in 2 ml of RSB and 0.3 ml of the mixed detergent solution is added. The mixed detergent solution is composed of two parts of a 10% solution of Tween 40 and one part of 10% solution of sodium deoxycholate. The use of mixed detergents to prepare nuclei was first reported by Traub *et al.* (1964). The choice of a nonionic detergent is not critical, and we have found that Tween 80 and NP 40 can be substituted. Probably detergents such as Brij 58 and Triton X-100 would serve equally well.

In order to complete the stripping of the outer nuclear membrane, gentle shear is necessary. This is accomplished by shaking the conical tube containing the nuclei detergent preparation with a vortex type mixer for about 4 seconds at top speed. It might seem that nuclei would prove to be fragile at this point and easily damaged by vigorous shaking. This is not the case, and large variations in detergent treatment technique yield invariant results.

The detergent preparation is then centrifuged again at 2000 rpm for

2 minutes and the supernatant removed. It is necessary at this point to consider carefully how to dispose of the supernatant which contains the remaining cytoplasm and the perinuclear ribosomes. The supernatant obtained following the detergent treatment is, of course, full of detergents. If added to the previously extracted cytoplasm, it liberates the lysosomal enzymes which degrade polyribosomes and other RNA-containing structures. If a polyribosome preparation is desired, it is best to discard the last nuclear supernatant or else add it in the presence of an RNase inhibitor such as dextran sulfate. If only total RNA or protein is desired from the cytoplasm, then the nuclear supernatant can be added to the previously extracted cytoplasm in the presence of an agent such as sodium dodecyl sulfate (SDS) which terminates the degradative process started by the liberated lysosomal enzymes.

After nuclei have been treated with detergents and centrifuged, the resultant pellet cannot be dispersed by gentle pipetting as before. Apparently, after the nuclear envelope is removed, the nuclei become "sticky" and after centrifugation a recalcitrant mass is obtained. Just what to do with this recalcitrant nuclear mass depends on what is desired of the nuclear pellet. The pellet can be dispersed by resuspending it in high salt buffer (HSB) (0.5 *M* NaCl, 0.05 *M* $MgCl_2$, 0.01 *M* tris pH 7.4) and digesting with DNase, preferably of an electrophorectically purified variety. The buffer is designed to have a high magnesium content so that DNase is still active in spite of the high ionic strengths.

If 20 lambdas of a 2 mg/ml solution of purified DNase is added to the viscous nuclear preparation which is then incubated at 37°C with gentle agitation, the viscosity of the preparation will rapidly decrease. If a larger than usual mass of cells is used and a small quantity of chromatin remains at the end of the DNase digestion, a second addition of DNase always completes the digestion. Vigorous stirring on a vortex mixer before the addition of DNase helps disperse the clumped chromatin and increases the rate at which DNase digests the sample.

If total nuclear RNA is desired, the DNase digest may be directly extracted with phenol. The RNA obtained will consist of the nucleolar ribosomal precursors and the heterogeneous nucleoplasmic RNA. The optical density tracing should show less than a tenth of 1% of the cells's 18 S RNA associated with the nuclear fraction. In order to obtain nearly 100% recovery of nuclear RNA, special techniques of extracting with phenol and detergent must be used. These will be described shortly. First, it is worth noting that the nuclear digest obtained after exposure to high ionic strength and DNase can be further fractionated with comparative ease. Thus, it is possible with little additional effort to obtain a nucleolar fraction well separated from the remaining nucleoplasmic component (Penman *et al.*, 1966).

The simplest separation of nucleoli and nucleoplasm can be accomplished by differential centrifugation. The nuclear digest is placed in a 15 ml heavy-walled centrifuge tube and centrifuged for 5 minutes at 10,000 rpm in an International B-20 or a Sorvall RC-2. The pellet from such a centrifugation will consist primarily of nucleoli slightly contaminated with nucleoplasm, and the supernatant will be primarily nucleoplasm, possibly containing the most mature parts of the nucleoli. The results of such a separation are shown in Fig. 1. Most striking is the complete localization of the 45 S ribosomal precursor in the nucleolar fraction and the occurrence of heterogeneous RNA in the nucleus and cytoplasm and not in the nucleolus. It can be seen that the 18 S associated with the nuclear and nucleolar fractions is extremely small. There is a large peak at 32 S in the nucleus and a smaller peak corresponding to 28 S RNA in the nucleoplasm. The species are labeled only after a fairly lengthy period of incorporation of radioactive isotope. Long periods of chase using either radioactive nucleic acid precursor or methyl-label methionine, which specifically labels 45 S RNA initially, show that the 32 S RNA in the nucleolus and the 28 S RNA in the nucleus are precursors to cytoplasmic 28 S RNA (Greenberg and Penman, 1966; Holtzman *et al.*, 1966; Penman, 1966). It is our present thought that the 28 S RNA found in the nucleoplasm is probably an artifact produced by the high ionic strength and that it is most probably physiologically associated with the nucleolus. It appears to represent the most mature RNA in the nucleolus.

A careful examination of the RNA obtained in the nucleolar and nucleoplasmic fractions by the above methods indicates that the separation of the nucleolus from the nucleoplasmic RNA is possibly not complete. This is indicated by the occurrence of some heterogeneous RNA heavier than 45 S in the nucleolar fraction. Recent experiments indicate that this RNA is not normally associated with the nucleolus. The separation of nucleolus from nucleoplasm can be improved by using more sophisticated techniques than simple differential centrifugation.

Almost complete separation of nucleoli and nucleoplasm can be accomplished by zonal centrifugation of the nuclear digest (Willems *et al.*, 1968). A 15–30% sucrose gradient using high salt buffer is formed in a 17 ml centrifuge tube such as is used in the Spinco 25.3 rotor. The total gradient volume is 15 ml. The nuclear DNase digest is layered on top of the gradient. Centrifugation for 15 minutes at 17,000

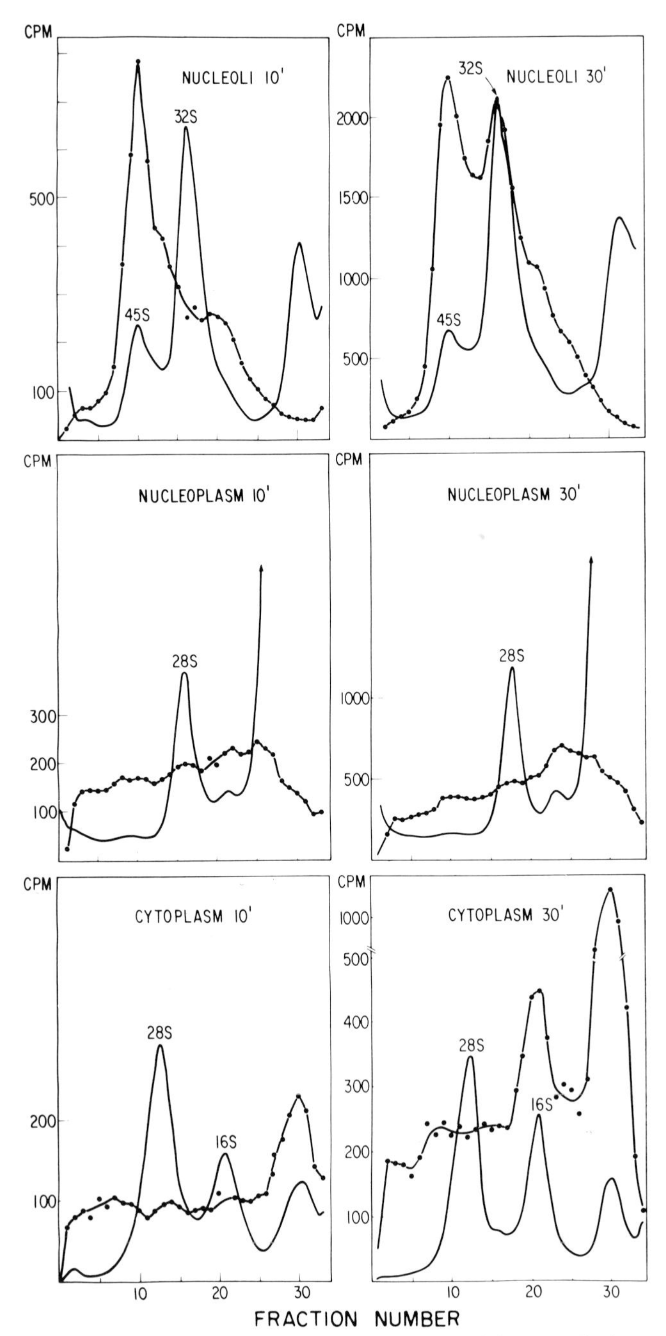

FIG. 1. Sucrose gradient analysis of the RNA extracted from nucleolar, nuclear, and cytoplasmic fractions. HeLa cells growing at a concentration of 4×10^5 cells/ml were concentrated to 2×10^6 cells/ml. Results are unaffected for at least several hours by this procedure. Uridine-^{14}C (20 μC/μmole specific activity) was added to a final concentration of 0.1 μC/ml. The incubation medium was made 10^{-5} *M* in thymidine and deoxy-

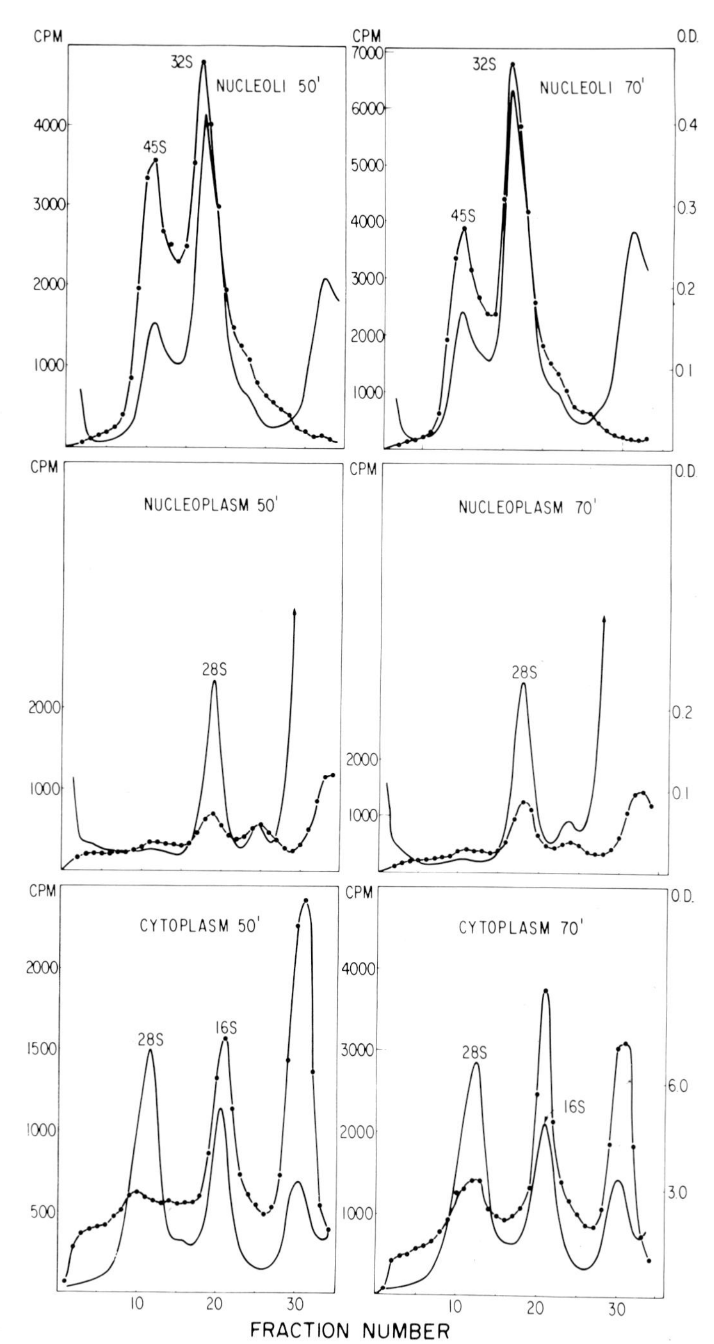

cytidine. Samples containing 6×10^7 cells were removed at the indicated time. Sucrose gradients (15-30%) were made with SDS buffer (10^{-1} *M* NaCl, 10^{-2} *M* tris, pH 7.4, 10^{-3} *M* EDTA, 0.5% sodium dodecyl sulfate) and centrifuged (Spinco SW 25.3 rotor) for 16 hours at 25°C. Centrifugation speed was 21×10^3 rpm for the cytoplasm fractions: (●) radioactivity; (——) optical density, 260μm.

rpm completely deposits the nucleolar fraction on the bottom of the tube and leaves the nucleoplasmic components distributed through the sucrose gradient. The gradient can be decanted and the pellet resuspended in 1 ml of SDS buffer (0.1 *M* NaCl, 0.001 *M* EDTA, 0.01 *M* tris pH 7.4, 0.5% sodium dodecyl sulfate). The resuspended nucleolar pellet can be extracted with phenol directly.

If the nucleoplasmic RNA is desired it must be extracted from the decanted sucrose gradient. Since this constitutes a volume of 15 ml, a direct extraction would be somewhat inconvenient. (Our techniques have been designed so that extraction of RNA with phenol is done with sample volumes of 2 ml or less.) We have found that the nucleic acids in the sucrose gradients supernatant to nucleolar pellet can be precipitated by adding two volumes of 95% ethanol directly to the supernatant fluid and centrifuging the precipitate after allowing the alcohol to stand at −20°C for at least 1 hour. This procedure brings down a considerable amount of nuclear protein, but the pellet obtained can be easily resuspended in SDS buffer and phenol extracted in the same manner as the nucleolar pellet.

Some comments on the method of phenol extraction of nuclear material are in order. Let us consider, first, the extraction of the total nuclear digest since this is the most difficult type of sample to extract. It is an old observation that the nucleic acids of the nuclei tend to remain trapped with the interfacial proteins during phenol extraction. The hot phenol SDS procedure of Scherrer and Darnell (1962) was the first method to permit recovery of the nuclear nucleic acids. The method described here is a modification of the technique of Scherrer and Darnell which has proved to yield reliably quantitative recoveries of RNA and incidentally, DNA.

It is first important to realize that the presence of divalent ions such as magnesium makes extraction with SDS extremely difficult. The procedure to be described depends on nearly quantitative removal of the SDS into the organic phase of the extraction mixture. This will not happen if high magnesium concentrations are present. Therefore, the first step is to add sufficient EDTA to chelate all free magnesium. We have added EDTA (the pH is adjusted to 7.4) to a final concentration of 30 m*M* to chelate the 50 m*M* Mg ions of the HSB buffer. Following the addition of EDTA, the mixture is made 0.5% in SDS. The mixture will appear quite cloudy since the SDS protein complexes are only partially soluble at the high ionic strength of the digestion buffer. Raising the pH to approximately 8 solubilizes the SDS protein complexes which is necessary if an aliquot is desired at this time but is not necessary if the next steps in phenol extraction are to be performed.

Phenol is added to a volume equal to that of the aqueous phase (1 or 2 ml). We have always used phenol that is supplied without preservatives, and we have used it without redistillation. It is possible that redistilling phenol in the presence of an oxygen atmosphere as is commonly done introduces more undesired breakdown products than it removes. The only precaution we take with phenol is to keep it in the refrigerator and we have found no change in the RNA obtained by phenol extraction even when phenol several months old is used.

A 15 ml conical centrifuge tube has been found to be convenient for phenol extractions of samples whose initial volume is 2 ml or less. After the addition of phenol, the tube is placed in a 55°C water bath and allowed to come to temperature for about 1 minute. The tube is then shaken vigorously on a vortex-type mixer for about 10 seconds. This procedure can be repeated once.

If the phenol–aqueous solution is centrifuged now, a voluminous fluffy interface will be found dispersed through the phenol and in the aqueous phase. One of the basic problems in phenol extraction is encountered at this point, i.e., the removal of phenol without any of the interfacial proteins which still have entrapped nucleic acid. In order to achieve a good separation of the organic phase from the interfacial denatured proteins, the following step has been added. After vigorous shaking of the phenol–aqueous mixture, a volume of chloroform equal to the volume of phenol is added, the mixture is warmed to 55°C and is then shaken again on the vortex mixer. The addition of chloroform raises the density of the organic phase so that there is no tendency for denatured proteins to sink into the organic phase.

The mixture is centrifuged and a clear separation of organic phase from aqueous phase can be seen. There is considerable white precipitate distributed through the organic phase which is SDS that has come out of solution. If desired, the tube can be warmed gently and the SDS will go into solution making the separation between aqueous and organic phase clear. There will be a large, fluffy precipitate in the aqueous phase which may occupy the entire aqueous phase. This is not a cause for alarm and the following steps should be followed.

The phenol–chloroform phase is removed with a Pasteur pipette, and the procedure is now repeated using chloroform alone; the mixture is warmed, shaken, and the chloroform removed. The amount of chloroform used corresponds to twice the volume of the aqueous phase. Three or four repetitions of the chloroform extraction will have reduced the fluffy precipitate to a thin layer of denatured interfacial proteins found at the surface of the chloroform phase. At this point, the aqueous phase can be removed, leaving the denatured proteins behind. If extremely efficient protein extraction is desired, as is necessary when using methionine as a label of RNA, then the whole procedure is repeated after the aqueous phase has been separated from the interface.

The phenol-chloroform extraction procedure is also used for the precipitates resuspended in SDS buffer when the nucleoli are separated from the nucleoplasm. Nucleic acid recoveries are customarily better than 95% with this procedure. This is apparently because the repeated extractions with chloroform removes SDS from the fluffy interface and so reduces the tendency of nucleic acids to remain trapped at the interface. As might be expected from a method that yields a good recovery of RNA, nuclear DNA is also present in the aqueous phase and can constitute a problem during further procedures. The nucleic acids from either the total nuclear digests or from the separated nucleolar and nucleoplasmic fractions is then precipitated with 2 volumes of alcohol and resuspended in whatever buffer system is desired for further analysis. If DNase digestion is to be included as part of the subsequent step, the resuspension buffer should be made fairly high in magnesium content since some EDTA is often carried through the alcohol precipitation and will prevent added DNase from being active.

The emphasis on the above extraction procedures has of course been on RNA. If nuclear DNA is desired, a rather different technique would be required. The digestion step in high salt buffer would of necessity be avoided. The nuclear aggregate can be dispersed by sonication and the DNA obtained by phenol extraction. This, of course, will yield degraded DNA. If high molecular weight DNA is desired, it is best to omit the cleaning of nuclei with a double detergent since obtaining DNA from clumped nuclei is difficult. Extraction of high molecular weight DNA is best done on a crude nuclear preparation while the nuclei are still dispersed.

There is one point about the procedure which is not obvious. The high salt buffer used to digest the nuclei was originally designed to remove a fraction of the histones from DNA and make a sufficient number of sites on DNA available to DNase, thus breaking the nucleohistone gel. The ionic strength of the HSB buffer has also been found to be the highest ionic strength to which ribosomes can be exposed without a significant alteration in physical structure. It has become apparent that the high salt buffer has another important effect. Both the nucleus and the nucleolus are apparently rich in nuclease activity. The nucleolus will continue to break down the 45 S ribosomal precursor if exposed to elevated temperature, unless the ionic strength is high (Vesco and Penman, 1969). Apparently the ionic strength of the digestion buffer is sufficient to inhibit endogenous ribonuclease activity to undetectable levels without inactivating the added DNase. Warming of a nuclear preparation in the absence of high salt buffer is very dangerous when undegraded RNA is desired.

The procedure outlined above was designed for HeLa cells and will probably work with most cells of human origin. For other cell types, the procedure has to be modified. Our experience with other cell types will be outlined briefly in order to indicate the types of problems that can be encountered and the modifications of the techniques which will meet these problems.

Cells of rodent origin are commonly used for tissue culture and for nucleic acid investigation. We have found that both L cells and the 3T3 line developed by Howard Green are refractory to the initial homogenization in hypotonic buffer. In order to achieve 100% breakage of cells, the ionic strength of the homogenizing buffer must be lowered. This can be most conveniently accomplished by diluting 1 volume of RSB buffer with 2 volumes of distilled water for the initial mechanical homogenization. Subsequently, all steps of washing and detergent treatment can be carried out using normal RSB buffer.

The developing sea urchin embryo presents a wide variety of problems since the cells fractionate differently at different stages of development. During the early blastula stage the cells are very easily fractionated in RSB buffer, but the nuclei do not maintain their integrity if exposed to the double detergents in this low ionic strength medium. It has been found that if nuclei are resuspended in a buffer that is 100 m*M* NaCl and 20 m*M* in magnesium, the double detergent treatment can be applied and clean, stable nuclei are obtained. The situation changes drastically in late blastula. The nuclei are quite stable even at low ionic strength buffer when exposed to double detergent mixture. At this stage of development, the nuclei can no longer be digested with high salt buffer. The work with sea urchin nuclei is preliminary and is only mentioned here to indicate the general method of approach which is to raise the ionic strength during treatment with the mixed detergents until nuclei become stable.

There is one other major innovation of technique that should be described. In this modified technique, mechanical breakage of the cells is omitted and the initial fractionation into cytoplasm and crude nuclei is accomplished with a nonionic detergent. This method is particularly suitable for fractionating large numbers of samples, especially when comparatively small numbers of cells must be handled.

The technique of fractionating with detergents alone consists of swelling washed cells in buffer containing 0.5% of the detergent NP 40 produced by the Shell Corp. As reported by Borun *et al.* (1967), a good fractionation of cytoplasm and nuclei is obtained in the sense that all the cells are broken and the majority of the cytoplasm is removed from the nuclei. The treatment with NP 40 can be done either in a hypotonic buffer such as RSB, or in isotonic saline which has been made 10 m*M* in magnesium and is suitably buffered with either tris or phosphate. The use of isotonic saline appears to preserve the nuclear morphology much better than the treatment in hypotonic buffer.

The nonionic detergent accomplishes much the same thing as mechanical shearing in that the cytoplasm is removed down to the perinuclear membrane and some cytoplasmic tabs remain attached to the nuclei. The crude nuclear preparation can be centrifuged out of the detergent mixture, resuspended in RSB, and then treated with the double detergent previously described. This removes the outer nuclear membrane. The purified nuclei are then centrifuged again, and the supernatant decanted and added to the previous extract, which is now the cytoplasmic extract.

The major drawback to this method is the degradation of RNA-containing structures in the cytoplasm which occurs as consequence of the release of the lysosomal enzymes. We have done a fairly extensive study of the ribonuclease activities found in the cytoplasm of HeLa cells. There is a soluble ribonuclease with pH optimum of 8. This nuclease can be rendered inactive by low temperature. It possesses an extremely high temperature coefficient and its activity, although considerable at 37°C, is undetectable at 0°C. This enzyme appears to be inhibited by most detergents so that if preparations of cytoplasm are kept cold or are treated with detergent the soluble nuclease is not responsible for extensive degradation. However, the lysosomal particulate RNase presents a different problem. The pH optimum of the lysosomal enzyme is 5, and this enzyme is not inactivated by low temperature. Most cytoplasmic preparations are made at pH 7.4 and although this is far from the pH optimum of the lysosomal enzyme, the enzyme is sufficiently active to cause structural alterations such as changes in polyribosome distribution if the lysosomes have been disrupted by detergent. However, one can make use of the pH dependence of the lysosomal enzymes. If the extraction buffer to which NP 40 is to be added is adjusted to pH 8.5, the lysosomal enzyme is greatly reduced in activity and practically undegraded polyribosomes and other structures can be obtained.

It is perhaps best to end this discussion on a note of caution. One should note the reservations that must be kept in mind in interpreting new experimental data using these techniques, especially that obtained from virus. It is clear that the nucleic acids bound to large structures remain in the nucleus. This is true of most of the cellular DNA presumably because it is in the form of chromatin and it is certainly true of the ribosomal precursors which are associated with the nucleolus. There is in addition a large amount of heterogeneous RNA which appears to be confined to the nucleus and never enters the cytoplasm. Upon fractionating the nucleus, it is found that this heterogeneous RNA is also associated with some type of protein-containing structure in the nuclear fraction, possibly chromatin. The main problem is to ascertain whether nucleic acids not associated with large structures preserve their intracellular location during isolation.

It is clear, for instance, that small molecules such as amino acids and nucleotides are completely leached from the purified nuclei. Recently we have found that both the unmethylated precursor to transfer RNA and 5 S RNA unassociated with ribosomes appear very rapidly in the cytoplasm. It is impossible to determine whether these molecules normally flow to the cytoplasm immediately after synthesis as the kinetic data implies, or whether they are lost from the nucleus during the extraction procedure. There is also a class of heterogeneous RNA associated with the cytoplasm. In base composition, kinetics of formation, sedimentation distribution, etc., this RNA is distinct from the heterogeneous RNA which remains with the isolated nuclei. It is still impossible to determine whether this RNA is normally associated with the cytoplasm in the unfractionated cell. These reservations must be applied to fractionation of infected cells when the intracellular sites of viral function are sought. If virions or other structures of interest are found in isolated nuclei, it can be safely assumed that they actually occur there and are not the result of cytoplasmic contamination. The converse statement however cannot be made strongly without extensive work comparing the morphology of cells before and after fractionation.

ACKNOWLEDGMENTS

The author would like to thank Mr. Robert Weinberg for many helpful suggestions in preparing this chapter. He would also like to thank Mrs. Maria Penman who carried out the experiments which eventually led to the conclusions presented here.

REFERENCES

Borun, T., Scharff, M., and Robbins, E. (1967). *Biochim. Biophys. Acta* **149**, 302.
Earle, W. (1943). *J. Natl. Cancer Inst.* **4**, 165.
Greenberg, H., and Penman, S. (1966). *J. Mol. Biol.* **21**, 527.
Holtzman, E., Smith, I., and Penman, S. (1966). *J. Mol. Biol.* **17**, 131.
Penman, S. (1966). *J. Mol. Biol.* **17**, 117.
Penman, S., Smith, I., and Holtzman, E. (1966). *Science* **154**, 786.
Scherrer, K., and Darnell, J. (1962). *Biochem. Biophys. Res. Commun.* **9**, 451.
Traub, A., Kaufmann, E., and Ginsberg-Tietz, Y. (1964). *Exptl. Cell Res.* **34**, 371.
Vesco, C., and Penman, S. (1968). *Biochim. Biophys. Acta* **169**, 188.
Weinberg, R., Loening, U., Willems, M., and Penman, S. (1967). *Proc. Natl. Acad. Sci. U.S.* **58**, 1088.
Willems, M., Wagner, E., Laing, R., and Penman, S. (1968). *J. Mol. Biol.* **32**, 211.

6. Preparation of Polyribosomes from Cells Grown in Tissue Culture*

Sheldon Penman, Hanna Greenberg,† and Margherita Willems‡

Massachusetts Institute of Technology
Cambridge, Massachusetts

It has been known for a long time that ribosomes are sites of protein synthesis in cells of all types (Siekevitz, 1952). More recently, it was shown that active ribosomes are arranged so that many ribosomes are associated with a single strand of messenger RNA (Penman *et al.*, 1963; Warner *et al.*, 1963; Wettstein *et al.*, 1963). This finding was important because of its intrinsic interest and because it has permitted many interesting conclusions about the protein synthesizing mechanism of cells. This is particularly true in the case of virus-infected cells since the virus specific polyribosomes are often different from the host polyribosomes in detailed characteristics (Penman *et al.*, 1963). In some cases, it has been shown that certain polyribosome distributions are characteristic of different stages of virus maturation.

In some tissues it is quite simple to prepare undegraded polyribosomes; in others it is almost impossible. The difference appears related to the amount and nature of the endogenous ribonucleolytic activities of the cells under investigation. Polyribosomes are particu-

*This work was carried out under the National Institutes of Health, Grant No. CA-08416-03, and the National Science Foundation, Grant No. GB 5809. Dr. Sheldon Penman is a recipient of a Career Development Award No. GM-16127. Dr. Hanna Greenberg is recipient of a fellowship from the American Cancer Society.

†Present address: Sudbury Valley School, Framingham, Massachusetts.

‡Present address: Massachusetts General Hospital, Boston, Massachusetts.

larly sensitive to nucleolytic attack. The ribosomes themselves are fairly well protected from ribonuclease degradation by their structural proteins, but the messenger RNA holding them together is exquisitely sensitive.

Cells grown in tissue culture are particularly easy to work with and will be the subject of this report.

The preparation of relatively undegradated polyribosomes is fairly simple and straight forward. However, when the characteristics of polyribosomes are considered in detail, it is found that small amounts of degradation are introduced in many of the commonly used procedures. When detergents are added to cytoplasmic extract, the lysosomal enzymes are activated and some polyribosome degradation results. In some cases, e.g., picornovirus infected cells and liver, most of the polyribosomes seem to be associated with the membrane fraction and cannot be obtained without detergents. The optimum strategy for obtaining undegraded polyribosomes from both uninfected and infected cells will be considered in detail.

Polyribosome preparation and analysis consists of obtaining a cytoplasmic extract and subjecting this extract to zonal sedimentation in a sucrose density stabilized gradient. Single ribosomes sediment at 74 S and the polyribosomes up to about 500 S. The major fraction of the remaining cell components sediment either more rapidly or more slowly than ribosomes. The polyribosomes are distributed in a sucrose gradient with relatively little contamination from other cell structures.

The following method of obtaining cytoplasmic extract has been used with HeLa cells. It is the simplest procedure and works well with cultured cells of human origin. A sample consisting of 1 to 4×10^7 cells is collected from suspension culture by centrifugation at 1600 rpm for 3 minutes in a swinging bucket rotor, such as the International PR-2. If cells are growing in monolayer they can be trypsinized off the vessel surface and handled exactly as cells collected from suspension culture.

The size of the sample is not critical. However, if fewer cells are used there will be too little optical density to record with available equipment. In this case, a criterion rather than optical density, such as labeled nascent polypeptides, must be used to measure the polyribosome distribution. Larger samples can be handled but the resolution obtained in the sucrose gradient decreases. This loss of resolution occurs when the sucrose density gradient is unable to stabilize the sedimentation zones as they become more concentrated.

The cells are washed once with cold Earle's saline and deposited again by centrifugation at 2000 rpm for 2 minutes. It is convenient to transfer them into a small conical tube for this centrifugation since this reduces the amount of liquid remaining with the cell pellet when the saline is decanted. The cell pellet is resuspended in 1–2 ml of hypotonic buffer. The buffer commonly used for HeLa cells is the formulation first developed by Jon Warner (Warner *et al.*, 1963) and termed RSB (reticulocyte standard buffer). Its composition is commonly 0.01 *M* NaCl, 0.003 *M* $MgCl_2$ and 0.01 *M* tris, pH 7.4. While RSB is quite hypotonic, the ionic strength and divalent ion concentration preserve polyribosome structure.

The cells are allowed to swell for 5 minutes in the hypotonic buffer, then homogenized with a tight-fitting ball homogenizer, originally described by Dounce (Penman *et al.*, 1964). We have had ball homogenizers machined from stainless steel using a ball bearing for the ball and a precision-bored barrel for the main body of the homogenizer. The difference in diameters between the ball and the barrel is 0.002 inch. The stainless steel homogenizer has the advantage of unbreakability and a constant bore through the length of the homogenizer. These are two characteristics that are not shared by the commercially supplied glass homogenizers. However, the glass homogenizers are perfectly adequate, though one must be prepared to see a favorite homogenizer broken periodically.

The cells can be completely disrupted with 10 strokes of the homogenizer pestle. The number is not critical and large variations of personal style seem to result in little differences in extraction efficiency. Recently, we have used the motor driven Potter homogenizer with Teflon pestle to prepare very concentrated extracts. Somewhat surprisingly even this very vigorous procedure results in no polyribosome degradation and very little nuclear breakage when used with HeLa cells. However, this probably cannot be generalized to all cell types and certainly not to homogenization buffers of very different ionic strength.

The RSB buffer used for homogenization of HeLa cells is not ideal for some other cell types. Cells of rodent origin such as L cells or 3T3 fibroblasts do not break easily in RSB buffer. We have found that reducing the ionic strength by diluting RSB, two parts distilled water to one part buffer, results in nearly complete cell breakage.

The homogenate is placed in a conical centrifuge tube and centrifuged for 2 minutes at 2000 rpm in the PR-2 or similar centrifuge. The nuclei are deposited quantitatively. The supernatant is removed with a Pasteur pipette and is designated cytoplasmic extract. At this point it is necessary to consider the experimental design since the question as to whether or not to use detergents must be answered.

The cytoplasmic extract can be layered on a sucrose density gradient with no detergent treatment. A 15–30% or 5–20% sucrose gradient made with the same buffer used for homogenization may be used. The 5–20% gradient requires less centrifugation since the viscosity of the sucrose is lower, but because of the lower stability of the shallower gradient the resolution suffers.

Polyribosome profile, in optical density obtained from HeLa cells, is shown in Fig. 1. The resolution is quite good, and detailed measurements indicate that very little polyribosome degradation results from this procedure.

HeLa cell polyribosomes may be sedimented without detergent treatment because the bulk of the cellular polyribosomes are not attached to membranes (Penman *et al.*, 1964). This appears to be characteristic of rapidly growing cells. However, even in HeLa cells about 15% of the cellular polyribosomes are apparently associated with membranes. Other cell types with more highly developed endoplasmic reticulum have a larger percentage of membrane-associated polyribosomes. In poliovirus-infected cells most, if not all, of the polyribosomes are associated with the membrane fraction. If cytoplasm from cells with extensive association between polyribosomes and membranes is layered on a gradient without detergent most of the polyribosomes sediment quickly to the bottom of the tube.

It is relatively simple to release polyribosomes from their associated membranes with a mild detergent. Sodium deoxycholate is most commonly used. It is not strong enough to alter ribosome structure of itself. However, addition of sodium deoxycholate to cytoplasmic extract opens a Pandora's box of lysosomal enzymes. Lysosomal RNase is liberated and proceeds to hydrolyze polyribosomes. The pH dependence of this enzyme is shown in Fig. 2 "particulate." Since the optimum is pH 5 and extracts are usually made at pH 7.4, the hydrolysis of polyribosomes is slow but measurable.

The degradation caused by the liberation of the lysosomal enzymes can be avoided in two ways. Highly charged molecules can bind to ribonuclease and thus serve as inhibitors. Polyvinyl sulfate and dextran sulfate serve admirably in this application (Philipson and Kaufman, 1964). However, it must be noted that these charged polymers are not specific in their action. They bind to all basic proteins and therefore, to be effective, must be added in concentration high enough to saturate all the basic protein-binding sites. With the number of cells used in these preparations we have found that 1–2 mg of dextran sulfate added to the extract prevents measurable degradation of polyribosomes. The polyanions have the somewhat odd effect of dissociating the monomeric ribosomes into subunits while leaving the polyribosomes unaffected (Mayazawa *et al.*, 1967; Zylber, 1968). The RNase

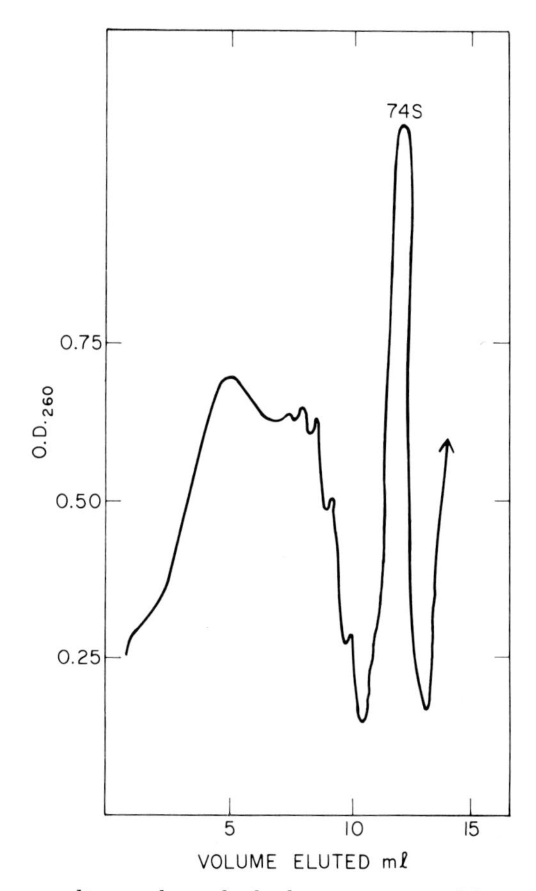

FIG. 1. Sucrose gradient analysis of polyribosomes prepared from HeLa cells. Cytoplasmic extract was prepared from 4×10^7 HeLa cells grown in suspension culture. The cytoplasm was extracted with a ball homogenizer after allowing cells to swell in hypotonic buffer, as described in the text. The extract in 1 ml of buffer was layered on a 27 ml, 15–30% sucrose gradient and centrifuged at 25,000 rpm at 5°C for 90 minutes. The gradient was eluted using a peristaltic pump and the optical density recorded continuously in a spectrophotometer. The polyribosomes shown here are heavier than those usually obtained from HeLa cells. This was accomplished by incubating cells at a concentration of 2×10^6 cells/ml for 1 hour prior to harvesting. This incubation apparently decreases the rate of translation relative to initiation and results in more densely packed polyribosomes. The bimodal distribution of the polyribosomes is characteristic of rapidly growing cells.

inhibitors must be added before the detergent but after the nuclei are removed from the extract since the polyelectrolytes lyse the nuclear envelope and cause the liberation of the chromatin material.

Another way of preventing polyribosome degradation is to take advantage of the pronounced pH dependence of the lysosomal enzyme.

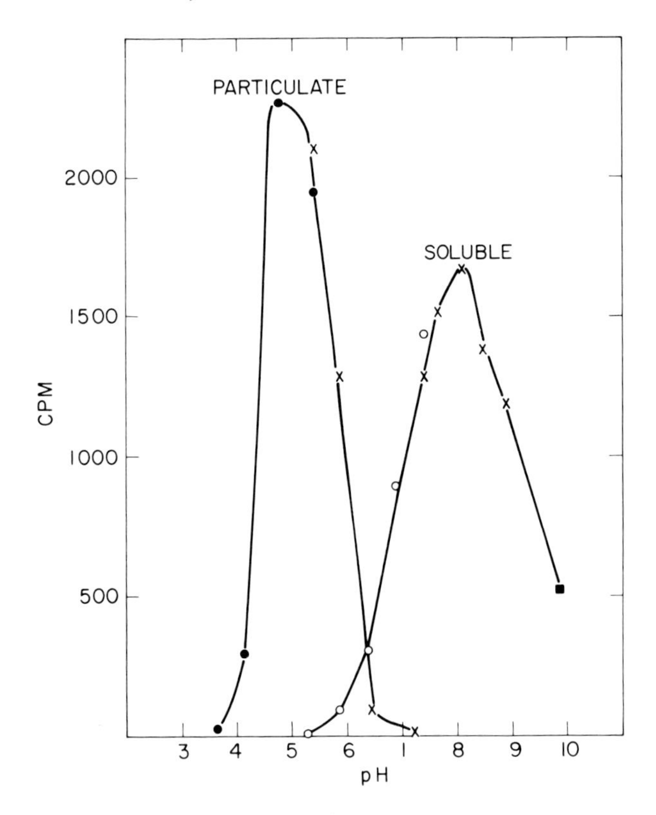

FIG. 2. pH dependence of the soluble and particulate ribonuclease activities from HeLa cell cytoplasm. Cytoplasmic extract was prepared as described in Fig. 1 and in the text. The extract was centrifuged in an angle rotor at 40,000 rpm for 90 minutes at 5° C. The supernatant was used directly as a source of the soluble activity. The pellet was resuspended in RSB buffer containing 0.5% sodium deoxycholate. The solution was centrifuged again at 40,000 rpm to remove ribosomes. One hundred microliters of each preparation were added to a reaction mixture containing 0.1 *M* buffer, 0.15 *M* $MgCl_2$, and ^3H-labeled ribosomal RNA from HeLa cells. The final volume was 0.4/ml. Buffers used were: acetate, from pH 4.2 to 5.3; cacodylate, from pH 5.4 to 7.3; tris, from pH 7.4 to 8.9; glycine-NaOH, from pH8.3 to 9.9. After 30 minutes of incubation the samples were assayed for acid-soluble radioactivity.

Its activity is strongly influenced by the pH, and raising the pH to 8.5 greatly diminishes its residual activity. We have found that polyribosomes are stable under these conditions.

Cytoplasmic extract can also be prepared using nonionic detergents to lyse cells. This method potentially yields a higher efficiency of polyribosome extraction than the mechanical preparation described above. It is also the method of choice when very small numbers of cells must be manipulated since the inevitable losses in homogenization and transfer can be completely avoided.

The method of detergent preparing cytoplasmic extract depends upon the fact that nonionic detergents solubilize cellular membrane and cytoplasmic components but do not affect the outer nuclear membrane. If the procedure is carried out with some care, all of the cytoplasm can be extracted with the exception of the perinuclear ribosomes associated with the outer nuclear membrane. These however, constitute a very minor fraction of the cells' polyribosomes. While all nonionic detergents tested such as Tween 40 and Brij 58 are moderately effective, the detergent NP 40, used for this purpose by Borun *et al.* (1967), seems to be the most effective. The lysis of cells with detergents can be carried out, either in RSB or in an isotonic buffer, which is 0.14 *M* NaCl, 0.02 *M* $MgCl_2$ and 0.01 *M* tris. When this isotonic buffer is used, the nuclear morphology does not undergo the change seen with hypotonic buffers. Thus, the chromatin appears, by light microscopy at least, to retain its characteristic distribution rather than becoming evenly distributed as in hypotonic buffers.

The remarks made above about the use of detergents causing the liberation of lysosomal enzymes applies to this method as well. Thus, if the extraction is carried out at pH 7.4 some polyribosome degradation ensues. If this degradation is to be avoided the pH can be raised to 8.5. This causes some nuclear clumping but not to a serious degree. The polyelectrolyte RNase inhibitors such as dextransulfate cannot be used in this case since as mentioned above they cause lysis of the nuclear envelope.

The gentle stirring of cells in the presence of NP 40 added to 0.5% is enough to cause complete lysis in about 5 minutes. The procedures are carried out at 0–4°C. Nuclei are deposited by centrifugation, and the cytoplasm handled as above.

The procedures described so far yield good polyribosome preparations when applied to HeLa cells and to most cells grown in tissue culture. However, problems arise in obtaining undegraded preparations from animal tissues. These problems stem from the cellular ribonucleases which have so far been ignored in this discussion. Let us first consider the cytoplasmic ribonucleases of HeLa cells which have been carefully studied.

It was stated above that the principal source of degradation in HeLa cell extracts occurs when detergents liberate lysosomal enzymes. This does not, however, mean that there are no other nucleases present. A very curious observation was made several years ago in our laboratory: The principal ribonuclease in HeLa cell cytoplasm appears to be a soluble nuclease with pH optimum of 8; the activity vs. pH dependence of this enzyme is shown in Fig. 2 "soluble." There is considerable nuclease activity in cytoplasm when assayed at 37°C. From the amount of the activity at 37°C and assuming a normal temperature dependence of enzymatic activity, it would be expected that this enzyme would result in degradation at 0°C. This does not happen since it was shown that polyribosomes prepared without detergents are undegraded. Furthermore, this enzyme is completely inhibited by sodium deoxycholate, yet it is in this situation, where the lysosomal enzyme is liberated, that degradation ensues. These paradoxical observations were somewhat difficult to resolve. Eventually it was found that the soluble ribonuclease in HeLa cells has an exceptionally large temperature coefficient. While it is quite active at 37°C, its activity is undetectable at 8°C. If preparations are kept cold, little or no polyribosome degradation occurs. The temperature dependence of the soluble enzyme is shown in Fig. 3a. For comparison, the temperature coefficient of the lysosomal enzyme assayed at pH 5 is also shown (Fig. 3b). The lysosomal enzyme is not nearly as severely inhibited by reduced temperatures.

When cytoplasmic extracts of HeLa cells are kept cold, the soluble enzyme does not function and undegraded polyribosomes are obtained. However, when incubations are carried out at 37°C, as, for example, in the case of an *in vitro* incorporating system, considerable endoribonucleolytic activity ensues and polyribosomes are rapidly degraded. It has been shown in our laboratory that this enzyme is associated with an inhibitor, much as the principal ribonuclease of rat liver (Blobel and Potter, 1966). This inhibitor can be inactivated with *para*-mercurochlorobenzoate.

There have been reports of success in preventing polyribosome degradation in cell extracts by addition of rat liver supernatant. Apparently there is excess inhibitor in the rat liver supernatant which can inhibit the soluble ribonuclease activity. However, our own experiments and those reported elsewhere, indicate that lysosomal enzyme appears insensitive to the soluble inhibitor present in the cytoplasm. Presumably, therefore, the rat liver inhibitor acts only on alkaline soluble ribonuclease. However, it is not possible to extrapolate from the experience with HeLa cells to that obtained from animal tissue. There is at least one report (Shortman, 1961) and an observation in another laboratory (Willems, 1968) of a ribonuclease associated with membranes but distinct from lysosomal enzyme. This enzyme is sensitive to ribonuclease inhibitor from rat liver supernatant. Whether it is similar to the soluble enzyme described above or still another ribonu-

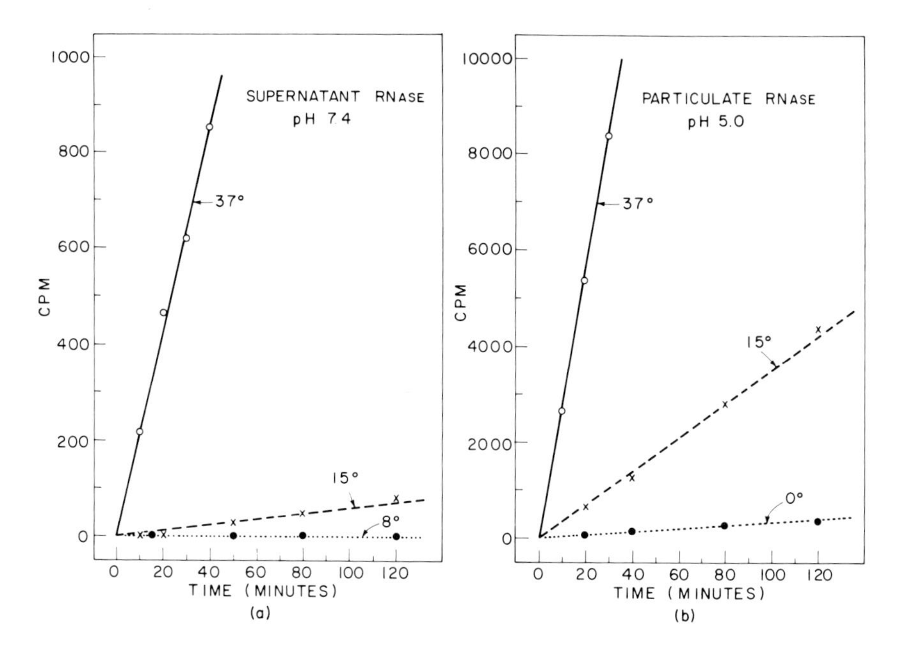

FIG. 3. Temperature dependence of the ribonuclease activities from HeLa cell cytoplasm. The enzyme preparations were made and their activities assayed as described in Fig. 2 except that 50 lambdas of particulate and 100 lambdas of the soluble preparations were used in the reaction mixtures.

clease activity remains to be elucidated. If none of the above techniques prevent polyribosome degradation, addition of 100,000 gm supernatant from rat liver to cell extracts would seem a reasonable strategy.

REFERENCES

Blobel, G., and Potter, V. (1966). *Proc. Natl. Acad. Sci. U.S.* **55**, 1283.

Borun, T., Scharff, M., and Robbins, E. (1967). *Biochim. Biophys. Acta* **149**, 302.

Mayazawa, F., Olijnyh, O., Tilley, C., and Tamaoki, T. (1967). *Biochim. Biophys. Acta* **145**, 96.

Penman, S., Scherrer, K., Becker, Y., and Darnell, J. E. (1963). *Proc. Natl. Acad. Sci. U.S.* **49**, 654.

Penman, S., Becker, Y., and Darnell, J. E. (1964). *J. Mol. Biol.* **8**, 541.

Philipson, L., and Kaufman, M. (1964). *Biochim. Biophys. Acta* **80**, 151.

Shortman, K. (1961). *Biochim. Biophys. Acta* **51**, 37.

Siekevitz, P. (1952). *J. Biol. Chem.* **195**, 549.
Warner, J. R., Knopf, P., and Rich, A. (1963). *Proc. Natl. Acad. Sci. U.S.* **49**, 122.
Wettstein, F., Staehlin, T., and Noll, H. (1963). *Nature* **197**, 430.
Willems, M. (1968). Private communication.
Zamencnik, P., and Keller, E. (1954). *J. Biol. Chem.* **209**, 337.
Zylber, E. (1968). Unpublished results.

7. Isolation and Fractionation of Mammalian Metaphase Chromosomes

N. P. Salzman

Laboratory of Biology of Viruses
National Institute of Allergy and Infectious Diseases
National Institutes of Health
Bethesda, Maryland

I. Introduction

When a chemical that produces metaphase arrest is added to a rapidly dividing mammalian cell culture, a fraction of the cell population will accumulate in metaphase. Milligram quantities of purified chromosomes can be isolated from these arrested cells. These chromosomes can be fractionated into several groups which show pronounced morphological and biochemical differences. The procedures that have been devised in this laboratory for chromosome isolation and fractionation are described in this article (Salzman *et al.*, 1966; Mendelsohn *et al.*, 1968).

II. Materials

Vinblastine sulfate (Velban, Eli Lilly and Co., Indianapolis, Indiana): The powder is dissolved in sterile 0.85% sodium chloride at a concentration of 1 mg/ml. This solution is diluted 1 to 10 with saline to give the working solution (100 μg/ml).

pH 3 buffer: A stock solution is prepared by mixing equal parts of *M* sodium acetate and N HCl solutions. The pH of this mixture is adjusted to 2.2 by addition of the required quantity of one or the other component solution. The final buffer is prepared by diluting this stock solution tenfold. The dilutent contains concentrations of $MgCl_2$, $CaCl_2$, and sucrose so that the final buffer contains 10^{-3} M $MgCl_2$, 10^{-3} M $CaCl_2$, and 0.1 M sucrose.

Ribonuclease A (Worthington RASE): It is obtained as a 1% solution in 0.1 M phosphate buffer. This solution is diluted to a concentration of 0.2% with 0.05 M acetate buffer, pH 5.1 and the solution is heated to 80°C for 10 minutes. It is stored frozen until it is used.

10 and 40% sucrose solutions: The composition of the solutions is stated as weight to volume. The solutions are prepared in pH 3 buffer.

1% sodium citrate: The sodium citrate solution contains 10^{-3} M $MgCl_2$ and 10^{-3} M $CaCl_2$.

10% Tween 80: The chemical is manufactured by the Atlas Chemical Industries and is obtained from Fisher Scientific Co.

Giemsa stain: A stock solution of dye is prepared by adding 1 gm of dye (Giemsa Stain, National Aniline Division, 40 Rector St., New York, New York) to 66 ml of glycerine. This mixture is held at 60°C for 2 hours with occasional agitation. The solution is brought to ambient temperature and 66 ml of methanol are added. The solution is stirred with a magnetic stirrer overnight, and it is then filtered through Whatman No. 4 paper. A buffer solution (pH 6.2) is prepared from 0.908 gm of KH_2PO_4 and 1.188 gm of Na_2HPO_4 contained in 100 ml of water. To stain slides, dilute 1 ml of dye solution and 1 ml of buffer to 50 ml with water.

Fixative solution: Methanol:glacial acetic acid 3:1 (v/v).

III. Methods

A. Cell Cultures

The HeLa and Chinese hamster (CH) cell lines that have been used were grown in suspension culture. The HeLa cultures were grown in Eagle's medium (Eagle, 1959) supplemented with 5% horse serum and 4 mM glutamine. The CH cell (V79-589 FR) was obtained from Dr. Mortimer Elkind of the National Institutes of Health and was recloned twice prior to use. Chinese hamster cells were grown in Ham's F-10 medium (Ham, 1963) supplemented with 10% fetal calf serum and 4 mM glutamine.

B. Accumulation of Cells in Metaphase Arrest

Vinblastine sulfate (100 μg/ml) is added to a cell culture at a final concentration of 0.1 μg/ml. The period during which cells are accumulated in metaphase arrest varies depending on the purpose of the experiment. When the intent of the experiment is to obtain a high yield of chromosomes, cells are allowed to accumulate in metaphase a period of time corresponding to approximately one-half of the cell generation time. This will result in a cell population in which 30–50% of the cells are in metaphase arrest. It is important to maintain the cell concentration in a range where the cells are undergoing division at an optimal rate during the time that cells are accumulated in metaphase. For the CH and HeLa cell cultures, this is approximately $2–3 \times 10^5$ cells/ml.

C. Hypotonic Treatment of the Cells

Cells that have accumulated in metaphase are collected by centrifugation at 1000 rpm for 10 minutes. (All centrifugations involved in the isolation procedure are done in an International Centrifuge, Model PR-2, at a temperature of 20°C.) The supernatant fluid is removed by aspiration. The cell pellet is resuspended in a 1% sodium citrate solution which was prewarmed to 37°C. Approximately 40 ml of solution is added to 8×10^7 cells. The cells are dispersed by gentle pipetting, and the solution is then incubated at 37°C. The period of incubation is determined for each cell line. The time is selected to effect hypotonic swelling of the cells but is terminated prior to the time that cell rupture begins. Chinese hamster cells are incubated for 10 minutes and HeLa cells are incubated for 30 minutes.*

*At the end of the incubation period in 1% sodium citrate, it is important to determine the fraction of the cell population that is in metaphase arrest. One-half ml of methanol:glacial acetic acid (3:1, v/v) is added dropwise to an aliquot of 0.5 ml of hypotonically treated cells in order to fix the cells. After standing at room temperature for 10 minutes, the cells are centrifuged at 500 rpm for 5 minutes. The pellet is then resuspended in 3 ml of methanol:glacial acid for an additional 5 minutes at room temperature. The cells are then centrifuged and resuspended in a small volume of fixative. A drop of this suspension is placed on a microscope slide which is air dried and then stained with Giemsa. The slide is immersed in the stain solution for 10 minutes and then washed with water twice, the first wash of 10 minutes duration and the second wash of 30 seconds duration.

D. Rupture of Hypotonically Swollen HeLa Cells

At the end of the 37°C incubation, the cells are collected by centrifugation at 800 rpm for 10 minutes. The cell pellet is then resuspended in 10 ml of pH 3 buffer. The cells are shaken either by hand or mechanically for 10–20 minutes in order to disrupt cells and liberate chromosomes. The effectiveness of this procedure is established by microscopic examination.* If the chromosomes in the metaphase cells are not effectively freed, the shaking treatment is extended for an additional period. The chromosomes contained in the pH 3 buffer can be stored at 4°C for extended periods. Even after 3 months, they maintain excellent morphological appearance.

E. Purification and Fractionation of Chromosomes by Velocity Gradient Centrifugation

The mixture of chromosomes and cellular components that had been stored at 4°C is brought to room temperature and is then centrifuged at 2500 rpm for 30 minutes. The supernatant fluid is removed by aspiration, and the pellet (from 8×10^7 cells) is resuspended in 2 ml of pH 3 buffer; 0.17 ml of the RNase solution is added and the mixture is incubated at 37°C for 1 hour. Then a sufficient quantity of a 10% solution of Tween 80 is added so that its final concentration is 1%. The mixture is shaken vigorously for 5 minutes. An aliquot of this solution is diluted twentyfold with pH 3 buffer and the optical density at 450 mμ is measured. It should read 0.350 ± 0.050. If the OD is higher than this value, the undiluted material is adjusted with pH 3 buffer to bring a 1 to 20 dilution of it into this OD range. Two milliliters of the undiluted solution are layered onto a 24 ml 10–40% linear sucrose gradient in pH 3 buffer contained in a $1 \times 3\frac{1}{2}$ inch siliconized (Siliclad, Clay Adams, Inc.) nitrocellulose tube. This gradient is centrifuged for 40

*To observe the nature of the preparation microscopically at this stage, a drop of material is placed at one end of a microscope slide and the drop is then drawn across the slide using the edge of a second slide to distribute the fluid. The slide is then dried in a current of warm air and fixed for 10 minutes in methanol:acetic acid. It is then stained with Giemsa. In some experiments and in certain fractions, the concentration of material is sufficiently high so that slides can be made directly without the necessity to first concentrate the material. At other stages, it is necessary to concentrate the material before it is examined microscopically. In the latter case, an aliquot of the mixture is removed and centrifuged at 2500 rpm for 10 minutes. Most of the supernatant fluid is removed, and the pellet is resuspended in a small volume of supernatant fluid. This concentrated sample is then used to prepare the slide.

minutes at 500 rpm. The tubes are tapped by puncture near the base, with care to avoid the large pellet at the bottom which contains primarily nuclei. Two milliliter fractions are collected and one drop aliquots of each fraction are examined on microscope slides (see dagger footnote). The appropriate fractions from different regions of the gradient are then combined into three pools, each containing chromosomes partially purified on the basis of size difference. In order to concentrate the three pools of chromosomes into small volumes, they are pelleted by centrifugation at 2500 rpm for 30 minutes and each pellet is resuspended in 2 ml of pH 3 buffer. They are then layered onto a series of three parallel 24 ml 10–40% sucrose gradients and centrifuged for 40 minutes. Fractions obtained from this second series of gradients are examined microscopically and scored for homogeneity with respect to size groups. Fractions from the second series of gradients which are homogeneous for a chromosome type are pooled to yield the final three chromosome fractions shown in Fig. 1. About half of the gradient fractions are unsuitable for this pooling step because of cross contamination between chromosome size groups. Discrete and reasonably homogeneous size groups are obtained from the smaller chromosomes. The fraction containing the large chromosomes shows a considerably broader degree of heterogeneity.

Chemical studies suggest that isolated chromosomes are admixed with ribosomes which bind to the chromosomes during the isolation procedure (Salzman *et al.*, 1966). This must be borne in mind with regard to any studies concerning "chromosomal protein" or "chromosomal RNA." The DNA extracted from each pool of fractionated chromosomes will represent a distinct class of molecules.

F. Alternative Procedures for Chromosome Purification

We have also described a procedure for the isolation of HeLa chromosomes (Salzman *et al.*, 1966) that consists of the following:

(1) Cells in suspension culture are incubated with 1 μg/ml of vinblastine for 10–14 hours.

(2) The cells are harvested by centrifugation, washed once with Eagle's medium, and pelleted.

(3) Pellets derived from 8×10^7 cells are suspended in 40 ml of 1% sodium citrate by gentle pipetting and are incubated at 37°C for 30 minutes. The hypotonically swollen cells are centrifuged at 800 rpm for 5 minutes.

(4) The pellet is resuspended in 10 ml of 2.5% citric acid-0.1 *M* su-

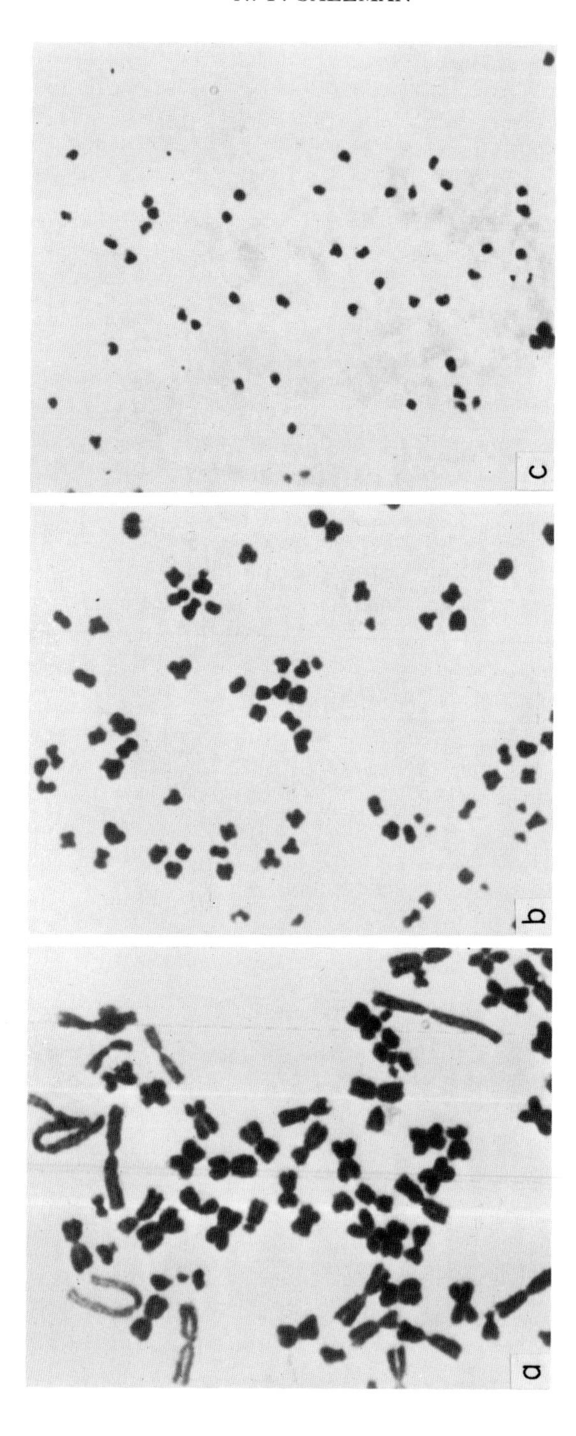

FIG. 1. Chromosome fractions obtained from metaphase Chinese hamster cells.

crose and is shaken vigorously for 5 minutes. The mixture is then made 0.1% with Tween 80 and shaking is resumed for an additional 5 minutes.

(5) The citric acid-sucrose-Tween 80 suspension is centrifuged at 500 rpm for 5 minutes.

(6) The supernatant fluid is transferred to a porous steel filter for suction filtration. A filter 3 cm in diameter is used for one sample derived from 8×10^7 cells.

(7) The filtrate is centrifuged at 2500 rpm for 30 minutes to pellet chromosomes. The supernatant fluid is discarded, and the chromosome pellet is washed twice by resuspension in 10 ml of citric acid-sucrose and centrifugation at 2500 rpm for 30 minutes.

Chromosomes stored in citric acid-sucrose at 4°C for 3 months remain intact as judged by the retention of their characteristic morphology. Complete experimental details are described in the publication by Salzman *et al.* (1966). This procedure does not effect a separation of chromosomes into distinct size groups. For this reason, the procedure described in detail in this article is considered more advantageous. Alternative procedures for the isolation of chromosomes have also been described (Chorazy *et al.*, 1963; Somers *et al.*, 1963; Lin and Chargraff, 1964; Cantor and Hearst, 1966; Huberman and Attardi, 1966; Maio and Schildkraut, 1967).

REFERENCES

Cantor, K. P., and Hearst, J. E. (1966). *Proc. Natl. Acad. Sci. U.S.* **55**, 642.

Chorazy, M., Bendich, A., Borenfreund, E., and Hutchinson, D. J. (1963). *J. Cell Biol.* **19**, 59.

Eagle, H. (1959). *Science* **130**, 432.

Ham, R. G. (1963). *Exptl. Cell Res.* **29**, 515.

Huberman, J. A., and Attardi, G. (1966). *J. Cell Biol.* **31**, 95.

Lin, H. J., and Chargaff, E. (1964). *Biochim. Biophys. Acta* **91**, 691.

Maio, J. J., and Schildkraut, C. L. (1967). *J. Mol. Biol.* **24**, 29.

Mendelsohn, J., Moore, D. E., and Salzman, N. P. (1968). *J. Mol. Biol.* **32**, 101.

Salzman, N. P., Moore, D. E., and Mendelsohn, J. (1966). *Proc. Natl. Acad. Sci. U.S.* **56**, 1449.

Somers, H. E., Cole, A., and Hsu, T. C. (1963). *Exptl. Cell Res.* Suppl. 9, 220.

8. Isolation of Surface Membranes of Tissue Culture Cells*

Leonard Warren and Mary C. Glick

Department of Therapeutic Research
School of Medicine
University of Pennsylvania
Philadelphia, Pennsylvania

I. Introduction

In this section three methods of isolation of surface membranes of tissue culture cells will be described. The methods given are for the L cell but the surface membranes of cells such as CHO, BHK 21, HeLa, KB, and others have been prepared by slight variations of the procedures described below. Surface membranes have also been obtained from Ehrlich ascites tumor cells. The zinc ion and tris methods described here are modified versions of procedures previously described (Warren *et al.*, 1966, 1967).

II. Materials

The chemicals employed are of reagent grade. Dounce homogenizers both small (7 ml) and large (40 ml) are purchased from Kontes Glass Co., Vineland, New Jersey. Loose-fitting (Type A) and tight-fitting pestles (Type B) are available. Fluorescein mercuric acetate (FMA) is purchased from Nutritional Biochemical Corp., Cleveland, Ohio. The solution of FMA is made to a concentration of approximately 2.2×10^{-3} *M* (saturation) with 0.02 *M* tris Cl buffer, pH 8.1. The

*Supported by U.S.P.H. Grant No. 1-R01 HD 0052-01 and the American Cancer Society Grant T-333.

FMA solution, after stirring for 1 hour, is adjusted to pH 8.1 with 2 *M* tris base. Some FMA does not go into solution and is filtered off. This solution is usable for 3 weeks.

Sucrose solutions are made according to the table in the "Handbook of Chemistry and Physics," twenty-seventh edition, 1943, p. 1556.

III. Methods

General: All work is carried on at 0–4°C. Fractions are harvested with a syringe fitted with a No. 15 needle whose terminal 6 mm is bent at a right angle to the shaft with the bevel facing upward. When harvesting small fractions a 5 ml syringe fitted with a bent No. 15 needle is used. In large scale isolations, fractions are removed from gradients in centrifuge bottles through a Pasteur pipette attached to a sidearm flask under suction. All steps of the procedures are monitored with a phase contrast microscope.

A. Fluorescein Mercuric Acetate Method

This is a scaled-down version of a method previously described (Warren *et al.*, 1966). Cells (3×10^6 to 10^8) are washed twice with physiological saline (0.16 *M* NaCl), and the cell pellet is suspended in 1 ml of saline. The suspension is transferred to a small Dounce homogenizing tube and 3.0 ml of FMA solution (0.0022 *M*, pH 8.1) is added while stirring. After 5 minutes at room temperature the tube is placed in ice until the suspension has reached 3°C. The cells are then broken with about 25 strokes of a tight pestle (Type B). The homogenizing process is monitored as are successive steps in the isolation by phase contrast microscopy. The surface membranes appear as large empty gray bags with a hole through which the nucleus and cytoplasm were expelled. Homogenizing should be gentle enough to prevent tearing and destruction of the cell ghosts. About 10–20% of the cells remain small, dense, and intact throughout the homogenizing.

Four milliliters of 60% sucrose solution are added to the homogenate. After stirring, the homogenate–sucrose mixture is placed on 10 ml of 45% sucrose solution in a 40 ml centrifuge tube with a blunt tip. The tube is centrifuged at 150 *g* (800 rpm) in the refrigerated International Centrifuge (PR-2) for 1 hour. The upper phase which contains membranes and fine debris is removed to within 1 mm of the meniscus by means of a syringe. The fluid in the meniscus region is harvested separately. This fraction contains cells and nuclei as well as membranes. The lower phase contains some cells, nuclei, and coarse debris. About 0.1 volume of water is added to the intermediate (meniscus) fraction, and it is recentrifuged on a solution of 45% sucrose for 1 hour at 125 *g* (750 rpm). The top layer is removed and combined with the top layer of the first centrifugation. The membrane fraction is virtually devoid of cells but contains fine debris. It is then diluted with 0.1 volume of water and placed on 10 ml of 35% sucrose solution in a 40 ml glass centrifuge tube; this is centrifuged at 1800 *g* (2900 rpm) for 1 hour. Fine debris stays in the upper phase while the membrane forms a pellet. A few drops of 35% sucrose solution are added to the pellet of surface membranes. After stirring, the suspension is transferred to a tube containing sucrose solutions in a linear gradient running from 45 to 65%. The tube is centrifuged in the SW-39 head of the Spinco model L-2 ultracentrifuge for 1 hour at 33,000 *g*. An orange band containing membranes forms in the middle of the tube. The band of purified membrane is harvested with a 2 ml syringe fitted with a No. 18 needle with a bent tip. The suspension of membranes in sucrose solution is diluted with distilled water to 12 ml, stirred, and then centrifuged at 4000 *g* for 30 minutes in an RC-2 centrifuge. The supernatant solution is removed, and 2 ml of water are added to the pellet. The final preparation contains virtually no nuclei, cells, or mitochondria. A minimum of debris is present. The yield of whole ghosts is 20–55%. Membranes are counted with the hemocytometer under the phase contrast microscope.

B. Zinc Ion Method

To 10 ml of a suspension of L cells (5×10^8) in saline, previously washed twice with cold 0.16 *M* NaCl solution, add 30 ml of 0.001 *M* $ZnCl_2$ and let stand at room temperature for 10 minutes. During this time the cells swell as the surface membranes become distinct and appear to separate from the underlying cytoplasm. The cell suspension is cooled to 5°C and homogenized gently in a large Dounce homogenizer fitted with a tight pestle (Type B). After 100–200 strokes the homogenate contains whole surface membranes, nuclei, cytoplasmic debris, and some whole cells which appear dense and will not yield their surface membranes.

To the homogenate add an equal volume of 60% sucrose solution and layer 40 ml onto two 150 ml Corex centrifuge bottles containing discontinuous gradients of 50, 48, 45, 43, 40, and 35% sucrose solutions 15, 10, 25, 20, and 10 ml, respectively. The gradients are centrifuged at 1500 *g* for 30 minutes in the Sorvall RC3 centrifuge (HG-4 rotor). The membranes are found in the 40 and 43% sucrose solutions and are removed from the gradients with suction as three fractions. The first of these fractions contains membrane fragments and cellular particles in addition to whole membranes. The middle area contains whole membranes, relatively free from contaminating cellular material while the lower part of the 43% sucrose solution contains nuclei and whole membranes. Three pellets of membranes are formed by centrifuging these fractions combined from both gradients and diluted to 35% sucrose concentration, at 6000 *g* for 15 minutes in the Sorvall RC3 centrifuge. Each of the three pellets is suspended in 35% sucrose solution, layered over a discontinuous gradient of 3 ml of 65 and 60%, 4 ml of 55%, 6 ml of 50%, 5 ml each of 45 and 40% sucrose solutions, and centrifuged for 1 hour at 90,000 *g* in the SW 25.1 rotor of the Spinco model L-2 ultracentrifuge. The membranes are harvested from the top of the 50 and 55% sucrose solutions, diluted to a concentration of approximately 35% sucrose, and centrifuged at 6000 *g* for 15 minutes. The membrane pellet is resuspended in 35% sucrose solution and is recentrifuged. These membranes are counted as a preliminary procedure for chemical or enzymatic analyses.

Surface membranes free from visible particulate or nuclear contamination can be obtained by this method in a yield of 20–30% of the starting cells. The yield can be increased considerably by recentrifuging fractions containing particulate matter or nuclei. The membranes are visibly stable for many months at −20°C in 35% sucrose solution.

C. Tris Method

To 10 ml of a suspension of L cells (5×10^8), washed twice with cold 0.05 *M* tris Cl buffer, pH 7.4, add 10 ml of the same buffer and 1.0 ml of 0.05 *M* $MgCl_2$. After 8 minutes at 3°C, the membranes are gently stripped from the cells with approximately 20 strokes of a tight-fitting pestle (Type B) in a Dounce homogenizer. The membranes are whole, the nuclei remain intact, but a lot of cytoplasmic debris is formed.

All sucrose solutions are 0.005 *M* with respect to $MgCl_2$. The homogenate is suspended in an equal volume of 20% sucrose solution, and 5 ml is layered onto a discontinuous gradient in a 40 ml centrifuge tube containing 5 ml each of 60, 50, 40, 30, and 20% and 10 ml of 35% sucrose solutions. The gradients are centrifuged at 1380 *g* for 15 minutes in a refrigerated International Centrifuge PR-2, rotor No. 269. After centrifugation the upper layer contains most of the debris. The membranes, which are found in the 35 and 40% sucrose bands, are harvested with a syringe and are centrifuged to form a pellet at 6000 *g* for 15 minutes in the RC2 centrifuge (HB-4 rotor). The supernatant fluid, containing some debris and no membranes is discarded. The pellet is suspended gradually in 2 ml of a 30% sucrose solution by stirring and then placed on a layered gradient consisting of 5 ml each of 60, 55, and 50%, 10 ml each of 48 and 45%, and 4 ml each of 43 and 40% sucrose solutions in the centrifuge tube of an SW 25.2 rotor of a Spinco ultracentrifuge. After centrifugation at 90,000 *g* for 1½ hours, the membranes are harvested from the top of the 48 and 45% sucrose solutions. After diluting the combined fractions to a concentration of approximately 35% sucrose the membranes are centrifuged at 5000 *g* for 20 minutes. The whole membranes are resuspended in 35% sucrose solution and are counted. The yield of membranes is 15–25%.

The yield can be increased considerably by purifying the fractions from the first gradient containing cells and nuclei. These fractions are combined and placed on a low speed gradient similar to the first gradient. The second high speed gradient is identical to the one described above with the exception that 10 ml of 50% and 5 ml of 48% sucrose solutions are used.

Whole surface membranes made by this method are particularly suitable for enzymatic studies since no interfering chemicals are present. Membranes can be obtained at a pH range from 7.0 to 8.2 at 3°C. The yield of membranes is higher at the higher pH, but these membranes appear to be less stable. However, the method can be modified for work with a particular enzyme.

IV. Comments

Surface membranes are isolated mainly as whole cell ghosts. Thus quantitation can be placed on a per cell basis. The FMA method is the most versatile and can be used on a variety of tissue culture cells. Since sulfhydryl groups are blocked by FMA, many enzymes of the membrane are undoubtedly inactivated. However preparation of membranes isolated by the FMA method do contain H-2 antigen (Manson *et al.*, 1969). The tris method though best for enzymatic studies is the most difficult and least predictable of the methods. Membranes isolated by the zinc ion method are enzymatically active and are capable of incorporating labeled amino acids into hot trichloroacetic acid (TCA) precipitable material (Glick and Warren, 1968, 1969).

It should be emphasized that the methods described above are for L cells. In general, the following points should be noted. Cells should be washed with saline rather than with phosphate-buffered or tris-buffered saline. It has been found by using the FMA method that one can obtain membranes from some cells only if the cells are allowed to stand for 5–10 minutes in hypotonic solutions (0.05 or 0.1 *M* NaCl) before adding the solution of FMA. This treatment is especially beneficial when small dense cells with large nuclei are being processed. The times of treatment and the concentration of FMA solution can be varied. Cells being processed by the FMA or tris procedure should be used as soon after washing as possible. It is important that homogenizing be gentle rather than vigorous. Homogenizing in a small Dounce tube (7 ml) usually gives better membrane preparations than when a large 40 ml tube is used. In determining the optimal times and speeds for centrifugation it has frequently been observed that centrifugation at lower speeds for longer periods is better than higher speeds for shorter periods of time.

REFERENCES

Glick, M. C., and Warren, L. (1968). *Federation Proc.* **27**, 299.

Glick, M. C., and Warren, L. (1969). *Proc. Natl. Acad. Sci. U.S.* (in press).

Manson, L. A., Hickey, C., and Palm, J. (1969). *In* "Biological Properties of the Mammalian Surface Membrane" (L. A. Manson, ed.). Wistar Inst. Press, Philadelphia, Pennsylvania (in press).

Warren, L., Glick, M. C., and Nass, M. K. (1966). *J. Cellular Physiol.* **68**, 269.

Warren, L., Glick, M. C., and Nass, M. K. (1967). *In* "The Specificity of Cell Surfaces" (B. D. Davis and L. Warren, eds.), pp. 109–127. Prentice-Hall, Englewood Cliffs, New Jersey.

III. Concentration and Purification of Viruses

9. Purification of Polyoma Virus

Lionel V. Crawford

Imperial Cancer Research Fund
Lincoln's Inn Fields
London, England

I. Introduction

Polyoma is a highly resistant virus and can be pelleted by centrifugation and exposed to dense salt solutions without loss of infectivity. Its purification therefore presents few problems once the virus has been obtained free of cell debris and other hemagglutination inhibitors. The virus adsorbs reversibly to receptors which are found on most mammalian cells. At high pH and temperature the virus is released from these sites (Crawford, 1962) and the receptors are destroyed by treatment with receptor destroying enzyme (RDE) from *Vibrio cholerae* (Hartley and Rowe, 1959). These adsorption properties are used to obtain a concentration of the virus while it is still attached to the infected cell debris, thus making it possible to obtain high titer virus suspensions without high speed centrifugation.

II. Estimation of Virus Quantities

To assist in calculating the amounts of virus during purification of polyoma virus some equivalent values may be useful. They are only meant to be "rules of thumb" and are accurate only to an order of magnitude.

The most convenient rapid assay of polyoma is by hemagglutination. Assays are performed by making doubling dilutions of virus in phosphate-buffered saline at 4°C. To each virus dilution (in a volume of 0.2 ml) 0.2 ml of guinea pig red blood cell suspension (0.75%) at 4°C is added, the suspension mixed, and the cells allowed to settle at 4°C. The number of hemagglutinating units (HAU) in the initial suspension is the reciprocal of the highest dilution which causes agglutination. Doubling dilutions are usually not very accurate and high titer virus suspensions should be diluted accurately 100- or 10,000-fold before starting doubling dilutions. This will ensure that the end point is achieved after only a few doubling dilutions.

One HAU $= 10^5$ pfu $= 10^7$ physical particles in the electron microscope.
2×10^{11} "full" particles $= 2 \times 10^4$ HAU $= 8\ \mu g$ virus $= 1\ \mu g$ DNA.
$1\ \mu g$ DNA $= 10^3$ to 10^4 pfu assayed as DNA.
One infected cell yields about 10^3 pfu $= 10^5$ physical particles.
Hence, one roller bottle of 10^8 cells yields about 10^{13} particles, 10 ml of a suspension with a titer of 10^5 HAU/ml.

Some relevant characteristics of polyoma virus are given in the accompanying tabulation.

Electron microscopic appearance	Buoyant density (gm/ml)	Corresponding refractive index of isopycnic solution of	
		RbCl	CsCl
"Full"	1.32	1.3720	1.3670
"Empty"	1.29	1.3680	1.3630

These refractive indices are approximate and refer to solutions containing tris buffer (0.05 *M*, pH 7.5). Accurate values for CsCl in water can be obtained from the equation (valid up to a density of 1.38 gm/ml): density (in gm/ml) = 10.2402 (refractive index) − 12.6483 (Bruner and Vinograd, 1965).

III. Virus Production and Preliminary Concentration

The method described requires good, large scale, tissue culture facilities and makes maximum use of the mice available. Where tissue culture facilities are not available on a sufficiently large scale the method of Winocour (1963), using larger numbers of mice but reducing the tissue culture requirements, may be preferable. The polyoma strain which is normally used is small plaque virus but large plaque virus can also be produced by the same procedure.

(a) Cultures of primary or secondary whole mouse embryo cells are grown to confluence in 80 ounce roller bottles rotated horizontally on their long axes at 1 rpm or less (House and Wildy, 1965). Each bottle contains about 10^8 cells at confluence and requires 100–200 ml of medium (Eagle's medium plus 10% calf serum). Other flat-sided bottles or plates may also be used but require more medium and more manipulation for a given amount of virus.

(b) Cultures are infected with about 1 pfu/cell and kept at 37°C for a week before harvesting.

(c) The cells are shaken or scraped off the glass into the medium (ethylenediaminetetraacetate may also be used to detach the cells from the glass but this should not be necessary if the cultures are heavily infected). The cells and medium from each bottle are then transferred to a centrifuge bottle, 5% by volume of 0.4 *M* phosphate buffer (pH 5.6) added and the bottles cooled to 4°C. The low pH and temperature ensure that most of the virus is adsorbed to the cells, leaving a minimum in the medium (10^2 HAU/ml or less). The bottles are then centrifuged at low speed (15 minutes at 2000 *g*) and the supernatant discarded.

(d) The cells are then suspended in 2.5 ml per 10^8 cells of tris saline (TD of Smith *et al.*, 1960) and samples taken to check for bacterial contamination. The bottles are stored at 4°C while awaiting the results of the tests. Samples free from contamination are then grouped (4×10^8 cells from four bottles in 10 ml of TD makes a convenient unit). The cells are now transferred to flasks and frozen and thawed three times.

(e) To each 10 ml of suspension 2.5 ml of RDE is added and the suspension incubated at 37°C for 24 hours. The RDE can be prepared as described by Burnet (1948) or House (1967) or commercial preparations used. For large scale operation it is well worthwhile to prepare RDE since impure preparations are quite usable. Commercial RDE is often unnecessarily pure and may contain undesirable preservatives but for small scale operation may be convenient. After RDE treatment the suspension is made alkaline by adding 5% by volume of *M* $NaHCO_3$, warmed to 37°C and the cell debris spun off (15 minutes at 2000 *g*). The pellet is then washed with 10 ml of warm tris saline and resuspended in 10 ml of tris saline.

All fractions from (e) onward are retained and the RDE treatment monitored as follows. A small sample (0.1 ml) is taken from each fraction (including the resuspended cell debris) and diluted 100- and 10,000-fold in phosphate-buffered saline. The dilutions are incubated at 37°C for 30 minutes to allow the virus to dissociate from any HA inhibitors present. Hemagglutination assays are then made and a balance sheet constructed to account for all the virus, making due allowance for the different volumes of the various fractions. If more than 10–20% of the virus is left in the cell debris after one RDE extraction it may be worthwhile to recycle this material, adding another 2.5 ml of RDE and proceeding as described in (e).

With experience the RDE treatment may be adjusted, adding more enzyme if it is often necessary to recycle samples, or reducing the amount of enzyme to economize and reduce the carryover of RDE into the virus stocks.

The RDE extracts prepared as above have titers of 10^5 to 10^6 HAU/ml and may be used directly for many purposes. The RDE and other enzymes in the suspension do not interfere with virus adsorption for transformation or infection of cells when the suspensions are diluted 50-fold or more.

The strain of polyoma virus used will affect the details of the procedure to some extent. Large plaque virus adsorbs less strongly, under the same conditions, than small plaque virus (Diamond and Crawford, 1964). This means that it is necessary to be more careful to keep suspensions cold and acid to prevent the virus coming off the cell debris. Also, the HA assay must be done in the cold with cold reagents to obtain correct values. With small plaque virus this is relatively unimportant.

IV. Concentration and Purification

Any dilute virus suspension may be concentrated by spinning down the virus (80,000 *g* for 2 hours) and resuspending in a small volume. Samples in which HA inhibitors are present are best treated with RDE [as described in (e)], after concentration, if not already so treated. Treatment with nucleases and proteolytic enzymes may also be inserted at this stage if desired. Since polyoma virus particles also contain pieces of host DNA there is little point in trying to reduce external contamination to a very low level at this stage.

The basic operation, once the virus has been concentrated, is equilibrium density gradient centrifugation. Using the SW 39 rotor of the Spinco model L centrifuge the following quantities are convenient.

Five grams of RbCl are dissolved in tris buffer (0.05 *M*, pH 8.0, 7.6 ml) and distributed, 3 ml into each of three plastic centrifuge tubes (2 by ½ inch). One milliliter of virus suspension is then layered onto each tube and stirred into the top half of the gradient. After spinning at 30,000 rpm for 24 hours at 10 ± 5° the tubes are inspected in a beam of light. If there is sufficient virus two major opalescent bands will be visible, one in the lower third of the tube (full particles) and another near the middle of the tube (empty particles). Cell membrane fragments and soluble proteins are left at the top of the gradient. Visible bands can be collected from the top of the tube with a fine Pasteur pipette held in the meniscus or from the bottom of the tube by collecting drops. If there is not enough virus to give opalescent bands the gradients can be fractionated and HA assays performed to locate the virus bands.

Refractive index determinations are also useful to determine the density at various points in the gradient. If such determinations are to be made samples must be read as soon as possible after collection, before significant evaporation can occur. All other determinations can be made later without affecting results.

A simple way of collecting gradient fractions is as shown in Fig. 1. The tube is held in a vertical position and sealed with a rubber bung penetrated by a short piece of glass tubing. Attached to the glass tubing is a short piece of rubber tubing which can be closed with a screw clip. The bottom of the centrifuge tube is then wiped clean and a thin film of silicone grease applied to it. The screw clip is then opened and closed and a *small* hole made in the bottom of the tube with a pin or needle, preferably slightly off center. Avoid jerking the tube at any time, particularly during this operation. The gradient is now ready for collection and the containers for the samples are placed in position. The screw clip is loosened until drops come out at a suitable rate. The tube can be illuminated during collection and the opalescence in the drops observed as they form. This allows a more precise separation of the visible bands.

It should be emphasized that it is not necessary to use swinging bucket rotors for these gradients. Fixed-angle rotors are quite suitable, although it is then necessary to add mineral oil (liquid paraffin) on top of the gradients to keep the highly corrosive salt solution away from the metal tube cap. Angle heads do in fact give better resolution, as well as increased capacity. Using the No. 50 or No. 50 Ti rotors of the Spinco model L, 40,000 rpm would be a suitable speed. Nor is it necessary to spin gradients at high speeds. Higher speeds generate steeper gradients and therefore reduce the radial distance between particles of different densities. Setting up the gradients by layering has several advantages. The gradients form more quickly, although preformed gradients would of course be even quicker, but necessitate

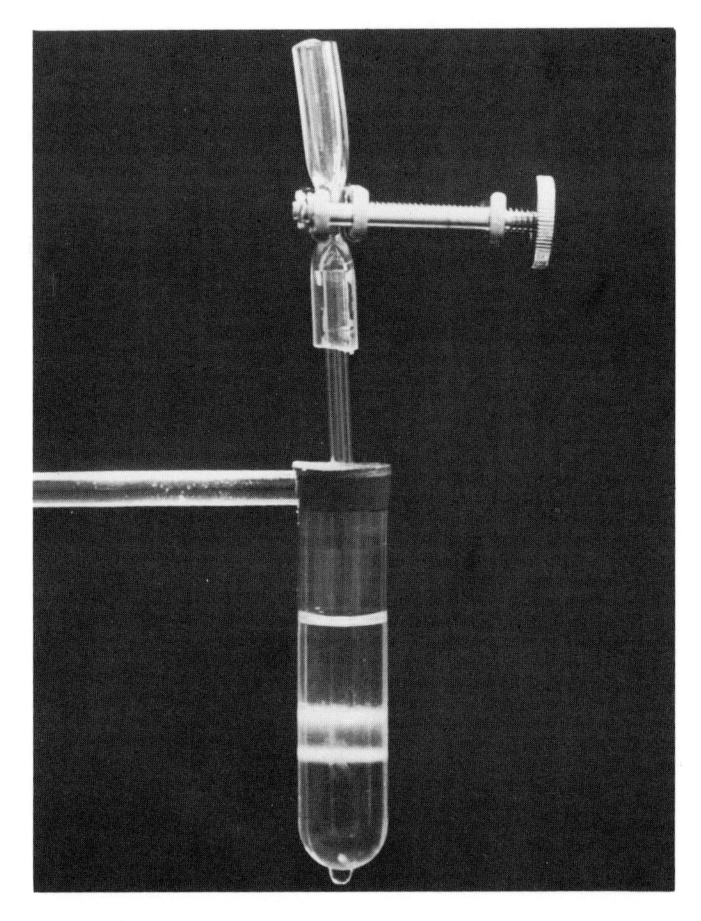

FIG. 1. Equilibrium density gradient in the process of collection.

more manipulations. More important is that an element of velocity centrifugation is introduced. The virus sediments to its equilibrium position almost as soon as the gradient has formed, but small molecules may still be far from their equilibrium positions at the end of the run and well clear of the virus bands. An alternative recipe using CsCl instead of RbCl as described would require 4.8 gm of CsCl and 7.8 ml of buffer for three SW 39 tubes, each taking 1 ml of virus suspension. For larger scale operation these amounts are simply increased as needed, keeping the same ratio between the weight of CsCl and the total volume of buffer plus virus suspension.

It is not necessary to use RbCl or CsCl of very high purity for these gradients. As long as the solutions are not discolored the buffer present should ensure that the pH is not disturbed by impurities present in the salt. If there is insoluble material in the salt this should be removed by filtration through filter paper (preferably "hardened" type) otherwise it may make drop collection difficult. If for some purposes it is desirable to avoid Rb or Cs ions, saturated NaBr can be substituted for RbCl.

The dense salt from gradient fractions can be removed by dialysis or the samples can be diluted with the required buffer and the virus spun down (80,000 *g* for 2 hours, or longer if the samples are diluted less than 1:4). Cross contamination between full and empty bands should only be of the order of a few percent. This can be reduced by recycling the virus through another equilibrium density gradient (as described above) after ultrasonicating the suspension to break up any aggregates present. Alternatively, the virus can be further purified by zone centrifugation through sucrose density gradients, full particles (240 S) and empty particles (140 S) being easily separated from aggregates.

REFERENCES

Bruner, R., and Vinograd, J. (1965). *Biochim. Biophys. Acta* **108**, 18.
Burnet, F. M. (1948). *Lancet* **I**, 254.
Crawford, L. V. (1962). *Virology* **18**, 177.
Diamond, L., and Crawford, L. V. (1964). *Virology* **22**, 235.
Hartley, J. W., and Rowe, W. P. (1959). *Virology* **7**, 249.
House, W. (1967). *Lab. Pract.* **16**, 321.
House, W., and Wildy, P. (1965). *Lab. Pract.* **14**, 594.
Smith, J. D., Freeman, G., Vogt, M., and Dulbecco, R. (1960). *Virology* **12**, 185.
Winocour, E. (1963). *Virology* **19**, 158.

10. Purification of Influenza Virus

W. G. Laver

Department of Microbiology
John Curtin School of Medical Research
Australian National University
Canberra, Australia

I. Introduction

The purification of influenza virus presents problems which are not encountered with the nonenveloped viruses. These result from the nature of the virus and the way it is released (by budding) from cells. Particles of these viruses contain, as integral and essential constituents, lipids and carbohydrates from the host cells and possibly host cell proteins as well, although the presence of these in the virus has never been conclusively demonstrated. Therefore, purified preparations of influenza virus will always contain host cell material and it is difficult to decide what proportion of this represents part of the virus and how much is contaminating cell debris. In addition, the virus particles are not uniform in size and probably vary to some extent also in density.

Influenza viruses are usually grown in the allantoic sac of 11-day-old chick embryos, but they may also be grown in a variety of cultured cells. The virus particles are best purified from infected allantoic fluid or from infected growth media by adsorption onto and elution from erythrocytes followed by differential centrifugation and banding in density gradients. Yields of virus are usually followed by assaying for hemagglutinin activity (Fazekas de St. Groth and Webster, 1966). Assays for infectivity (Fazekas de St. Groth and White, 1958) complement fixation or neuraminidase activity (Laver, 1963) may also be carried out.

II. Apparatus

(a) Refrigerated centrifuge.
(b) Ultracentrifuge: Spinco model L with SW 25 rotor.
(c) Machine for making and sampling linear sucrose gradients such as the apparatus described by Britten and Roberts (1960).
(d) Water bath (37°C).

III. Reagents

(a) Supply of fresh chicken or human red cells.
(b) Bacterial (*V. cholerae*) neuraminidase: This may be obtained from Behringwerke AG, Marburg, Germany.

IV. Procedure

A. Adsorption onto and Elution from Erythrocytes

Influenza viruses adsorb to red cells in the cold, attaching by means of their hemagglutinin subunits to specific mucoprotein receptors on the surfaces of the cells. When the cell-virus complexes are warmed up, the viral neuraminidase destroys these receptors and the virus elutes from the cells. Some strains of influenza virus, e.g., A_0/NWS, have no neuraminidase activity when grown under standard conditions; the enzyme of these strains is very heat labile and is usually inactivated completely before the allantoic fluid is harvested. These viruses can only be eluted from red cells after the addition of bacterial (*V. cholerae*) neuraminidase. On the other hand, there are some strains with full neuraminidase activity, which will neither elute from red cells spontaneously nor after the addition of bacterial neuraminidase (e.g., $A_2/RI/5^+$; Choppin and Tamm, 1960). Others (e.g., A_0/BEL) will elute spontaneously from chicken red cells but not from human red cells. Therefore the method of adsorption-elution described below, while generally applicable, may need to be modified for use with certain strains.

Virus-infected allantoic fluid (or media from infected cell cultures) is centrifuged (2000 *g*, 15 minutes) and the supernatant is filtered through glass wool to remove floating debris. The fluid is chilled (0-2°C) in an ice bath and cold, washed, packed chicken or human red cells are stirred in. The volume of cells added will depend on the amount of virus in the infected fluid. Fluid having a hemagglutinin titer of $10^{3.3}$ hemagglutinin units/ml requires 2% (v/v) of chicken red cells for complete adsorption. (One hemagglutinin unit is defined as the amount of virus causing partial agglutination—15% dimers—of 0.25 ml of 0.5% chick erythrocytes.) If less virus is present, proportionally less red cells should be added.

The cells are stirred gently for 1 hour at 0°C, then centrifuged in the cold. The supernatant is removed and assayed for hemagglutinin to determine if all of the virus has been adsorbed by the cells. If an appreciable amount of virus (more than about 10%) is present in the supernatant, this should be saved and readsorbed later with more cells. Otherwise it is discarded. The heavily agglutinated cells are washed once with a volume of ice-cold saline (0.15 *M* NaCl) equivalent to that of the original allantoic fluid. The washings are discarded and the cells are then suspended in warm saline (one-tenth the volume of the original allantoic fluid) and the virus is allowed to elute for 1 hour at 37°C. The amount of virus which has eluted should be tested by removing samples at intervals, centrifuging off the cells and assaying the supernatants for hemagglutinin activity. [If bacterial (*V. cholerae*) neuraminidase is used to elute the virus, the cells must be suspended in saline containing 0.1% (w/v) $CaCl_2$.] After 1 hour when the virus has usually eluted completely the cells are removed by centrifugation and the virus eluate (the supernatant fluid) is stored at 4°C with 0.08% (w/v) sodium azide added to prevent bacterial growth. With some strains of virus considerable hemolysis occurs, even if fresh cells are used, and the eluates are colored red. With other strains no hemolysis occurs, and the eluates are almost colorless and slightly opalescent. Approximately 80-100% of the virus in the allantoic fluid should be recovered in the eluate.

B. Sedimentation through a Sucrose Gradient

The virus is further purified by centrifugation at low speed (4000 *g*, 15 minutes) to remove particulate contaminants and then at high speed (40,000 *g*, 30 minutes) to pellet the virus particles. These are resuspended in saline (one-tenth the volume of the eluate), centrifuged at low speed (2000 *g*, 10 minutes) to remove large particles, and the supernatant is layered onto sucrose gradients. The concentrated virus suspension (1–2 ml) is layered onto a 28 ml linear sucrose gradient (10–40% sucrose in saline buffered with 0.01 *M* sodium phosphate, pH 7.5) and centrifuged in the Spinco SW 25 rotor at 15,000 rpm for 40 minutes. A hole is then made in the bottom of the tube, just to one side of the pellet, and fractions (2 ml) are collected through this hole. The main virus band will have sedimented about one-third the way down the tube and should be opalescent and easily visible. The main band should contain about 65% of the virus applied to the gradient (assayed as hemagglutinin). Virus is also distributed throughout the bottom of the gradient and is present in the pellet, but these last two fractions are discarded. The main virus fraction is diluted with saline and centrifuged (40,000 *g*, 2 hours). The pellet of virus, straw-colored and quite clear, is resuspended in saline containing 0.08% sodium azide to give a white, highly opalescent suspension, and stored at 4°C. Preparations of virus from eluates heavily contaminated with hemoglobin may contain adsorbed hemoglobin and be red in color. Often this dissociates from the virus after standing at 4°C for several weeks, and the virus particles may then be recentrifuged and resuspended.

V. Assessment of Purity

A number of criteria can be applied when assessing the purity of preparations of influenza virus, but none is really satisfactory. Electron microscopy will show whether particulate contaminants are present and a measure of the hemagglutinin/dry weight ratio will give a rough estimate of the degree of purification achieved. It is possible to prepare radioactively labeled uninfected allantoic fluid, to mix this with the infected, nonradioactive fluid, purify the virus using radioactively labeled red cells, and measure the amount of radioactive host cell and red cell contaminants present in the final virus preparation. Unfortunately, because of the way in which the virus is budded off from the cell surface, the main contaminants likely to be present are pieces of membrane from disrupted cells containing viral antigens. These will adsorb to and elute from red cells like virus and will, of course, be absent from the radioactive (uninfected) allantoic fluid. Thus, measurement of the amount of label in the purified virus may give an overoptimistic estimate of the purity of the virus particles. Immunological tests for the presence of host cell contaminants cannot easily be used because host antigens are incorporated also into the virus particles.

VI. Alternative Methods of Purification

A very large number of methods have been described for the purification of influenza viruses, but most of these appear to offer few advantages over the method outlined here. However, if pure virus of high infectivity is required, a method such as that described by Pons (1967) may be more suitable. Methods for the large scale purification of influenza virus using a zonal-ultracentrifuge rotor have also been described (Reimer *et al.*, 1966).

REFERENCES

Britten, R. J., and Roberts, R. B. (1960). *Science* **131**, 32.
Choppin, P. W., and Tamm, I. (1960). *J. Exptl. Med.* **112**, 895.
Fazekas de St. Groth, S., and Webster, R. G. (1966). *J. Exptl. Med.* **124**, 331.
Fazekas de St. Groth, S., and White, D. O. (1958). *J. Hyg.* **56**, 151.
Laver, W. G. (1963). *Virology* **20**, 251.
Pons, M. W. (1967). *Virology* **31**, 523.
Reimer, C. B., Baker, R. S., Newlin, T. E., Havens, M. L., Van Frank, R. M., Storvick, W. O., and Miller, R. P. (1966). *J. Bacteriol.* **92**, 1271.

11. Temperature-Sensitive Mutants of Animal Viruses: Isolation and Preliminary Characterization

E. R. Pfefferkorn

Microbiology Department
Dartmouth Medical School
Hanover, New Hampshire

I. Introduction and Definition of Terms

Fenner (1965) has pointed out that many problems related to the genetics of animal viruses can be attacked through the use of conditional-lethal mutants. The most readily selected conditional-lethal mutants are temperature-sensitive (*ts*) mutants, which form plaques at a low (permissive) temperature but not at a high (nonpermissive) temperature. At the molecular level, these mutants are defective in intracellular growth because an altered amino acid sequence in some essential virus-determined protein renders that protein incapable of assuming or perhaps maintaining a functional configuration at the nonpermissive temperature. These mutants thus depend upon a fundamental property common to all proteins rather than upon a specific function. Mutants defective in a given protein can be isolated even though nothing is known of that protein's function.

We present here our current procedures for the study of *ts* mutants of Sindbis virus in chick fibroblast cultures (Burge and Pfefferkorn, 1966a,b) together with suggestions for the study of other viruses.

II. Definition of the Wild Type Virus and Choice of Permissive and Nonpermissive Temperatures

Any convenient strain of virus can be designated the "wild type." The most desirable characteristic of a wild type strain is the ready formation of plaques over a reasonably wide range of temperature. The first task, in fact, is the determination of this range of temperature in a series of trials at intervals of 1°C and then 0.5°C. Incubators with good temperature control (±0.3°C) and minimal thermal gradients are essential, especially when the maximum temperature is sought. Several standardized thermometers should be used simultaneously to detect any gradient. We use anhydric incubators of the National Appliance Co., Portland, Oregon for closed bottles, although water-jacketed models would probably be preferable.

The nonpermissive temperature actually used in the selection of mutants should be 0.5°C below the maximum to allow for minor fluctuations in incubator temperature. Precise control of the lower temperature is not as critical. Hence, any convenient permissive temperature can be used. A greater difference between the chosen permissive and nonpermissive temperatures makes the isolation and study of *ts* mutants easier. However, a very long incubation for plaque formation at the low temperature may test both the patience of the investigator and the integrity of the cells.

Our plaque assays for Sindbis virus are incubated at 40°C for 40 hours (nonpermissive) or at 28–30°C for 3–4 days (permissive).

III. Mutagenesis

Spontaneous mutation to a *ts* genotype is probably rare in most animal viruses. Hence, prior chemical mutagenesis greatly facilitates the isolation of *ts* mutants. In our limited experience only nitrosoguanidine and nitrous acid have conclusively increased the frequency of *ts* mutants. The single mutant ascribed to ethylmethane sulfonate may well have been spontaneous (Burge and Pfefferkorn, 1966a).

It is advisable to take all possible measures to avoid the repeated isolation of the same mutant. Hence, before chemical mutagenesis a wild-type stock should be freed of possible preexisting *ts* mutants by growth at the nonpermissive temperature. We infect cultures with a multiplicity of about 0.01pfu/cell and incubate at 40°C for 12 hours. The culture medium is then stored at −60°C.

For nitrous acid mutagenesis, 1 ml of tissue culture medium containing virus is mixed with 1 ml of 1 *M* potassium phosphate buffer, pH 6.7, and 2 ml of freshly prepared 4 *M* $NaNO_2$. Infectivity is reduced at an exponential rate until the reaction is slowed by more than 100-fold at 2 hours by adjusting the pH to approximately 8.0 with 0.45 ml of 1 *N* KOH. All of the residual nitrite is removed at 4°C by extensive dialysis against Hanks' BSS (bicarbonate omitted). After the addition of rabbit serum to preserve infectivity the nitrous acid-treated virus is stored at −60°C for subsequent scoring.

The point at which killing by nitrous acid should be halted depends in part upon the initial titer of virus used. We have found that when the titer of Sindbis virus is reduced by a factor of 10^{-5} approximately 1% of the survivors are *ts* mutants.

The acid lability of Sindbis virus requires that nitrous acid treatment be carried out at a high pH. A high buffer concentration is used to insure good pH control in the presence of 2 *M* $NaNO_2$. Any virus not so sensitive to acid could be treated at a lower pH with reduced buffer and $NaNO_2$ concentrations. In defining the conditions for nitrous acid treatment, a control in which NaCl replaces $NaNO_2$ should always be included to insure that the lethal event is actually associated with HNO_2. Care should be taken to remove the nitrite completely before storage of the treated virus to prevent continued reaction that will reduce the titer even at −60°C.

In mutagenesis with *N*-methyl-*N′*-nitro-*N*-nitrosoguanidine (Aldrich Chemical Co., Milwaukee, Wisconsin) 100 μg of the crystalline compound is dissolved in 1 ml. of tissue culture fluid containing Sindbis virus. After 15 minutes at room temperature, we remove the nitrosoguanidine by extensive dialysis at 4°C and store the virus at −60°C as described above. This treatment with nitrosoguanidine reduces the viral titer by a factor of about 10^{-3}. We know nothing of the kinetics of killing. Approximately 1% of the survivors are *ts* mutants.

Caution: Nitrosoguanidine should be considered a potent carcinogen and handled with extreme caution to avoid ingestion, contact with the skin, or inhalation of aerosols.

The choice of chemical mutagens undoubtedly depends upon the nature of the particular virus employed. For example, we have had no success with fluorouracil although this analog is a potent mutagen for the production of *ts* mutants of polio virus (Cooper, 1964).

We do not regrow viral stocks after mutagenesis with nitrous acid or nitrosoguanidine because the genome of Sindbis virus is single stranded. For those viruses that contain double stranded RNA or DNA, regrowth after chemical mutagenesis should increase the probability of isolating *ts* mutants. Since these mutants are by definition recessive, the nonmutagenized strand should mask the effect of most induced mutations. Regrowth will yield genomes in which the mutation is represented in both strands. However, regrowth after mutagenesis poses the danger of repeated isolation of the progeny of one mutant. To eliminate this possibility the mutagenized virus can be regrown in a series of independent cultures. Each of the resulting stocks should be discarded as soon as one mutant has been isolated from it. A high input multiplicity, for example, 10 pfu/cell, will increase the chances that each stock contains an induced mutant.

IV. Isolation of *ts* Mutants from Mutagenized Viral Stocks

There is no generally reliable way to select *ts* mutants; they are usually found by blindly scoring viral clones for ability to form plaques at the permissive and nonpermissive temperatures. We isolate clones of Sindbis virus from single plaques produced at the permissive temperature. Both the usual plaque assay using an agar overlay of monolayer cultures (see Chapters 14–18) or the agar-cell suspension method described by Cooper (1955) are used. The latter method has the advantage that the plaques, which lie on the surface, are more accessible. In either case a plaque is sampled by removing a plug of agar with a sterile Pyrex tube. This plug is transferred to a tube containing 1 ml of Hanks' BSS containing 2% rabbit serum and held at 4°C for 1 day. At the end of this time the fluid contains 300–3000 pfu. Although reasonably well isolated plaques are chosen for the clones, absolute elimination of contamination from adjacent plaques is *not* essential at this point. If 99% of the virus comes from one clone its genotype (*ts* or wild) is easily defined.

Since chemical mutagenesis increases the frequency of *ts* mutants to only 1%, many wild types have to be tested and rejected to secure each mutant. For convenience, we prefer to test each clone initially only at the nonpermissive temperature. A volume of 0.25 ml serves as the inoculum in a standard plaque assay on monolayers in 1 ounce prescription bottles. In this step most of the clones produce an uncountably large number of plaques and are discarded. A few yield 0–10 plaques; the refrigerated samples corresponding to these clones are reassayed at the nonpermissive temperature (undiluted) and at the permissive temperature (undiluted and at a 10^{-2} dilution). Those clones that appear on reassay to be *ts* mutants are cloned again by inoculating a culture with virus from a well-isolated plaque from the 10^{-2} dilution. After 24 hours at 28°C the culture medium is removed and stored at −60°C.

This blind selection of mutants is tedious but reliable. Much time is saved when *ts* mutants can be distinguished from the wild type by plaque morphology. Fields (1968) has used incubation at two temperatures to make this distinction with reovirus. An agar-overlayed culture is incubated at the permissive temperature for the minimal time required for plaque formation. The locations and particularly the diameters of the resulting plaques are then indicated by suitable marks on the culture vessel. The culture is then incubated at the nonpermissive temperature for a period sufficient for significant enlargement of wild type plaques. Those plaques that fail to increase in diameter during the second incubation period contain potential *ts* mutants. In our hands, this method does not work with Sindbis virus. But its simplicity recommends it to all laboratories seeking *ts* mutants of animal viruses.

If the newly isolated mutant strain is to be optimally useful, its back mutation frequency should be relatively low. This parameter is determined from plaque titrations performed at both the permissive and nonpermissive temperatures. The ratio of wild type revertants to mutants (the back mutation frequency) is less than 5×10^{-5} for about half of the *ts* mutants that we isolate.

Stocks of *ts* mutants prepared for use in genetic and biochemical experiments should contain minimal numbers of back mutants to the wild type. To prepare such stocks it is necessary to know the back mutation frequency of the primary stock used to supply the inoculum. We use a dilution of the primary stock so great that it is unlikely that any wild type virus is introduced. For example, if the back mutation frequency is 10^{-5} an inoculum of 10^3 pfu would have only a 1% chance of containing a wild type. New back mutations will, of course, occur during the growth at the permissive temperature but this procedure will minimize their frequency in the final stock, especially if, as is often true, the wild type grows more rapidly than the *ts* mutant even at the permissive temperature. With certain mutants it may be necessary to grow several stocks simultaneously and keep only the ones that, by chance, have the lowest frequency of back mutants.

After one *ts* mutant has been isolated an alternative approach to mutant selection is possible. At some temperature between the permissive and nonpermissive levels this mutant will produce microplaques. Similar microplaques will be found when mutagenized virus is titrated at this intermediate temperature, and a significant fraction of these will prove to represent *ts* mutants. But it is important to note that some *ts* mutants may not be detected by this method since the intermediate temperature for microplaque formation may not be the same for all.

V. Preliminary Characterization of *ts* Mutants

The detailed genetic and biochemical study of *ts* mutants is beyond the scope of this discussion. In brief, two approaches are available for the genetic analysis, recombination and complementation. In each approach two different *ts* mutants are used to infect three cultures. Two of the cultures, the controls, receive solitary infections with each of the mutants at an adsorbed multiplicity of 5 to 20 pfu/cell. The third, experimental, culture is mixedly infected with the same multiplicities of both mutants. To detect complementation the three cultures are incubated at the nonpermissive temperature, and the viral yield of the mixed infection is compared with the sum of the yields from the control infections (all titrated at the permissive temperature).

With Sindbis *ts* mutants, we measure the virus produced between 1 and 6 hours after infection. Typical results of complementation between Sindbis virus mutants have been recorded (Burge and Pfefferkorn, 1966b).

If the two mutants complement one another the mixed infection will be significantly more productive although its yield may not approach that of the wild type virus under similar conditions. A positive result in a complementation test suggests that the two mutants are defective in different functions but the possibility of intracistronic complementation cannot be ignored (Fincham, 1966).

To detect recombination the three cultures described above are incubated at the permissive temperature. The resulting viral crops are titrated at both the permissive and the nonpermissive temperatures. The yields measured at the permissive temperature should be quite similar. If recombination has occurred, the yield from the mixedly infected culture should contain a higher fraction of pfu's able to form plaques at the nonpermissive temperature. No recombination has, as yet, been detected between *ts* mutants of Sindbis virus (Burge and Pfefferkorn, 1966b).

Perhaps the most fundamental biochemical characteristic of *ts* mutants is the ability or inability to stimulate the synthesis of viral nucleic acid at the nonpermissive temperature. This property can easily be detected with most small RNA and DNA viruses by extracting nucleic acid from the infected cell and titrating its infectivity (see Chapters 14 and 17). There are several alternatives to direct assay of infectious nucleic acid; for example, incorporation of a labeled precursor into RNA in the presence of actinomycin D can be used with several different RNA viruses. The DNA of several herpes viruses has a much higher guanine-cytosine ratio than cellular DNA, allowing separation on the basis of buoyant density (see Chapter 45).

Further analysis of the individual defects of *ts* mutants will lead into biochemical and morphogenetic problems that can be attacked by many of the techniques described in this volume.

VI. Scope and Limitations

Temperature-sensitive mutants provide the best available method to explore the entire genome of an animal virus although there are cistrons in which *ts* mutations cannot be isolated. By definition, only essential cistrons can yield conditional-lethal mutants; the thymidine kinase function of vaccinia virus, for example, is known not to be essential (Dubbs and Kit, 1964). Moreover, extensive experience with bacteriophage has suggested that *ts* defects in certain essential proteins may be very rare or perhaps impossible (Epstein *et al.*, 1963). Supressor-sensitive (*su*) mutants have proved to be a profitable alterative to *ts* mutants in bacteriophage (Epstein *et al.*, 1963). A detailed consideration of the nature of these conditional-lethal mutants is beyond the scope of this discussion. The permissive and nonpermissive conditions for *su* mutants are not temperature but growth in two genetically different host cells. The cells differ in their capacity to translate messenger RNA that contains certain triplets. Mutants that have lost the ability to grow in certain cells but not others have been described in rabbit pox virus (Sambrook *et al.*, 1966). Whether these actually resemble the *su* mutants of microbial systems must await further understanding of their nature.

REFERENCES

Burge, B. W., and Pfefferkorn, E. R. (1966a). *Virology* **30**, 204-213.
Burge, B. W., and Pfefferkorn, E. R. (1966b). *Virology* **30**, 214-223.
Cooper, P. D. (1955). *Virology* **1**, 397-401.
Cooper, P. D. (1964). *Virology* **22**, 186-192.
Dubbs, D. R., and Kit, S. (1964). *Virology* **22**, 214-225.
Epstein, R. H., Bolle, A., Steinberg, C. M., Kellenberger, E., Boy De LaTour, E., Chevalley, R., Edgar, R. S., Susman, M., Denhardt, G. H., and Lielausis, A. (1963). *Cold Spring Harbor Symp. Quant. Biol.* **28**, 375-394.
Fenner, F. (1965). *Perspectives Virol.* **4**, 34-45.
Fields, B. (1968). Personal communication.
Fincham, J. R. S. (1966). "Genetic Complementation." Benjamin, New York.
Sambrook, J. F., Padgett, B. L., and Tomkins, J. K. N. (1966). *Virology* **28**, 592-599.

12. Purification and Separation of Encephalomyocarditis Virus Variants by Chromatography on Calcium Phosphate

Alfred T. H. Burness

Virus Research Unit
Medical Research Council Laboratories
Woodmansterne Road
Carshalton, Surrey, England

I. Introduction

Calcium phosphate is capable of adsorbing at low phosphate buffer concentrations a wide range of materials, including nucleic acids, proteins, and viruses, which can usually be recovered by elution with higher concentrations of phosphate buffer. This property is used in the chromatographic purification of viruses by selecting conditions for adsorption and elution of the virus which differ from those required by the contaminating material.

Linear gradient elution is used to determine the concentrations of phosphate required to elute the virus and contaminants, respectively. Then a more complex gradient is designed which will give maximum separation of these phosphate concentrations in the chromatographic profile, thus leading to greater separation of virus from contaminants.

Calcium phosphate chromatography is also capable of separating variants present in uncloned virus. Linear gradient elution gives information on the concentration of phosphate buffer to elute the leading and trailing edges of the virus peak. Then a gradient is devised which will give maximum separation of these phosphate molarities and subsequently the variants eluted by them.

The use of this approach will be illustrated using as a model first the purification and then the separation of variants of the K-2 strain (Hoskins and Sanders, 1957) of encephalomyocarditis (EMC) virus. The elution gradients required for this purpose may not apply to other viruses or even to other strains of EMC virus, but it is considered that the principles involved should apply generally.

II. Materials and Methods

A. Reagents

Most of the chemicals required are common laboratory reagents and all are obtainable from the British Drug Houses, Ltd., Poole, Dorset, England.

0.5 *M* calcium chloride: This is mixed with 0.5 *M* Na_2HPO_4 to make the calcium phosphate, 80 ml being required for a single column. Dissolve 109.5 gm of $CaCl_2 \cdot 6H_2O$ in 1000 ml of water.

0.5 *M* disodium hydrogen phosphate: The minimum required is 120 ml per column. Dissolve 179.1 gm of $Na_2HPO_4 \cdot 12H_2O$ in 1000 ml of water. Add chloroform to both solutions as a preservative.

1 *M* phosphate buffer, pH 6.8–7.0: Dissolve separately 95.1 gm of anhydrous Na_2HPO_4 and 44.9 gm of KH_2PO_4, each in 500 ml of water, then mix with vigorous stirring. 0.5 *M*, 0.32 *M*, 0.05 *M* and 0.005 *M* phosphate buffers: These are required for gradient elution and, in addition, the 0.005 *M* phosphate is used for washing the calcium phosphate. Prepare by dilution of 1 *M* phosphate buffer.

Bromocresol purple: This is used for checking the uniformity of packing of the calcium phosphate column. Dilute standard indicator solution with 2 volumes of 10% sucrose in 0.005 *M* phosphate buffer.

Reagents for phosphate determination.

10 *N* sulfuric acid: Dilute 70 ml concentrated H_2SO_4 in water to 250 ml.

2.5% ammonium molybdate in water.

Reducing agent: Dissolve 15.0 gm of sodium metabisulfite and 0.5 gm of sodium sulfite together in 250 ml of water using gentle heat to 60°C; add slowly with stirring 0.25 gm of 1-amino-2-naphthol-4-sulfonic acid until dissolved. Store the reagent in a brown bottle and use within 2 weeks.

Stock 0.01 *M* potassium dihydrogen phosphate: Dissolve 0.1361 gm of freshly dried KH_2PO_4 in 100 ml of water. Dilute 1 in 100 as a standard for phosphate determination.

B. Apparatus

Chromatographic pumps, with adjustable output: These are required (1) in the preparation of calcium phosphate by pumping at 1.7 and 2.6 ml/minute, 0.5 *M* $CaCl_2$ and 0.5 *M* Na_2HPO_4, respectively, simultaneously, and (2) for pumping at 3 ml/minute the eluting phosphate buffers during chromatography. A single DCL (Distillers Company Limited) micropump, Series II, fitted with three size 1 plunger heads, and made by F.A. Hughes & Co., Ltd., Great Burgh, Epsom, Surrey, England, is ideal.

100, 50, and 25 ml graduated cylinders and stopwatch: These measure flow rates from the chromatographic pumps and make up the autograd.

500 ml graduated, glass cylinder and magnetic stirrer with bar: These are used for mixing $CaCl_2$ and Na_2HPO_4 to make calcium phosphate.

Glass chromatography column: A 2.5 cm diameter by 20 cm length is used. A Pharmacia Sephadex column, reduced in length, allows a fast flow rate and is ideal.

Autograd: This is a multichambered device for preparing simple or complex gradients (Peterson and Sober, 1959); the one made by the Technicon Co. is used.

Three glass reservoirs: Two supply the pumps with $CaCl_2$ and Na_2HPO_4 for making calcium phosphate, while the third contains 0.005 *M* phosphate for washing the column.

Fraction collector: One which can accommodate up to 80 tubes of 8 ml capacity or more is necessary.

Spectrophotometer: A Unicam SP500, capable of measuring optical densities at a wavelength of 260 mμ, is required.

Tygon tubing: This is used for carrying eluting solvent from the autograd via the pump to the chromatography column and then on to the fraction collector.

Disposable pipettes: These are useful for applying sample to column.

C. Assay Procedures

Hemagglutinin activity is measured on column samples in plastic serology trays, using sheep red blood cells (0.1% v/v) in a diluent consisting of 1 part glucose solution (4.5% w/v) plus 1 part phosphate-buffered saline with gelatin (0.05% w/v) added.

Infectivity assays using mice or plaque assay (Sanders *et al.*, 1958) are not convenient as routine procedures because of the time required for the result (2–3 days), but are necessary if the distribution of plaque size variants in the chromatographic profile is being sought.

Ultraviolet light (uv) absorption measurements are made routinely at 260 mμ. Once the relationship between the points of elution of virus and of uv absorbing contaminants have been determined for crude virus, the contaminants can be used as internal markers. Alternatively, if the virus has been partially purified and is reasonably free of uv absorbing impurities and is in sufficient quantity (equivalent to 1 ml containing about 8.0 optical density units at 260 mμ or 1 mg for EMC virus per column), it can be detected by its optical density.

The radioactivity of virus labeled with ^{32}P, ^{14}C, ^{3}H, etc., can be detected in the collected fraction with conventional counting equipment.

Phosphate determinations are required to check that the elution gradient is correctly set up and essential if the design of a different gradient to achieve better resolution in a particular part of the elution profile is contemplated. Every other sample is tested by using essentially the technique of Fiske and Subbarow (1925) in the following way. Take 2 ml sample diluted to about 0.0002 *M* phosphate concentration, which will produce an optical density of about 0.6 at 800 mμ. Add 0.1 ml of 10 *N* H_2SO_4, 0.2 ml 2.5% molybdate, and 0.1 ml reducing agent, mixing thoroughly between additions. Run a blank containing water together with 0.0001 *M* phosphate standards at the same time. After 10 minutes read at 800 mμ. Phosphate molarity of undiluted sample = 0.0001 × OD at 800 mμ of dilute sample × dilution/OD at 800 mμ of 0.0001 *M* standard.

D. Chromatographic Procedures

1. Preparation of Calcium Phosphate (Brushite Form)

Pump 0.5 *M* $CaCl_2$ and 0.5 *M* Na_2HPO_4 at 1.7 and 2.6 ml/minute,[1*] respectively, simultaneously into a 500 ml graduated cylinder already containing 50 ml of water being slowly stirred magnetically, until the volume reaches 250 ml. Wash the calcium phosphate so produced six times to remove "fines" by addition of 0.005 *M* phosphate to the 500 ml mark, inverting the cylinder two or three times, allowing the cal-

*Superscript numbers refer to numbered paragraphs in Section II, E.

cium phosphate to settle[2] for 5 minutes, then discarding the supernatant. Use the calcium phosphate immediately or, alternatively, store[3] under 0.005 *M* phosphate until required.

2. *Preparation of Columns*

Discard most of the 0.005 *M* phosphate supernatant and mix the calcium phosphate into a slurry. Transfer the contents of one cylinder to a glass chromatography column. Connect the column to a pump delivering 0.005 *M* phosphate at about 3 ml/minute[4] and wash the calcium phosphate for an hour or so until it has settled to a constant volume. Check for channels or cracks by adding about 1 ml of bromocresol purple to the column and pumping the dye through with 0.005 *M* phosphate; if the indicator contains 5-10% sucrose it is unnecessary to remove the liquid above the column surface for this test. If there is any skewing or channeling stir the calcium phosphate gently using a glass rod and allow to settle before retesting with dye.

3. *Elution Gradients*

(1) A 0.05-0.5 M linear gradient for initial experiments to determine the points of elution of virus and of contaminants: Add 165 ml 0.05 *M* and 160 ml[5] (i.e., an equal weight) 0.5 *M* phosphate buffer to chambers 1 and 2 of the autograd,[6] respectively.

(2) Gradient A, suitable for *purification* of EMC virus: Use eight chambers[7] of an autograd and to each, starting at chamber 1, add 40 ml[8] of one of the following in the order: 0.005 *M*, 0.005 *M*,0.32 *M*, 0.005 *M*, 0.005 *M*, 0.32 *M*, 0.5 *M*, and 1.0 *M* phosphate buffer.

(3) Gradient B, for *separation* of EMC virus variants: Use eight chambers[7] of an autograd, and to each, starting at chamber 1, add 40 ml[8] of one of the following in the order: 0.005 *M*, 0.005 *M*, 0.5 *M*, 0.005 *M*, 0.005 *M*, 0.5 *M*, 0.5 *M*, and 1.0 *M* phosphate buffer.

4. *Operation of Column*

Wash the prepared column with 0.005 *M* phosphate buffer to check the fraction collector and pump, etc. Disconnect the 0.005 *M* phosphate buffer line and add the virus[9] to the column carefully in order not to disturb the surface of the calcium phosphate. When the sample has entered the column bed wash the last traces onto the column with about 5 ml of 0.005 *M* phosphate. Add a further 5 ml[10] 0.005 *M* phosphate buffer, reconnect the column to the 0.005 *M* phosphate buffer supply, and wash for 10 tubes, 8 ml/tube, in order to wash clear material not adsorbing. Change the line supplying the column with 0.005 *M* phosphate buffer to the autograd line. At the completion of the run, as the last trace of gradient leaves the autograd, switch to the 0.005 *M* line to ensure that the concentrated part of the gradient is collected and to wash the strong phosphate out of the pump and lines. Subject individual fractions to analysis.

E. Comments on Chromatographic Procedures

1. Preliminary investigations were made to compare the quality of calcium phosphate prepared in a 500 ml graduated cylinder with that made in a vessel with a much wider diameter, such as a beaker, using both fast and slow stirring. The pump rates were set arbitrarily, but it was considered desirable to have an excess of phosphate ions. The graduated cylinder with slow stirring gave a product with the fastest flow rate using these pump rates. Any change in condition may require using a vessel other than a measuring cylinder to obtain suitable mixing.

2. Calcium phosphate, which gives columns with fast flow rates, will settle to the 150 ml mark or less in the cylinder during this 5 minute standing. Failure to pass this test is usually because of incorrect rates of either pumping or of stirring and such calcium phosphate is rejected.

3. The maximum storage time has not been determined, although after a month the product has a noticeably slower flow rate. It is found convenient to prepare sufficient batches for 1–2 weeks' work.

4. The flow rate under gravity is usually faster than 3 ml/minute. The purpose of the chromatographic pump is not to force the eluting buffers through the column but to maintain a constant flow rate. Experience shows that the application of pressure can be self-defeating, since this causes packing of the calcium phosphate, which then requires a higher pressure to maintain a reasonable flow rate, which causes further packing, and so on. Since the calcium phosphate produced as described gives fast flow rates the pump may be dispensed with, and it should be possible to supply eluting buffers by the use of gravity alone.

5. These volumes equal the total volume required for either complex gradients A or B. Normally when using an autograd equal volumes are added to each chamber, but since the density of 0.5 *M* phosphate buffer is markedly greater than that of 0.05 *M* phosphate buffer, it is essential to use an equal weight rather than an equal volume in each chamber. All variants in stock K-2 EMC virus are eluted by 0.5 *M* buffer, but it is conceivable that some viruses may require higher con-

centrations of phosphate for elution, in which case chamber 2 should be made up with an equal weight of 1.0 *M* phosphate buffer.

6. An autograd is not essential for making a linear gradient. All that is required are two similar shaped vessels, preferably cylinders, which are open at the top, joined at the bottom by a tube containing a tap, and with an outlet from one of the vessels to take the eluting buffers to the column. This latter vessel must be stirred to mix the contents flowing in from the second vessel.

7. The autograd supplied by the Technicon Co. contains nine chambers, but owing to a mishap ours contains eight chambers! Use could be made of the ninth chamber by adding a further 40 ml of 1 *M* phosphate buffer to ensure that the gradient is not exhausted before all the virus is eluted.

8. The volume of 40 ml/chamber was decided upon as being one which occupies a reasonable volume in the autograd. A smaller autograd than the one made by Technicon would be useful.

9. The starting material for chromatography is infected cell supernatant, containing the virus, clarified at 10,000 g for 15 minutes. A single column can accommodate up to 200 ml of this crude virus (i.e., about 200 mg of protein). If preliminary concentration or purification is attempted it is important to ensure that the phosphate concentration is not too high, say, 0.02 *M*, or some viruses may not adsorb.

10. Only a small volume of liquid is maintained on the surface of the calcium phosphate in order not to delay changes in the concentration of phosphate buffer in the elution profile.

III. Results

A. Purification of EMC Virus

1. Use of a Linear Gradient

Chromatography of 60 ml of crude virus using a linear gradient yields two peaks of uv absorption, the first being due to nonadsorbed material and the second to material which has been adsorbed but is eluted when the phosphate concentration reaches about 0.1 *M* (Fig. 1). Hemagglutinin activity is eluted immediately following the second uv absorbing peak. The separation of virus from the uv absorbing material could be increased by using a gradient with a plateau at a concentration of about 0.12 *M* which would wash the uv absorbing material clear before a rapid rise in phosphate molarity eluted the virus. Therefore, gradient A was prepared following the procedure of Peterson and Sober (1959).

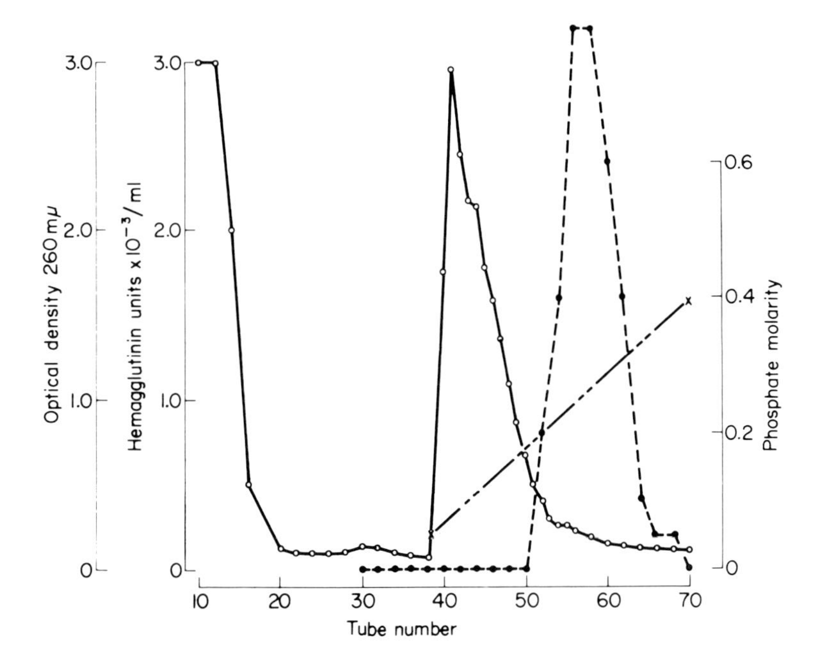

FIG. 1. Calcium phosphate chromatography using a 0.05–0.5 *M* linear gradient. Sixty milliliters of crude virus added to column, which was then washed for 10 tubes (8 ml/tube) with 0.005 *M* phosphate buffer before beginning elution with a 0.05–0.5 *M* phosphate linear gradient: (○) optical density at 260 mμ, (●) hemagglutinin activity, and (X) phosphate molarity.

2. *Use of Gradient A*

Chromatography of 50 ml of crude virus using gradient A gives a distribution of optical density (Fig. 2) very similar to that obtained with the linear gradient. However, gradient A elutes the hemagglutinin activity well clear of the second peak of uv absorbing material.

Chromatography on calcium phosphate gives 50–100% recovery of infectivity and achieves about a 15-fold purification, based on recovery of hemagglutinin activity (HA) compared either with nucleic acid or with protein (Table I).

B. SEPARATION OF VARIANTS

1. *Chromatography of Stock Virus*

The linear gradient reveals no sign of heterogeneity of hemagglutinin activity in stock virus but the peak eluted was broad (Fig. 1). Gradient B is designed to give a plateau at a phosphate concentration

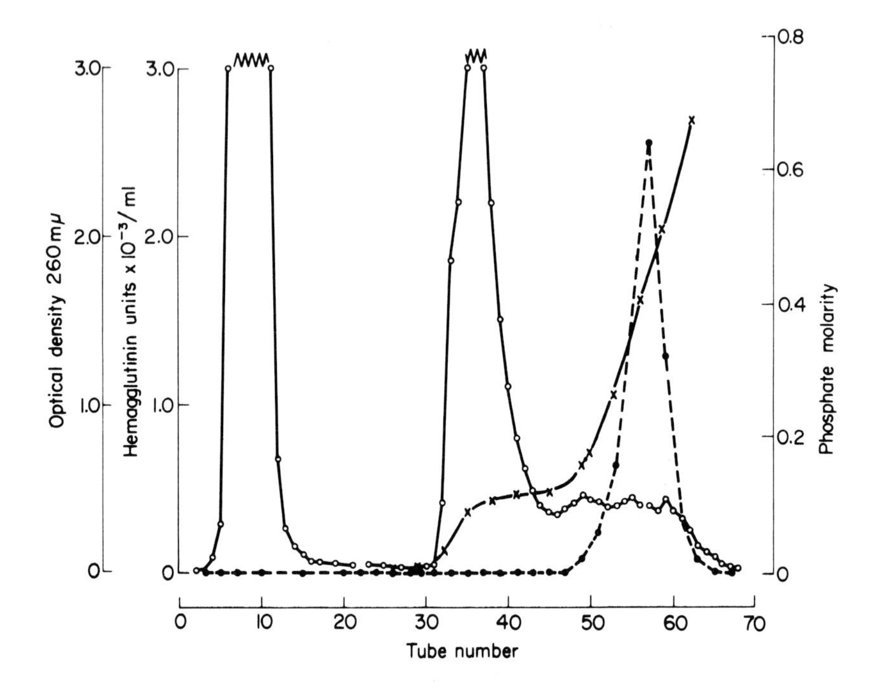

FIG. 2. Chromatography using gradient A. Fifty milliliters of crude virus added to column, which was then washed for 20 tubes with 0.005 *M* phosphate buffer before beginning elution with gradient A. Symbols as in Fig. 1.

TABLE I
PURIFICATION OF EMC VIRUS ON CALCIUM PHOSPHATE[a]

Assay	Starting material	After chromatography
HA units/ml	20480	20480
% recovery	—	100
Protein μg/ml	925	60
% recovery	—	6.5
HA units/μg protein	22.1	341.3
Relative purification	—	15
Nucleic acid (μg/ml)	73.6	4.2
% recovery	—	5.7
HA units/μg nucleic acid	278	4819
Relative purification	—	17

[a]For details see Fig. 2.

of about 0.18 *M*, which is about that present at the beginning of elution of this broad peak, followed by a rapid rise in phosphate concentration after the plateau region. Chromatography of 100 ml of crude virus using gradient B gives an optical density profile (Fig. 3) very similar to that obtained using the 0.05–0.5 *M* linear gradient and gradient A, but the hemagglutinin activity now appears as two peaks. One of the few differences detected between material in these peaks is that there is a tendency for large plaque variants to be eluted in the first peak and small plaque variants in the second peak (Burness, 1967).

2. *Chromatography of Cloned Virus*

The resolution possible using gradient B is shown by chromatography of a partially purified large plaque variant, LPP (Fig. 4) and of a small plaque variant, SPP (Fig. 5), which are eluted by 0.16 *M* and

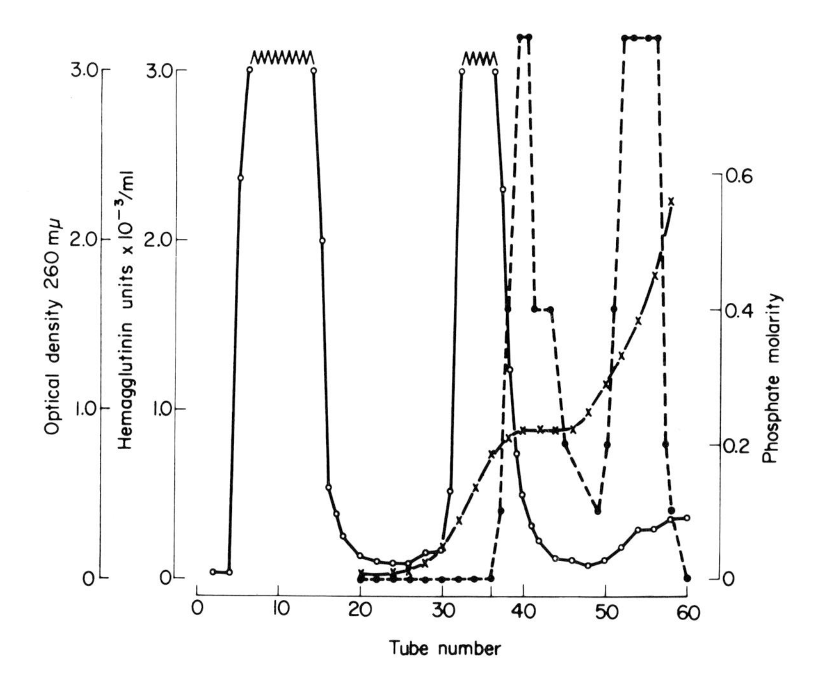

FIG. 3. Chromatography using gradient B. One hundred milliliters of crude virus added to column, which was then washed for 10 tubes with 0.005 *M* phosphate buffer before beginning elution with gradient B. Symbols as in Fig. 1.

0.43 *M* phosphate buffer, respectively. It is interesting to compare the sharp, symmetrical peaks of the cloned variants with those obtained on chromatography of crude stock virus (Figs. 3 and 7), where the separated peaks show signs of heterogeneity suggesting that several kinds of variants are present.

IV. Alternative Procedures

A. Virus Purification

Calcium phosphate chromatography has been used for the purification of a number of viruses, including influenza virus (Taverne *et al.*, 1958), herpes virus (Taverne and Wildy, 1959), arbovirus (Smith and Holt, 1961), adenovirus (Simon, 1962), EMC virus (Faulkner *et al.*, 1961; Kaighn *et al.*, 1964), and mengovirus (Krug and Franklin, 1964).

The main differences in technique between these previous reports and the present article are as follows.

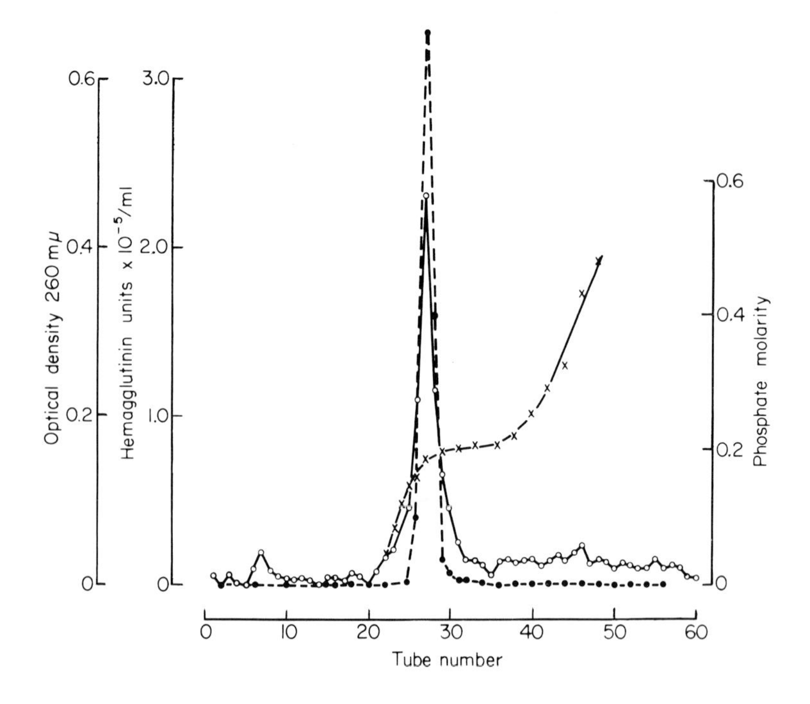

FIG. 4. Chromatography of a large plaque variant (LPP) of EMC virus using gradient B. Symbols as in Fig. 1.

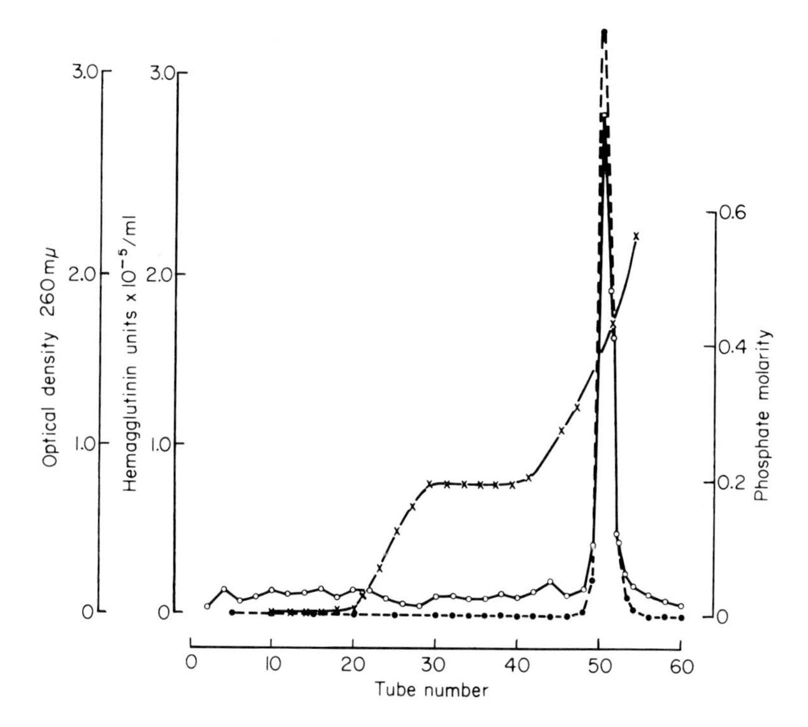

FIG. 5. Chromatography of a small plaque variant (SPP) of EMC virus using gradient B. Symbols as in Fig. 1.

1. *Preparation of Calcium Phosphate*

The previous reports used calcium phosphate prepared following the procedure of Tiselius *et al.* (1956) by running equal volumes of 0.5 *M* $CaCl_2$ and 0.5 *M* Na_2HPO_4 from two separating funnels into a flask fitted with a mechanical stirrer. We find the calcium phosphate produced in this way is of variable quality, particularly in its flow rate, and often requires pressure to maintain a reasonable rate, whereas a very reproducible product is obtained using pumps to add the $CaCl_2$ and Na_2HPO_4.

2. *Use of Hydroxylapatite*

Brushite ($CaHPO_4{\cdot}2H_2O$) is the form of calcium phosphate prepared by mixing $CaCl_2$ and Na_2HPO_4 at ambient temperatures. It can be converted to hydroxylapatite, $Ca_5(PO_4)_3OH$, which is the most stable form of calcium phosphate, by treatment with alkali (Tiselius *et al.*, 1956). Kaighn *et al.* (1964) obtained better recoveries of EMC vi-

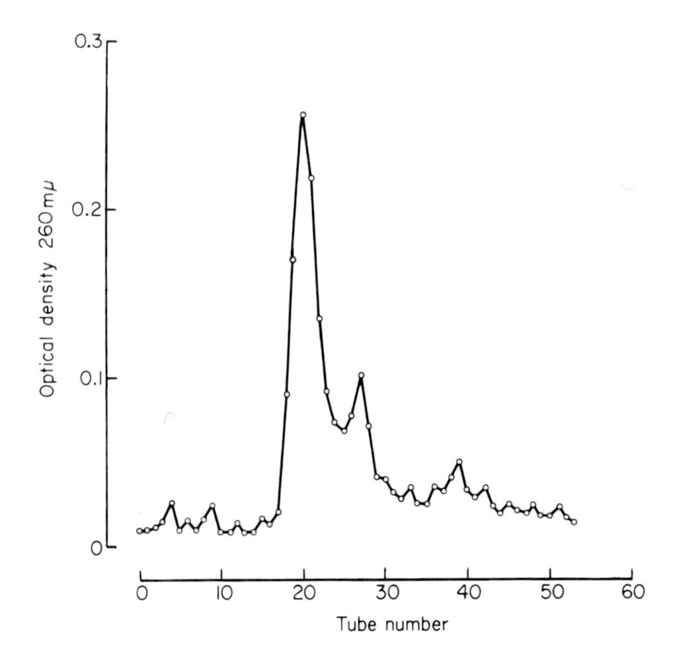

FIG. 6. Chromatography of partially purified stock EMC virus using a 0.1–0.4 *M* phosphate buffer linear gradient. Symbols as in Fig. 1.

rus from hydroxylapatite than from brushite columns. We still prefer to use brushite, which is easier to prepare than hydroxylapatite and we find gives faster flow rates. However, if a virus requires alkaline conditions for stability, then the use of hydroxylapatite should be considered.

3. *Elution Conditions*

Taverne *et al.* (1958) used stepwise elution when they introduced chromatography on calcium phosphate for the purification of animal viruses. Stepwise elution has the advantage of simplicity both in operation and in apparatus required but is more time-consuming, lacks the resolution of which gradient elution is capable, and subjects the virus to sudden changes in ionic conditions, which may be undesirable for certain viruses.

Most workers since have used linear gradient elution, which is comparatively easy to operate and can give adequate separation of virus from contaminants (Fig. 1). The introduction of more complex gradients produced by an apparatus such as the autograd offers the possibility of further improving the purification achieved (Fig. 2).

It should be made clear that virus purified only by calcium phosphate chromatography is not sufficiently pure for serious physical and chemical studies. However, Faulkner *et al.* (1961) obtained crystalline EMC virus from calcium phosphate chromatography effluents simply by pretreating the crude virus with ultracentrifugation and trypsin before chromatography. In addition, Krug and Franklin (1964) used the same procedure to purify mengovirus and concluded that after calcium phosphate chromatography no further purification could be achieved by CsCl density gradient centrifugation. Calcium phosphate has many advantages compared with other forms of column chromatography for purifying virus since it is easy to prepare, operates at neutral pH with simple buffers, gives fast flow rates, and appears to be able to take up considerable amounts of virus and contaminants which means preliminary purification is not required.

B. Separation of Virus Variants

Mutants of both poliovirus (Koza, 1963; Ozaki *et al.*, 1965) and of ECHO virus (Dömök and Simon, 1966) had different elution charac-

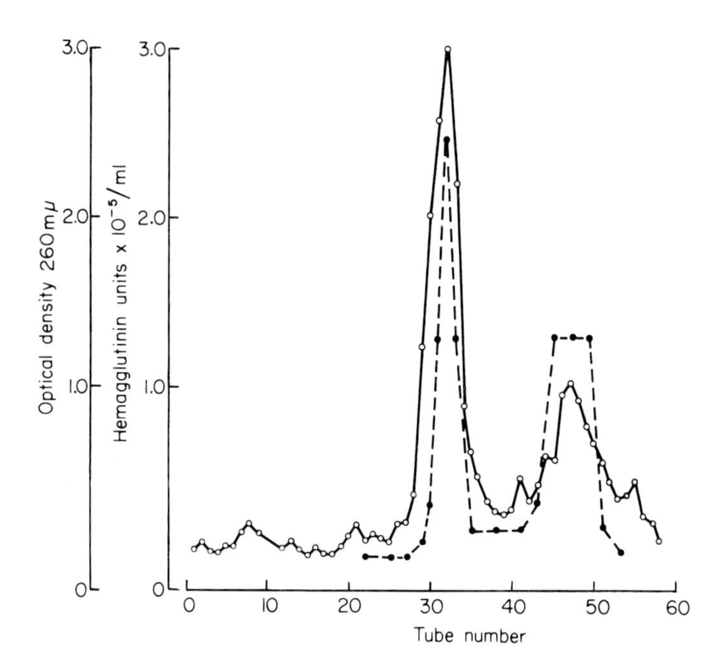

Fig. 7. Chromatography of partially purified stock EMC virus using gradient B. Symbols as in Fig. 1.

teristics when examined separately, and herpes virus (Taverne and Wildy, 1959) yielded more than one peak of virus activity, on calcium phosphate prepared essentially by the procedure of Tiselius *et al.* (1956) as described in Section IV, A,1 and with stepwise elution. The resolution achieved was not as clear as that given by gradient B with EMC virus variants (Figs. 4 and 5).

Although many viruses have been subjected to calcium phosphate chromatography using linear gradients, as far as is known no reports described the separation of variants from stock virus, possibly because, using a 0.05–0.5 *M* linear gradient, for instance, the phosphate molarity is changing too rapidly to achieve adequate separation (Fig. 1). A less steep 0.1–0.4 *M* linear gradient applied to partially purified stock virus does result in some resolution of the single virus peak, giving a small additional peak on the high phosphate molarity side (Fig. 6). However, the superiority of gradient B compared with a linear gradient is well illustrated by subjecting the same preparation of virus to chromatography using the complex gradient. Two major well-separated peaks of uv absorption with coincident hemagglutinin activity are eluted (Fig. 7). The late eluting peak in particular shows further signs of heterogeneity which no doubt could be resolved to some extent by rechromatography of this peak using a gradient with a plateau region at this higher molarity. Heterogeneity in the early eluting peak has already been shown by using a modified gradient (Burness, 1967).

REFERENCES

Burness, A. T. H. (1967). *J. Virol.* **1**, 308.

Dömök, I., and Simon, M. (1966). *Virology* **29**, 553.

Faulkner, P. E., Martin, E. M., Sved, S., Valentine, R. C., and Work, T. S. (1961). *Biochem. J.* **80**, 597.

Fiske, C. H., and Subbarow, Y. (1925). *J. Biol. Chem.* **66**, 375.

Hoskins, J. M., and Sanders, F. K. (1957). *Brit. J. Exptl. Pathol.* **38**, 268.

Kaighn, M. E., Moscarello, M. A., and Fuerst, C. R. (1964). *Virology* **23**, 183.

Koza, J. (1963). *Virology* **21**, 477.

Krug, R. M., and Franklin, R. M. (1964). *Virology* **22**, 48.

Ozaki, Y., Diwan, A. R., Takizawa, M., and Melnick, J. L. (1965). *J. Bacteriol.* **89**, 603.

Peterson, E. A., and Sober, H. A. (1959). *Anal. Chem.* **31**, 857.

Sanders, F. K., Huppert, J., and Hoskins, J. M. (1958). *Symp. Soc. Exptl. Biol.* **12**, 123.

Simon, M. (1962). *Acta Virol. (Prague)* **6**, 302.

Smith, C. E. G., and Holt, D. (1961). *Bull. World Health Organ.* **24**, 749.

Taverne, J., and Wildy, P. (1959). *Nature* **184**, 1655.

Taverne, J., Marshall, J. H., and Fulton, F. (1958). *J. Gen. Microbiol.* **19**, 451.

Tiselius, A., Hjertén, S., and Levin, Ö. (1956). *Arch. Biochem. Biophys.* **65**, 132.

13. Aqueous Polymer Phase Systems in Virology

Lennart Philipson

Department of Cell Biology
The Wallenberg Laboratory
University of Uppsala
Uppsala, Sweden

I. Introduction

Liquid-liquid partition was first refined for countercurrent separations of small molecules and peptides (for a review, see Craig, 1960).

The introduction of polymer phase systems (Albertsson, 1960) opened partition methods for wide application with viruses, cell particles, and macromolecules.

Two different polymers in water are usually not compatible even at low concentrations, and consequently a mixture will separate into two phases, each composed of a solution of one polymer dissolved in water. In such a system the partitioning of an introduced macromolecular component will depend upon its size and surface properties and also upon the ionic strength, hydrogen ion concentration, and the ions present. This treatise describes the application of aqueous phase systems in virus concentration, the separation of virus mutants and nucleic acids, and also in the study of virus-antibody interaction.

II. Material and Methods

A. Polymers

1. Dextran (D)

Dextran, a branched polyglucose, is available from several sources. We have used a dextran fraction supplied by Pharmacia Fine Chemicals, Uppsala, Sweden as Dextran 500. This has a limiting viscosity number (n) of 48 ml/gm, a number-average molecular weight (M_n) of 180,000, and a weight-average molecular weight (M_w) of 460,000. The product should be checked to see it is free of NaCl.

Stock solutions containing 10–20% (w/w) dextran (with correction for 5–10% moisture of the powder) are used. Their concentration can be accurately measured by optical rotation since the specific rotation $[\alpha]_D^{25}$ for dextran is +199°. These solutions can be steam-sterilized at 100°C.

2. *Sodium Dextran Sulfate (DS)*

Dextran 500 is supplied in a sulfated form with the trade name Dextran Sulfate 500 by Pharmacia Fine Chemicals, Uppsala, Sweden. Its sulfur content is 17%. Stock solutions of 10–20% (w/w) in water can be steam-sterilized at 100°C for 15 minutes if adjusted to pH 7. In the original report (Philipson *et al.*, 1960) DS of higher molecular weight was used, but the same results are obtained with Dextran 500.

3. *Methyl Cellulose (MC)*

Methocel 4000, U.S.P. grade, from the Dow Chemical Co., has a molecular weight of around 140,000. Stock solutions of 1–2% (w/w) are prepared by vigorously dispersing 10 gm of dried powder in 300–500 ml of hot (80–90°C) water. Cold water is then added with vigorous shaking to a final weight of 1 kg, and the solution clears if kept overnight at 4°C. Solutions may be autoclaved.

4. *Polyethylene Glycol (PEG)*

Polyethylene glycol 6000 (Carbon and Carbide Chemical Co.) is kept in 30% (w/w) aqueous solution which can be autoclaved. An ultraviolet adsorbing impurity may first be removed from the PEG powder by dissolving 300 gm in 6 liters of warm acetone and precipitating with 3 liters of ether. The precipitate is washed with acetone–ether (2:1) and dried.

B. Equipment

Separatory funnels of different types are useful for exploratory experiments on different phase systems and for concentration of viruses. Figure 1a shows a small graduated separatory funnel suitable for determining the K value of different solutes and the volume ratios between phases. Figure 1b shows a separatory funnel used for 100–1000-fold concentration of virus from large volumes. Plastic centrifuge tubes can also be used and the bottom phase collected by puncturing

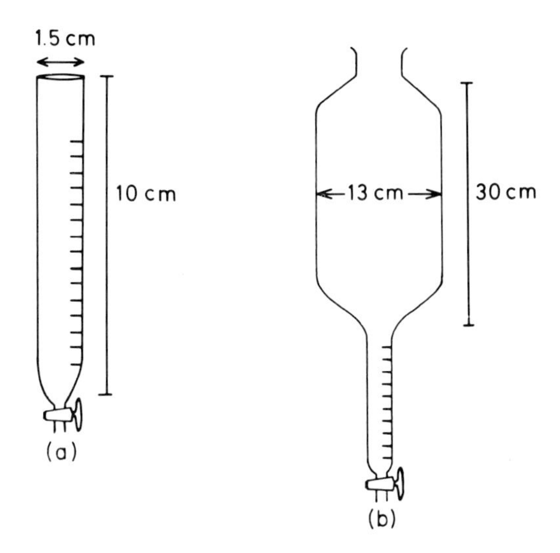

FIG. 1. Funnels used (a) for determining K values and (b) for concentration of viruses.

the tube. Centrifugation (1000 g for 10 minutes) can then be used to speed up separation.

Countercurrent distribution has been carried out in hand-driven batteries of 20 tubes or in automatic fractionators from E. C. Apparatus Co., Swarthmore, Pennsylvania. However, in this equipment the separation time for aqueous phase systems is as high as 10–30 minutes mainly because of the low density differences and high viscosities of the polymers and most countercurrent experiments are now carried out with 1–2 ml unit volumes in a micromethod developed by Albertsson (1965a). The fractionator consists of two close-fitting cylindrical plates, a stator and a rotor, as shown in Fig. 2. The bottom phases are in the stator and the top phases are in the rotor which is moved stepwise either manually or automatically. An automatic version has been produced by Incentive Research and Development AB, Stockholm, Sweden.

C. REMOVAL OF POLYMERS

1. Dextran Sulfate

Dextran sulfate can be quantitatively precipitated by potassium, barium, or cesium ions (Albertsson, 1960). About 1 ml of 3 M KCl or 2.5 ml of 0.1 M $BaCl_2$ is required to remove more than 99% from 5 ml

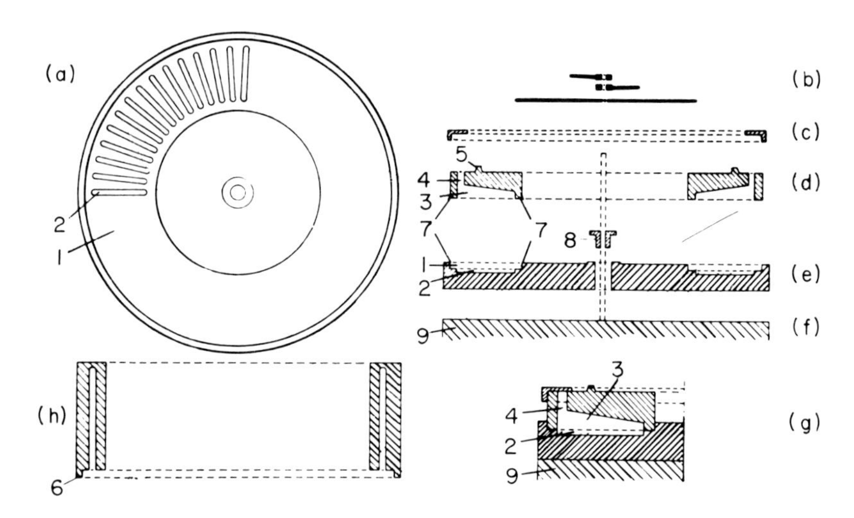

FIG. 2. Drawing of countercurrent distribution apparatus (reduced 10 times). The volume of the bottom phase cavity is 0.7 ml and the number of cavities is 60. (a) Plan view of the stator. (b)-(f) Cross sectional view of the assembly on a rotary shaker (f, 9); (e) is the stator with a shallow anular grove 1 and shallow cavities 2 which contain the bottom phase; (d) is the rotor with the lower surface 7 in contact with the stator and with inlets 4 to the cavities 3. Two knobs 5 facilitate the manual turning of the rotor. At assembly silicon grease is applied at 7 to seal the rotor and the stator; (c) is a circular cover over the inlets 4; (b) is a metal disc and two screwed-on knobs which keeps the rotor in position during shaking; (g) is a cross section of one cavity at assembly of the rotor and the stator; (h) is an annular fraction collector in cross section, which contains 8 cm by 8 mm holes corresponding in size to the inlet 4 and which can be fitted coaxially on top of the rotor by a rim 6 (Albertsson, 1965a).

aliquots of 2% DS (Philipson *et al.*, 1960). The sample is left 2 hours at 4°C and centrifuged for 10 minutes at 2000 rpm. The dextran sulfate together with any cellular debris is removed by this procedure, but virus remains in the supernate.

2. *Methyl Cellulose*

Methyl cellulose can be precipitated to 99.4% with 10% (w/w) $(NH_4)_2SO_4$ (Philipson *et al.*, 1960). At 16% (w/w) $(NH_4)_2SO_4$ precipitation is quantitative while viruses or proteins are not lost. It is desirable to filter the MC precipitate to get rid of its last traces.

3. *Polyethylene Glycol*

The following procedures have been used:

(a) Polyethylene glycol can be quantitatively extracted with chloroform since the K value in water-chloroform is 0.001 (Rudin and Albertsson, 1967).

(b) A 2:1 molar mixture of dibasic and monobasic potassium phosphate is added to the PEG solution in a concentration of 23% (w/w). The phase system obtained contains PEG in the top and the macromolecules in the salt-rich bottom phase (Albertsson, 1960; Alberts, 1967).

(c) Polyethylene glycol is "salted out" by concentrated salt and in a cesium chloride gradient it floats to the top and does not interfere with the banding of macromolecules (Alberts, 1967).

(d) Gel filtration techniques may be used since the molecular weight of the PEG used is only around 6000.

Methods (a), (b), and (c) have been found useful with nucleic acids and (c) and (d) with viruses.

4. *Dextran*

No general method to remove dextran is available, but since it is uncharged, ion exchange chromatography may be used to separate out biological macromolecules.

D. Definitions of Terms

1. *Partition Coefficient*

The ratio between the concentrations of a solute in the top and bottom phase of a two phase system is its partition coefficient (K). The smaller the value of K the more the solute favors the bottom phase, and vice versa at high K values the partition favors the top phase.

2. *Phase Diagrams*

The phase characteristics of mixtures of any two polymers must be known before a particular composition is selected for a phase system. When polymers are mixed together in a specified ionic environment only some proportions and total concentrations will yield a phase system. This is expressed in a *phase diagram*. Thus, all combinations of the two polymers above the curved line (Fig. 3) will form two phases but those below will not. This curve is called the *binodial* and its shape varies with temperature and if the polymers are changed on the ionic composition. In Fig. 3 a system composed of polymer 1 and polymer 2 represented by point A will have a bottom phase with a composition shown at point B and a top phase with composition C. The points B and C are referred to as *nodes* and the line CAB is called a *tie line*. The volume ratio between B and C phases is the same as the length ratio between CA and AB. The tie line becomes shorter as the overall composition approaches the point D, the *critical point*, where both the top and bottom phases have the same composition and volume. Phase systems should generally be selected sufficiently far from the critical point so that minor changes in temperature or composition will not interfere with their formation. The books of Treybal (1963), Zernike (1955), and Albertsson (1960) discuss phase diagrams further.

3. *Countercurrent Distribution*

To resolve two solutes which partition with similar K values, phase system separation must be made in multiple steps by the countercurrent distribution technique (for a review, see Craig, 1960). This technique uses a set of tubes loaded with the phase system. The system is shaken and then allowed to separate, the top or the bottom phase is moved to the next tube in the set, and the same sequence is repeated until the solutes are clearly separated. Then each solute will show a normal distribution among the tubes and its partition coefficient (K) may be calculated by

$$K = \frac{r_{max} + 0.5}{n + 0.5 - r_{max}}$$

where r_{max} is a function of the number of the tube containing the maximum amount of solute and n designates the number of transfers;

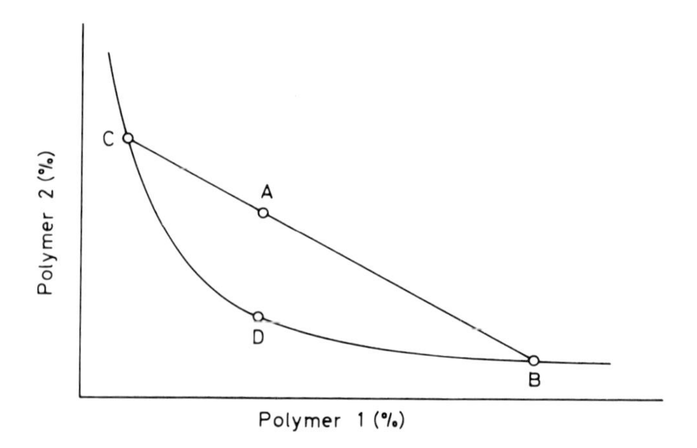

FIG. 3. Phase diagram of a theoretical polymer system showing the concentration of polymer 1 on the abscissa and polymer 2 on the ordinate. See text for symbols.

which should be > 24 to obtain reliable K values; r_{max} is calculated with the following formula:

$$r_{max} = \frac{0 \cdot a + 1 \cdot b + 2 \cdot c + \ldots + n \cdot z}{a + b + c + \ldots + z}$$

where 0, 1, 2 $\cdots$ n designates the number of the tube and $a, b, c \cdots z$ is the amount of solute found in each tube. The countercurrent technique can separate solutes which differ in K values by a factor of only 1.5–2. The separation of two substances will be best if a system is selected to give $K_1 \cdot K_2 = 1$, where K_1 and K_2 refer to the partition coefficients of the two substances. With an unknown mixture one therefore seeks a system where the overall partition coefficient is around 1.

4. *Nomenclature of Phase Systems*

The composition of a phase system is abbreviated PI_y–PII_z; subscript y is the final percent concentration (w/w) of the first polymer (PI) and z the final concentration of the second polymer (PII). In the systems described here PI may be dextran (D), dextran sulfate (DS), or methyl cellulose (MC), while PII always is polyethylene glycol (PEG). The final molar concentration of NaCl is also indicated. A selected system may thus be written D_5–PEG_4 (0.3 *M* NaCl) which means 5% (w/w) dextran and 4% (w/w) polyethylene glycol in 0.3 *M* NaCl.

5. *Preparation of Phase Systems for Countercurrent Distribution*

Countercurrent distribution requires a volume ratio between top and bottom phase of one in the equipment from E. C. Apparatus Co., but it can be varied in the micromethod. The phase systems are made up in large quantities, and each phase is separately recovered and filtered through sintered glass to remove impurities. They are then stored separately and mixed in the correct proportions prior to filling the chambers of the apparatus. A separate phase system containing the solutes to be separated should be made for the first chamber in the fractionator.

III Theory of Operation

The selection of a phase system for particles of biological origin is a major problem. Some guiding principles will be presented later. It is generally expected that larger particles will have a greater tendency to one-sided distribution between the phases. Brønsted (1931; Brønsted and Warming, 1931) predicted that the partition coefficient (K) should be determined by the following formula:

$$K = \exp[(M\lambda)/(kT)] \tag{3}$$

where M is the molecular weight, k the Boltzmann constant, T the temperature, and λ a constant characteristic for the substance and the phase system. For globular particles M should be replaced by A, the particle surface area. For large particles and viruses the K values appear to be proportional to the surface area rather than the molecular weight. The formula cannot be applied in practice when K values approach $10^{\pm 3}$ probably because the two phases do not separate completely (Albertsson and Frick, 1960). The constant λ is influenced by the ionic composition. With particles and macromolecules which have a high M value, a small shift in λ from positive to negative will cause a drastic shift from one phase to the other. This has been observed with viruses when the sodium chloride concentration is varied (Philipson *et al.*, 1960) and with nucleic acids when the magnesium or monovalent ion concentration is varied (Albertsson, 1965b; Öberg *et al.*, 1965).

It is equally evident from Brønsted's formula that small molecular weight material will not show such strong one-sided distribution and concentration of particles or viruses will be accompanied by a substantial purification from low molecular weight material.

IV. Concentration of Viruses

A. Selection of Phase Systems

A phase system for virus concentration should give a one-sided distribution of the virus in the bottom or top phase and the volume of the virus-rich phase should be in the order of 1/100–1/1000 of the total volume. Two systems have been useful.

1. The Dextran Sulfate–Polyethylene Glycol System

The phase diagrams for this system (Fig. 4) show that the binodials vary with the salt concentration. The first step is to determine the partition coefficient of the virus at different salt concentrations and preferably with volume ratios between top and bottom phase of around 1,

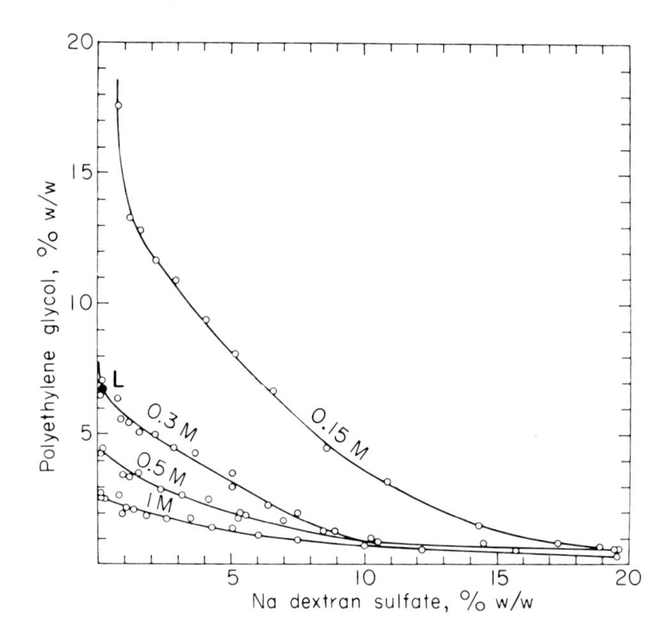

FIG. 4. Binodials of the DS-PEG system at different NaCl concentrations (Albertsson, 1960).

since if one phase is extremely large, equilibration may take considerable time. Table I shows that small viruses distribute in favor of the bottom phase at low salt concentrations but in the top phase at high concentrations. Large viruses collect at the interface in low salt and in the top phase in high. The virus is concentrated 100–1000-fold in the favored phase. Thus if a system is selected which reduces the volume 50–100-fold, there will be no substantial loss of virus. Such a system with a large volume difference between the virus-rich and the virus-depleted phase has the composition $DS_{0.2}$-$PEG_{6.5}$ (0.3 *M* NaCl). This is indicated by the point L in the phase diagrams of Fig. 4, the bottom phase is only 1/100 of the total volume. This system could be tried with almost any virus but the interface should be collected together with the bottom phase since some viruses, particularly the larger ones, concentrate at the interface.

2. The Dextran Sulfate–Methyl Cellulose System

A system of DS and MC at 0.15 *M* NaCl may be used to purify larger viruses or large particles. Table II gives the *K* values for different viruses in a system with volume ratios around one. Only viruses similar

TABLE I
THE INFLUENCE OF NACL CONCENTRATION UPON THE PARTITION OF DIFFERENT VIRUSES IN THE DS-PEG SYSTEM

Phase system[a]	NaCl (molarity)	Partition coefficient (K) in log units for different viruses			
		Polio	ECHO	Adeno	T 2
$DS_{3.0}$-$PEG_{2.0}$	1.0	2.5	2.5	2.2	2.8
$DS_{3.0}$-$PEG_{3.0}$	0.5	0.3	0.2	1.2	0.8[b]
$DS_{4.0}$-$PEG_{4.0}$	0.3	−1.8[b]	−2.0	0.3[b]	–
$DS_{6.0}$-$PEG_{7.0}$	0.15	−2.2[b]	−2.2	−2.9[b]	−2.5[b]

[a]The variation in polymer concentration affects the *K* values only to a minor degree but keeps the volume between the two phases around one.
[b]Denotes appreciable accumulation of virus at the interface.

or larger in size to adenovirus favor the bottom phase and salt concentration does not strongly influence the partition. Large viruses have been concentrated with $DS_{0.22}$-$MC_{0.51}$ (0.15 *M* NaCl) where the ratio top to bottom phase is 15 (Philipson *et al.*, 1960).

B. CONCENTRATION PROCEDURE

The following procedure is currently in use in this laboratory to concentrate small viruses with DS and PEG. Large viruses can also be concentrated if the interface is collected with the bottom phase. The polymers and sodium chloride are added in dry powder to tissue culture fluid or phage lysates to a final concentration of 0.2% w/w DS, 6.45% w/w PEG, and 0.3 *M* NaCl. The nomogram shown in Fig. 5 is used to determine the necessary amounts of the polymers and salts. It

TABLE II
PARTITION COEFFICIENT OF VIRUSES IN THE DS-MC SYSTEM[a]

Virus	Partition coefficient (*K*) in log units
ECHO	−0.3
Polio	−0.4
Adeno	−1.8
Influenza	−2.0
Parainfluenza	−2.3
Phage T 2	−2.6

[a]$DS_{0.40}$-$MC_{0.48}$(0.15 *M* NaCl).

is important to take the salt concentration of the tissue culture fluid or phage lysate into account and the nomogram is calculated with a presumed initial concentration of 0.15 *M* NaCl in the virus solution. The polymers and salt dissolve in 3 hours with magnetic stirring. The phase system is then transferred to the separatory funnel shown in Fig. 1*b* and allowed to separate for 24 hours at 4°C; the bottom phase is then 1/100 of the total volume of the system and together with the interface contains most of the virus. Dextran sulfate is precipitated by adding 0.7 ml of 3 *M* KCl per milliliter of collected material and removed by low speed centrifugation. The virus is further purified by either CsCl-equilibrium centrifugation or gel filtration on columns of sphere condensed agarose (Bengtsson and Philipson, 1964). When virus collects entirely at the interface both the top and bottom phases can be discarded and the interfacial solids washed in 1% DS solution after low speed centrifugation without any loss of virus. Dextran sulfate can subsequently be removed as described above.

C. Comparison with Other Methods

Polymer phase systems offer a simple method to concentrate those viruses which burst from the cells to give the major yield in the media.

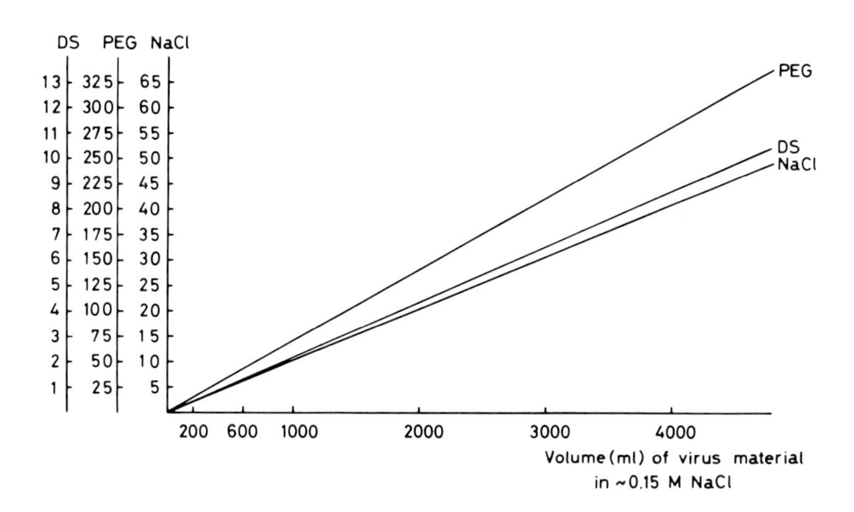

FIG. 5. Nomogram for the addition of polymers and salt to tissue culture fluid or phage lysate to obtain the system $DS_{0.2}$-$PEG_{6.5}$ (0.3 *M* NaCl). It has been assumed that the NaCl concentration in the tissue culture fluid or phage lysate is already 0.15 *M* (Bengtsson, 1965).

Almost all phages belong to this category and the procedure has been successfully applied to the concentration of phage T2 (Albertsson, 1967),ϕX174 (Sinsheimer, 1966), and RNA phages (Watanabe and August, 1967). The method is also suitable for animal viruses, such as picorna viruses, which accumulate in the medium (Philipson *et al.*, 1960; Norrby and Albertsson, 1960) and possibly also for viruses formed at the cell surface such as the myxoviruses (Wesslén *et al.*, 1959). Viruses which accumulate inside the cells, such as adenoviruses, may be concentrated from the cell phase.

Tobacco mosaic virus (TMV) has also been concentrated by a procedure analogous to those described here (Venekamp and Mosch, 1964). In this case the system used contained only PEG (6% w/w) and NaCl (0.5 *M*) and high virus concentrations are required to achieve a quantitative precipitation.

When polymer phase systems are used for concentration, virus is also substantially purified; conventional concentration procedures such as flash evaporation or pressure dialysis do not achieve this. The method is also more gentle than ultracentrifugation to a pellet, which may cause considerable denaturation. The recently introduced ultrafiltration methods (Strohmaier, 1967) with controlled membrane porosity may be comparable to the phase systems and also have some additional advantages, but the phase systems require less attendance and the presence of polymers may not be a serious drawback if other purification steps are to be used subsequently. The polymers may also stabilize against denaturation.

V. Countercurrent Distribution of Virus Mutants

To completely separate particles of similar surface area or size, a multiple sequence of extraction steps may be needed. Countercurrent distribution is then suitable.

A. Selection of Phase Systems

The resolving power of countercurrent distribution is highest if the *K* value for the unresolved mixture is close to one. A system composed of DS and PEG has been worked out for poliovirus, and Table III shows the exploratory experiments performed to determine the most suitable composition. The effect of salt and polymer concentration upon the *K* value was utilized in selecting the system $DS_{1.2}$-$PEG_{1.2}$ (0.60 *M* NaCl).

TABLE III
PARTITION OF A HETEROGENEOUS POLIOVIRUS TYPE 1 STRAIN IN DIFFERENT DS-PEG SYSTEMS[a]

Concentration of PEG (% w/w)	NaCl molarity	Percent recovery of virus infectivity	Interface adsorption	Partition coefficient (*K*)
1.0	0.70	19	0	>12
1.2	0.60	69	0	0.57
1.3	0.50	60	+	< 0.05
1.3	0.55	100	+	0.05
1.3	0.60	62	0	0.2

[a]All systems were 7% w/w DS.

B. SEPARATION OF VIRUS MUTANTS

Countercurrent distribution experiments show that plaque-purified strains of poliovirus type 1 fall in two categories, one with high and one with low *K* values (Fig. 6). Strains not subjected to biological purification are heterogeneous. All of the poliovirus strains with low *K* values, around 0.3, show minute plaques under DS overlay, the *m*– marker (Nomura and Takemori, 1960) which shows covariation with the *d*– marker (Vogt *et al.*, 1957). The strains with high *K* values of around four exhibit the *m*+ marker. It could also be shown by countercurrent distribution that live vaccine stocks of Sabin type 1 poliovirus contained a low proportion of *m*+ mutants amounting to 1 in 2×10^{-3} *m*– variants (Bengtsson and Philipson, 1963).

Both *m*+ and *m*– mutants have been found for poliovirus type 2 while no true *m*– mutants of poliovirus type 3 have been detected with this technique (Bengtsson, 1966).

The basis for the difference in partition between the *m*+ and *m*– variants probably resides in the protein coat of the virus and it appears that *m*– variants attach to dextran sulfate and are therefore retarded at phase transfer (Bengtsson *et al.*, 1964; Bengtsson, 1965). Phase systems may have application in the purification of stocks of live poliovirus vaccine. The method may also be useful in the genetic analysis of viruses exhibiting the *m*– character, such as foot and mouth disease virus (FMDV) (Dinter and Sibalin, 1958), encephalomyocarditis (EMC) (Liebhaber and Takemoto, 1963), herpes simplex (Takemoto and Fabisch, 1964), and some myxoviruses (Takemoto and Fabisch, 1963).

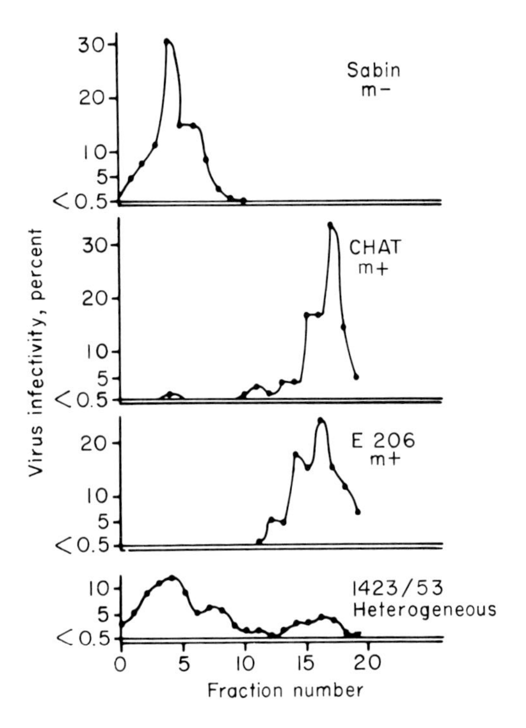

FIG. 6. Countercurrent distribution patterns of different poliovirus type 1 strains in the phase system DS_7-$PEG_{1.2}$ (0.6 *M* NaCl). Infectivity is given as the percentage of total found in respective fractions (Bengtsson and Philipson, 1963).

VI. Phase Systems as Tools in Studies of Virus-Antibody Interaction

The phase systems may also be used to study molecular interaction, especially if the complexes formed differ significantly in size or structure from the reactants. Under favorable conditions, reaction kinetics may be measured since the complex could be partitioned to one phase and uncombined molecules to the other. Systems have been worked out for the study of antigen-antibody interaction (Albertsson and Philipson, 1960; Philipson *et al.*, 1966; Philipson, 1966).

A. SELECTION OF PHASE SYSTEMS

It would be useful in virus-antibody studies to find a system which distributes the virus in the top phase and γ-globulin in the bottom phase. Several systems were investigated with the aid of purified P^{32}-

labeled virus and purified γ-globulin. Figure 7a shows the distribution of poliovirus and Fig. 7b of γ-globulin. It is evident that an increase in salt concentration favors the distribution of both reactants to the top phase. $DS_{3.0}$-$PEG_{3.0}$ (0.35 *M* NaCl) was examined further. At higher pH values an increase in the *K* value was observed for both virus and γ-globulin, but virus–antibody complexes partitioned in the bottom phase irrespective of the pH as shown in Fig. 8. Since this system was subsequently used for countercurrent distribution it was buffered to pH 7.0 with 0.05 *M* phosphate to keep the *K* values of the reactants close to one.

B. VIRUS–ANTIBODY INTERACTION

It was demonstrated that the primary interaction between IgG antibodies and poliovirus have single-hit kinetics and the reaction is pseudo first order, but depends on both antibody and virus concentration. No dissociation of virus from the complex could be detected (Philipson, 1966). The countercurrent distribution technique also demonstrated that the persistent fraction of unneutralized virus (Dulbecco *et al.*, 1956) resided in virus–antibody complexes and not in uncombined virus.

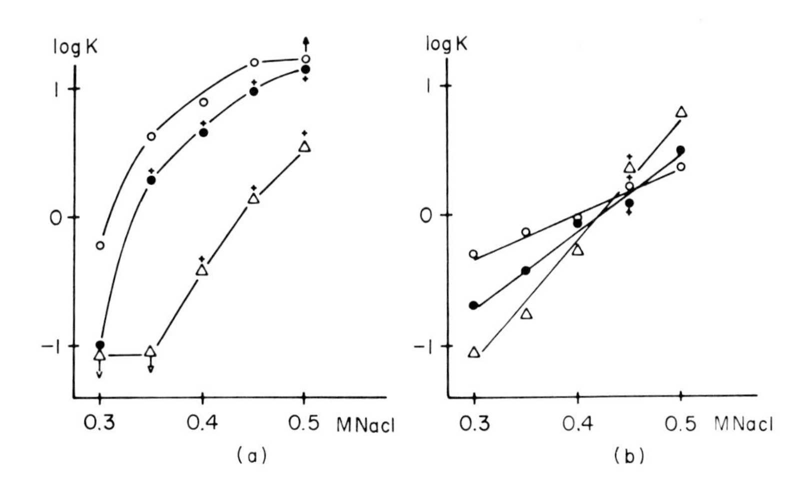

FIG. 7. Distribution of (a) ^{32}P-poliovirus type 1 and (b) human γ-G-globulin in polymer phase systems of different composition. The ordinate gives the partition coefficient (*K*) in logarithms and the abscissa the molar concentration of sodium chloride in the systems. Arrows indicate values off scale. Crosses indicate interface adsorption, (○) DS_3-PEG_3 (●) $DS_{3.5}$-$PEG_{3.5}$, and (△) $DS_{4.0}$-$PEG_{4.0}$ (Philipson *et al.*, 1966).

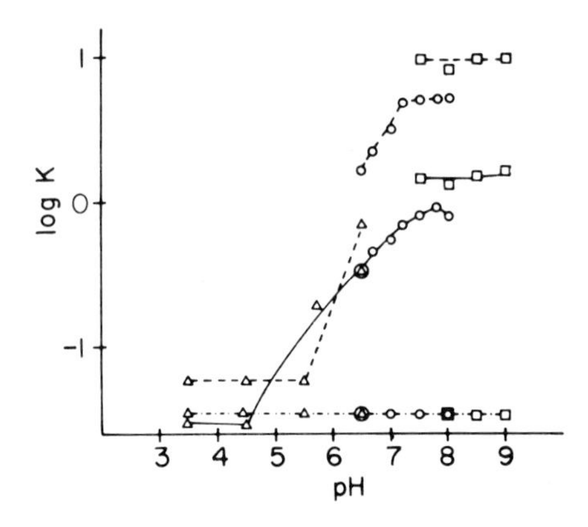

FIG. 8. The influence of hydrogen ion concentration on the distribution of ^{32}P-labeled poliovirus, (- - - -) γ-G-globulin (———), and poliovirus-antibody complexes (–.–) in the system $DS_{3.0}$-$PEG_{3.0}$ (0.35 *M* NaCl). The ordinate gives the distribution coefficient (*K*) in logarithms. The following buffers were investigated: (△), citrate-phosphate buffer, (○), phosphate buffer, and (□), tris HCl buffer.

IgM antibodies interacted at a slower rate than IgG antibodies, and the reaction did not appear to be first order.

Cleavage products of IgG did not change the *K* value of free virus while reduced and alkylated IgG produced complexes with slightly altered properties in this system (Philipson and Bennich, 1966). The phase systems appear to have an advantage over gel filtration in that phase separation is rapid enough to allow kinetic analysis.

VII. Phase Systems for Separation of Nucleic Acids

It may be expected that the distribution of highly asymmetric macromolecules with a polyelectrolyte character will be strongly influenced by the ionic composition of a phase system. Nucleic acids may accordingly be partitioned in either phase depending on the salt concentration and system composition. This can be utilized for separation of nucleic acids from proteins and possibly for the separation of different types of nucleic acids which differ in base ratio or conformation.

A. Selection of Phase Systems

A phase system containing dextran and polyethylene glycol with the phase diagram shown in Fig. 9 has been used for nucleic acid separation. Neutral polymers were used in the system since the introduced macromolecules are polyelectrolytes. Although polymer concentration strongly influences the partition of nucleic acids (Albertsson, 1965b; Alberts, 1967), partition can most easily be controlled by changing the ionic environment and therefore the system D_5-PEG_4 has been used exclusively in our laboratory for both single extractions and countercurrent distribution. Albertsson (1965b) has shown that in this system the partition of native DNA is influenced by both anions and cations. The divalent anions HPO_4^{2-} and SO_4^{2-} usually give higher *K* values than monovalent anions. With sodium halides decreasing *K* values are observed in the order $F^- > Cl^- > J^- > Br^-$ at final concentrations of 0.005 *M*. Decreasing *K* values with 0.01 *M* alkaline chlorides have the order $Li^+ > Na^+ > Cs^+ > K^+ \sim Rb^+$. This order is the same irrespective of the anion used. The same patterns also hold for RNA (Öberg *et al.*, 1965) although high molecular weight RNA goes more readily than DNA into the bottom phase and lithium phosphate buffer must be used to achieve sufficiently high *K* values. Both the conformation and after denaturation base composition of DNA and RNA appear to strongly influence the *K* values in this phase system as shown in Fig. 10, where synthetic polynucleotides and native or denatured DNA have been partitioned.

B. Application of Nucleic Acid Partition in Virology

The only report in this field concerns the purification of Qβ polymerase enzyme from nucleic acids using the phase system $D_{1.6}$-$PEG_{6.4}$ plus a complex salt mixture (Eoyang and August, 1967).

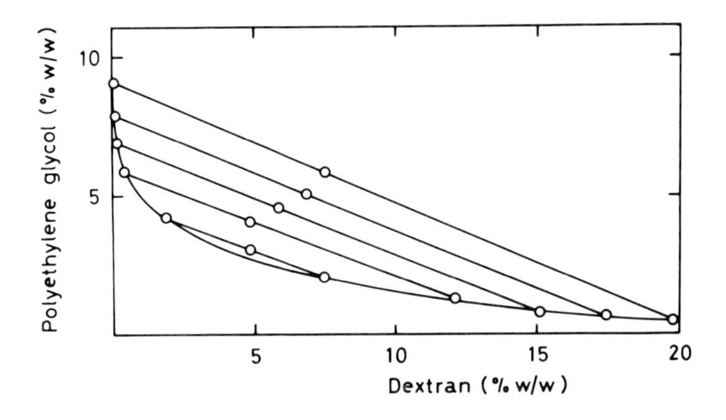

FIG. 9. Binodial of the D-PEG system at 0°C in 0.01 *M* phosphate buffer, pH 7.2 (Albertsson, 1967).

Additional applications can be easily foreseen (Favre and Pettijohn, 1967). Since both conformation and base composition of nucleic acids may influence the partition and a difference of 10^2–10^4 in the K values between single- and double-stranded DNA has been observed (Alberts, 1967), these systems are of interest for the isolation of complementary strands of nucleic acids and also for the separation of linear and cyclic structures of nucleic acids. Preliminary studies along these lines indicate that TMV RNA can be partially resolved from poliovirus RNA by countercurrent distribution although their differences in size and base ratios is very small (Öberg *et al.*, 1965).

VIII. General Evaluation of the Polymer Phase Systems

Aqeous polymer phase systems have been used in concentration of virus from large volumes (Albertsson, 1967; Watanabe and August, 1967). The two major difficulties with this method have been the selection of suitable phase systems and the removal of polymers after phase separation. This survey has emphasized the selection of phase systems for virus and nucleic acid separation. The polymers remaining after phase separation can often be removed if additional purification steps are included or may also be precipitated or extracted as described in Section II. When the initial difficulties have been overcome, the method is preferable to conventional virus concentration procedures because of the simplicity of the operations involved and because it requires only minor attendance.

The method may, however, have an even higher potential in studies of macromolecular interaction as exemplified by virus–antibody interaction. It may be generally applicable in this field since macromolecular complexes could be separated from the free reactants and kinetic experiments may thus be carried out. Countercurrent distribution may then resolve different classes of molecules or complexes. Current chromatographic or electrophoretic methods such as agarose gel filtration of viruses (for a review, see Philipson, 1967) and acrylamide gel electrophoresis of nucleic acids (Loening, 1967) may compete with the phase systems in resolving macromolecules, but single extractions in phase systems are more rapid and may be advantageous for preserving complexes formed by molecular interaction. There is furthermore no limit to the particle size that can be partitioned and it is possible that phase systems may even be suitable for studying the interaction of macromolecules and cell organelles or intact cells.

Finally, it is worth pointing out that the energy required for transfer of, for instance, nucleic acid molecules from one phase to another is

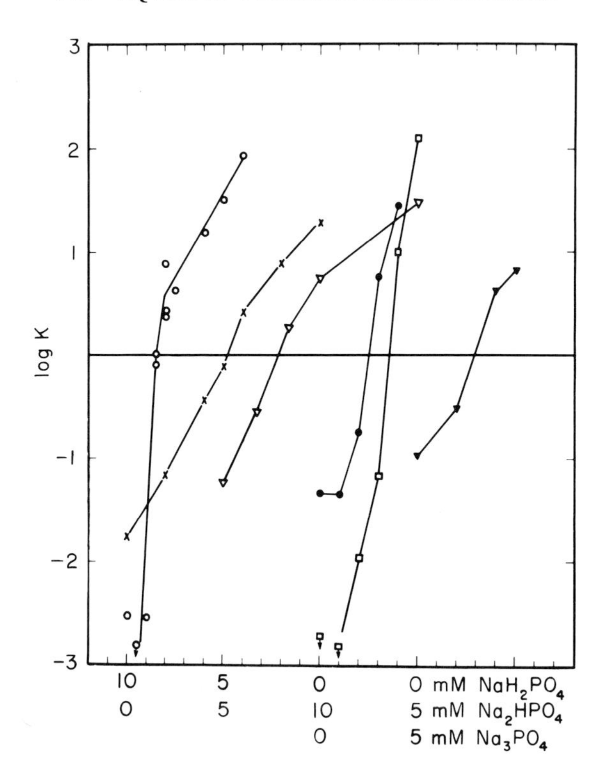

FIG. 10. Partition of different polynucleotides in D_5-PEG_4 at different concentrations of sodium phosphate: (○) DNA, (X) denatured DNA, (▽) poly-U, (●) poly-C, (□) poly-A, and (▼) Poly-I. (Albertsson, 1965b).

very low. A shift in K value of 10^4 may reflect a difference between the DNA molecules in the top and bottom phase of only 5100 cal/mole, an energy change which could be only about 1 cal/mole of nucleotide residues. This high sensitivity with which DNA reacts to small changes in the surrounding polymeric phases suggests the possibility, as pointed out by Albertsson (1965b) and Alberts (1967), that similar phenomena might change the distribution and condensation of genetic material within the living cell.

REFERENCES

Alberts, B. M. (1967). *Biochemistry* **6**, 2527.

Albertsson, P. Å. (1960). "Partition of Cell Particles and Macromolecules." Wiley, New York.

Albertsson, P. Å. (1965a). *Anal. Biochem.* **11**, 121.
Albertsson, P. Å. (1965b). *Biochim. Biophys. Acta* **103**, 1.
Albertsson, P. Å. (1967). *In* "Methods in Virology" (K. Maramorosch and H. Koprowski, eds.), Vol. 2, p. 311. Academic Press, New York.
Albertsson, P. Å., and Frick, G. (1960). *Biochim. Biophys. Acta* **37**, 230.
Albertsson, P. Å., and Philipson, L. (1960). *Nature* **185**, 38.
Bengtsson, S. (1965). Unpublished data.
Bengtsson, S. (1965). *Proc. Soc. Exptl.* Biol. Med. **118**, 47.
Bengtsson, S. (1966). *Acta Pathol. Microbiol. Scand.* **68**, 68.
Bengtsson, S., and Philipson, L. (1963). *Virology* **20**, 176.
Bengtsson, S., and Philipson, L. (1964). *Biochim. Biophys. Acta* **79**, 399.
Bengtsson, S., Philipson, L., Persson, H., and Laurent, T. C. (1964). *Virology* **24**, 617.
Brønsted, J. N. (1931). Z. *Physik. Chem.* A Bodenstein Festband, 257.
Brønsted, J. N., and Warming, E. (1931). Z. *Physik. Chem.* **A155**, 343.
Craig, L. C. (1960). *In* "Laboratory Manual of Analytical Methods of Protein Chemistry" (P. Alexander and R. J. Block, eds.), Vol. 1, p. 103. Pergamon Press, Oxford.
Dinter, Z., and Sibalin, M. (1958). *Arch. Ges. Virusforsch.* **8**, 385.
Dulbecco, R., Vogt, M., and Strickland, A. G. (1956). *Virology* **2**, 162.
Eoyang, L., and August, J. T. (1967). *Methods Enzymol.* **12B**, 530.
Favre, J., and Pettijohn, D. E. (1967). Europ. J. Biochem. **3**, 33.
Liebhaber, H., and Takemoto, K. K. (1963). *Virology* **20**, 559.
Loening, U. E. (1967). *Biochem. J.* **102**, 251.
Nomura, S., and Takemori, N. (1960). *Virology* **12**, 154.
Norrby, E., and Albertsson, P. Å. (1960). *Nature* **108**, 1047.
Öberg, B., Albertsson, P. Å., and Philipson, L. (1965). *Biochim. Biophys. Acta* **108**, 173.
Philipson, L. (1966). *Virology* **28**, 35.
Philipson, L. (1967). *In* "Methods in Virology" (K. Maramorosch and H. Koprowski, eds.), Vol. 2, p. 179. Academic Press, New York.
Philipson, L., and Bennich, H. (1966). *Virology* **29**, 330.
Philipson, L., Albertsson, P. Å., and Frick, G. (1960). *Virology* **11**, 553.
Philipson, L., Killander, J., and Albertsson, P. Å., (1966). *Virology* **28**, 22.
Rudin, L., and Albertsson, P. Å. (1967). *Biochim. Biophys. Acta* **134**, 37.
Sinsheimer, R. L. (1966). *In* "Procedures in Nucleic Acid Research" (G. L. Cantoni and D. R. Davies, eds.), p. 569. Harper, New York.
Strohmaier, K. (1967). *In* "Methods in Virology" (K. Maramorosch and H. Koprowski, eds.), Vol. 2, 245. Academic Press, New York.
Takemoto, K. K., and Fabisch, P. (1963). *Proc. Soc. Exptl. Biol. Med.* **114**, 811.
Takemoto, K. K., and Fabisch, P. (1964). *Proc. Soc. Exptl. Biol. Med.* **116**, 140.
Treybal, R. E. (1963). "Liquid Extraction," 2nd ed. McGraw-Hill, New York.
Venekamp, J. H., and Mosch, W. H. M. (1964). *Virology* **22**, 503.
Vogt, M., Dulbecco, R., and Wenner, H. A. (1957). *Virology* **4**, 141.
Watanabe, M., and August, J. T. (1967). *In* "Methods in Virology" (K. Maramorosch and H. Koprowski, eds.), Vol. 3, p. 337. Academic Press, New York.
Wesslén, T., Albertsson, P. Å., and Philipson, L. (1959). *Arch. Ges. Virusforsch.* **9**, 510.
Zernike, J. (1955). "Chemical Phase Theory." N. V. Uitgevers-Maatschappij, Æ Kluwer, Deventer, Antwerp, Djakarta.

IV. Quantitative Assay Procedures for Virus Infectivity

14. Plaque Assay for Poliovirus and Poliovirus Specific RNAs

J. Michael Bishop and Gebhard Koch†*

Laboratory of Biology of Viruses
National Institute of Allergy and Infectious Diseases
National Institutes of Health
Bethesda, Maryland
and
Heinrich Pette-Institut
Hamburg, Germany

I. Introduction

Dilute suspensions of virus particles can induce discrete lytic lesions ("plaques") in confluent sheets of sensitive tissue culture cells. This phenomenon provides a convenient means for quantitation of virus preparations by measurement of infectivity and thus represents one of the keystones of modern animal virology. An effective "plaque test" was first developed for Western equine encephalitis virus by Dulbecco (1952), and was promptly adapted to use with poliovirus (Dulbecco and Vogt, 1954). In these initial procedures, plaques were produced in monolayers of cells growing on glass. Subsequently, it was found that similar results could be obtained with cells suspended in a layer of soft agar (Cooper, 1955, 1961) in a manner analogous to that employed in the assay of bacterial viruses. The protocol presented below incorporates this agar-cell suspension technique into a

*Present address: Department of Microbiology, University of California, School of Medicine, San Francisco, California.

†Present address: Institut für Mikrobiologie, Medizinische Hochschule Hannover, Hannover, Germany.

procedure which allows the rapid, simultaneous assay of whole virus and isolated viral RNA. The polycations DEAE-dextran (where DEAE stands for diethylaminoethyl) and poly-L-ornithine are used as enhancers for the intrinsically low infectivity of RNA (Koch *et al.*, 1966). Attention is given to the optimal conditions for assay of both single- and double-stranded poliovirus RNA (Bishop and Koch, 1967). Finally, an effort is made to indicate the general range of applicability of this procedure as opposed to the more conventional technique employing cell monolayers and osmotic shock (Koch *et al.*, 1960).

II. Materials

A. Tissue Culture

Clonal strain S_3HeLa cells are grown in suspension at cell densities between 2 and 8×10^5/ml in Eagle's medium supplemented with 5% pooled horse serum. For optimal results, the cells should be in continuous logarithmic growth phase with a generation time of 18–22 hours. In the procedure to be described, cells are harvested after reaching a concentration of $4\text{–}6 \times 10^5$/ml.

B. Reagents

1. Suspension Culture Medium

Purchased as dehydrated powder ("Eagle's Medium No. 2, altered for spinner culture with glutamine and $NaHCO_3$") from Grand Island Biological Co., 3175 Stanley Road, P. O. Box 68, Grand Island, New York. Reconstituted with demineralized, doubly distilled water for use at designated multiples of the standard concentration. Sterilized by membrane filtration.

2. Serum

Either horse or calf serum is satisfactory. Prior to use in large scale assays, individual lots of serum must be tested for the presence of nonspecific virus inhibitors which occasionally occur spontaneously in both horse and bovine serum (Takemori *et al.*, 1958). It is also possible to heat inactivate the serum (65°C, 30 minutes), or to use randomly pooled sera, but pretesting offers the most reliable results.

3. Agar

Difco Special Agar-Noble from Difco Laboratories, Detroit, Michigan. Certain mutant strains of poliovirus (and other viruses) are inhibited by sulfated polysaccharides which are present in agar (Takemori and Nomura, 1960; Takemoto and Liebhaber, 1961), but this presents no problem to the routine assay of wild type strains. When required, these inhibitors can be counteracted by the addition of polycations, such as DEAE-dextran, to the agar (Liebhaber and Takemoto, 1961).

4. *Phosphate-Buffered Saline-Magnesium (PSM)*

0.15 *M* NaCl, m*M* $MgCl_2$, 0.02 *M* sodium phosphate buffer, pH 7.2. Sterilized by filtration and saturated with chloroform prior to storage at 4°C.

5. *Poly*-L-*ornithine*

Molecular weight 45,000. Obtained from Mann Research Laboratories, 136 Liberty Street, New York, New York. Stock solution of 500μg/ml in PSM. Stored in 10 ml aliquots at −20°C.

6. *DEAE-dextran*

Molecular weight approximately 2×10^6. Obtained from Pharmacia, Uppsala, Sweden. Stock solution of 100 μg/ml in chloroform-saturated PSM; stored at 4°C. This solution is used to prepare dilutions of RNA. The presence of chloroform counteracts trace bacterial contaminants often encountered if the RNA has been subjected previously to multiple manipulations such as column chromatography, passage through automatic recording equipment, etc.

C. Equipment

1. *Plastic Petri Dishes*

Standard bacteriological type, 10 cm diam.

2. *Sterile Wasserman Tubes*

Approximately 10 by 100 mm with loose fitting metal covers.

3. *Water Bath at 56°C*

4. *Shaker Bath (for RNA assay only)*

Should be capable of maintaining a temperature of 37 ± 1°C. The amount and type of agitation is critical. A short, rapid excursion of the sample carriage serves best to keep the cells thoroughly suspended during periods of incubation. A suitable bath is available from Lab-Line Instruments, Inc., Melrose Park, Illinois.

5. *Incubator*

Capable of maintaining a temperature of 37 ± 1°C. A humidified atmosphere containing 5% CO_2 is necessary unless the assay procedure is adapted to some form of closed system such as sealing the plates in plastic boxes in the presence of a small quantity of solidified CO_2.

D. Virus Samples

The preparation of high titer (1-5 × 10^9 pfu/ml) virus stocks, using concentrated suspension cultures, has been described (Levintow and Darnell, 1960). Unless the growth cycle has been allowed to proceed to the point of complete lysis (18–20 hours under conditions of single step growth) the cell suspension must be frozen and thawed three times prior to sampling in order to obtain accurate and maximum titers.

E. Preparation of Viral RNAs

Single-stranded RNA can be isolated from highly purified virus (Levintow and Darnell, 1960) by phenol extraction at 60°C, or by repeated column chromatography (methylated albumin-kieselguhr) of the RNA extracted from infected cells with phenol (Kubinski and Koch, 1962). Double-stranded "replicative form" RNA is obtained by extracting RNA from infected cells with phenol at 60°C, precipitating the RNA with 1 *M* NaCl, and chromatographing the supernatant on columns of methylated albumin-kieselguhr (Bishop and Koch, 1967) or cellulose (Franklin, 1966).

III. Assay Procedure

It is feasible for one person to assay as many as 100–150 samples in a single procedure. However, we have found that for the purposes of rapid, efficient, and accurate assay 60 plates represent a convenient maximum number. Therefore, the quantities given in the following description are intended for an assay of that size.

A. Preparation of Basal Layer

1. *Materials*

a. Twofold concentrated suspension culture medium containing 6% serum.

b. Agar, 2% in distilled water, freshly autoclaved.

c. Petri dishes. Equal volumes of the medium and molten agar are combined and thoroughly mixed. Approximately 15 ml of this mixture is poured into each petri dish and allowed to harden on a perfectly level surface. These plates can be prepared in large numbers and stored in a cool, moist environment for up to several weeks. Prior to use, they should be placed in a 37°C incubator and allowed to warm.

B. Agar (1.4%) for Cell-Suspension Pour Layer

1. Materials

a. Twofold concentrated medium containing 3% serum, prewarmed to 56°C (45 ml).

b. Agar, 2.8% in distilled water (1.5 gm of agar, 55 ml of water), freshly autoclaved.

c. Capped Wasserman tubes, (60) prewarmed to 56°C. Equal volumes of the medium and agar are combined, and 1 ml aliquots are put into each of the Wasserman tubes. These are left in the 56°C bath until their final use (see below).

C. Dilutions

Samples should be diluted so that individual plates will contain less than 100, and preferably from 30 to 50 plaques. Higher numbers of plaques lead to inaccurate counting, primarily because of plaque overlap. Virus preparations can be diluted in either medium without serum or in PSM. Artificially low titers resulting from aggregation of virus particles are not generally encountered in the case of crude poliovirus stock, although it has been claimed that the inclusion of deoxycholate in the initial dilution improves plating efficiency (Cooper, 1961).* RNA samples are diluted in the DEAE-dextran:PSM solution. Virus and RNA dilutions are completely stable at room temperature for the length of time required to perform the assay. The presence of DEAE-dextran in RNA dilutions is important in this regard because of its capacity to protect RNA against the action of trace amounts of RNase (Vaheri and Pagano, 1965; Koch and Bishop, 1968). For longer periods of time, dilutions should be stored at or below 4°C. Before initiating the following portions of the assay procedure, ali-

*However, concentrated preparations of highly purified virus may aggregate to an extreme extent, and this undoubtedly influences the titers obtained with such preparations.

quots of the virus (0.5 ml) and RNA (0.1 ml) dilutions should be distributed into Wasserman tubes at room temperature.

D. Polyornithine Treatment of Cells for RNA Assay

(This and the succeeding step are omitted if only virus is being titered.) Cells are collected from suspension culture (250 ml) by centrifugation (1400 rpm, 4 minutes, International Centrifuge PR-2), washed once with warm PSM (100 ml), and resuspended in PSM (2.5 ml) to give a cell density of approximately 4×10^7/ml. Polyornithine (0.25 ml of stock solution) is added to a final concentration of 40 μg/ml. After incubation for 5 minutes at 37°C with continuous shaking, the cell suspension is diluted approximately 15-fold with PSM (40 ml) in order to reduce the concentration of polyornithine. This averts the possibility of complex formation between RNA and polyornithine which has not been bound to the cells. Complexing of this sort has been shown to inactivate the infectivity of RNA (Koch and Bishop, 1968).

E. Adsorption of RNA to the Polyornithine-Treated Cells

A 0.5 ml portion of the diluted cell suspension is added to each of the Wasserman tubes containing 0.1 ml of RNA dilution. The tubes are incubated with thorough agitation for 45–60 minutes. This long period of incubation is necessary to achieve maximum adsorption of single-stranded RNA to the host cells. In the case of double-stranded RNA, 15 minutes is sufficient time (Koch and Bishop, 1968). Vigorous agitation must be maintained throughout the course of incubation in order to keep the cells in suspension and to avoid the formation of large cell clumps.

F. Agar-Cell Suspension Pour Layer

(Virus assay resumes here.) While the foregoing incubation is in process, cells are collected from suspension culture (1800–2000 ml) by centrifugation and resuspended at a concentration of $1\text{–}2 \times 10^7$/ml in warm medium containing 2% serum (60 ml). A 1 ml portion of this "indicator cell" suspension is added to each of the Wasserman tubes containing either the RNA:cell mixture or 0.5 ml of virus dilution. Note that no special adsorption period is required for virus. After gentle shaking, the content of each tube is emptied into one of the tubes containing 1.4% agar. The cell suspension and agar solution are quickly mixed, poured evenly over the basal layer by rocking and rotating the petri dish. The plates are then left undisturbed at room temperature until the agar has hardened (20–30 minutes).

There are several critical aspects at this stage of the procedure. First, it is essential that the basal agar layer be level and that the pour layer in turn be allowed to harden with the plates on a perfectly level surface. Second, if the surface of the basal layer is too dry as a consequence of prolonged storage, the agar-cell suspension does not solidify in a uniform fashion. This causes discontinuities in the cell sheet and erratic plating efficiencies. Finally, if the agar solution is used to form the pour layer too soon after autoclaving, the initial temperature of the final agar-cell mixture may be high enough to damage the cells. Preparing the agar in advance and distributing it into Wasserman tubes in a 56°C water bath as described above obviates this problem.

G. Incubation of Plates and Plaque Counting

The plates are inverted and incubated in a humidified 5% CO_2 atmosphere at 37°C. Plaques are best seen against the indirect light of a fluorescent desk lamp. They can usually be counted after 48 hours, but should be rechecked after 72 hours. If desired, the cell sheet can be stained by carefully layering 5 ml of 0.01% neutral red in phosphate buffer onto the surface of the agar and then incubating the plates for another 3 hours. However, this is a tedious procedure because the staining solution tends to dissect between the soft agar pour sheet and the basal layer. If the assay is performed as described, and a proper concentration of cells is obtained in the pour layer, staining should not be necessary.

H. Assay of Productively Infected Cells ("Infectious Centers")

The titration of RNA just described is in itself an assay for the infectious centers formed by exposing polyornithine-treated cells to RNA. It is therefore easily adapted to other situations in which it must be determined what portion of a cell population has been productively infected by virus or RNA. The cell population containing potential infectious centers should be diluted as required in medium containing 5% serum and 0.5 ml portions of the dilutions added to indicator cells (1.0 ml) as in the case of the virus assay. The agar pour layer is then formed as usual. It should be emphasized that the presence of serum in the diluent is essential. In its absence, infectious centers do not survive dilution, presumably because of a general reduction in cell viability.

IV. Alternate Procedures

A. Simplified Assay

It is possible to omit polyornithine from the procedure and to perform the assay as follows. The cells which are to be used for the formation of infectious centers with RNA are resuspended in PSM:DEAE-dextran. Aliquots (0.5 ml) are then added to the RNA dilutions, and the remainder of the assay carried out exactly as before. By using this procedure, one sacrifices a portion of the assay's sensitivity for single-stranded RNA (see Table I). However, it is extremely simple to execute and is less toxic to the host cells than that using polyornithine. Moreover, it offers nearly optimal titers with double-stranded RNA.

B. Virus-Induced Infectious Centers as Control for RNA Assay

Routine titration of virus preparations is performed most conveniently by adding dilutions to the indicator cells immediately before forming the agar-cell pour layer. However, the same results can be obtained if the virus dilutions are incubated with the polyornithine-treated cells as is done in the case of RNA. This modification can be used as an internal control for the RNA assay because it serves to indicate whether the pretreated cells are capable of forming infectious

TABLE I
Specific Infectivity of Single- and Double-Stranded RNA

Polycation used in assay	Titer[a]	
	Single-stranded RNA (PFU/μg)	Double-stranded RNA (PFU/μg)
None	1.6×10^{-1}	3.1×10^{-1}
Polyornithine	6.7×10^{4}	2.3×10^{6}
DEAE-dextran	1.6×10^{2}	1.1×10^{6}
Polyornithine and DEAE-dextran	6.7×10^{4}	2.3×10^{6}

[a]Purified RNA preparations were titered with the procedure described in the text except that where indicated one or both of the polycations was omitted.

centers after exposure to virus, which is more stable and more efficient than RNA.

C. Cell Monolayers with Agar Overlay

The original procedure of adsorbing virus (Dulbecco, 1952) or RNA (Koch *et al.*, 1960) to confluent monolayers of cells and then overlaying these with agar is still in widespread use. Under certain circumstances, it offers some advantages over the agar-cell suspension assay. First, laboratory facilities or virus-sensitive cell lines may not be adaptable to the suspension procedure. Second, rapid and repeated washings of the cells are sometimes necessary. This would apply both to studies concerning adsorption of virus or RNA to the host cell and to experiments in which the environmental conditions of the cells are to be changed for controlled periods of time. Finally, monolayers allow direct exposure of cells to chemical and physical agents (such as metabolic inhibitors and ultraviolet radiation) at selected times after infection.

The conventional assay for infectious RNA is of sufficient interest to merit brief description here. Confluent monolayers of virus-sensitive cells are washed successively with 0.15 *M* and 0.6 *M* NaCl, buffered with sodium phosphate, pH 7.4. A suitable dilution of RNA in 1 *M* NaCl is then placed on the cell sheet in a volume just sufficient to cover the entire surface (0.1 ml for 40 mm diam petri dishes). After an appropriate adsorption period (usually 20–30 minutes), the monolayer is overlayed with a molten agar solution similar in composition to that used to prepare the basal layer for the agar-cell suspension assay. Once the agar has solidified, the plates are inverted and incubated for 72 hours. Then the cell sheet is stained with neutral red in order to visualize the plaques.

D. Monolayer Assay for Infectious Centers

Monolayers can also be used for the detection of productively infected cells (infectious centers). The cells representing potential infectious centers are allowed to settle out of suspension and adhere to an indicator monolayer prior to the addition of agar overlay (Ellem and Colter, 1960). However, if the infected cells have been damaged by the conditions required to initiate infection, or by necessary experimental manipulations, their ability to adhere to the monolayer will be impaired, and the final titer of infectious centers will be inaccurate. This artifact can be avoided if the infected cells are fixed in close proximity to the monolayer by immobilization in a very thin agar layer. Subsequently, a nutrient agar overlay is added.

Under most circumstances, the agar-cell suspension assay is the preferred technique for measuring infectious centers. It is inherently free of the technical difficulties and artifacts just discussed. All cells which successfully support a single infectious cycle will register as infectious centers.

E. Adaptation of a Virus-Host Cell System to the Suspension Assay of Infectious RNA

In approaching the assay of a viral RNA with which there is no relevant previous experience, it might be wise to proceed as follows. Test first the infectivity of RNA on appropriate monolayers in the presence of DEAE-dextran, the least toxic and simplest to use of the polycations. Next, determine the value of the additional use of polyornithine pretreatment of the host cells. Having standardized the conditions for stimulating RNA infectivity, adapt the system to agar-cell suspensions as desired.

Polybasic compounds are easier to use and considerably less toxic than is osmotic shock. It remains to be seen whether they are as universally effective in augmenting the infectivity of viral nucleic acids. To date, polycations have been applied successfully to the assay of RNA from a variety of small animal viruses and to the infection of spheroplasts with isolated bacteriophage RNA (Iglewski and Franklin, 1967).

V. Discussion

A. The Nature of a Plaque: Clonal Purification of Virus Strains

There is a direct and linear relationship between the concentration of infecting virus and plaque yield (Fig. 1). Such a relationship indicates that each plaque results from infection with a single virus particle (Dulbecco and Vogt, 1954). This fact has an important consequence: the progeny virus contained in a well-isolated plaque is genetically homogeneous (Dulbecco and Vogt, 1955). Picking virus from such plaques thus offers the most convenient approach to purification of genetic strains. The agar is removed from the central portion of the plaque with a sterile Pasteur pipette and suspended in 0.5–1.0

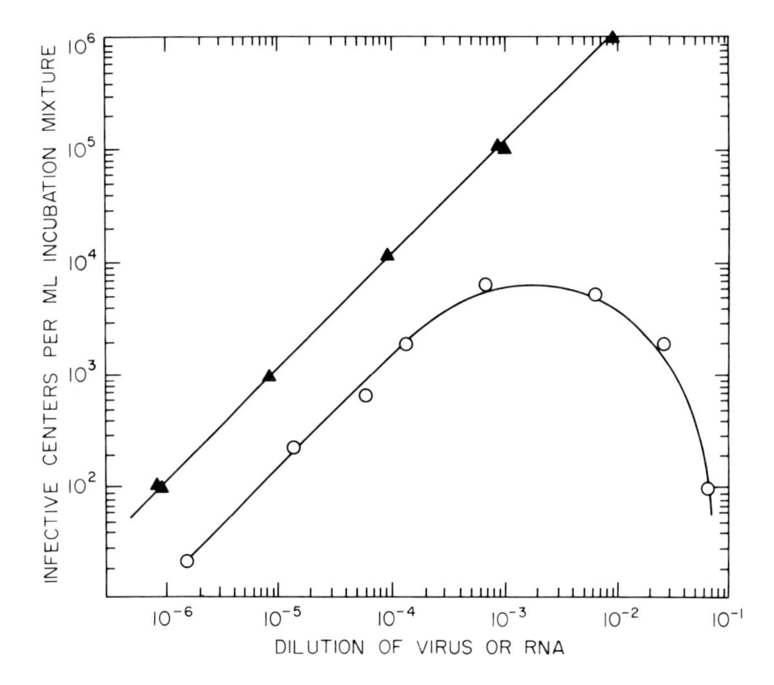

FIG. 1. Relationship between concentration of infecting units and infectious center yield. Concentrated cell suspensions were infected with appropriate dilutions of (▼) poliovirus and poliovirus (○) single-stranded RNA as described in the text. After incubation, the cell suspensions were diluted as required and assayed for infectious centers.

ml of medium. After storage overnight at 4°C such a suspension will usually contain 10^4–10^5 pfu. It can be used for repeated cloning of the virus strain in the manner just described or as inoculum for regrowth of the purified virus.

When using the plaque technique to purify virus strains, several sources of contamination should be kept in mind (Dulbecco and Vogt, 1954, 1955). First, virus of multiple origin might be present because of plaque overlap. Second, virus may have diffused from adjacent plaques. Third, on rare occasions mutations could occur during the virus growth which is responsible for plaque development. In general, extremely pure virus strains can be obtained if one takes the following precautions: (1) use plates containing 10 or less plaques, (2) select plaques which are separated from adjacent plaques by a distance of at least 10 mm, and (3) perform 3 or 4 serial plaque passages.

It is also possible to separate and purify virus strains by repeated passages at limiting dilutions (Burnet *et al.*, 1953). A series of inoculations is made with virus stock which has been diluted so that productive infection occurs in a very low percentage of cases. Under these conditions, the probability that infection was initiated by a single particle becomes relatively high. The reader should consult the previous literature for further details (Isaacs, 1957).

B. Efficiency of the Assay

As determined by comparing the results of bioassay with particle counts from electromicrographs, between 0.01 and 0.1% of a population of poliovirus virions will give rise to lytic infectious cycles and thereby register as plaque-forming units (Schwerdt and Schaffer, 1955). The exact cause of this relatively low pfu:particle ratio is not known. No effort to substantially improve the low efficiency of bioassay has ever met with consistent success, although on occasion a pfu:particle ratio as high as 1:20 has been observed (Schwerdt and Fogh, 1957).

There are similar severe restrictions on the efficiency of assay of infectious RNA. In the case of poliovirus, RNA titers range between 0.1 and 1% of those expected on the basis of the viral equivalents of RNA contained in the preparation. Moreover, these figures represent optimal results obtained only with the assistance of special agents such as the polycations employed in the procedure described above. The factors which limit the infectivity of RNA are multiple, and none are well understood. Enzymatic degradation of the RNA and poor adsorption to and penetration into the host cell are the most commonly suggested explanations, but it is clear that the polycations employed here also have beneficial effects on some other aspect of the RNA-host cell interaction (Koch and Bishop, 1968).

Plaque yield is directly proportional to the amount of infecting RNA over a considerable range of RNA concentrations (Fig. 1). This proportionality is considered to have the same implication as in the case of whole virus: A single molecule of RNA is sufficient to initiate infection. However, if the concentration of RNA is raised beyond a certain point, the number of infectious centers declines sharply (Fig. 1). This reduction of plating efficiency is actually a function of the ratio of RNA molecules per host cell rather than of the absolute concentration of RNA (Koch and Bishop, 1968), and therefore is probably not caused by aggregation of RNA. Apparently, adsorption of large numbers of RNA molecules has an adverse effect on the host cell. Whatever its cause, this phenomenon has important practical significance: The amount of RNA present in the incubation mixture must be kept below the inhibitory concentration level (1 μg/ml as the assay is performed here) if optimal titers are to be obtained.

C. Polycations and the Infectivity of RNA

Dose-response curves for the effect of four polycations on the infectivity of single-stranded RNA are shown in Fig. 2. All of the substances tested have toxic effects on the cells causing aggregation and reduction in cloning efficiency. This may explain the sharp decrease

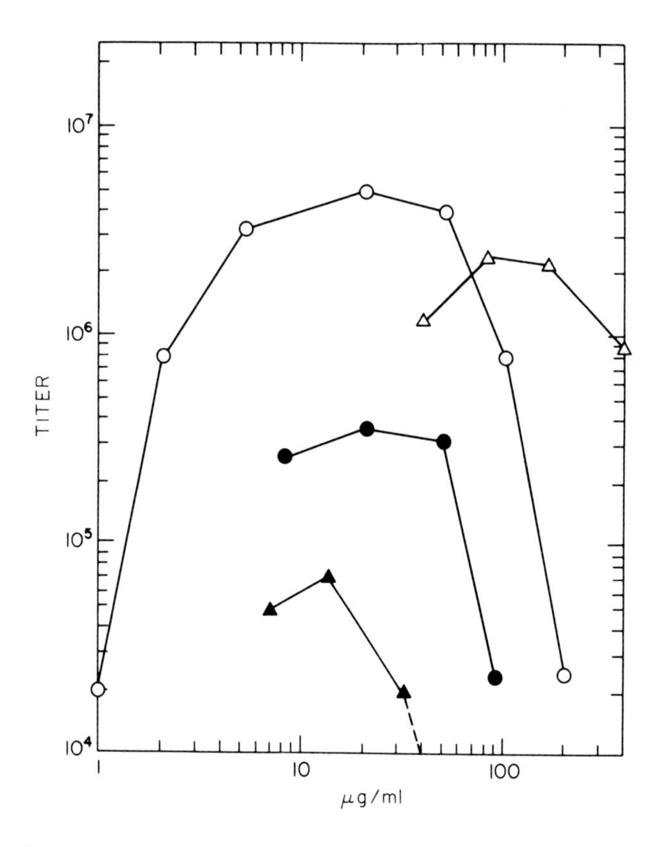

Fig. 2. Dose-response curves for the effect of polycations on the infectivity of poliovirus single-stranded RNA. A standard dilution of RNA was assayed as described in the text except that (a) the concentration of polycation used was varied as indicated and (b) polylysine and methylated albumin were added only after exposure of cells to RNA. The ordinate refers to plaque-forming units per milliliter of the standard RNA solution (300 μg/ml). (○) Poly-L-ornithine, (●) methylated albumin, (◄) poly-L-lysine, and (△) DEAE-dextran.

in RNA titers at high polycation concentrations. As shown in Table I, polyornithine, used at optimal concentrations, causes an increase of at least 10^5 in the titer of both single- and double-stranded RNA. When used alone, DEAE-dextran yields an intermediate rise in titer but has no additive effect in combination with polyornithine. It is included in the assay because of its ability to protect RNA against the action of RNase.

D. Assay Precision

The precision of the assay for any single set of determinations is on the order of $\pm 20\%$. This is comparable to Dulbecco's statement that if 100 plaques are counted the highest and lowest counts in a series of parallel assays should differ by a factor of not more than 1.5 (Dulbecco, 1955). In the case of RNA, larger variations may be observed on a day-to-day basis. These variations reflect the fact that productive interaction of RNA with host cells is difficult to achieve, requiring a stimulus (either osmotic shock or polycations) which is toxic to the cells.

E. Advantages of the Agar-Cell Suspension Assay

The primary advantage of the agar-cell suspension technique is the fact that no advance preparation of cell monolayers is necessary. Cells maintained in suspension culture can be harvested whenever desired and used immediately. This allows great flexibility in planning the size and frequency of plaque tests. When the suspension assay is performed as described above, it offers two additional useful features. First, virus and infectious RNA can be titered simultaneously in a single, rapid procedure. Second, the infectious centers formed after adsorption and penetration of RNA are detected with a separate lot of "indicator cells." These are not exposed to the deleterious conditions under which RNA infection is initiated, a fact which undoubtedly improves the reliability of the assay and also facilitates a variety of experiments with the initial RNA-cell complex which would not be possible otherwise.

In general, we consider the agar-cell suspension procedure to be the method of choice whenever its use is feasible. Suspension cultures are not essential. Cells can be maintained as monolayers (or prepared as primary cultures by trypsinization), placed into suspension when needed, and used exactly as described above. Care must be taken to achieve the recommended concentration of cells in the agar layer (1–2 × 10^7 cells per 10 cm diam petri dish). Failure to do so may have major effects on plaque size and number, and on cell viability (Cooper, 1955).

ACKNOWLEDGMENTS

The procedure presented above was developed with the expert assistance of Miss Nancy Quintrell. Some of the technical details are derived from Dr. J. Maizel's unpublished modification of Cooper's agar–cell suspension assay for infectious virus (Cooper, 1961).

REFERENCES

Bishop, J. M., and Koch, G. (1967). *J. Biol. Chem.* **242**, 1736.
Burnet, M., Fraser, K. B., and Lind, P. E. (1953). *Nature* **171**, 163.
Cooper, P. D. (1955). *Virology* **1**, 397.
Cooper, P. D. (1961). *Virology* **13**, 153.
Dulbecco, R. (1952). *Proc. Natl. Acad. Sci. U.S.* **38**, 747.
Dulbecco, R. (1955). *Physiol. Rev.* **35**, 301.
Dulbecco, R., and Vogt, M. (1954). *J. Exptl. Med.* **99**, 167.
Dulbecco, R., and Vogt, M. (1955). *Ann. N.Y. Acad. Sci.* **61**, 790.
Ellem, K. A. O., and Colter, J. S. (1960). *Virology* **11**, 434.
Franklin, R. M. (1966). *Proc. Natl. Acad. Sci. U.S.* **55**, 1504.
Iglewski, W. J., and Franklin, R. M. (1967). *Proc. Natl. Acad. Sci. U.S.* **58**, 1019.
Isaacs, A. (1957). *Advan. Virus Res.* **4**, 111.
Koch, G. and Bishop, J. M. (1968). *Virology* **35**, 9.
Koch, G., Koenig, S., and Alexander, H. E. (1960). *Virology* **10**, 329.
Koch, G., Quintrell, N., and Bishop, J. M. (1966). *Biochem. Biophys. Res. Commun.* **24**, 304.
Kubinski, H., and Koch, G. (1962). *Virology* **17**, 219.
Levintow, L., and Darnell, J. E., Jr. (1960). *J. Biol. Chem.* **235**, 70.
Liebhaber, H., and Takemoto, K. K. (1961). *Virology* **14**, 502.
Schwerdt, C. E., and Fogh, J. (1957). *Virology* **4**, 41.
Schwerdt, C. E., and Schaffer, F. L. (1955). *Ann. N.Y. Acad. Sci.* **61**, 740.
Takemori, N., and Nomura, S. (1960). *Virology* **12**, 171.
Takemori, N., Nomura, S., Nakano, M., Morioka, Y., Henmi, M., and Kitaoka, M. (1958). *Virology* **5**, 30.
Takemoto, K. K., and Liebhaber, H. (1961). *Virology* **14**, 456.
Vaheri, A., and Pagano, J. S. (1965). *Virology* **27**, 434.

15. Plaque Formation by Influenza Viruses

Edwin D. Kilbourne

Department of Microbiology
Mount Sinai School of Medicine of
The City University of New York
New York, New York

I. Introduction

Although the influenza viruses are among the best studied of viruses and are of special interest because of their mutability and participation in genetic recombination, their study has been handicapped by the lack of suitable plaque-forming systems. During the past few years a clone of cells (clone 1-5C-4) derived from a variant (Wong-Kilbourne) of the aneuploid Chang human conjunctival cell line (see Fig. 1) has proved useful in genetic and antigenic analyses of influenza viruses.* Clones of the Wong-Kilbourne variant are uniquely susceptible among human aneuploid cell lines† to the cytocidal effects of influenza viruses in low multiplicity and in their capacity to produce infective viruses (Wong and Kilbourne, 1961). As a consequence, many standard laboratory strains of virus can produce plaques in monolayers of clone 1-5C-4 cells (Sugiura and Kilbourne, 1965). The cells have been distributed widely throughout the world and are available to investigators from the American Type Culture Collection

*The development of this system has been principally due to the efforts of Dr. Akira Sugiura. Others who have made major contributions are Dr. Sam C. Wong, Dr. Matilde Krim, and Dr. Rene Jahiel.

†See, however, the recent report of Hatano and Morita (Table III).

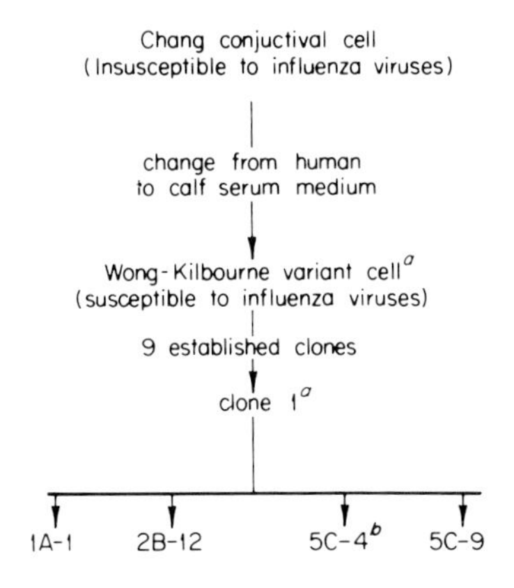

FIG. 1. Derivation of clone 1-5C-4. [a]Contained SV5-like paramyxovirus. [b]Clone free of virus (clone 1-SC-4).

and from commercial sources. They are readily propagated and have proved stable with respect to their viral susceptibility. In contrast to primary or secondary cell cultures clone 1-5C-4 cells provide a relatively homogeneous substrate for the study of influenza virus-cell interaction. For the foregoing reasons the present description of a technique for influenza virus plaque formation will be principally concerned with the methods developed in the author's laboratory employing clone 1-5C-4 cells. Alternative methods are reviewed in Section III, E.

II. Materials

A. CELLS

The cells have been partially described in Section I, and their genealogy is summarized in Fig. 1. Chang conjunctival cells (R. S. Chang, 1954) obtained from Dr. Seymour Levine were adapted by Wong and Kilbourne to growth in Morton and Parker's medium 199 with 10% calf serum (Wong and Kilbourne, 1961). The cells were found to be susceptible to the cytocidal effects of A_0/NWS and swine (S15) virus. A series of clones was established by Puck's technique and these were found to differ slightly in susceptibility. During this study, hemadsorption in uninoculated cells disclosed the presence of a contaminating noncytocidal virus identified as an SV5-like paramyxovirus. Clone 1-5C-4 was established as a maximally susceptible mycoplasma-free, virus-free clone. Continued monitoring in the author's laboratory and by the American Type Culture Collection has not revealed any reappearance of the paramyxovirus. The cell has been identified as human by chromosomal and antigenic analyses. It is aneuploid with a modal chromosome number of 72. It may be frozen by conventional techniques and stored for more than 2 years at −60°C or lower temperatures.

B. Culture Media

The constituents of fluid growth and maintenance media and of the media used in agar overlays added following viral inoculation are listed in Table I. It is not essential that fetal calf serum be used, and γ-globulin-free serum has not effected discernible advantages. Eagle's MEM may be substituted for 199 in the growth medium.

C. Incubators

Water-jacketed double door incubators with attachments for gas control (Boekel) have proved satisfactory for cell propagation and maintenance.

D. Viruses

A number of standard laboratory strains of influenza A and B viruses produce plaques on initial passage in clone 1-5C-4 cells (see Table II). Efficiency of plaque formation is increased by serial propagation of some viruses (e.g., the S15 strain of swine influenza virus) but not with viruses such as A_0/NWS with which the efficiency of plaque formation related to chick embryo infective dose (EID_{50}) is initially high (Wong and Kilbourne, 1961). It is regrettable that the majority of A_2 strains tested have produced only small plaques or none at all. However, most such strains have been passaged exclusively in eggs and may have become attenuated in their virulence for mammalian cells. Passage of egg-propagated strains of A_2/RI/5^+ and A_2/RI/5^- in monkey kidney cells has produced virus capable of producing small plaques in the present system. However, a 1956 A_1 strain and a 1963 swine virus formed plaques readily although previously passed only in eggs (Sugiura and Kilbourne, 1965). There has been little opportunity to explore the potential of clone 1-5C-4 cells for direct recovery of influenza viruses from man, but two strains of influenza B virus were recovered as plaque-forming viruses by the author in 1966. Simultaneous inoculation of chick embryos with the same throat washings was unsuccessful. In addition, direct isolation of the new Hong Kong

TABLE I
COMPOSITION OF MEDIA[a,b]

Ingredients	Growth medium	Fluid maintenance medium	Primary agar overlay[c]
10 × 199 (without $NaHCO_3$) Hanks base[d]	10.0[e]	10.0	10.0
Water, distilled, demineralized	90.0	90.0	55.0
$NaHCO_3$, 5%	0.5	0.4	1.5
Fetal calf serum Δ56 C, 30′[d]	5.0	–	–
Bovine albumin 35%[f]	–	0.3	0.3
Eagle's MEM amino acids 50x[d]	–	–	2.0
Eagle's MEM vitamins 100x[d]	–	–	1.0
DEAE-dextran, 1%[g]	–	–	1.0
Ionagar No. 2, 2%	–	–	30.0

[a]Modified from Sugiura and Kilbourne (1965).
[b]To each medium penicillin and streptomycin are added in final concentrations of 100 units mg/ml, respectively.
[c]Secondary (staining) overlay contains 0.5 part 1% neutral red (Nutritional Biochemical) substituted for 0.5 part of water. For optimal demonstration of "red" border plaques, one-half this concentration is recommended.
[d]Microbiological Associates. Eagle's MEM may be substituted for 199.
[e]Parts.
[f]Midwest Pentex Co.
[g]Pharmacia Co.

TABLE II
PLAQUE ASSAYS OF VARIOUS STRAINS OF INFLUENZA VIRUS IN CLONE 1-5C-4 CELL CULTURE[a]

Type or subtype	Strains	Maximal count (days after infection)	Efficiency of plaque formation[b] (%)	Average plaque diameter (mm)	Plaque border
Swine	S15	5	12	2.5	Sharp
A_0	NWS	4	70	3	Sharp
	WSN	4	NT[c]	3	Diffuse
	WS	4	NT	3	Diffuse
	Mel	6	2	1	Diffuse
A_1	CAM	6	40	2	Red
A_2	RI/5+(MK)	7	58	0.5	Sharp
	RI/5–(MK)	5-7	NT	0.5	Sharp
B	Lee	6	2	0.5-1	Diffuse, very faint

[a]Adapted from Sugiura and Kilbourne (1965).
[b]Expressed as a ratio of pfu to EID_{50} (egg infective dose).
[c]Here, NT stands for not tested.

variant has been accomplished, and all of those 1968 strains thus far tested have produced plaques in these cells.

In addition to the swine viruses, certain avian influenza A viruses have produced plaques in clone 1-5C-4 cells (Pereira, 1967).

In recombination experiments in the author's laboratory, parental and recombinant seed viruses are maintained as allantoic fluid suspensions from chick embryos inoculated at 10–11 days of age. Recloning of virus from plaques in clone 1-5C-4 cells has not appeared to be necessary to maintain plaquing efficiency and plaque size. However, the point has not been systematically studied for each virus. It can be stated that obvious genetic changes in viral stocks after three consecutive egg passages have not been discovered. Yields of virus from clone 1-5C-4 cell monolayers under fluid maintenance medium have been low (see Section III, C, 2) so that propagation of viral seed stocks in eggs is a convenience that outweighs the risk of host-induced virus variation.

III. Procedures

A. Growth and Maintenance of Clone 1-5C-4 Cells

Cells may be grown in screw-capped 200 ml milk dilution bottles or on 250 ml plastic flasks (Falcon). After seeding with 0.5×10^6 cells, 20 ml of growth medium (Table I) are added. Medium is replaced after 3–4 days in order to maintain the pH of cultures in the neutral range. Monolayers are complete in 6–7 days. Yields from a 250 ml plastic flask approximate 15×10^6 cells. Cells are removed with Versene for passage.*

1. Preparation of Petri Dish Cultures for Viral Inoculation

Plastic petri dishes (60 mm; Falcon) are seeded with $0.5\text{–}1.0 \times 10^6$ cells per dish, covered with fluid growth medium, and then incubated for 2–4 days at 37°C in a humidified atmosphere with a CO_2 concentration of about 3% until complete monolayers are formed. One medium change may be necessary during this period.

*Versene solution: NaCl, 8.0 gm; $KHPO_4$, 0.2 gm; KCl, 0.2 gm; Na_2HPO_4 (anhydrous), 1.15 gm; Versene, 0.4 gm in 1 liter double-distilled H_2O. Autoclave 120°C, 15 minutes.

B. Growth and Maintenance of Influenza Viruses

(See also Section II, D.)

Virus seed stocks are routinely produced by inoculation of 10–11-day-old chick embryos in the allantoic sac with 10^3 EID_{50} of virus and eggs are then incubated for 40–48 hours. Eggs are refrigerated at 4°C for 6–18 hours before harvest to minimize bleeding into the allantoic sac. Pooled fluids are titrated for hemagglutinating, and infective virus and tested for bacterial sterility. Pools are then quick-frozen in ethanol-CO_2 in aliquots and stored at −60°C in a Dry Ice chest or at −95°C in a mechanical (REVCO) deep freeze. Aliquots of virus are thawed slowly under running cold tap water before use and are not reused.

C. Plaque Formation

1. *Inoculation of Viruses*

Medium is removed. (Monolayers are washed once with 15 ml of phosphate-buffered saline (PBS) only if inhibitor-sensitive viruses are used.) Virus appropriately diluted in maintenance medium is added in a volume of 0.2 ml and allowed to adsorb to the monolayer for 15 minutes at 37°C. Ten milliliters of the primary agar overlay medium (Table I) are then added without removing the inoculum. Infected cultures are incubated at 35°C in an atmosphere of 3% CO_2 for a period optimal for plaque development for the virus employed (Table II), but not longer than 7 days, because monolayers are not well maintained after this time. Hydrocortisone incorporated in the overlay has a favorable effect on cell maintenance (Omura *et al.*, 1967) but also may be inhibitory to plaque development (Kilbourne, 1965).

2. *Kinetics of Viral Multiplication and Yield of Virus per Cell*

a. Adsorption. Fifty percent of A_0/NWS virus is adsorbed by 10 minutes after inoculation, and by 30 minutes 75% of the final plaque count is achieved. Removal of residual virus after inoculation does not change the plaque count (Sugiura and Kilbourne, 1965).

b. Virus multiplication. Under conditions of high input multiplicity (30 pfu/cell), increase in hemagglutinating and infective virus is detectable at 6 hours. Thereafter there is a period of exponential increase (6–12 hours) and peak yields of infective virus are attained at 20 hours after infection. The calculated yield of infective virus averages 5 pfu per cell with multiplicities of infection of 1–30. In estimating virus/cell multiplicity in the present system it may be assumed that there are 2×10^6 cells in a complete monolayer in a plastic petri dish of 60 mm diam (Sugiura and Kilbourne, 1965). Intranuclear S antigen appears at 3 hours after infection and cytoplasmic hemagglutinin and neuraminidase 4 hours after infection (Maeno and Kilbourne, in preparation).

3. Increase of Plaque Radius with Time

In the influenza virus-clone 1-5C-4 system, plaque growth kinetics are linear with respect to plaque radius (Jahiel and Kilbourne, 1966). The frequency distribution of the radii of plaques produced by recombinant X-7 virus are plotted in Fig. 2 together with the standard deviation as percentage of mean plaque radius. The X-7 virus produces large clear plaques similar to those produced by its A_0/NWS parent.

4. Demonstration and Counting of Plaques

a. Vital staining. Although the large (2–4 mm), clear, sharp-bordered plaques of certain influenza viruses may be seen by the unaided eye in unstained monolayers, the use of a dye that is taken up by viable cells is necessary for precise plaque counts. Neutral red is taken up rather slowly by clone 1-5C-4 cells but when added in the form of a second agar overlay (5 ml/dish) 12–18 hours before the day of reading (Table I, footnote *c*) it provides an adequate background stain for undamaged viable cells (Fig. 3a). Plaques are counted with an automatic recording pen with the aid of a magnifying lens and a green filter on a standard colony counter. Approximate plaque size is determined with a 1.0 mm ruler. Precise measurement of plaques requires that cell monolayers be fixed and stained and viewed by projection microscopy (see Section III, C, 3*b* below). Phenotypic variation in plaque radius (SD = 17–30%) is noted even with recently cloned viruses, but median plaque size and plaque morphology are genetically stable characteristics of most influenza viruses.

"Red" plaques—Certain influenza viruses possess as a stable, transferable genetic characteristic the capacity to produce plaques with red borders or margins (Sugiura and Kilbourne, 1966). This effect is related to an increased uptake of neutral red by infected (but still viable) cells at the plaque margin. It is best demonstrated (Fig. 3b) by reduction of the neutral red concentration in the secondary agar overlay (Table I, footnote *c*).

b. Picking of plaques for cloning of virus. Cloning of viruses may be accomplished by removal with a Pasteur pipette of a plug of agar

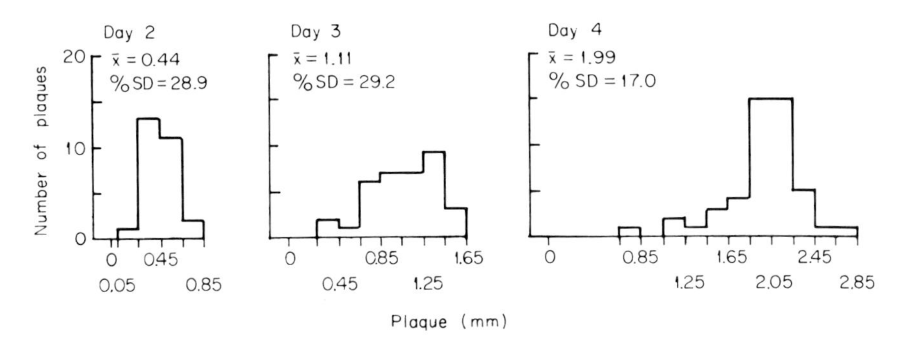

FIG. 2. Frequency distribution of X-7 plaque radii with time after viral inoculation. Abbreviations: $\bar{x}$, mean plaque radius; % SD, standard deviation as percentage of mean plaque radius (from Jahiel and Kilbourne, 1966).

overlying a well-isolated plaque. This plug, appropriately diluted in maintenance medium may then be inoculated into chick embryos or onto monolayers of clone 1-5C-4 cells. In the author's laboratory, two successive "plaque pickings" have been found to constitute an adequate cloning from viral mixtures as long as input multiplicity of virus has been low and results in no more than 10–20 well-demarcated plaques on a 60 mm petri dish.

c. Direct staining and fixation with crystal violet in ethanol. Because neutral red uptake is subject to considerable variation related to the physiologic state of the monolayer, the dark-contrast staining of fixed monolayers with crystal violet or hematoxylin is preferred for precise counts and measurements. A simple method involves the removal of the agar overlay with forceps, then immersion of the petri dishes in 0.1% crystal violet in 20% ethanol in H_2O for 1 minute. Plates are rinsed in tap water, then air dried. This technique also provides a semipermanent (>1 year) record of experiments if the plates are filed and cataloged. The variety of plaque types identifiable with this method is illustrated in Fig. 4.

d. Plaque counts and measurement. Plaque counts and measurement may be made by scanning plates with a projecting microscope (Bausch & Lomb Tri-Simplex) at a magnification of 21× or greater (Jahiel and Kilbourne, 1966). Submicroscopic plaques may thus be seen, but the occasional occurrence of nonspecific holes in the monolayer (<0.01 mm^2) limits the resolution of the method unless hemadsorption is used concomitantly (see Section III, C, 5*a* below).

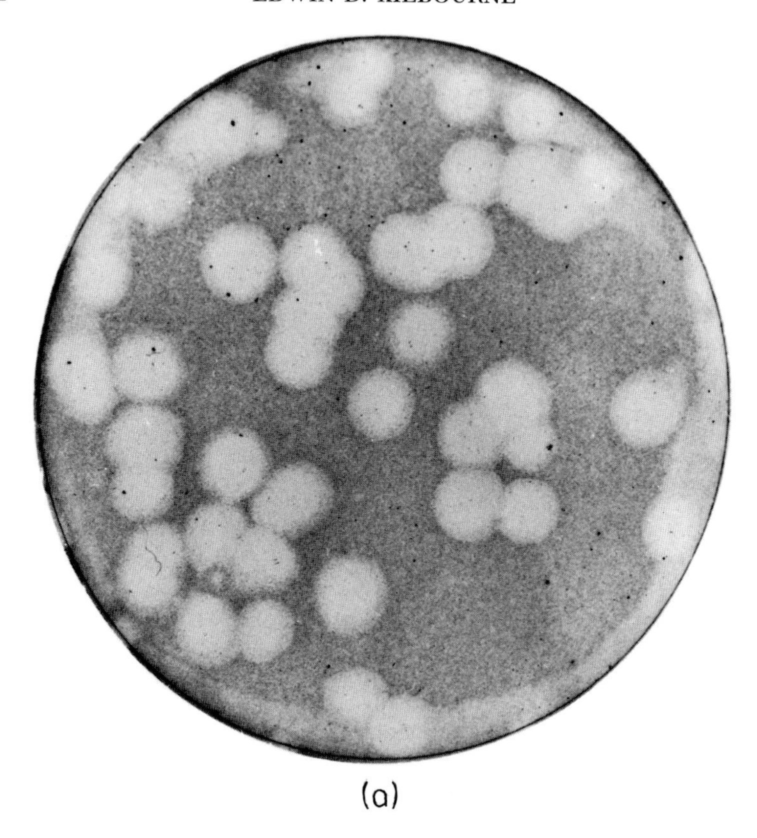

FIG. 3. Living monolayers of clone 1-5C-4 cells with neutral red stain: (a) 5 days after inoculation with A_0/NWS virus and (b) 4 days after inoculation of NWS r^+. One-half the usual neutral red concentration was used for optimal demonstration of the NWS r^+ "red" plaques.

e. Definition of plaques by hemadsorption. Microscopic plaques, or foci of infection in which cell damage is minimal, can be detected by the hemadsorption technique. After removal of the agar, petri dishes are washed twice with about 5.0 ml of PBS, then flooded with 2.0 ml of a 1% suspension of human group O red blood cells. After 10 minutes at room temperature, monolayers are again washed twice with PBS and fixed in Bouin's solution. Hemadsorption is then detected microscopically (Fig. 5). Hematoxylin may be used as a stain or plates can be read immediately after Bouin fixation (Jahiel and Kilbourne, 1966).

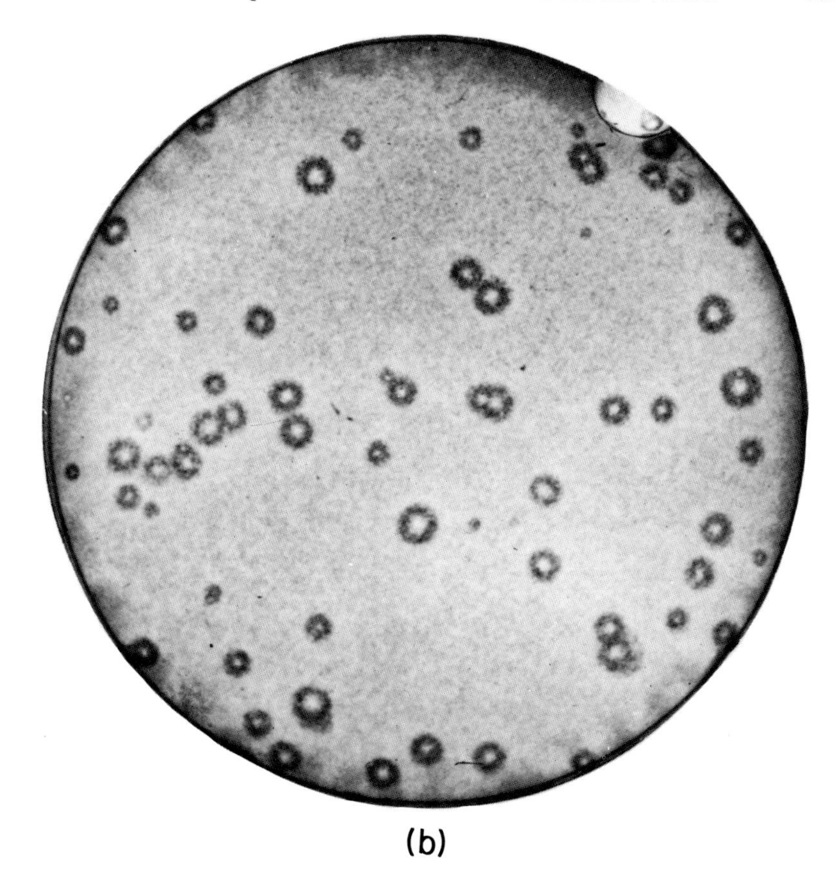

(b)

FIG. 3b. See opposite page for legend.

D. INHIBITION OF PLAQUE FORMATION WITH SPECIFIC ANTISERUM

1. Pre-inoculation (Conventional) Virus Neutralization

Conventional (plaque reduction) neutralization tests are readily carried out in the present system by mixture of virus and antiserum prior to inoculation, with reduction in plaque number as the end point.

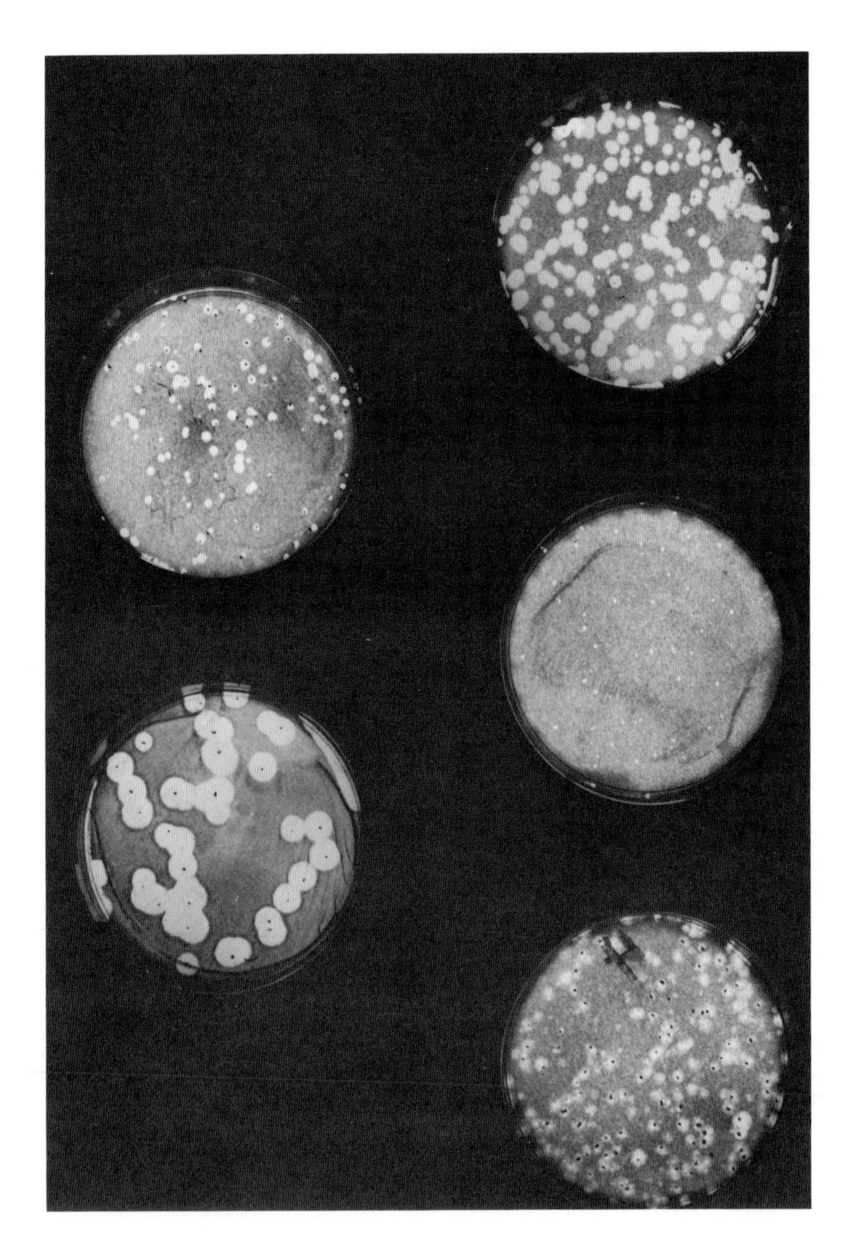

FIG. 4. Variety of plaque-type recombinants of A_0/NWS and A_2/RI/5$^+$ (from Kilbourne *et al.*, 1967).

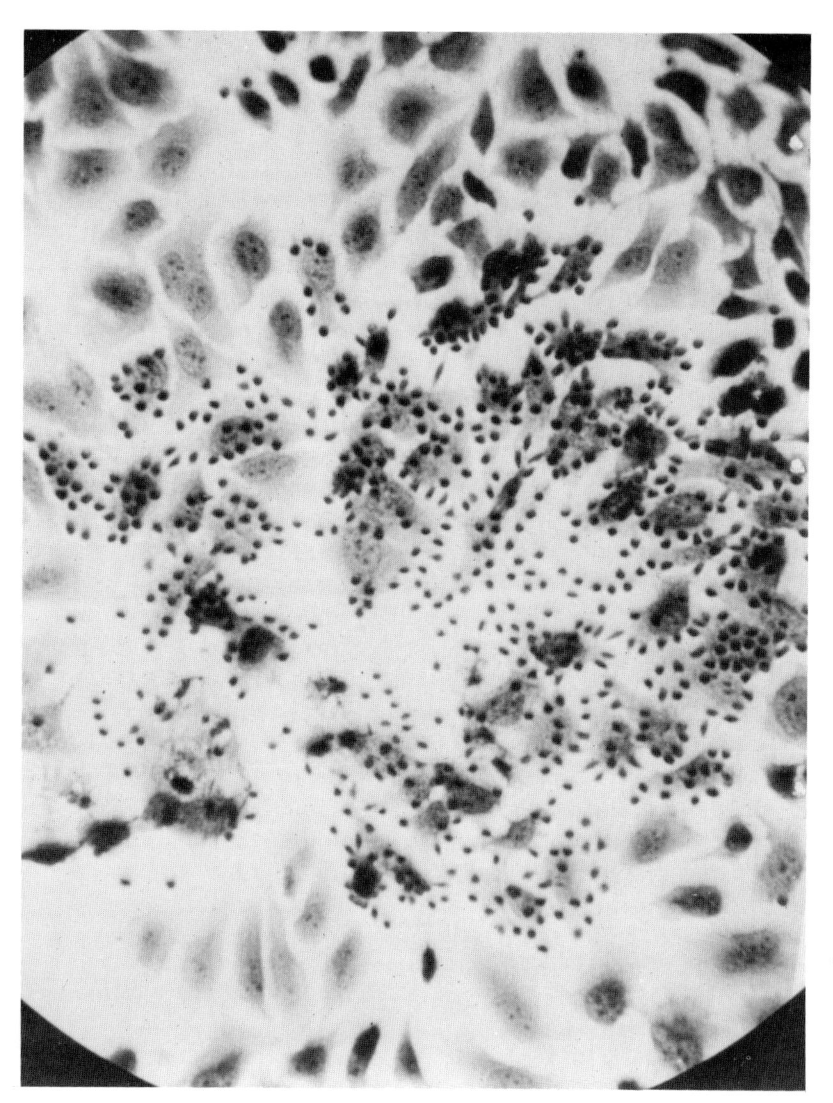

FIG. 5. Plaque demonstrated by microscopic hemadsorption; X-7 plaque after 4 days of incubation under an overlay containing RI/5^{+} antiserum. Hemadsorption followed by Bouin fixation and hematoxylin staining. 230×. (From Jahiel and Kilbourne, 1966.)

2. *Post-inoculation Neutralization (Antiserum-in-Overlay or Wecker Technique)*

In this method antiserum is incorporated into the medium used in the primary agar overlay and is added following inoculation of virus. Initial virus-cell contact therefore is not affected, but subsequent cell-to-cell spread of virus and consequent plaque development is inhibited. This method has permitted the demonstration of a minor antigenic component (the neuraminidase) of influenza virus that is not reactive in hemagglutination inhibition or conventional neutralization tests. In the presence of antibody to the viral neuraminidase, plaque *number* is not reduced, but reduction in plaque *size* (PSR) occurs (Kilbourne and Schulman, 1965; Jahiel and Kilbourne, 1966).

E. Scope and Limitations of the Procedure

Although clone 1-5C-4 cells support the multiplication of the majority of influenza viruses tested, they are not universally susceptible to all strains and are notably resistant to plaque formation with egg-line, nonadapted, A_2 strains. Furthermore, because the cells are aneuploid, viruses passaged through them cannot be considered for vaccine use. Also, the use of the cells for primary virus isolation is essentially unexplored. It must be kept in mind that optimal demonstration of plaques in clone 1-5C-4 cells as in other systems may be compromised by any environmental factor that affects the physiological integrity of the cells. Control of pH is especially important since neutral red uptake may be reduced in the cells not obviously damaged by an acid environment. Mycoplasma contamination has been found to reduce plaquing efficiency and plaque size. Clone 1-5C-4 cells have preserved their susceptibility to influenza virus under conditions of mass transfer in this laboratory for more than 3 years. However, other clones derived from the original variant cell differ quantitatively in their susceptibility so that the possibility of mutation of the line and the need for recloning should be kept in mind.

Cultures of rhesus monkey kidney have been extensively employed for virus isolation and for the production of experimental vaccines and can be used for demonstration of plaque formation with certain A_2 strains, usually after their serial passage in the cells (Table III).

A summary of other cell systems available to investigators is presented in Table III. Of the primary cultures, the most promising appear to be those of calf or hamster kidney cells or of chick embryo fibroblasts derived from 5-day-old embryos. The recently described

TABLE III
SUMMARY OF CELL SYSTEMS AVAILABLE FOR PLAQUE FORMATION BY INFLUENZA VIRUSES

Cell system	Type of culture	Influenza viruses	Plaquing efficiency[a]	Reference
Chick embryo fibroblasts	Primary (9 day)	A_0/WSN	1.0%	Granoff (1955)
Chick embryo lung	Primary (16 day)	A_0/PR8; Mel	0.2	Granoff (1955)
Chick embryo lung	Primary (14 day)		NS[b]	Ledinko (1955)
Chick embryo kidney-skin-muscle	Primary (18-20 day)	A_0/WS	10.0	Chang *et al.* (1966)
Chick embryo kidney	Primary (18-20 day)	A_0/PR8	4-100.0	Wright and Sagik (1958)
Chick embryo fibroblasts	Primary (11 day)	A_2/Jap.305	NS	Peters and Goedemans (1966)
Chick embryo fibroblasts	Primary (5 day)	A_0, A_1, A_2, B	NS	Mizutani and Nagase (1967)
Monkey kidney	Primary	A_1/575[c]	NS	Henry and Youngner (1957)
Monkey kidney	Primary	A_2/RI/5[c]	28-70	Choppin (1962, 1963)
Monkey kidney	Primary	A_2/Singapore[c]	6	Vonka (1965)
Monkey kidney	Primary	A_2/Conn/1/65		Walder and Hsiung (1967)
Calf kidney	Primary	Swine	10	Zimmermann and Schäfer (1959)
Calf kidney	Primary	Sw, A_0, A_1, B	10-300	Lehmann-Grube (1963)
Hamster kidney	Primary	A_0 A_1 A_2	0.1-10	Grossberg (1964)
Human conjunctival (clone 1-5C-4)	Aneuploid cell line	Avian, Sw, A_0 A_1, A_2, B	2-70	Sugiura and Kilbourne (1965)
Human bone carcinoma (G2)	Aneuploid (?) cell line	A_0, A_1, A_2	18->100	Hatano and Morita (1967)

[a] In relation to chick embryo infectivity (EID_{50}) as 100%.
[b] Here, NS stands for not stated.
[c] Monkey kidney adapted virus used.

G2 human cell line should provide either a complementary or alternative system to the clone 1-5C-4 cell system described in the present report.

REFERENCES

Chang, H., Wang, C., and In, C. (1966). *Acta Microbiol. Sinica* **12**, 158.
Chang, R. S. (1954). *Proc. Soc. Exptl. Biol. Med.* **87**, 440.
Choppin, P. W. (1962). *Virology* **18**, 332.
Choppin, P. W. (1963). *Virology* **21**, 342.
Granoff, A. (1955). *Virology* **1**, 252.
Grossberg, S. E. (1964). *Science* **144**, 1246.
Hatano, M., and Morita, O. (1967). *Arch. Ges. Virusforsch.* **20**, 305.
Henry, C., and Youngner, J. S. (1957). *J. Immunol.* **78**, 273.
Jahiel, R. I., and Kilbourne, E. D. (1966). *J. Bacteriol.* **92**, 1521.
Kilbourne, E. D. (1965). Unpublished data.
Kilbourne, E. D., and Schulman, J. L. (1965). *Trans. Assoc. Am. Physicians* **78**, 323.
Kilbourne, E. D., Lief, F. S., Schulman, J. L., Jahiel, R. I., and Laver, W. G. (1967). *Perspectives Virol.* **5**, 87-106.
Ledinko, N. (1955). *Nature* **175**, 999.
Lehmann-Grube, F. (1963). *Virology* **21**, 520.
Maeno and Kilbourne, E. D. Manuscript in preparation.
Mizutani, H., and Nagase, M. (1967). *Arch. Ges. Virusforsch.* **20**, 278.
Omura, E. F., Schwartz, M. S., Jahiel, R. I., and Kilbourne, E. D. (1967). *Proc. Soc. Exptl. Biol. Med.* **125**, 447.
Pereira, H. (1967). Personal communication.
Peters, A., and Goedemans, W. T. (1966). *Arch. Ges. Virusforsch.* **19**, 190.
Sugiura, A., and Kilbourne, E. D. (1965). *Virology* **26**, 478.
Sugiura, A., and Kilbourne, E. D. (1966). *Virology* **29**, 84.
Vonka, V. (1965). *Arch. Ges. Virusforsch.* **15**, 514.
Walder, R., and Hsiung, G. D. (1967). *Public Health Rept. (U.S.)* **82**, 689.
Wong, S. C., and Kilbourne, E. D. (1961). *J. Exptl. Med.* **113**, 95.
Wright, B. S., and Sagik, B. P. (1958). *Virology* **5**, 573.
Zimmerman, T., and Schäfer, W. (1959). *Z. Naturforsch.* **14b**, 213.

16. Hemadsorption-Negative Plaque Test for Viruses Inducing Intrinsic Interference

Philip I. Marcus and David H. Carver†*

Department of Microbiology and Immunology
Albert Einstein College of Medicine
Bronx, New York

I. Introduction

Plaque systems designed to detect and assay animal virus infectivity depend primarily on two events: (1) the continuous production of virions to support multiple cycles of infection, and (2) a cytopathic effect to distinguish uninfected from infected cells. The plaque technique as originally developed by Dulbecco (1952) provides the classical example. Many variations are possible and innumerable modifications have been tendered—all designed to maximize the expression of these two primary factors. Most viruses can be plaqued successfully as cytopathic agents including many of the oncogenic viruses. The latter type may also be scored by their transforming capacity. A new class of viruses was revealed by Vogel and Shelokov (1957), noncytopathic agents detectable because of their capacity to modify the cell surface through the incorporation of viral hemagglutinin. These infected cells bind erythrocytes to produce the so-called hemadsorption reaction. Modification of the cell surface by these viruses, primarily myxovirus-

*Address after September 1969: Microbiology Section, University of Connecticut, Storrs, Connecticut.

†Present address: Department of Pediatrics, Johns Hopkins School of Medicine, Baltimore Maryland.

es, is an extremely uniform feature of the infective process and the hemadsorption reaction can even be used as a reliable indicator of single infected cells (Marcus, 1962). Plaque assays that score hemadsorption-positive foci provide a reliable means of detecting and quantitating this type of virus (Deibel and Hotchin, 1961).

More recently, another class of noncytopathic viruses, those that are nonhemadsorbing, was revealed by their capacity to interfere with the replication of a specific myxovirus, Newcastle disease virus (NDV). Cells infected with this type of virus and subsequently challenged with NDV fail to initiate synthesis of viral hemagglutinin, providing the basis of a hemadsorption-negative plaque test. The state of refractoriness to NDV induced by these viruses has been termed *intrinsic interference*. Studies have shown that intrinsic interference: (1) is an intrinsic property of the virus-infected cell which does not extend to uninfected cells in the culture, (2) is induced under conditions that completely rule out interferon-mediated interference, and (3) is presumably brought about by the action of a protein(s) coded for by the genome of the inducing virus. *Intrinsic interference* is defined as a viral genome-induced cellular state of resistance to NDV,* coexistent with a state of susceptibility to a broad spectrum of other viruses (Marcus and Carver, 1965, 1967).

The hemadsorption-negative plaque test was developed originally as a means of accurately assaying rubella virus as a nonhemadsorbing, noncytopathic virus (Marcus and Carver, 1965). The test has proved to be highly reliable and has been extended to several other kinds of viruses (Marcus and Carver, 1967).

This article relates our experience with hemadsorption-negative assay systems and describes the various techniques used to reveal intrinsic interference. Thus, cells refractory to NDV may be scored as: (1) hemadsorption-negative (HAD^-) plaque areas standing out against a background of NDV-susceptible hemadsorption-positive (HAD^+) cells, (2) individual HAD^- cells in a population of widely dispersed single HAD^+ cells, or (3) as cell survivors (cells or colonies). The principal attribute of cells infected with viruses that induce intrinsic interference is their absolute resistance to NDV.

We do not know how many kinds of viruses will display intrinsic interference and be revealed by hemadsorption-negative assay systems, nor do we understand the apparently unique biological attribute of NDV that singles it out for exclusion from replication. However,

*Recent experiments of Wainwright and Mims (1967) indicate that this definition be broadened to include Sendai virus, suggesting that intrinsic interference may be directed against some macromolecular species common perhaps to the *paramyxoviruses*.

since the techniques used to demonstrate and quantify viruses of this type are relatively easy to carry out and reliable in their execution, they should facilitate our search for new infective agents.

II. Materials

A. Cell Cultures and Media

All cell types susceptible to NDV are potentially suitable host cells for detecting and assaying viruses that induce intrinsic interference. This broad spectrum of cells should include virtually all vertebrate and many invertebrate types since they possess specific receptors for myxovirus attachment. This favorable aspect indicates that a wide range of cell types should be available as suitable hosts for NDV. Thus, the spectrum of appropriate cells is limited primarily by their susceptibility to the viruses that induce intrinsic interference. The following cell types have been used to detect intrinsic interference by the hemadsorption-negative plaque test: primary human embryonic kidney, lung and skin; primary green monkey kidney; BSC-1, MA 134, and VERO lines of green monkey kidney; BHK line (hamster) and SV40 transformed BHK; rabbit corneal and GRKL line of rabbit kidney; primary chick embryo; 3T3, V6, and L cell mouse lines; fathead minnow line (fish). Primary and secondary mouse embryo cells have been used, but they present a special situation as discussed below (Section VII).

No particular medium can be singled out as peculiar to the requirements of the HAD$^-$ plaque test. Apparently any environmental milieu that supports cell growth is suitable for the development of intrinsic interference. Other than the obvious need of excluding from the medium viral inhibitory substances that might limit the spread of intrinsic interference-inducing viruses, no special requirement for growth medium has been noted. Even this limitation can be circumvented by scoring individually the initially infected cells, a procedure which obviates the need for multiple cycles of viral infection (Section III, B). However, at the time of challenge with NDV and during the incubation period for the synthesis of viral hemagglutinin and its incorporation into the cell surface, the medium should be free of any receptor-like substances or antihemagglutinins that might bind to viral hemagglutinin and block red blood cell (RBC) adsorption. Calf serum at $\leq 6\%$ final concentration is invariably free of such substances. In contrast, for example, fetal bovine serum (rich in sialic acid-containing fetuin) should not be used, although the inhibitory substances may often be removed by extensive rinsing with phosphate buffered saline (PBS) just prior to the addition of NDV as the challenge virus. Low temperature incubation prior to challenge with NDV may in some cells (primary human embryonic kidney) result in an increased "background" of HAD^- cells (Section VII). Very low concentrations of calf serum ($\simeq 2\%$) may also produce an elevation in "background."

Cold phosphate-buffered saline at pH 6 is used to rinse away unattached cells in the hemadsorption test. The low temperature and pH tend to minimize the activity of viral neuraminidase and hence prevent detachment of adsorbed erythrocytes (Sagik and Levine, 1957).

Routinely, most cell stocks were grown in NCI solution (Schwarz Biochemical) supplemented with 6% calf serum (attachment solution; Marcus and Carver, 1965) and 3% fetal bovine serum. Some cell lines, like the fathead minnow, require 15% fetal bovine serum. Incubation of this poikilothermic line and replication of viruses that induce intrinsic interference in it was always at 34°C. However, challenge with NDV and development of the hemadsorption-positive state always took place at 37°C. More exacting primary cultures, or cells such as the V5 line of mouse cells carrying Rauscher virus were grown in F10 medium (Ham, 1963) with 15% fetal bovine serum. Just prior to and during challenge with NDV, all cell cultures were rinsed and then incubated at 37°C in attachment solution (Marcus and Carver, 1965).

B. Viruses

1. *Intrinsic Interference-Inducing Viruses*

No unusual requirement for the growth of stock cultures of viruses that induce intrinsic interference has been noted. Seemingly, any growth condition that produces high yields of virus is acceptable. However, to eliminate or minimize the role of interferon-mediated interference, it may be advantageous to prepare virus stocks in heterologous cells. Barring this possibility, purified virus may be used. For reasons noted below* these precautions probably are not necessary.

Since each type of virus may require particular growth conditions and yet tolerate a wide latitude of variation without affecting its capacity to induce intrinsic interference, no attempt will be made to deline-

*Theoretically, interferon synthesized in the course of infection with intrinsic interference-inducing viruses could act to produce an extrinsic interference (interferon-mediated) and block hemagglutinin formation by NDV. However, NDV is so relatively refractory to the *action* of interferon that its inhibition by interferon in an intrinsic interference test is usually not a concern.

ate specific culture conditions. However, Sindbis virus has several attributes that recommend it as a model virus to test the hemadsorption-negative plaque or single cell assay system. Sindbis virus is obtained readily in high titer, is relatively stable, and develops intrinsic interference at a high rate in primary green monkey kidney cells. Furthermore, although some temperature-sensitive mutants (Burge and Pfefferkorn, 1967) and wild-type Sindbis virus are invariably cytopathic in chick embryo cells, intrinsic interference can be detected by the more rapid HAD^- particle assay (Section III). Sindbis virus stocks are prepared as follows: Young monolayers of primary chick embryo cells are established in Simpson-Hirst medium (Simpson and Hirst, 1961), infected at a multiplicity of 10 plaque-forming particles, and incubated at 34–35°C in that same medium for 15 hours. Baby hamster kidney cells also produce high yields of Sindbis virus. When assayed under optimal conditions (Carver and Marcus, 1967), stock preparations contain in excess of 10^9 pfp/ml. All virus stocks are stored at −70°C.

2. *Challenge Virus: Newcastle Disease Virus*

All strains of NDV thus far tested were equally effective as challenge virus. These include *California*, *Beaudette*, *Massachusetts-HiK*, and a vaccine strain (*Blacksburg*). Newcastle disease virus stocks of about 10^9 pfp/ml were obtained as allantoic fluid harvested from 9- or 10-day-old eggs 48 hours after inoculation with about 10^7 infectious particles. Newcastle disease virus stocks usually were used directly as challenge virus since 0.05–0.1 ml contains enough virions to result in an adsorbed multiplicity of about 10 hemadsorption-producing (equals plaque-forming) particles when added to a confluent monolayer of cells in a 50 mm petri dish.

A recent report by Wainwright and Mims (1967) indicates that Sendai virus (parainfluenza 1), also a paramyxovirus, may serve equally well as a challenge virus. Stock preparations of this virus are also obtained from eggs.

C. Newcastle Disease Virus Antiserum

Antiserum against NDV hemagglutinin was prepared in rabbits. Animals were inoculated intravenously with about 5×10^9 pfp at weekly intervals for 4 or 5 weeks. One week following the last inoculation, serum was obtained which at a dilution of 1:50 invariably inactivated 99% of the plaque-forming particle activity of NDV stock preparations within 15 minutes at 37°C.

D. Red Blood Cells

Any species of erythrocyte that adsorbs to NDV-infected cells may be used in the hemadsorption-negative plaque test. Chicken, turkey, goose, human, bovine, and guinea pig red blood cells have been used. Bovine and guinea pig erythrocytes have been used most frequently because their small size increases the resolution of hemadsorption-negative cells or plaques. This is especially helpful when the host cell is relatively small. Erythrocyte preparations can be kept for relatively long periods without hemolysis if stored concentrated as collected in plasma, at 4°C. Cells were washed two or three times in phosphate-buffered saline before use at about 3–6 × 10^7 RBC/ml. Occasionally, RBC preparations must be discarded because they become contaminated with bacteria (*Pseudomonas* sp.) that mimic a hemadsorption reaction by binding simultaneously to the erythrocyte and the surface of *uninfected* or NDV-refractory cells, or the petri dish surface itself.

III. Scoring Intrinsic Interference

A. Hemadsorption-Negative Plaque Test

The basic steps and controls carried out in the hemadsorption-negative plaque test are outlined in schematic form in Fig. 1. Susceptible host cells are grown to confluency, usually in 50 mm plastic petri dishes (Falcon Plastics, No. 3002) containing 5 ml of suitable growth medium. This medium is removed at the time of infection, and the intrinsic interference-inducing (test) virus contained in 0.3 ml of attachment solution (AS) is adsorbed for a suitable period, usually 30–60 minutes at an appropriate temperature, usually 35°C. The plates are then rinsed once with AS, flooded with 5 ml of growth medium, and incubated undisturbed in a water-saturated atmosphere of continuously flowing CO_2 and air. To reveal the hemadsorption-negative plaque areas at the end of the incubation period, usually 1–5 days, medium is removed from the infected monolayers and NDV is added to an attachment multiplicity of 10–20 plaque-forming or hemadsorption-producing particles (Marcus, 1962). Routinely, this is achieved by adding about 0.1 ml of NDV stock to a monolayer of cells that has been rinsed with AS and to which 0.2 ml of AS has been applied.

Virus in this 0.3 ml volume is attached for about 30–60 minutes at 37°C. Unattached virus is removed, and the monolayer rinsed once

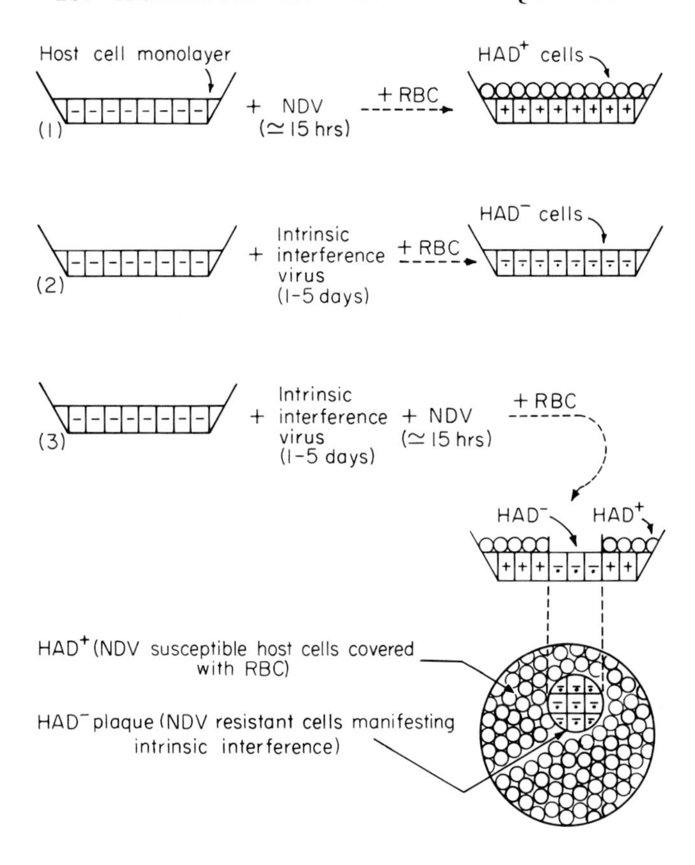

FIG. 1. Schematic representation of the hemadsorption-negative plaque test to assay viruses inducing intrinsic interference. Row 1, control for host cell susceptibility to NDV. All cells should score as HAD^+ 15 hours after challenge with NDV. Row 2, control for adventitious virus in host cells or test virus stock. All cells should score as HAD^-. Row 3, complete test, presence of viruses inducing intrinsic interference revealed by foci of HAD^- (NDV-refractory) cells present in a monolayer of otherwise HAD^+ (NDV-susceptible) cells.

with 2 ml of AS. To preclude spurious binding of red blood cells owing to the presence of residual input virus on the surface of otherwise hemadsorption-negative (HAD^-) cells, the rinsed monolayer is exposed to 0.5 ml of NDV antiserum at a concentration which neutralizes over 99% of the plaque-forming particle activity of NDV stock preparations within 15 minutes at 37°C.* Antiserum is removed after 20 minutes; the monolayer is washed once with 2 ml of AS, flooded with 5 ml of this solution, and incubated for about 15 hours at 37°C to develop the HAD^+ state in all cells susceptible to NDV. The medium is removed, the cell layer rinsed with cold PBS and replaced with 3 ml of a suspension of erythrocytes (bovine most commonly used) at about 6×10^7/ml in PBS. Red blood cell adsorption is carried out for 20 minutes at 4°C (refrigerator), and the plates are rinsed gently eight to ten times with copious amounts of cold PBS (pH 6) to remove unattached erythrocytes. Care is taken to minimize elution of RBC and loss resulting from mechanical trauma in the washing procedure. The rinsing procedure is carried out best by adding the cold PBS to the edge of a tilted petri dish, thereby not directing the stream of liquid on the monolayer proper. Several milliliters of cold PBS are added to the plate immediately after the final rinsing.† The hemadsorption-negative plaques stand out as dark areas when examined by illumination obtained from viewing the underside of plates held up to a light source at the ceiling (Fig. 3). Plaques remain stable for about 1 day in cold PBS (pH 6), or they may be fixed with OsO_4 (Marcus, 1962) and sealed in Gurr's water-mounting solution for a permanent record.††

In Fig. 1, row 1 represents a control on the susceptibility of the host

*This step is not always necessary. Experience with the single cell hemadsorption technique (Marcus, 1962) has demonstrated that infection with high multiplicities of myxovirus sometimes results in a small amount of red blood cell adsorption owing to residual surface-bound virus. This "background" can be eliminated completely by exposing the NDV-infected cells to specific viral antiserum, thus coating the viral hemagglutinin. The addition of NDV-antiserum is included routinely in the HAD^- plaque test since it is not possible to predict *a priori* whether the background level of hemadsorption will be high or low for a given lot or type of cells.

†This is an important step. If, after the final rinsing with PBS, the plates are allowed to dry out slowly, enormous surface tension changes result from evaporation and red blood cells are often sheared from the surface of NDV-infected cells. We have also noted that attached red blood cells are sensitive to mechanical shearing forces. Thus, if a plaque plate is dropped onto a hard surface—even for a small distance—many of the adsorbed RBC will dislodge. Such a plate can be used if fresh RBC are added and the adsorption period repeated.

††Photographic reproduction of unfixed preparations is accomplished readily by placing the plaque plate directly on high contrast glossy photographic paper and exposing it for an appropriate period to the light from a photographic enlarger. Development of the paper for high contrast provides an image which reproduces with high fidelity the appearance of the unfixed plaque plate. The resolution is such as to reveal individual cells when the photographs are examined with a hand lens. Figures 2–5 were obtained in this manner.

cells to NDV, and a test for the presence of adventitious agents that may produce or mimic intrinsic interference. As illustrated schematically in Fig. 1 (row 1) and photographically in Fig. 2, all cells of the NDV-infected monolayer should become saturated with erythrocytes and present a continuous sheet of red blood cells. In this control, any discontinuity in the sheet of erythrocytes is taken as evidence of cells' inherently or physiologically resistance to NDV or the presence of an agent that renders cells refractory to NDV.

Row 2 of Fig. 1 represents a control for the presence of adventitious hemadsorbing agents in the test virus stock or as a contaminant of the host cell. After the hemadsorption test, all cells in the monolayer should be free of erythrocytes. In this control, the presence of any hemadsorption is taken as evidence of contamination by hemadsorbing agents.* Note also that contaminated erythrocytes would be detected in this control.

Row 3 of Fig. 1 illustrates schematically the complete HAD^- plaque test as described above. The entire procedure is outlined in brief below:

(1) Infect cells with virus inducing intrinsic interference (30–60 minutes).
(2) Incubate virus–cell complexes to develop intrinsic interference (1–5 days).
(3) Challenge infected cells with NDV at $m \simeq 10$ pfp (30–60 minutes).
(4) Neutralize residual surface-NDV hemagglutinin with antibody (20 minutes).
(5) Incubate to incorporate NDV hemagglutinin into surface of susceptible cell ($\simeq$ 15 hours).
(6) Perform hemadsorption test (20 minutes).
(7) Count HAD^- plaques.

Figure 3 shows hemadsorption-negative plaques as they appear after the final rinse with cold PBS (pH 6).† The plaques illustrated, re-

*A noncytopathic hemadsorbing simian virus contaminating primary green monkey kidney cells was detected in this manner. Its presence obliterated the HAD^- plaques that had been produced by rubella virus. In this case the NDV-refractory state (intrinsic interference) was detected by colony (clone) survival (Section III, C).

†Certain experimental designs might benefit from quantitative information on the extent of interference with NDV-induced hemadsorption. The *average* reduction in total RBC binding to infected monolayers can be ascertained by measuring the amount of adsorbed erythrocytes spectrophotometrically through their content of hemaglobin (Ginzburg and Traub, 1959) or radioisotopically by counting ^{51}Cr-labeled RBC (Burge and Pfefferkorn, 1967). Details of these assay procedures are described in the original articles.

produced at actual size, resulted from a 3 day incubation period with rubella virus prior to challenge with NDV. Upon continued incubation, plaque areas become larger and eventually coalesce. They appear as shown in Fig. 4. Further incubation produces a cell monolayer that is totally refractory to NDV and scores as 100% hemadsorption-negative, as seen in Fig. 5. If larger virus inocula are used these results are obtained in correspondingly shorter intervals. When the yield of infectious virus is high and the effective cycling of infection in liquid medium more rapid, one day may suffice for the detection of plaques. In such instances, it may be expedient to add an agar overlay (attachment solution with 0.9% agar) to slow the diffusion of newly released virus. At the time of challenge with NDV, the agar overlay can be removed readily by first incubating the plate with 3 ml of AS for about 15 minutes at 37°C, rimming the overlay with a spatula, and then flipping off the agar. The cell monolayer remains bound tenaciously to the plastic plate and can be rinsed with AS and challenged with NDV as usual to define the HAD^- plaque areas.

In certain circumstances (for example, where the yield of infectious virus is low or the effective latent period particularly long) it may be advantageous to score individual HAD^- cells, or small foci, in a monolayer of HAD^+ cells. This is achieved by examining the plate with phase-contrast optics. The long-working distance condensors of the Unitron model BPHM are particularly useful and permit excellent viewing of unfixed preparations. Figure 6 illustrates the resolution of a focus of three cells rendered refractory to NDV by infection with rubella virus 20 hours before challenge. The hemadsorption-negative areas increase in size upon further incubation and may contain individual HAD^+ cells that have not yet become refractory to NDV. These too are readily resolved by phase-contrast optics as illustrated in Fig. 7.

1. Proportionality between Virus Concentration and Plaque Count

The number of HAD^- plaque areas on a plate increases linearly with the concentration of virus,* as illustrated in Fig. 8. This constitutes evidence that each plaque area is initiated by a single infectious unit of virus (Dulbecco, 1952). The exponential rate of inactivation by ultraviolet light of two viruses that induce intrinsic interference, rubella and Sindbis virus, offers support to the hypothesis that this infectious unit is most likely a single virion and that significant clumping of infectious particles does not occur in stock preparations.

*Tested for rubella and Sindbis virus (Marcus and Carver, 1965) and for lymphocytic choriomeningitis virus (LCM) (Wainwright and Mims, 1967).

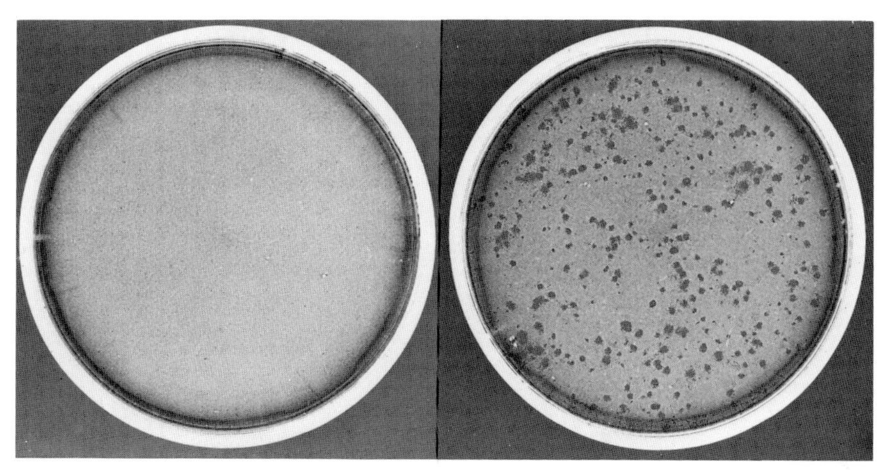

FIG. 2 (*Left*). Monolayer of green monkey kidney cells inoculated with NDV, incubated for 15 hours at 37°C, and subjected to the hemadsorption test. All cells are HAD^+, i.e., susceptible to NDV. Actual size (see last footnote on p. 168).

FIG. 3 (*Right*). Hemadsorption-negative plaques of rubella virus. Treatment as in Fig. 2, except monolayer was inoculated with rubella virus and incubated for 3 days at 35°C prior to challenge with NDV. The nonhemadsorbing (NDV-refractory) cells stand out as dark areas against a light background of bovine erythrocytes which cover the hemadsorption-positive (NDV-susceptible) host cells. Actual size.

FIG. 4 (*Left*). Hemadsorption-negative plaque area of rubella virus. Conditions as in Fig. 3 except size of rubella virus inoculum was doubled, and incubation at 35°C carried out an additional 24 hours for a total of 4 days prior to challenge with NDV. Approximately 80% of the cells are refractory to NDV, i.e., HAD^+. Actual size.

FIG. 5 (*Right*). Conditions as in Fig. 4 but incubation at 35°C extended for an additional 24 hours for a total of 5 days prior to challenge with NDV. One hundred percent of the cells are refractory to NDV, i.e., HAD^-. Actual size.

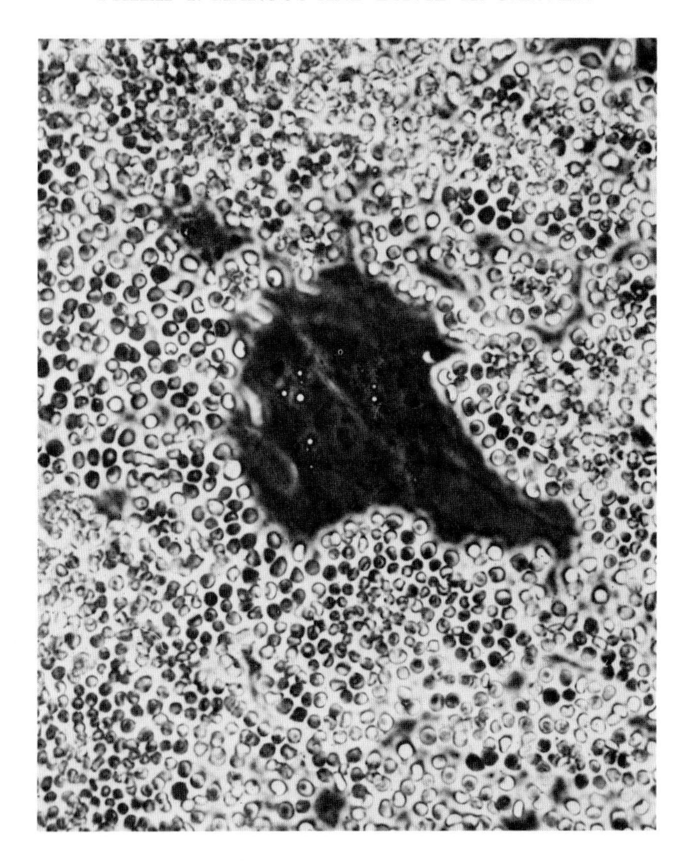

FIG. 6. Hemadsorption-negative plaque induced by rubella virus. Conditions as noted in Fig. 3 but cell monolayer challenged with NDV just 20 hours after infection with rubella virus. Three hemadsorption-negative cells comprise the plaque area. These NDV-refractory cells are surrounded by a confluent background of NDV-susceptible cells, not visible beneath the layer of adsorbed, bovine red blood cells. Phase-contrast, living cells. Diameter of RBC, 6 μ.

B. HEMADSORPTION-NEGATIVE PARTICLE ASSAY

Individual cells infected with a virus that incorporates viral hemagglutinin into its cell surface can be detected and scored quantitatively by the so-called hemadsorption-producing particle assay (Marcus, 1962).* From the Poisson distribution the fraction of cells that escape infection (HAD^-) can be used to calculate the effective multiplicity of

*The entire procedure also can be carried out with cells in suspension (White *et al.*, 1962).

infection (Luria and Darnell, 1967; Marcus, 1959). Conversely, cells made refractory to NDV by prior infection with a virus-inducing intrinsic interference can be scored as individual hemadsorption-negative cells. In this case, the fraction of hemadsorption-positive cells represents cells refractory to infection by the test virus. Similar calculations provide a measure of the number of virions capable of inducing intrinsic interference. The steps involved in the HAD^- particle assay are identical to those of the HAD^- plaque test, except that just prior to incubating cells for the development of viral hemagglutinin (step 5 in Section III, A), the NDV-challenged monolayer is trypsinized [0.05% trypsin (1:300 Nutritional Biochemical Corp.) in Ca^{++},

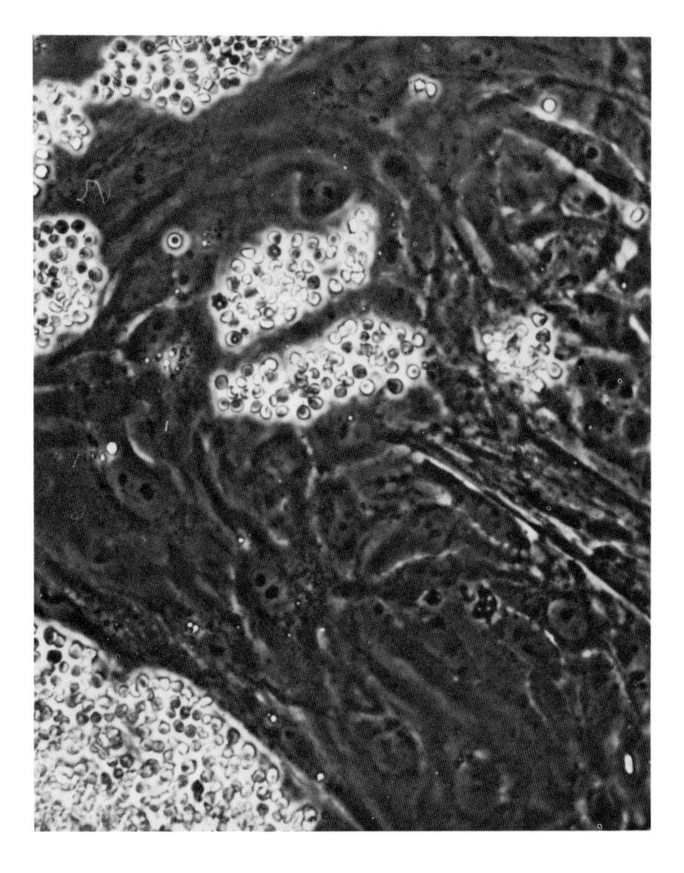

FIG. 7. Portion of a hemadsorption-negative plaque induced by rubella virus. Conditions as in Fig. 6 except that the cells were challenged with NDV 72 hours after infection with rubella virus. The few remaining individual cells that do adsorb bovine erythrocytes stand out against the background of those that do not.

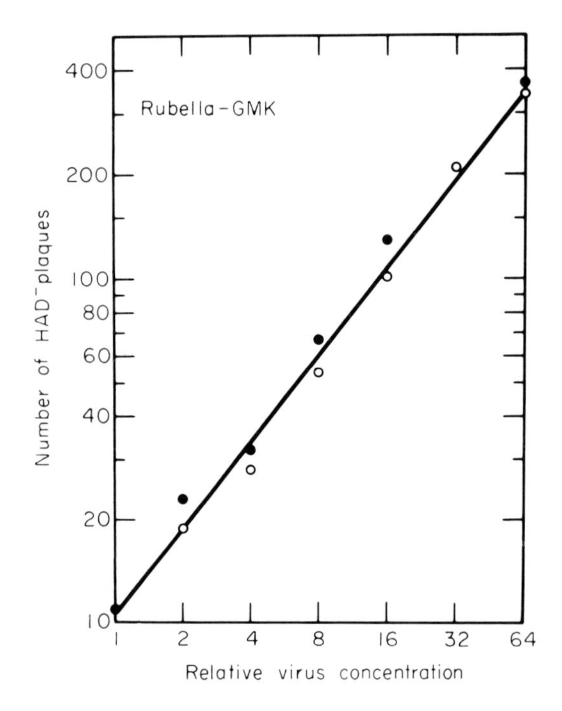

FIG. 8. Proportionality between the relative concentration of rubella virus and the number of hemadsorption-negative plaques observed (two different experiments).

Mg^{++}-free saline containing 0.005 *M* EDTA, usually 3 ml/50 mm petri dish, for 15 minutes at 37°C]. Monodisperse cells are counted in a hemocytometer and plated in attachment solution as single cells, usually 5–10 $\times$ 10^4 cells per 35 mm plastic petri dish. The hemadsorption test (step 6 in Section III, A) is then carried out as described. In the final step the fraction of cells manifesting intrinsic interference is determined by counting microscopically HAD^- (NDV-refractory) and HAD^+ (NDV-susceptible) cells. Hundreds of cells may be scanned rapidly, and the fraction of HAD^- cells ascertained to a high degree of accuracy. After the 15 hour incubation period allowed for NDV hemagglutinin incorporation into the surface of infected cells, essentially all of the HAD^+ cells are saturated with respect to the number of adsorbed RBC, as in control preparations, and the contrast between HAD^+ and HAD^- cells is maximal as illustrated in Fig. 9.

When the hemadsorption test used to resolve individual HAD^+ and HAD^- cells is carried out under optimal conditions, the binding of a single erythrocyte to a host cell is significant (Marcus, 1962).

C. Colony Survivors

Colony survival as a means of scoring intrinsic interference has been used less extensively than the HAD$^-$ plaque or particle assay technique, primarily because it requires more time. The first five steps are the same as those outlined in Section III, A, but in step 6, instead of performing the hemadsorption test, the plates are incubated until maximum cytopathicity is expressed in NDV-sensitive cells, usually 2 or 3 days after challenge with NDV. Surviving cells, stand-

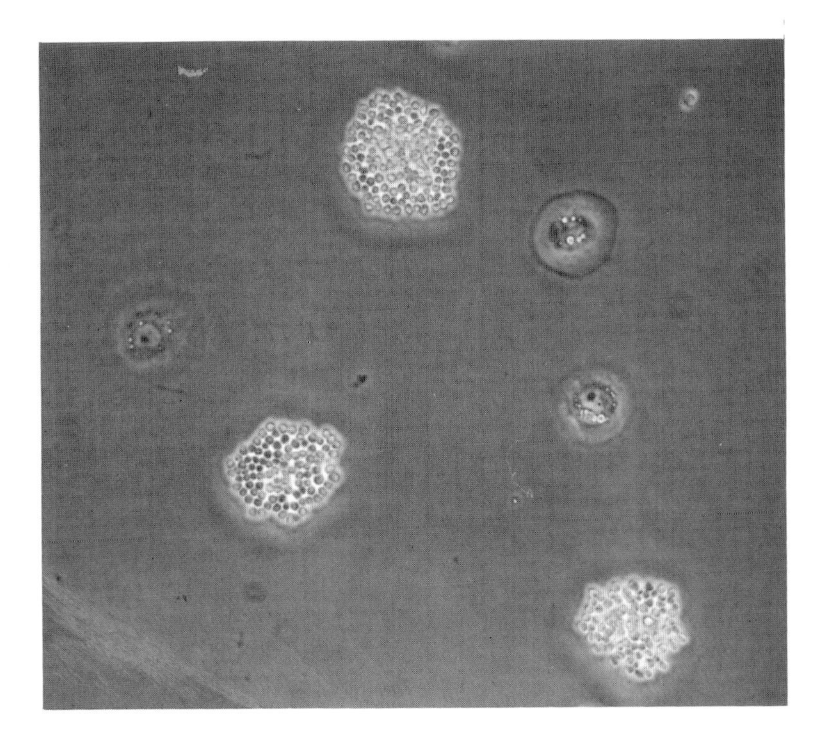

Fig. 9. Single cell hemadsorption test to detect individual cells rendered refractory to NDV, i.e., hemadsorption-negative (HAD$^-$), by a virus-inducing intrinsic interference. Green monkey kidney cell monolayers were infected with Sindbis virus (multiplicity, 5 pfp), challenged 11 hours later with NDV (multiplicity, 10 pfp), trypsinized and plated as single cells, incubated an additional 15 hours and tested for their hemadsorption reaction. Cells susceptible to NDV, i.e., not manifesting intrinsic interference, are represented by the three HAD$^+$ cells covered entirely with bovine erythrocytes. Cells demonstrating intrinsic interference are refractory to NDV and appear as three HAD$^-$ cells. Bovine erythrocytes have a diameter of about 6 μ. Phase-contrast, living cells.

ing out as islets, may be stained vitally with neutral red (1:10,000) in AS or PBS for 1 or 2 hours, or fixed with 10% formalin in PBS and stained with Giemsa.

IV. Viruses Inducing Intrinsic Interference

Viruses may be screened for their capacity to induce intrinsic interference by a simple test of their ability to produce HAD^- plaques or single cells. Table I lists the viruses which have been scored thus far in this manner. Some of these viruses have been subjected to further tests to establish more exacting criteria for defining intrinsic interference. These criteria are: (1) the ability to induce an NDV-refractory state in the presence of actinomycin D, and (2) the susceptibility of the NDV-refractory cells to a broad spectrum of other viruses (Section V).

By the very nature of the HAD^- plaque test only noncytopathic viruses can be scored; however, the HAD^- particle assay (Section III, B) is quicker, and if the cytopathic effect is sufficiently delayed then acquisition of the NDV-refractory state can be measured. The limiting factor is the length of time required to develop the hemadsorption-positive state in susceptible cells.* Most cells infected with NDV show saturated hemadsorption (the maximum number of adsorbed RBC) by about 15 hours, sometimes as early as 10–12 hours, if the multiplicity is high.

Not all noncytopathic viruses appear to induce intrinsic interference. Thus, cells overtly infected with, or carrying in most of their cells, parainfluenza viruses (Hermodsson, 1963; Maeno *et al.*, 1966), including simian virus SV5 (Choppin, 1967), and hog cholera virus (Kumagai *et al.*, 1961), appear to be as sensitive, or more so, to NDV infection as uninfected control cells. Cells transformed by Rous sarcoma virus (Temin, 1967) or SV40 (unpublished results) do not appear to be refractory to NDV. The situation with Rauscher virus-carrying mouse cells is complicated by the presence of viral (?) agents that apparently render cells refractory to NDV.

V. Viruses Insensitive to Intrinsic Interference

One prime characteristic of NDV-refractory cells is their sensitivity to a broad spectrum of other challenge viruses. Table II lists the vi-

* The NDV-refractory state induced by virulent poliovirus became measurable when guanidine was added to delay the onset of cytopathicity (Marcus and Carver, 1967).

TABLE I
VIRUSES THAT INDUCE INTRINSIC INTERFERENCE

Virus	Designation	Host cell
Rubella	F8 strain and fresh isolates	GMK, L cell, human embryo kidney
Sindbis	Group A arbovirus	GMK, FHM[a], HeLa
West Nile	Group B arbovirus	GMK
Poliovirus	MEF1, type 2	GMK
Poliovirus[b]	Type I	HeLa
Lactic dehydrogenase virus	LDH virus, Riley's agent	Primary mouse embryo cells
JLS-V5 mouse cell agent[c]	JLS-V5 line carrying Rauscher murine leukemia virus	JLS-V5 mouse cell line
Mouse cell agent[c]		Present in 8 of 10 different lots of primary mouse embryo cell cultures
Lymphocytic choriomeningitis virus[d]	WE_3	U cells (human amnion), chick and mouse embryo cells
Infectious bronchitis virus[e]	Strains *Conn.*, *Mass.*, and *Iowa*	Primary chick kidney cells
Cytomegalovirus[f]	Strain AD169	WI-38 human fibroblasts
Reovirus[g]	Type 3	L cells

[a]This line of cells is infected with a *Mycoplasm* sp. but shows 100% HAD^+ cells when challenged with NDV.

[b]Cytopathic, see Marcus and Carver (1967) for special test conditions.

[c]Cells and supernatant fluids were tested by J. Loveless and V. Riley and found to be free from LDH virus. Possible identical nature of all agents in mouse cell cultures has not been ruled out.

[d]From Wainwright and Mims (1967).

[e]From Beard (1967).

[f]From Seto and Carver (1969).

[g]From Marcus and Zuckerbraun (1969).

ruses that can infect cells made refractory to NDV by the intrinsic interference-inducing viruses shown in Table I. All challenge viruses were used at high multiplicities, i.e., ≃ 10 infectious particles. Cytopathic effects resulting from the action of these viruses on NDV-refractory cells were indistinguishable in their time of onset and severity from control cells challenged at the same time. In the special case of the noncytopathic, hemadsorbing simian virus included in Table II, infectivity was scored by the hemadsorption-positive state it conferred on cells. For comparison, Table II also notes the reaction of the four strains of NDV thus far tested, showing all are excluded by intrinsic interference. Sendai virus also appears to be excluded by intrinsic interference (Wainwright and Mims, 1967).

TABLE II
VIRUSES AND THEIR CYTOPATHIC EFFECT ON CELLS MANIFESTING INTRINSIC INTERFERENCE

Virus	Cytopathicity on NDV-refractory cells[a]
ECHO virus 11	+[b]
Encephalomyocarditis virus	+
Influenza B	+
Poliovirus	+
Vaccinia	+
Vesicular stomatitis virus	+
Simian virus, noncytopathic, hemadsorbing	+[c]
Newcastle disease virus	
California	—[d]
Beaudette	—
Mass-HiK	—
Blacksburg, vaccine	—
Sendai virus	—[e]

[a]All cell types listed in Section II were susceptible to NDV, and most cell types were susceptible to the majority of the test viruses.

[b]Denotes complete cell destruction within 24 hours, indistinguishable from control cultures similarly infected at a high multiplicity.

[c]For this noncytopathic, hemadsorbing virus, + denotes infection scored by hemadsorption.

[d]Denotes the complete absence of a cytopathic effect and cell appearance indistinguishable from uninfected controls.

[e]From Wainwright and Mims (1967).

VI. Basic Characteristics of Intrinsic Interference

Enumeration of some basic attributes of intrinsic interference may be of benefit in designing experiments to detect and assay elusive viruses. Some important characteristics of this type of interference are elaborated briefly in the sections that follow. More details are available in the papers by Marcus and Carver (1965, 1967).

A. RATE OF INDUCTION AND HALF-LIFE OF THE INTERFERENCE

The higher the multiplicity of infection, the shorter the time of induction to a state of intrinsic interference. For example, when primary green monkey kidney cells are infected with Sindbis virus at a multiplicity of 100 pfp, by 5 hours 50% of the cells are refractory to NDV. At a multiplicity of 5 pfp it takes more than twice as long to establish intrinsic interference in half of the cells. Once established in all of the cells of a monolayer, the NDV-refractory state may persist indefinitely if the cell sheet is not disrupted and is maintained in a healthy state with adequate changes of medium. However, intrinsic interference has a measurable half-life under certain conditions. When NDV-refractory cells from monolayers are dispersed with trypsin and plated at lesser cell densities in fresh medium, the HAD^- state is maintained in all of the cells for about 1 or 2 days and then is lost at a relatively rapid and constant rate, showing a half-life of about 10–15 hours.

B. Requirement for Active Virus and Protein Synthesis, and an Insensitivity to Actinomycin D

The capacity to induce intrinsic interference is lost after inactivation of plaque-forming capacity with ultraviolet light. Thus, only active virus appears to render cells refractory to infection by NDV.

The induction of intrinsic interference also requires protein synthesis, but it takes place in the presence of actinomycin D under conditions that preclude synthesis of cellular messenger RNA.

In concert, these results point out the necessity of protein synthesis coded for by a functional viral genome that brings about the state of interference (Marcus and Carver, 1967; Zuckerbraun and Marcus, 1969).

C. The Intrinsic Nature of the Interference

As documented previously (Marcus and Carver, 1965), the NDV-refractory state is an intrinsic property of the individual cell that has been infected with active virus, in contrast to cells manifesting interferon-mediated interference. The latter type of interference is characterized by cellular resistance to a broad spectrum of viruses and may be induced in uninfected cells by the addition of an extrinsic factor, interferon. Intrinsic interference is not mediated by the action of interferon since intrinsic interference can develop (even at an enhanced rate) in cells blocked by actinomycin D, or in cells inherently defective in producing interferon (Zuckerbraun and Marcus, 1969).

D. Mechanism of Action

The molecular basis for intrinsic interference is not known, but it appears to involve a step in the NDV growth cycle beyond that of viral attachment, entry, and eclipse. Presumably, the action of a viral genome-coded protein(s) brings about the NDV-refractory state, but does not alter the susceptibility of the cell to a whole spectrum of other viruses (Table II). Recent results indicate that viral proteins of the RNA polymerase complex may interfere directly with replication of the NDV genome, possibly by binding to NDV-RNA to form a nonfunctional complex (Zuckerbraun and Marcus, 1969). Further experimentation is needed to establish this point.

VII. Special Considerations and Precautions

A. "Background" Hemadsorption-Negative Cells

Perhaps the most common, yet least understood, factor that affects the performance of an HAD⁻ test is the presence of "spontaneously" appearing HAD⁻ cells that constitute the so-called "background." In some cell lines, this fraction is nonexistent or negligible, i.e., virtually 100% of the cells are infectable with NDV and score as HAD⁺. In the worst case, almost all cells of a culture may be "inherently" refractory to NDV. Since this latter condition represents a real problem in the routine assay of known viruses and a serious limitation in the search for new viruses, we shall relate our specific experiences in this area. To what extent "background" represents contamination by viral or other microbial agents remains to be determined.

1. Green Monkey Kidney Cells

Usually 1-5% of the cells in a primary culture of green monkey kidney (GMK) are refractory to NDV. This small percentage usually does not increase with time of incubation and does not affect the resolution of HAD⁻ plaques in a monolayer. Most HAD⁻ foci contain only one cell, often a giant cell. Some lots of cells have been tested where virtually all of the cells were sensitive to NDV and became HAD⁺. However, on one occasion, upon continued incubation, essentially all of the cells became refractory to NDV. This was taken as presumptive evidence of the presence of a simian virus-inducing intrinsic interference.

Most of the established lines of GMK cells (BSC-1, MA 134, VERO) show a uniformly low background of HAD⁻ cells, but occasionally we have observed nearly 50% HAD⁻ cells in a culture of VERO cells challenged with NDV. This extremely high background was virtually eliminated by growing the cells in medium containing kanamycin at 50 μg/ml. In this case, the implication is clear that mycoplasma may be responsible for the high "background." Yet, in cultures of L cells or fathead minnow known to contain *Mycoplasma* sp., little or no "background" is noted. Apparently only certain species of mycoplasma may be implicated in interference with NDV infection. More work in this area is needed.

2. *Mouse Cells*

On most occasions primary and secondary monolayers of embryonic mouse cells are highly refractory to infection by NDV, making it extremely difficult to resolve discrete HAD^- areas.* Many times, over 90% of the cells are refractory to NDV. The situation is somewhat improved in the case of some established lines of mouse cells. For example, L cells are almost always uniformly sensitive to NDV, producing monolayers that are 100% HAD^+, even when *Mycoplasma* sp. can be isolated from such cultures. However, L cell lines have been encountered which are almost totally refractory to infection by NDV (Marcus, 1967).

About 85% of the cells in the V5 line of mouse cells carrying Rauscher leukemia virus are refractory to NDV. In contrast, only a few percent of the V6 line of mouse cells, kept in parallel culture, manifest resistance to NDV. Closer study of the V6 line showed that a minimum number of HAD^- cells (about 1%) was present when the cells were challenged with NDV within a few hours after trypsinization. The fraction of HAD^- cells then increased gradually with incubation and leveled off at about 10% to 15% by 5 or 6 days, usually 1 or 2 days after the cell sheet had become confluent (Caputa *et al.*, 1967).

Some lines of mouse cells transformed by oncogenic viruses are highly refractory to NDV; others are not (Marcus, 1968). Clearly the situation is complex and requires further study. On the other hand, cells of the chick embryo seem uniformly susceptible to NDV.

3. *HeLa Cells*

HeLa cell lines usually contain a small, but variable fraction of cells refractory to NDV. With this cell in particular, it is important to note that at very high multiplicities some cells may be rendered refractory through the cumulative action of viral neuraminidase and subsequent elution of virus. This so-called cell-sparing phenomenon is most evident at multiplicities in excess of 20 pfp and adsorption at room temperature. Cell-sparing may be minimized by adsorbing NDV at 4°C

*This difficulty has been noted by Wainwright and Mims (1967) in their use of the HAD^- plaque test for LCM virus.

and starting the engulfment process by rapidly raising the temperature to 37°C (Marcus, 1959).

VIII. Potential Use of Intrinsic Interference to Detect and Study New Viruses

The justification for writing a "methods" paper would appear to stem from the potential use of the method. Some appreciation of this potential with the HAD⁻ plaque test may be gained by noting its recent use to study the kinetics of antibody neutralization (Rawls *et al.*, 1967), and the growth of rubella virus in the brains of suckling mice (Carver *et al.*, 1967). In this connection, the report by Wainwright and Mims (1967) is most encouraging. They point out that for the past 30 years the virus of lymphocytic choriomeningitis has been assayed in mice by intracerebral inoculation. Their successful application of the HAD⁻ plaque test to the titration of this virus portends new knowledge of the biochemistry and genetics of this heretofore elusive virus.

Intrinsic interference as detected by the hemadsorption-negative plaque and particle techniques defines a new property of viruses and, hopefully, may reveal the existence of a whole spectrum of unknown, noncytopathic, nonhemadsorbing viruses.

Recent insights into the mechanism of induction of intrinsic interference may prove valuable in the detection and assay of a new type of virus, or viral activity. Thus, studies with temperature-sensitive (ts) mutants of Sindbis virus led to the discovery that cells from most lots of primary green monkey kidneys contain a factor that, in terms of intrinsic interference, substitutes completely for the defective function of some ts mutants (Zuckerbraun and Marcus, 1969). Whether the activity that complements ts mutants is derived from a new class of viruses remains to be determined.

ACKNOWLEDGMENTS

Figures 3, 6, and 7 reproduced with permission from P. I. Marcus and D. H. Carver, *Science* (**149**: 983, 1965), copyright 1965 by the American Association for the Advancement of Science. Figure 8 and Tables I and II (modified) reproduced with permission from P. I. Marcus and D. H. Carver, *J. Virology* (**1**: 334, 1967). This work was supported by grants from the U.S. Public Health Service (AI-03619 and GM-12646). P. I. M. is a recipient of a Research Career Development Award (5-K3-GM-15,461). D. H. C. is a Kennedy scholar.

REFERENCES

Beard, C. W. (1967). *Avian Diseases* **11**, 399.
Burge, B. W., and Pfefferkorn, E. R., (1967). *J. Virol.* **1**, 956.
Caputa, E., Marcus, P. I., and Carver, D. H. (1967). Unpublished observations.
Carver, D. H., and Marcus, P. I. (1967). *Virology* **32**, 247.
Carver, D. H., Seto, D. S. Y., Marcus, P. I., and Rodrigues, L. (1967). *J. Virol.* **1**, 1089.
Choppin, P. (1967). Personal communication.
Deibel, R., and Hotchin, J. (1961). *Virology* **14**, 66.
Dulbecco, R. (1952). *Proc. Natl. Acad. Sci. U.S.* **38**, 747.
Ginzburg, Y., and Traub, A. (1959). *Virology* **9**, 671.
Ham, R. G. (1963). *Exptl. Cell Res.* **29**, 515.
Hermodsson, S. (1963). *Virology* **20**, 333.
Kumagai, T., Shimizu, T., Ikeda, S., and Matumoto, M. (1961). *J. Immunol.* **87**, 245.
Loveless, J., and Riley, V. (1967). Personal communication.
Luria, S. E., and Darnell, J. E. (1967). "General Virology," Chapter 3. Wiley, New York.
Maeno, K., Yoshii, S., Nagata, I., and Matsumoto, T. (1966). *Virology* **29**, 255.
Marcus, P. I. (1967, 1968). Unpublished observation.
Marcus, P. I. (1959). *Bacteriol. Rev.* **23**, 232.
Marcus, P. I. (1962). *Cold Spring Harbor Symp. Quant. Biol.* **27**, 351.
Marcus, P. I., and Carver, D. H. (1965). *Science* **149**, 983.
Marcus, P. I., and Carver, D. H. (1967). *J. Virol.* **1**, 334.
Marcus, P. I., and Zuckerbraun, H. L. (1969). Unpublished observations.
Rawls, W. E., Desmyter, J., and Melnick, J. L. (1967). *Proc. Soc. Exptl. Biol. Med.* **124**, 167.
Sagik, B. P., and Levine, S. (1957). *Virology* **3**, 401.
Seto, D. S. Y., and Carver, D. H. (1969). Unpublished observations.
Simpson, R. W., and Hirst, G. K. (1961). *Virology* **15**, 436.
Temin, H. (1967). Personal communication.
Vogel, J., and Shelokov, A. (1957). *Science* **126**, 358.
Wainwright, S., and Mims, C. A. (1967). *J. Virol.* **1**, 1091.
White, D., Oliphant, H., and Batchelder, E. (1962). *Nature* **196**, 792.
Zuckerbraun, H. L., and Marcus, P. I. (1969), *Bacteriol. Proc.* [p. 168].

17. Assay of Infectious DNA*

Joseph S. Pagano

Departments of Medicine and Bacteriology
University of North Carolina School of Medicine
Chapel Hill, North Carolina.

I. Introduction

Deoxyribonucleic acids (DNA) have been isolated relatively easily from many DNA-containing animal viruses; with an increasing number the molecular integrity of the DNA can evidently be preserved. Yet a convincing demonstration of biological activity and, ultimately, specificity of the DNA is available mainly for the papovaviruses. Perhaps this is because viral nucleic acids apparently have no intrinsic capacity for entering cells. In any case, this incapacity poses a barrier to infectiousness, which is tantamount to, if not the only way of showing, specific activity. Consequently, the new methods that have been developed for the assay of the infectivity of viral nucleic acids, and which are based chiefly on providing an efficient entry mechanism, may lead to an increase in the remarkably small number of DNA viruses that remain active after deproteinization (Vaheri and Pagano, 1965; Pagano and Vaheri, 1965; Koch *et al.*, 1966).

These methods, while also empirical, are far more sensitive as well as more nearly reproducible than those formerly available; and they may, in fact, work by simulating what takes place when an intact virus enters a cell (Pagano *et al.*, 1967). One method is based on the use of diethylaminoethyl-dextran (DEAE-D), a polycationic substance first used for the assay of infectious poliovirus RNA. The method has the additional important advantage of making it possible to keep assay

*This work was supported by grants from the U.S. Public Health Service (CA 10169-02) and the National Science Foundation (GB 4992) and by an award to the author from the Sinsheimer Foundation.

cells in physiological media throughout the process of initiation of infection.

What follows is a method, incorporating DEAE-D, for the assay of infectious SV40 DNA (McCutchan and Pagano, 1968). Its virtues are: (1) it is a precise and quantitative plaque method, (2) it is simple, (3) it is sensitive enough to permit the recovery of DNA of sufficiently high titer to initiate synchronous infections of cell cultures, and (4) it is potentially suited for other purposes besides assay of infectivity of viral DNA.

II. Reagents

A. Phenol, Water-Saturated

Prepare water-saturated phenol from crystallized phenol without preservative (Allied Chemical),* redistill until crystal clear, saturate with deionized water (about 80/20 v/v), and store in a low actinic glass bottle at 4°C. Before use remelt completely; avoid using top (water) layer.

B. Sodium Dodecyl Sulfate

A 10% stock solution is made with sodium dodecyl sulfate (SDS) (Fisher, U.S.P.) recrystallized from ethanol. This detergent is of value because it can denature some proteins; free cell-bound, and especially intranuclear, virus; deproteinize virus; and inhibit nuclease activity. A 5% solution in ethanol:water (45:55) gives better emulsions of SDS.

C. Buffers

Phosphate-buffered isotonic saline solution (0.14 *M* NaCl) (PBS) without Mg^{++} or Ca^{++} (pH 7.4); 0.02% disodium ethylenediaminetetraacetate (EDTA; Versene) in PBS; 0.2 *M* tris(hydroxymethyl)-aminomethane (tris) HCl, pH 7.4, for buffering saline solution and BME; tris-buffered (0.05 *M* tris, pH 7.4) isotonic saline solution.

Tris-buffered BME (Eagle's basal medium in Earle's balanced salt solution) is composed of 3 parts BME without $NaHCO_3$ and 1 part 0.2 *M* tris, pH 7.4. The resulting medium, used to dilute DNA and the DEAE-D stock, is about 0.283 osmolal. If the cells are cultured in a

*Any reliable source can be used.

medium other than BME this can be tried as the diluent. Tris-buffered saline solution can be used.

D. Pronase

Pronase (*Streptomyces griseus* protease, Calbiochem) 500 μg/ml in phosphate buffer, pH 8.2. Hold at 37°C for 60 minutes to digest contaminating nucleases.

E. Bentonite

Bentonite (Fisher, U.S.P.) Starting concentration is 5% in water. To prepare a suspension of uniform, finely divided particles carry out 2 cycles of differential centrifugation at 750 *g* (save supernatant) and 7700 *g* (save sediment). The sediment from the first cycle is resuspended in 0.1 *M* EDTA, pH 7, for 48 hours, and the sediment from the second cycle is suspended in 0.01 *M* acetate, pH 6. After a final centrifugation at 7700 *g* add enough acetate buffer to give a concentration of 1.5-6% bentonite as determined by dry weight (Fraenkel-Conrat *et al.*, 1961).

F. Polymers

DEAE-D (Pharmacia, $M_w = 2 \times 10^6$), 100 mg/ml is dissolved in 0.14 *M* tris HCl, pH 7.5. The insoluble residue is removed by centrifugation at 12,000 *g* for 30 minutes. The stock is stored at 4°C; it can be sterilized by filtration. Heparin sodium, 100 units/mg (Nutritional Biochemicals), is dissolved in tris-buffered isotonic saline, pH 7.4, and stored in aliquots at −20°C to prevent contamination.

G. Nucleases

Ribonuclease (crystallized 5×, Nutritional Biochemicals) and deoxyribonuclease (crystallized 2×) are dissolved in PBS containing Mg^{++} and Ca^{++}. Heat RNase at 80°C for 10 minutes in 0.14 *M* NaCl, pH 5, to inactivate DNase.

III. Materials and Procedures

A. General Comments about the Method

The key variable that must be controlled for success in the assay of infectious SV40 is the condition of the cell cultures. Since SV40 has a relatively long growth cycle, plaques taking 2–3 weeks to develop fully, conservation of a healthy monolayer of cells without contamination by bacteria or fungi is the primary necessity. It is worth devoting time to selection of liquid and solid media that produce cell monolayers that remain morphologically in perfect condition for at least 3 weeks; one criterion of a healthy monolayer is an even uptake of vital stain even at the edge of the cell monolayer. Success with liquid media does not automatically mean that the cells will survive with equivalent solid media. For example, toxic vapors in the incubator, such as mercury from broken thermometers, can insidiously accumulate in the overlay. Microorganisms contaminating the incubator, especially fungi and pseudomonas species, are a constant problem because the incubator must be well humidified. In these long-term plaque assays we have found amphotericin B in concentrations as low as 5 μg/ml to be toxic. Finally, however, any cell system that gives reproducible quantitative results in the assay of the infectivity of an intact virus can be expected to give as good, or in some cases even better, results with its infectious DNA, once this has been obtained.

B. Cell Cultures

Primary African green monkey kidney (MK) cells (*Cercopithicus aethiops*) from a reliable source are suspended in Eagle's basal medium in Earle's balanced salt solution (BME), 10% calf serum, penicillin G (200 units/ml) and streptomycin (120 μg/ml). Neomycin sulfate (Upjohn), 50 μg/ml, is a good alternative to these antibiotics. Five milliliters of the suspension (10^6 cells) are dispensed in 60 mm plastic petri dishes and placed at 37°C in a clean humidified atmosphere containing about 4.5% CO_2 until confluent monolayers form. An index of adequate growth is filling out of holes at the edges of the cell sheet; this usually takes 6–8 days. Well-dispersed suspensions are necessary for formation of an even monolayer. Occasionally on the sixth or seventh day the medium needs to be supplemented by 3 ml or changed if the monolayer is not developing satisfactorily.

Since a suspended cell system is not available for cultivation of SV40, BSC-1 cells (Hopps, 1963) are grown in sealed 75 cm^2 plastic bottles by seeding with 2.4×10^6 cells and allowing confluence of growth to occur (usually in 1 week); these cells require medium enriched with double amounts of amino acids, fetal calf serum, and careful control of pH. Alternatively bottles are seeded with $1.2\text{–}1.8 \times 10^6$ primary MK cells or with selected later passages (third to sixth); for quantity production BSC-1 and MK cells do well in roller-bottle systems (Flow, Bellco). Because of their presumed freedom from adventitious agents BSC-1 cells are preferable, but growth and susceptibility to SV40 are somewhat variable. Recently we have found two other continuous lines of MK cells to be preferable for cultivation in roller tubes; they are MA-134 cells (Microbiologic Associates) and Vero cells (Flow Laboratories). The use of chlortetracycline HCl (Lederle), 2.5 μg/ml, to prevent contamination with mycoplasma species is advisable.

C. Virus

The "red mutant" strain of SV40 (Riggs and Lennette, 1965), selected because of its high yield of virus per cell and the large plaques it forms, is propagated by infecting thirty 75 cm^2 cell monolayers with an exposure multiplicity of 10–30 pfu/cell (about 1 ml of 10^8 pfu-containing virus per monolayer). The adsorption period is 90 minutes at 37°C, and the medium then added is BME with 2% inactivated fetal calf serum. The supernatant fluids and cell debris are harvested by freezing and thawing the bottles twice when there is advanced cytolysis (5–6 days); the contents (900 ml) are collected and clarified by centrifugation at 4080 g for 20 minutes.

The supernatant fluids are concentrated and the virus is purified as follows: The virus-containing fluids are concentrated by dialysis against polyethylene glycol, 20,000 (Fisher) to approximately one tenth the original volume, dialyzed against PBS, and then centrifuged at 65,000 g for 240 minutes. The pellets are suspended in 5 ml of PBS.

The next step is optional. The virus is put through a 2.5 by 30 cm Sepharose 2B (Pharmacia) column with a flow rate of 25 ml/hour, efflux being from the top; the buffer is PBS containing 0.5% butanol or 0.04% sodium azide. The void volume of the column is about 37 ml. The fractions comprising the first peak, distinguished by an absorbance 260/280 of >1, and coming through the column at approximately 42 ml, are collected and centrifuged at 80,000 g for 120 minutes.

After resuspension in PBS, 3.3 ml of the virus are mixed with 2.0 ml buffered cesium chloride (Gallard & Schlesinger or Varlacoid) of density $= 1.86$ gm/ml to give a final density of 1.33 and centrifuged at 100,000 g (R_{av}) for 18 hours. The lower visible band appearing in the middle of the tube at density 1.33 is collected, diluted with PBS, and dialyzed against 3000 ml of PBS for 6 hours. At this point virus can be divided into aliquots and frozen for storage.

For production of large quantities of SV40 in a typical result fluids harvested from 9 roller tubes (1400 ml), containing a total of $10^{13.1}$ pfu, concentrated and purified as described (Sepharose fractionation omitted) yielded a total of $10^{12.3}$ pfu in the final product.

D. Extraction of DNA

An optional first step for use especially with unpurified virus is carried out by suspension of the virus in 4 ml of pronase (500 μg/ml) in phosphate buffer, pH 8.2, sonication for 2 minutes and incubation at 37°C for 60 minutes. This treatment destroys nucleases, reducing the likelihood that traces of DNase will be carried through the extraction process.

Ten percent SDS (0.5 ml), 1% bentonite (1 ml), and 0.02% EDTA in PBS (4 ml) are added either directly to the pronase-treated virus (4 ml) or to untreated virus suspended in 4 ml of 0.2 *M* phosphate buffer, pH 7.2. Ten milliliters 80% phenol are then added, and the mixture is shaken by hand for 8 minutes at room temperature. After centrifugation at 750 *g* for 15 minutes the aqueous (top) phase and the viscous interphase are carefully transferred to another centrifuge tube by means of a wide-bore pipette fitted with flexible tubing and a mouthpiece. This material is reextracted once more by gently shaking 8 minutes with 10 ml 80% phenol.

After removal of the aqueous layer from the second extraction 5 ml of TBS are added to the residual aqueous layer on the interphase, the tube is shaken for about 2 minutes, centrifuged again, and the aqueous layer is added to the solution collected earlier. This step is necessary because of trapping of the DNA in the interphase.

The aqueous material is mixed with 2½ volumes of cold ethanol saturated with NaCl and brought to −20°C for at least 2 hours. After centrifugation at 3000 *g* for 15 minutes, the precipitate is washed twice with saturated ethanol. After the precipitate is dissolved in the desired buffer, residual phenol can be eliminated by two extractions with aldehyde-free ethyl ether followed by bubbling of N_2 through the solution until the odor of ether has gone. This step is unnecessary if the preparation is used at dilutions of 1:100 or more.

If the DNA is to be diluted before use it is best to make aliquots of a 1:10 dilution of the extract in 0.14 *M* PBS free of Ca^{++} and Mg^{++}, pH 7.4, containing 0.02% EDTA before storage, preferably at −60°C, although diluted aliquots are stable at −20°C for at least 6–9 months. If the DNA is to be applied to cell cultures without further dilution EDTA must be omitted.

E. Assay of Infectivity of DNA with DEAE-D

The DNA preparation is diluted and mixed with solutions of DEAE-D in clean dry glass tubes (0.3 ml of DNA solution and 0.3 ml of DEAE-D of twice the desired final concentration), the DNA being thawed and serially diluted just before mixing with the DEAE-D solution since addition of the polymer before dilution may cause precipitation. In all these manipulations too vigorous pipetting of the DNA or contamination by nucleases from fingertips or breath is to be avoided.

Duplicate MK cell monolayers are rinsed once with 5 ml of PBS without antibiotics. After 5 or 10 minutes at room temperature, the rinse fluid is removed as completely as possible by aspiration, and the cells are inoculated with 0.2 ml of DNA and DEAE-D. After a further 15–20 minutes at room temperature, the inoculated cells are rinsed with 5 ml of Hank's balanced salt solution (BSS) containing antibiotics and overlaid with the same medium used for virus plaque assays.

The overlay consists of BME with 0.11% crystalline bovine albumin (Nutritional Biochemicals) in 0.5% melted agarose (Sea Kem) kept at 43°C and allowed to harden at room temperature after application. The first overlay is 5 ml; the second (3 ml) is added 7 days later; and the third overlay (3 ml) containing 0.01% neutral red is added on the twelfth or thirteenth day. Plaques can be counted up to the twentieth day.

F. Factors That Influence the Sensitivity of the Assay

We have recovered between 0.1 and 0.01% of the infectivity of the intact virus in the DNA extract; this has been accomplished both with relatively crude and with highly purified virus as the starting material. The keystone of the procedure leading to high yields of active material seems to be the method employed for the assay of infectivity.

1. Contamination with Fungi

The habit of common rhizopus fungus allows it to infiltrate closed petri dish cultures by growing up the outside of the lower dish. The bottom of every dish should be clean and dry with no spilled media allowed to remain.

2. Buffering

Since DEAE-D is acid and, in high doses, toxic, it should be well buffered to maintain a physiological pH.

3. Blocking Substances

Anions such as phosphate as well as amphoteric antibiotics may interfere with the action of DEAE-D. A tris-buffered growth medium such as BME without $NaHCO_3$ (and without, of course, any serum) is effective and gives 8-fold greater sensitivity than PBS. Tris-buffered isotonic saline may be used, and it is preferable with relatively concentrated DNA solutions.

4. *Washing*

The initial washing of the cells helps to remove surface nucleases. Only one washing is necessary unless the cells are older than ideal (see below). The post-inoculation washing is necessary to remove free or excess DEAE-D; with concentrations up to 1000 μg/ml DEAE-D one post-inoculation washing is sufficient. There is another way of eliminating excess DEAE-D, discussed later.

5. *Conditions of Adsorption*

The best conditions for exposure of cells to DNA may vary depending on the method of cell culture. In general, brief exposure times should be employed, especially if the cultures are kept at 37°C rather than at room temperature (23°C). If on testing there is no appreciable difference in sensitivity at the two temperatures, 23°C is preferable for convenience and reproducibility.

6. *Dose of DEAE-D*

The optimum dose of DEAE-D should be determined for each viral system. In general it would be expected to fall within a range from 100 to 1000 μg/ml. Excessive amounts of DEAE-D reduce the sensitivity of the assay. Concentrated solutions of highly polymerized DNA precipitate with DEAE-D; colloids may also form (Maes *et al.*, 1967).

7. *Sequence of Application of DEAE-D and DNA*

It is advantageous to mix the nucleic acid preparation with DEAE-D before applying it to cells in order to gain earlier the benefit of the stabilizing action of DEAE-D against nucleases. However, in some cases it may be desirable to expose the cells to DEAE-D first before inoculating them with DNA. This can be done by pretreating with DEAE-D for 5 or 10 minutes at room temperature and then inoculating the cells with the buffered DNA solution, either after aspiration without washing or after washing of the cell monolayers several times. If the treated cells are washed before application of the DNA, the sensitivity of the assay drops by 20- or 30-fold; the loss can be partly compensated by larger doses of DEAE-D. This maneuver may be of use with concentrated DNA.

8. *Age of Cells*

Cell monolayers should be used for assays within a day or two of the time that they have attained confluent growth. At least in the case of

RNA assays with primary MK cells, the sensitivity of the assay is reduced up to 40-fold if week-old monolayers are used. The loss of sensitivity can be only partly restored by extra pre-inoculation cell rinses.

G. Complementary Use of a Polyanion

Another way of clearing excess DEAE-D from the assay besides washing is through the use of a polyanion to neutralize the cationic polymer. Heparin is nontoxic in doses of 1000 μg/ml or more and can be applied directly to the DNA-inoculated cells after the adsorption period, or it can be included in the post-inoculation washing. Theoretically there is special merit in this procedure in the case of SV40 since DEAE-D inhibits plaque formation by intact virus (McCutchan and Pagano, 1968). Even relatively small amounts of the residual DEAE-D might be capable of producing this effect. However, each DNA-infected focus is the site of production of such overwhelming quantities of progeny virus as to make any increase in plaque counts with heparin trivial.

More important is the fact that the incorporation of heparin enables the use of larger doses of DEAE-D if this happens to be desirable, and the possibility that the polyanion may repair subtle damage to the cell surface membrane produced by the polycation. This possibility could be of crucial importance for DNA transformation. Before heparin is used its effects on plaque formation of the intact virus should be tested (in the case of SV40, no effect, or slight enhancement). Heparin itself does not demonstrably interact with either DNA or cell surfaces.

IV. Comments

A. Other Uses of the DEAE-D Method

Also, DEAE-D enhances the infectivity of several single-stranded viral RNAs. The magnitude of enhancement and the procedure are essentially the same as the plaque method described for viral DNA. In addition, DEAE-D is effective in infective-center or agar cell suspension systems and in cytolytic quantal assays of infectious RNA. The enhancing effect in all cases is obtained with physiological or isotonic media. The combination of DEAE-D and older methods that employ hypertonic media does not confer additional sensitivity. These effects are quite independent of cell type, cells of both primate and nonprimate origin—including primary and continuous-line MK, HeLa, porcine and L—having been utilized successfully (Pagano, 1970).

To facilitate the induction by SV40 DNA of the noninfectious early neoantigen known as "T" in MK cells (Pagano and McCutchan, unpubl.) DEAE-D was used. Since the number of cells in which synthesis of this specific protein is initiated is dependent on the multiplicity of incoming viral DNA, it is not surprising that the efficient rate of infection made possible by DEAE-D greatly increases the ratio of cells that produces the T antigen after a single cycle of virus growth. This is excellent evidence, incidentally, that the plaques formed by SV40 DNA with the DEAE-D method are in fact SV40 plaques because of the unique specificity of the SV40 T antigen.

B. Other Methods of Assay of Infectious Nucleic Acids

The available methods can be classified according to whether they require hypertonic, both hypertonic and hypotonic, or isotonic conditions. In the case of infectious DNA, methods requiring hypertonic media make plaque assays difficult and erratic. As far as we know the anisosmotic methods possess no single advantage; they are reviewed here briefly in case a special application might arise requiring their use.

1. *Hypertonic*

After the assay cells have been washed with Hank's BSS, 1 *M* NaCl is placed on them for 20 minutes and then removed. The cells are inoculated with DNA in PBS (30 minutes at 23°C). Alternatively, the 1 *M* NaCl washing is omitted, the DNA inoculum being diluted in 1 *M* NaCl instead of PBS; in this case a post-inoculation washing is needed (Ito *et al.*, 1966). This method, taken from an assay of rabbit kidney vacuolating virus DNA, is essentially the one that was used for the assay of polyoma DNA, the first animal virus DNA of proven infectivity (DiMayorca *et al.*, 1959). A similar method has also been used for the plaque assay of SV40 DNA, but the percent recovery of infectivity was infinitesimal (Black and Rowe, 1965).

Gerber (1962), who first demonstrated the infectivity of SV40 DNA by a cytolytic quantal assay, used Alexander's mixed hypertonic medium consisting of 0.9 *M* NaCl, 8% sucrose, and 0.01 *M* tris, pH 8.2. Before inoculation, the cell cultures were washed twice with 0.6 *M* PBS. After 25 minutes at room temperature, the inoculum was removed and replaced with liquid maintenance medium.

For assay of infectious RNA other hypertonic diluents have been used including $MgSO_4$ and sucrose, as reviewed by Crick *et al.* (1966). Dimethylsulfoxide (DMSO), because of its peculiar capacity to act as a carrier and penetrant, has been tried with DEAE-D (Pagano and Vaheri, 1965), by itself (Amstey and Parkman, 1966) or with sucrose (Tovell and Colter, 1967) on a single-stranded RNA with limited success.

With polyoma DNA Warden and Thorne (1968) recently found that the efficiency of the DEAE-D method was about 100 times greater than that of a hypertonic plaque method used for comparison (Weil, 1961); with DEAE-D the specific infectivity of the 20 S DNA component was 6×10^5 pfu/μg.

2. Hypotonic–Hypertonic

Sanders (1964) described a method for assay of infectious RNA of encephalomyocarditis virus that is of use in cells resistant to the osmotic shock provided by the ordinary hypertonic media (Krebs II ascites cells in his sytem). The method is based on application of a double osmotic shock, the cells being suspended first in a hypotonic buffer (0.001 *M* phosphate) and then exposed to a solution of nucleic acid in hypertonic (1.3 *M*) phosphate-buffered sucrose. In such a case the DEAE-D method ought to be tried first since it does not depend on osmotic effects.

3. Isotonic

Other substances besides DEAE-D are now known to exert an enhancing effect on infectivity of viral RNA under isotonic conditions. Some of these substances are more active in hypertonic media. The enhancing agents have in common a cationic nature; they include nuclear histones, protamine (Amos and Kearns, 1963), polyamines (Moscarello, 1965), poly-L-lysine, and poly-L-ornithine, all used for the assay of RNA from picornaviruses. If there is any correlation between M_w of the compound and enhancing power—and in the case of DEAE-Ds of graded M_w there is, in fact, a good correlation—most of the other compounds, being of comparatively low M_w, may be at a disadvantage. However, dependence of enhancement on M_w of the polymer may not pertain in all systems, and Koch *et al.* (1966) devised an efficient assay with poly-L-ornithine, the M_w of which was 45,000.

Ryser (1967) found that polycations stimulate animal cells to take up albumin; there was good correlation between uptake and M_w of the polymers tested including poly-L-ornithine, poly-L-lysine, poly-D-lysine, and DEAE-D. None of these materials has been tested in a DNA assay system.

4. Assay of Infectivity of DNA from Larger Viruses

The nucleic acids from viruses containing DNA molecules larger than those of the papovaviruses have not been shown to be infectious, let alone precisely assayable. The possible exceptions to this generalization may give clues as to what is required for infectivity. Is it merely necessary, for instance, to succeed in extraction of the intact DNA from complex viruses to enable demonstration of infectivity, or is there an inner-coat constituent of enveloped viruses needed to trigger replication that is lost through deproteinization? (Pagano, 1970).

What follows is a resumé of several methods that have been applied to extraction of DNA from large viruses. At many points the approach is based on the work of Marmur (1961) with bacterial DNA. These examples are selected because they yield intact or nearly intact DNA, and they are therefore candidates for recovery of biologically active nucleic acid; indeed in two cases minimal activity seems to have been detected. Essentially combinations of lipid solvents, protein-reducing agents and proteolytic enzymes, in addition to the standard reagents, the detergent, SDS, and the denaturing agent, phenol, are involved.

Sodium dodecyl sulfate alone was used by Watson and Littlefield (1960) for deproteinization of Shope papilloma virus; they described the characteristic clearing and increase in viscosity accompanying release of viral DNA brought about by raising of temperature of the SDS-containing virus suspension to 50°C. A hypertonic salt solution was then added to precipitate the denatured protein and SDS. Partially purified virus having been the starting material, a nonselective precipitation of the DNA by ethanol was employed. DNA obtained by a basically similar procedure was shown by Chambers and Ito (1964) to be biologically active through capacity to induce tumor formation, the only available assay system for this virus.

This relatively gentle method of extraction has been used with some modifications in attempts, apparently successful, to extract intact DNA from far larger viruses including equine abortion (herpes) virus (M_w of DNA $= 93 \times 10^6$) and fowlpox virus ($M_w = 240 \times 10^6$), as well as from African swine fever virus (Soehner *et al.*, 1965; Randall *et al.*, 1966; Adldinger *et al.*, 1966). In the case of both large viruses the detergent-salting out sequence was followed with the addition of chloroform–butanol extraction. A phenol extraction step was included for the equine abortion virus but omitted for fowlpox extraction. In contrast to SV40 DNA, these large DNAs could be spooled on a glass rod during precipitation in ethanol. There was considerable evidence of a low level of infectivity in the extracted material, although final proof that the activity was due wholly to isolated viral DNA is not yet in.

Pfau and McCrea (1962) in attempting to isolate infectious DNA from vaccinia virus discarded phenol extraction and treated purified virus washed in organic solvents with 2% 2-mercaptoethanol for

18-24 hours at 4°C. This was followed by three successive exposures of the virus to pronase for 12, 8, and 4 hours at 37°C. The procedure yielded more than 90% of the viral DNA, the bulk of it in a double-stranded form (Pfau and McCrea, 1963). Nevertheless, the material was not infectious; however, no evidence was given to show that the DNA was intact.

Joklik (1962), using a rather similar extraction procedure with cow-pox virus, except that he included treatment with SDS after the 2-mercaptoethanol, substituted papain for pronase and added two phenol extractions, obtained a homogeneous double-stranded DNA (M_w of 80×10^6) which, however, probably represented half pieces of the intact DNA ($M_w = 160 \times 10^6$). The material was not infectious. It would be of great interest to attempt to stabilize the DNA with DEAE-D during extraction (Maes *et al.*, 1967) since breakage evidently occurs as the DNA is liberated. If intact DNA were preserved in this way, infectiousness might then be demonstrable with the DEAE-D method.

More recently, Sarov and Becker (1967) have succeeded in obtaining intact vaccinia DNA by extraction of purified virus after layering on a sucrose gradient; in this way it was possible to separate by zonal centrifugation DNA of M_w 170×10^6 without breakage.

ACKNOWLEDGMENTS

The author wishes to thank his colleagues, Dr. James H. McCutchan and Dr. Antti Vaheri, for their advice and criticism of the manuscript.

REFERENCES

Adldinger, H. K., Stone, S. S., Hess, W. R., and Bachrach, H. L. (1966). *Virology* **30**, 750.
Amos, H., and Kearns, K. E. (1963). *Exptl. Cell Res.* **32**, 14.
Amstey, M. S., and Parkman, P. D. (1966). *Proc. Soc. Exptl. Biol. Med.* **123**, 438.
Black, P. H., and Rowe, W. P. (1965). *Virology* **27**, 436.
Chambers, V. C., and Ito, Y. (1964). *Virology* **23**, 434.
Crick, J., Lebedev, A. I., Stewart, D. L., and Brown, F. (1966). *J. Gen. Microbiol.* **43**, 59.
DiMayorca, G. A., Eddy, B. E., Stewart, S. E., Hunter, W. S., Friend, C., and Bendich, A. (1959). *Proc. Natl. Acad. Sci. U.S.* **45**, 1805.
Fraenkel-Conrat, H., Singer, B., and Tsugita, A. (1961). *Virology* **14**, 54.
Gerber, P. (1962). *Virology* **16**, 96.

Hopps, H. E., Bernheim, B. C., Nisalak, A., Tjio, J. H., and Smadel, J. E. (1963). *J. Immunol.* **91**, 416.
Ito, Y., Hsia, S., and Evans, C. A. (1966). *Virology* **29**, 26.
Joklik, W. K. (1962). *J. Mol. Biol.* **5**, 265.
Koch, G., Quintrell, N., and Bishop, J. M. (1966). *Biochem. Biophys. Res. Commun.* **24**, 304.
McCutchan, J. H., and Pagano, J. S. (1968). *J. Natl. Cancer Inst.* **41**, 351.
Maes, R., Sedwick, W., and Vaheri, A. (1967). *Biochim. Biophys. Acta* **134**, 269.
Marmur, J. (1961). *J. Mol. Biol.* **3**, 208.
Moscarello, M. A. (1965). *Virology* **26**, 687.
Pagano, J. S., and McCutchan, J. H. (1968). Unpublished data.
Pagano, J. S., and Vaheri, A. (1965). *Arch Ges. Virusforsch.* **17**, 456.
Pagano, J. S., McCutchan, J. H., and Vaheri, A. (1967). *J. Virol.* **1**, 891.
Pagano, J. S. (1970). *Progr. Med. Virol.* **12**. In press.
Pfau, C. J., and McCrea, J. F. (1962). *Nature* **194**, 894.
Pfau, C. J., and McCrea, J. F. (1963). *Virology* **21**, 425.
Randall, C., Gafford, L. G., Soehner, R. L., and Hyde, J. M. (1966). *J. Bacteriol.* **91**, 95.
Riggs, J. L., and Lennette, E. H. (1965). *Science* **147**, 408.
Ryser, H. J.-P. (1967). *Nature* **215**, 934.
Sanders, F. K. (1964). *In* "Techniques in Experimental Virology" (R. J. C. Harris, ed.), pp. 277–304. Academic Press, New York.
Sarov, I., and Becker, Y. (1967). *Virology* **33**, 369.
Soehner, R. L., Gentry, G. A., and Randall, C. C. (1965). *Virology* **26**, 394.
Tovell, O. R., and Colter, J. S. (1967). *Virology* **72**, 84.
Vaheri, A., and Pagano, J. S. (1965). *Virology* **27**, 434.
Warden, D., and Thorne, H. V. (1968). *J. Gen. Virol.* **3**, 371.
Watson, J. D., and Littlefield, J. W. (1960). *J. Mol. Biol.* **2**, 161.
Weil, R. (1961). *Virology* **14**, 46.

18. Focus Assay of Rous Sarcoma Virus*

Peter K. Vogt

Department of Microbiology
University of Washington Medical School
Seattle, Washington

I. Introduction

Rous sarcoma virus (RSV) belongs to the few tumor viruses which induce neoplastic transformation in the majority of the infected cells. This unusual oncogenic effectiveness of RSV has been used for some time to assay virus infectivity. Rous sarcoma virus inoculated onto the chorioallantoic membrane (CAM) of chicken embryos produces small ectodermal and mesodermal tumors termed "pocks." The number of these tumors is approximately proportional to the virus concentration, and can thus serve as a basis for virus titration (Keogh, 1938; Rubin, 1957). However, this technique has severe drawbacks. Identical virus inocula often produce grossly varying numbers of pocks in different eggs. This variation is not attributable to the inoculation procedure per se but appears to result from genetic resistance to RSV as well as interference with RSV by congenital infection of the embryo with avian leukosis viruses (Payne and Biggs, 1964a,b, 1965). Further, the CAM technique allows only one virus sample to be assayed per egg, excluding any sort of comparative studies on the same embryo. The CAM assay is also in a sense terminal. It is not possible to follow the process of infection and transformation beyond the production of pocks, and to manipulate infected or transformed cells.

The focus assay of RSV in chick embryo cell cultures avoids all

*Work supported by U.S. Public Health Service Research Grant CA 10569 from the National Cancer Institute and by Grant E 302 from the American Cancer Society.

these difficulties. The number of foci produced in a culture plate by a given inoculum of RSV is highly reproducible (Manaker and Groupé, 1956; Temin and Rubin, 1958). The relationship between virus concentration and focus count is strictly linear, indicating that a single particle of RSV is sufficient to produce a focus. Genetic resistance and congenital infection of chick embryos with avian leukosis viruses can be recognized with the tests discussed below. Embryos yielding cells with undesirable characteristics can thus be eliminated. The cells from a single chicken embryo are sufficient to assay hundreds of virus samples. The RSV-infected chick embryo cells can be transferred and cultured *in vitro* for prolonged periods, they can be cloned, and they can be stored for months in the frozen state (Temin, 1962; Hanafusa *et al.*, 1963; Trager and Rubin, 1966; Dougherty, 1964). All stages of the focus assay are easily accessible to microscopic inspection. Although the focus assay is commonly carried out with fibroblasts, epithelial cells are also susceptible to transformation by RSV *in vitro* (Ephrussi and Temin, 1960). The shape of the transformed cell as well as the architecture of Rous sarcoma foci are largely controlled by the viral genome (Temin, 1960; Vogt, 1967a). Foci may be either compact, containing only transformed cells (Bryan high titer strains, Harris strains) or diffuse with interdispersed normal-appearing cells (Schmidt-Ruppin strain, Fujinami sarcoma virus). Foci may be multilayered as with the Bryan high titer strain or predominantly monolayered as with the Prague and Harris strains. Individual transformed cells appear refractile and swollen, their contours may be round (most strains of RSV) or fusiform (morph *f* mutants of RSV). To a smaller extent these focus characteristics are also influenced by the physiological state of the culture. For instance, beef embryo extract in the medium tends to enhance multilayering. Cultures which have been transferred several times may show a greater tendency to respond with the production of fusiform Rous sarcoma cells.

The following technique is based on the use of chicken embryos, but is also applicable to other avian embryos especially those of all other *Galliformes* and *Anseriformes*.

II. Materials

A. Animal Products

1. *Chick Embryos*

Fertile eggs are obtained from a commercial flock. Many of these open flocks have only a low (less than 5%) incidence of congenital leukosis virus infection. Among those tested and found satisfactory belong flocks of the following breeders in the United States: Kimber, Hyline, Hubbard, and Heisdorf & Nelson. Some breeders also offer leukosis-free eggs: SPAFAS, Inc., Norwich, Connecticut and Kimber Farms, Niles, California. However, an absolute guarantee for the absence of leukosis virus in individual embryos cannot be given, and in crucial experiments tests for leukosis virus in the embryo are advisable. White leghorns are the breed most frequently used. Flocks of the large breeders in the United States contain some genetic resistance to subgroup B avian tumor viruses: approximately half of the embryos yield cell cultures susceptible to subgroups A, B, and C; the other half produces cultures selectively resistant to subgroup B (Hanafusa, 1965; Vogt, 1965). Heavy breeds often carry genetic resistance against several avian tumor virus subgroups but are not as well studied as white leghorns.

2. *Calf Serum*

Not all serum lots offered commercially will support focus formation by RSV in tissue culture, and samples of several lots should be tested before larger quantities are purchased. Satisfactory sera have been obtained from Hyland Laboratories, Los Angeles, California; Microbiological Associates, Bethesda, Maryland; Colorado Serum Co., Denver, Colorado; and Grand Island Biological Company, Grand Island, New York. Calf sera available from local slaughter houses frequently have been unacceptable for the RSV focus assay. Calf sera are not inactivated. They may be stored for as much as 1 year at −20°C.

3. *Chicken Serum*

Chicken serum is also purchased from tissue culture supply houses. It is not used in the RSV assay proper but in the growth of primary fibroblast cultures. However, antibody to RSV should be absent. Chicken sera must be inactivated at 56°C for 2 hours to eliminate infectious avian leukosis virus which may be present. Storage at −20°C for up to 1 year is permissible.

4. *Beef Embryo Extract*

Embryos weighing from 250 to 500 gm are obtained with the amniotic sac intact from a local slaughter house. They are removed from the amniotic sac under sterile conditions and homogenized in an electric blender with an equal volume of one of the cell culture media listed below. The homogenate is clarified at 5000 rpm for 10 minutes, and then centrifuged at 9,000–12,000 rpm for 20 minutes. The material is vialed and stored frozen for as much as ½ year at −20°C. Commercially available beef embryo extract is acceptable but too costly for routine use.

5. *Chick Embryo Extract*

Chick embryo extract is produced from whole 10-day-old chick embryos according to the procedure described above for beef embryo extract.

B. Maintenance Media and Reagent Solutions

1. *Cell Culture Media*

Several media have been found satisfactory. Medium 199 (Morgan *et al.*, 1951) is commonly used. It may be substituted by minimal essential medium (Eagle, 1959), F10 (Ham, 1963), or Scherer's maintenance medium (1953). These are needed in single and double concentrations. Melnick's medium A in single concentration is used for special purposes only (1955). Although the commercially available solutions and powders are acceptable, larger quantities of media are preferably prepared in the laboratory. The tissue culture media are sterilized by pressure filtration through Millipore filters (0.22 μ average pore size).

2. *Saline Solutions*

Tris-buffered saline consists of NaCl 8 gm/liter, KCl 0.37 gm/liter, Na_2HPO_4 0.1 gm/liter, glucose 1 gm/liter, tris hydroxymethylaminomethane 3 gm/liter, 10 *N* HCl 1.8 ml/liter.

3. *Trypsin*

Trypsin is prepared as a 0.25% solution in tris-buffered saline from Trypsin 1:250 or Trypsin 1:300 (Difco Laboratories, Detroit, Michigan or Mann Research Laboratories, New York, New York), Millipore filtered (0.45 μ average pore size) and stored at −20°C.

4. *Bacto Tryptose Phosphate Broth*

Bacto tryptose phosphate broth is prepared according to the manufacturer's (Difco Laboratories) instructions and sterilized by autoclaving.

5. *Bacto Agar*

Bacto agar (Difco Laboratories) is prepared in 1.8% concentration and autoclaved. Purified agar (Difco Laboratories) is preferable to Bacto agar for the nutrient overlay of primary cultures but is not acceptable for the RSV focus assay. Nobel agar and agarose also appear unsuitable for the RSV focus assay.

6. *Sodium Bicarbonate*

Sodium bicarbonate 2.8% solution in distilled water. Sterilize by autoclaving.

7. *Yeast Extract*

Fresh yeast extract is prepared by adding 250 gm of dry baker's yeast (Standard Brands, Inc.) to 1 liter of boiling, distilled water. The extract is filtered through Whatman No. 12 paper, vialed, and stored at −20°C (Hayflick, 1965).

C. Complex Media

1. *List of Complex Media*

The solutions listed above are combined in several complex media. These are: growth medium for primary cultures (PGM), growth medium for secondary cultures and further transfers (GM), seeding medium (SM), soft agar overlay for primary cultures (POL), and hard agar overlay for the focus assay (OL). The composition of these media is given in Table I.

TABLE I
Composition[a] of Complex Media for RSV Assay

Component	PGM	GM	SM	POL	OL
Medium 199, single strength[b]	40	40	40	20	–
Medium 199, double strength[b]	–	–	–	10	20
Tryptose phosphate broth	5	5	5	5	5
Calf serum	4	2.5	0.5	4	2.5
Chicken serum	1	–	–	1	–
2.8% $NaHCO_3$	1	1	1	1	1
Bacto agar[c]	–	–	–	–	20
Purified agar[c]	–	–	–	10	–

[a]Expressed in parts of the total.

[b]May be replaced by F10, minimal essential medium, or Scherer's maintenance medium. In the case of seeding medium (SM) Melnick's medium A may be used and is the most economical.

[c]Melted in a boiling water bath, then cooled in a 45°C water bath for 30 minutes and mixed with the remainder of the components which have been prewarmed to 45°C. Mixed POL and OL can be kept for several hours at 45°C.

2. *Transfer Buffer*

Tris-buffered saline with 10% calf serum (TBC) is used to handle cells during transfer operations outside the incubator.

3. *Freezing Medium*

Freezing medium (FM) consists of 11 parts GM, 5 parts calf serum, and 4 parts dimethyl sulfoxide.

4. *Antibiotics*

Penicillin and streptomycin are added to all complex media as well as to tris-buffered saline and trypsin solutions at concentrations of 10^5 units/liter and 25 mg/liter, respectively. Other antibiotics which may be used without harmful effect on cells or virus are 1 mg/liter of Amphothericin B, 100 mg/liter of Kanamycin, 50 mg/liter of Aureomycin, 100 mg/liter of Neomycin, and 10,000 units/liter of Nystatin.

D. EQUIPMENT

(1) Tissue culture glass and plastic ware: flasks, centrifuge tubes, measuring cylinders, and serological pipettes. Number 12-318 hand pipettes (Bellco Glass, Inc., Vineland, New Jersey), Falcon tissue culture dishes (Falcon Plastics, Los Angeles, California).

(2) Egg punch (Tri R Instrument Co., Jamaica, New Jersey).

(3) Sterile surgical instruments to handle embryos: three stainless steel forceps, one No. 90L-312 stainless steel hook (Lawton Co., New York, New York), and one stainless steel spatula (Fig. 1) per embryo.

(4) A low speed, clinical centrifuge (International Equipment Co.).

(5) Magnetic stirrers: A multiple stirring unit (Lab-Line Co., Melrose Park, Illinois) is most suitable for preparing primary cultures from several chicken embryos. One inch, Teflon-covered stirring bars with spinning ring (Lab-Line Co.).

(6) A humidified incubator gassed with 95% air-5% CO_2 and regulated between 38 and 39°C.

(7) Inverted microscope fitted with a mechanical stage which has at least 75 mm free movement in both directions; 2.5× and 10× planachromat or achromat objectives and 10× eyepieces. A glass plate with a 2 mm^2 grid is fixed to the slide holder of the stage and serves as support for petri dishes during counting of foci. Grid plates can be obtained from Technical Instrument Co., San Francisco, California or may be 3 by 4 inch photographic transparencies of 2 mm graph paper

with a large cover slip bonded to the emulsion side of the photographic plate.

(8) For preparation of secondary cultures and further transfer of cells an electronic cell counter (Coulter Electronics, Hialeah, Florida) with a 100 μ aperture is desirable. It should be standardized with cell suspensions of known concentration.

III. Procedures

A. Primary Chick Embryo Cell Cultures

Nine- to eleven-day-old embryos are candled and the air sac is marked. The shell over the air sac is disinfected with 70% ethanol, broken with the egg punch and removed with forceps. In all following steps, instruments and pipettes should not be used with more than one embryo, in order to avoid possible cross contamination with avian leukosis viruses. The shell membrane is peeled off with forceps, and the embryo is lifted with the hook into a petri dish. The head of the embryo is removed with forceps, and the embryo is placed in a 50 ml Erlenmeyer flask containing a 1 inch, Teflon-covered stirring bar. Using the blunt end of the spatula the embryo is then minced, and red blood cells are washed off with 10 ml of tris-buffered saline. Five milliliters of 0.25% trypsin (37°C) are added, and the mince is stirred in a magnetic stirrer at medium speed for 3 minutes. After settling of the large clumps the supernatant containing cells is decanted into a 50 ml Corex glass centrifuge tube containing 10 ml of PGM and placed in crushed ice. This extraction is repeated 3–4 times, at each time 5 ml of 0.25% trypsin are added to the embryo fragments. In between extractions fragments may be broken up by *gentle* pipetting with a wide mouth serological pipette. If a large proportion of the cells are damaged during the trypsin extractions it is advisable to use 0.25% trypsin only for the first cycle and replace it in the remaining ones with tris-buffered saline warmed to 37°C. After the extractions the pooled cells of each embryo are centrifuged (800 rpm, 10 minutes). The supernatant is decanted, and the cells are gently suspended in 20 ml of PGM with a wide mouth pipette. A small sample is diluted 1:10 in PGM and counted in a hemocytometer with a 10× or 40× objective. Red blood cells and grossly injured cells are disregarded. The yield from a 10-day-old embryo should lie between 0.9 and 1.4 × 10^8 viable cells. 1.6–2.5 × 10^7 cells are needed for a sensitivity assay. The remainder is

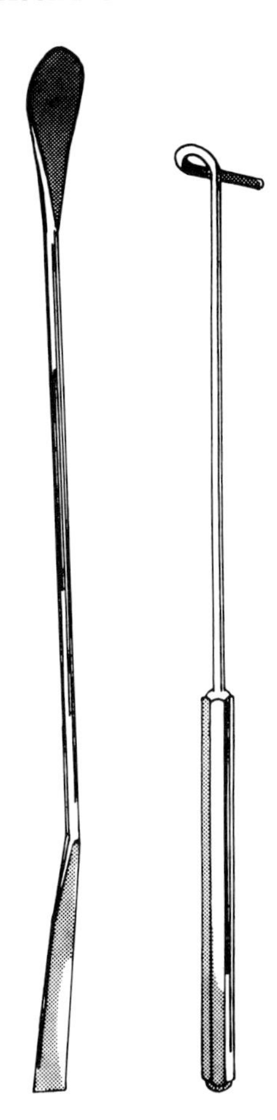

FIG. 1. Stainless steel spatula and hook.

seeded in 100 mm petri dishes with 10 ml of PGM (6–8 $\times$ 10^6 cells/plate) or in 150 mm petri dishes with 20 ml of PGM (1.5 $\times$ 10^7 cells/plate). Plates are equilibrated in the incubator for 2 hours before seeding and are returned to the incubator immediately after seeding. Smaller numbers of cells may be seeded in 100 mm petri dishes if the volume of PGM is reduced by up to 50%. However, in order to avoid drying out of such plates the PGM should be brought up to the volumes indicated above one day after seeding when the cells have settled and spread. The cells are overlaid with POL on the third or fourth day after seeding (10 ml/100 mm plate and 20 ml/150 mm plate). They may be used for secondary cultures from the fourth until the ninth day after seeding.

B. Sensitivity Assay of Primary Cells

In order to detect congenital infection with avian leukosis virus or genetic cellular resistance to RSV, a portion of the cells obtained from each embryo is seeded in 60 mm petri dishes containing 5 ml of PGM (4×10^6 cells/plate). These cultures are infected within 4 hours after seeding with a high and a low concentration of the RSV under study (approximately 10^4 and 10^2 focus-forming units per plate).

The inoculum is added to the medium and left on the plate until the next day when the PGM is replaced with 5 ml of OL, which is then allowed to harden at room temperature for 10 minutes before the plates are returned to the incubator.

The scope of the sensitivity assay depends on the RSV strains to be used. Since each avian tumor virus subgroup has a different host range and differs in its sensitivity to interference by avian leukosis viruses, the results with a given RSV will be representative only of other members of the same subgroup.

A qualitative reading of resistant and sensitive embryos can be taken on the third or fourth day after seeding, i.e., at the same time at which the large, uninfected plates of the same embryos have grown up sufficiently to be used for secondary cultures. This allows one to choose the cells with the desired qualities for experiments.

Cellular resistance of primary cultures against a given RSV may result from the genetic makeup of the cells or from congenital infection with an avian leukosis virus. The first type of resistance cannot be transmitted with the cell-free medium to susceptible cultures, the second kind can. Without carrying out such tests it is not possible to discriminate between the two causes of resistance. However, some experience with a given flock of chickens allows one to make guesses which are very likely correct. (In commercial white leghorn flocks most resistance against subgroup B is genetic, whereas practically all resistance against subgroup A is caused by congenital infection with a subgroup A leukosis virus.) Detailed discussions of genetic cellular resistance and subgroup specific interference may be found in several publications (Payne and Biggs, 1964a,b, 1965; Crittenden *et al.*, 1963, 1967; Crittenden and Okazaki, 1965; Vogt and Ishizaki, 1965, 1966; Vogt *et al.*, 1967).

The numbers of foci on the primary culture sensitivity test are counted and recorded on the seventh day after infection following the procedure described below for the RSV in secondary cultures.

C. Preparation of Secondary Chick Embryo Fibroblast Cultures

1. *Method 1*

The fluid medium or soft agar overlay is removed by suction from primary cultures showing confluent cell growth. The cell sheet is then washed once with tris-buffered saline and treated for approximately 3 minutes with trypsin (0.05% in tris-buffered saline, 5 ml/100 mm dish, 10 ml/150 mm dish). A 5 or 10 ml hand pipette with a rubber bulb of corresponding size is then used to suspend the cells. After a brief centrifugation (3 minutes, 800 rpm) the trypsin is discarded and the cells are resuspended in TBC (5–10 ml per harvested primary plate). A cell count is obtained with a hemocytometer or an electronic cell counter, $10–15 \times 10^6$ cells can be expected from a 100 mm primary plate. The cells are seeded in 60 mm Falcon dishes containing 4 ml of GM ($0.9–1.2 \times 10^6$ cells/dish; other sizes of dishes receive cells in proportion to their surface, about 3.5×10^4 cells/cm^2). The seeding concentration is critical for the RSV assay; especially overseeding leads to a suppression of focus formation (Rubin, 1960b).

2. *Method 2*

Medium is removed from the primary culture as above and the cells are washed with tris-buffered saline. Only 2.5 ml of 0.05% trypsin are added to a 100 mm plate (5 ml for a 150 mm plate). The cells are suspended with a 2 ml hand pipette and rubber bulb and are added to 3 ml of TBC. Centrifugation is omitted, and after determining the cell concentration the suspension is seeded directly in 60 mm Falcon dishes containing 3 ml of SM, at 1.2×10^6 cells/plate. The cells settle and spread rapidly. The medium is changed between ½ to 2 hours after seeding to 5 ml of GM. Method 2 is slightly more laborious because of the obligatory medium change, but it results in less cell damage.

D. Inoculation and Agar Overlay

Secondary cultures of chick embryo fibroblasts may be inoculated with RSV immediately after seeding if prepared according to method 1, or after the medium change if prepared according to method 2. At any rate, infection should follow within 4 to 6 hours after seeding. The cultures retain their physiological competence for RSV focus formation for about 1 day after seeding. Delay of inoculation beyond this time is likely to reduce the efficiency of the assay. However, the physiological competence of older chick fibroblast cultures can be restored at any time by transferring the cells onto new plates in the appropriate concentration (see below). The inoculum is added to the GM and left on the cells overnight. On the next day GM is replaced by OL (5 ml/60 mm plate). The OL is allowed to harden at room temperature for 10 minutes, and the cells are returned to the incubator. The extended incubation of RSV inoculum and cells overnight is possible because under these conditions of low multiplicity of infection detectable amounts of progeny RSV are not made until about 18 hours after infection. Secondary foci resulting from progeny virus are thus still avoided.

E. Counting of Foci

Rous sarcoma virus foci are usually best developed at the seventh day after infection, but counts may be taken any time between the fifth and the ninth day. The culture dish is placed on a plane glass plate with a 2 mm^2 grid firmly connected to the mechanical stage of the inverted microscope. Foci are counted with a 2.5× objective and 10× ocular. A 10× objective is useful to determine details of focus structure. Cell clumps may mimic RSV foci but can usually be distinguished from the latter by the presence of cells migrating radially away from the clump and by the absence of the swollen, refractile cell type which characterizes RSV foci. Foci become more easily recognizable if GM or SM is added on top of the agar about 2 hours before counting (2 ml/60 mm plate) and the plates are left outside the incubator. This is particularly important for those strains of RSV which do not cause piling up of cells within the focus (Harris RSV, Fujinami sarcoma virus, sometimes also Prague RSV).

F. Additional Transfers of Chick Embryo Fibroblast Cultures

Although secondary fibroblast cultures are used routinely for the RSV assay, the cells may be passaged several times before they are inoculated with RSV. Such transfers are necessary in interference tests for avian leukosis viruses (Rubin, 1961). The medium is removed by suction and replaced by 0.05% trypsin diluted in tris-buffered saline and warmed to 37°C (2 ml/60 mm dish). After 3 minutes the cells are suspended with a 2 ml hand pipette fitted to a rubber bulb of the same volume and are added to a tube with 2 ml of TBC. The cells are not centrifuged but are counted in a hemocytometer or electronic cell counter and seeded onto new plates (1.2×10^6 cells/60 mm plate containing 3 ml of SM). A medium change to 5 ml of GM is performed between ½ and 2 hours after seeding. Such plates grow to confluency within 2 to 3 days, and active cell growth often extends for more than 10 passages. Infection with RSV for focus assay is possible after the medium change on the day of seeding. In this case the fluid medium is replaced by OL on the next day as described under inoculation procedures above.

G. Frozen Storage of Chick Embryo Fibroblasts

Chick embryo fibroblasts may be frozen and stored in a similar manner as other cells (Dougherty and Rasmussen, 1964). The cells are suspended with 0.05% trypsin in tris-buffered saline as described in the transfer procedure above, added to TBC, and centrifuged (800 rpm, 3 minutes). They are then resuspended in GM at a concentration of about 5×10^6/ml. An equal volume of freezing medium is added slowly. The suspension is sealed in glass ampoules. If maximal survival rates are not required the ampoules may be stored in a deep freeze at–75°C. Slow freezing and storage in a nitrogen freezer improve survival.

IV. Difficulties and Remedies

Several factors can have an inhibitory effect on RSV focus formation. Cells which are genetically resistant or congenitally infected with avian leukosis virus are unsuitable for the RSV assay (Rubin, 1960a; Crittenden *et al.*, 1963). The assay cells should be vigorous but must not be offered a very rich medium, resulting in rapid growth. Increase in calf serum concentration or use of newborn or fetal calf serum will often lead to a reduction of focus formation at high virus dilutions and will thus make the assay not only inefficient but invalid because focus counts are no longer proportional to virus concentration (Rubin, 1960b). Suppression of focus formation may also be caused by too high an initial concentration of cells. Confluent cell sheets are poor focus formers. Excessive exposure of the cells to trypsin also tends to reduce the plating efficiency of RSV. Among the environmental conditions temperature is crucial. If an incubator is opened frequently during the day the temperature of the plates close to the door may drop below 35° C for prolonged periods of time. This results in an inhibition of focus formation. Even with these factors well under control some RSV strains may form only small, barely discernible foci. In such instances the addition of beef embryo extract to GM and OL may improve results drastically. Different batches of beef embryo extract vary in their effectiveness. The required concentration may lie between 0.1 and 1%. Beef embryo extract increases the number of foci per plate as well as the size of individual foci. Most batches of chick embryo extract have an effect similar to that of beef embryo extract. However since chick embryos may harbor an avian leukosis virus the usefulness of chick embryo extract is restricted to terminal experiments, unless tests are carried out to establish absence of an interfering virus from the preparation.

Beef embryo extract also improves the condition of cells kept for several transfer generations. Cells which are kept in fluid medium for repeated passage also profit from fresh yeast extract (0.2–0.5% in GM). However, this additive should be omitted from the RSV assay proper.

Even in genetically and physiologically susceptible chick embryo fibroblast cultures not all strains of RSV show optimal efficiency of plating. The plating of subgroup B and most subgroup C avian sarcoma viruses (Vogt *et al.*, 1967) can be substantially improved by pretreatment of the cell cultures with medium containing DEAE-dextran (10 μg/ml, 1 hour, Pharmacia Fine Chemicals, Inc., Piscataway, New Jersey) (Vogt, 1967b). DEAE-dextran may be replaced by other polycations of which Polybrene (10 μg/ml, Abbot Laboratories, Chicago, Illinois) is most effective (up to 40-fold enhancement of focus formation) and least toxic to the cells (Toyoshima and Vogt, 1969).

ACKNOWLEDGMENT

Most of the techniques described in this paper have been designed and perfected in the laboratory of Dr. Harry Rubin, University of California, Berkeley. The author is grateful to Dr. Rubin and to his technicians, Mrs. Lois Fanshier and Mrs. Ardra Brodale, for introducing him to the world of RSV.

REFERENCES

Crittenden, L. B., and Okazaki, W. (1965). *J. Natl. Cancer Inst.* **35**, 857.
Crittenden, L. B., Okazaki, W., and Reamer, R. (1963). *Virology* **20**, 541.
Crittenden, L. B., Stone, H. A., Reamer, R. H., and Okazaki, W. (1967). *J. Virol.* **1**, 898.
Dougherty, R. M., and Rasmussen, R. (1964). *Natl. Cancer Inst. Monograph* **17**, 337.

Eagle, H. (1959). *Science* **130**, 432.
Ephrussi, B., and Temin, H. M. (1960). *Virology* **11**, 547.
Ham, R. G. (1963). *Exptl. Cell Res.* **29**, 515.
Hanafusa, H. (1965). *Virology* **25**, 248.
Hanafusa, H., Hanafusa, T., and Rubin, H. (1963). *Proc. Natl. Acad. Sci. U.S.* **49**, 572.
Hayflick, L. (1965). *Texas Rept. Biol. Med.* **23**, Suppl., 285.
Keogh, E. V. (1938). *Brit. J. Exptl. Pathol.* **19**, 1.
Manaker, R. A., and Groupé, V. (1956). *Virology* **2**, 838.
Melnick, J. L. (1955). *Ann. N.Y. Acad. Sci.* **61**, 754.
Morgan, J. F., Morton, H. J., Healy, G. M., and Parker, R. C. (1951). *Proc. Soc. Exptl. Biol. Med.* **78**, 880.
Payne, L. N., and Biggs, P. (1964a). *Nature* **203**, 1306.
Payne, L. N., and Biggs, P. (1964b). *Virology* **24**, 610.
Payne, L. N., and Biggs, P. (1965). *Virology* **27**, 621.
Rubin, H. (1957). *Ann. N.Y. Acad. Sci.* **68**, 459.
Rubin, H. (1960a). *Proc. Natl. Acad. Sci. U.S.* **46**, 1105.
Rubin, H. (1960b). *Virology* **12**, 14.
Rubin, H. (1961). *Virology* **13**, 200.
Scherer, W. F. (1953). *Am. J. Pathol.* **29**, 113.
Temin, H. M. (1960). *Virology* **10**, 182.
Temin, H. M. (1962). *Cold Spring Harbor Symp. Quant. Biol.* **27**, 407.
Temin, H. M., and Rubin, H. (1958). *Virology* **6**, 669.
Toyoshima, K., and Vogt, P. K. (1969). In preparation.
Trager, G. W., and Rubin, H. (1966). *Virology* **30**, 275.
Vogt, P. K. (1965). *Virology* **25**, 237.
Vogt, P. K. (1967a). *Perspectives Virol.* **5**, 199.
Vogt, P. K. (1967b). *Virology* **33**, 175.
Vogt, P. K., and Ishizaki, R. (1965). *Virology* **26**, 664.
Vogt, P. K., and Ishizaki, R. (1966). *Virology* **30**, 368.
Vogt, P. K., Ishizaki, R., and Duff, R. (1967). *In* "Subviral Carcinogenesis" (Y. Ito, ed.), p. 297. Aichi Cancer Center, Nagoya, Japan.

19. Clonal Analysis of Virus-Induced Cell Transformation

Ian Macpherson

Imperial Cancer Research Fund
Lincoln's Inn Fields
London, England

I. Introduction

The transformation of cells *in vitro* by some oncogenic viruses is usually associated with easily recognizable changes in the cells' growth characteristics. Hamster or rat cells transformed by polyoma virus pile up and grow in disarray. Transformation occurs rapidly and is not accompanied by virus synthesis. It is therefore possible to obtain a measure of the oncogenic activity of polyoma virus by infecting cells and plating them at a dilution permitting the formation of discrete colonies. Uninfected cells and infected cells that have not undergone transformation grow in parallel array and tend to remain as a monolayer. The transformed colonies have the characteristics previously described. Systems in which cell transformation does not appear until several cell divisions after infection or in which secondary infections result from the synthesis of new virus cannot be analyzed quantitatively by colony analysis (e.g., mouse cells and polyoma virus or human cells and SV40 virus).

II. Method

Cultures of rapidly dividing cells may be infected *in situ* or may be trypsinized and infected in suspension. Since transformation is a very inefficient process in terms of total virus particles or plaque-forming units, a high concentration of virus is required to obtain the maximum transformation rate. Maximum transformation efficiency (10–20%) requires a multiplicity of 1000 pfu/cell in polyoma systems.

The virus is suspended in phosphate-buffered saline containing 2% calf serum and the infection of the cells is carried out at 37°C for 1 hour using some form of gentle agitation to increase the rate of virus adsorption and also, in the case of cells infected in suspension, to prevent the cells attaching to the glass. Some concentrated stocks of the small plaque variant of polyoma virus may cause the cells to agglutinate. This can be avoided by incubating the cells in growth medium at 37°C for 2 hours after virus adsorption. During this period the virus penetrates the cells and when they are resuspended they do not agglutinate.

After infection the cells are cultured in petri dishes at concentrations permitting the formation of discrete colonies. In order that the colonies are as representative as possible of the infected cell population, pains should be taken to obtain the maximum colony-forming efficiency (CFE). The use of X-irradiated cells (1500 r) as feeders usually help in this respect.

Cultures are incubated in a humidified CO_2 incubator at 37°C until the transformed colonies can be distinguished from the normal colonies. In the case of primary or secondary rat or hamster embryo cells this is about 10–14 days. With hamster cell lines such as BHK 21/13 (Macpherson and Stoker, 1962) or NIL 2 (Diamond, 1967) 7 or 8 days suffice.

The transformed colonies may be distinguished in living cultures if the dishes are illuminated from below with a microscope lamp. Normal colonies are irregularly shaped and have a "sheen" resulting from the parallel arrangement of the cells. Transformed colonies are round and opaque.

To count the colonies the medium is discarded and the cell sheet rinsed with buffered saline, fixed in methanol for 5 minutes, and stained with Giemsa. The stain is rinsed off with tap water, and the wet cultures examined with a low-power plate microscope. To eliminate bias when scoring, the control and infected cell cultures should be coded and randomized before being examined.

The transformation frequency is expressed either as transformed colonies per total cells plated (T/cell) or as the transformed colonies per total colonies (T/colony).

REFERENCES

Diamond, L. (1967). *Intern. J. Cancer* **2**, 143.

Macpherson, I., and Stoker, M. (1962). *Virology* **16**, 147.

20. Agar Suspension Culture for Quantitation of Transformed Cells

Ian Macpherson

Imperial Cancer Research Fund
Lincoln's Inn Fields
London, England

I. Introduction

Normal cells in tissue culture characteristically fail to undergo division when suspended in fluid medium or in medium rendered semisolid with a low concentration of agar. Apparently they require attachment and extension on a solid substrate in order to divide.

Cells with a high degree of autonomy *in vitro*, acquired either by spontaneous transformation or as the result of transformation by an oncogenic virus, usually lose this requirement and can multiply continuously in suspension.

This property has been utilized in a selective assay for cells transformed by a number of oncogenic viruses. Normal cells (or cell lines that grow poorly or not at all in suspension culture) are infected with virus and plated in agar suspension culture. Only transformed cells grow to produce large colonies in these conditions.

II. Materials and Methods

A. Components of the Medium

1. *Preparation of Agar Stock (1.25%)*

Add 12.5 gm of Difco Bacto agar granules to about 800 ml of cold glass-distilled water or deionized water tested as being suitable for use in tissue culture (agarose and Noble agar may also be used, but offer no special advantages over Difco Bacto agar). Boil to dissolve the agar granules and make up to 1000 ml with hot water. Dispense 80 ml amounts (±1 or 2 ml) of hot agar into 200 ml screw-capped bottles (8 ounce medical flats). Sterilize by autoclaving at low pressure with the screw caps tight. Cool to room temperature and tighten the screw caps. Store at room temperature. Melt agar in boiling water, cool bottles briefly at room temperature (to prevent bottles cracking) before transferring them to a water bath at 44°C.

2. *Synthetic Medium* (2×)

Prepare double-strength synthetic medium (i.e., with twice the normal concentration of all components). The phenol red should be reduced to one-tenth the normal level because colonies are easier to see in lightly colored medium. Sterilize medium by filtering through Millipore membranes. Dispense in 80 ml amounts in 200 ml screw-capped bottles. Store at 4°C for periods of up to 1 week.

3. *Serum*

Millipore-filtered calf or fetal calf serum. Store frozen.

4. *Tryptose Phosphate Broth*

Autoclaved Difco Bacto tryptose phosphate broth. Store at room temperature.

B. Preparation of Agar Medium

Add 20 ml of serum and 20 ml of tryptose phosphate broth to the 2× synthetic medium, warm to 44°C, and then add to the agar. Mix by inverting the bottle several times and maintain the complete medium at 44°C until used. This is the medium used routinely in our laboratory, but modifications involving the omission of tryptose phosphate broth and reducing the concentration of serum do not alter its essential properties. Inhibition of normal cell growth in agar is a function of the absence of a substrate to which the cells can attach. If the normal cells attach to small pieces of debris such as cotton wool or fiber glass in the agar, they will divide and form colonies.

C. Preparation of Base Layers

Pipette 7 ml of agar medium into 5 cm petri dishes and leave to set at room temperature. The dishes may be of glass or plastic. If the latter they need not be tissue culture grade since the cells do not come into contact with the surface of the dish. It is inadvisable to prepare the base layers a long time before use or to store them in the refrigerator since fluid is exuded from the base and this prevents the top layer making a firm attachment. The base layers provide the bulk of the nutrient supply for the cells in the top layer.

D. Preparation of Top Layer

Cells may be infected in suspension or as monolayers which are subsequently resuspended with trypsin. In either instance care must be taken to ensure that the suspension is free of cell aggregates. Some strains of small-plaque polyoma virus cause hamster cells to clump when the cells are infected in suspension with high concentrations of the virus. If this occurs, the virus should be adsorbed to monolayers. Following adsorption the cultures are fed with fluid medium and left for 1 or 2 hours to allow the virus to enter the cells. The cells may then be trypsinized.

One volume of cell suspension in medium is mixed with 2 volumes of 0.5% agar. It is unnecessary (and probably undesirable) to warm the cell suspension to 44°C before mixing it with the warm agar. The gelling time of such dilute agar is slow and allows ample time for mixing the suspension and pipetting it onto the base layers. The top layers should be applied very carefully to the base layers, since forceful pipetting may result in the cell suspension penetrating the base layer and consequently growing on the base of the dish.

The optimum number of cells plated per dish depends on the type of cells used and the number of transformed colonies expected. If well-separated colonies are required fewer cells should be plated. For BHK 21/13 cells and polyoma virus the optimum number of cells plated for estimations of transformation rates is 10^5 per dish, and for isolating transformed colonies 10^3 infected cells per dish.

Cultures are incubated at 37°C in a well-humidified atmosphere of 5-10% CO_2 in air. If a suitable incubator is not available the dishes may be enclosed in a gas-tight box containing the appropriate gas phase. Cells capable of dividing do so shortly after incubation has commenced, and grow progressively to form colonies 0.1-0.2 mm in diameter in 7-10 days.

E. Counting Colonies

Colonies are examined and counted unfixed and unstained with the aid of a plate microscope (25-50× magnification). Dishes may be left for several days in the refrigerator before being examined. Occasionally normal cells undergo a few divisions and form small colonies. By examining control cultures it is possible to determine the size of colony that should be considered as "background." The longer cultures are incubated the more obvious this distinction becomes. Transformed cell colonies increase in size more rapidly than the "abortive" normal cell colonies.

A more certain method of classifying colonies is to use an image-shearing eyepiece when counting (manufactured by W. Watson & Sons Ltd., Barnet, Herts., England). This splits the image of a colony into green and red components. The eyepiece may be calibrated for a particular colony size, say, 0.1 mm. Colonies of this size present two images, just touching. Colonies larger than 0.1 mm in diameter will have overlapping images, and colonies smaller than 0.1 mm will have separated images.

In cultures with many colonies a convenient method of counting is to lay a small cover glass (e.g., 5 × 20 mm) on the top layer surface and make a sample count of the colonies below the cover glass. A grid may be ruled on the cover glass with a ball-point pen.

If the incubation time must be extended for more than 10 days in order to obtain colonies (e.g., in the case of NIL 2 hamster cells transformed by adenovirus 12—see Table I) it is necessary to feed the cells by adding 1-2 ml of medium to the agar top layer. The medium should be renewed about twice a week.

F. Subculturing Colonies

Colonies may be removed from the agar with finely drawn Pasteur pipettes. The whole colony is transferred to a tube containing 1 ml of medium and pipetted until it breaks into several fragments. It is essential to remove the agar from the colony, otherwise the cells will be prevented from migrating onto the glass and dividing. A true assessment of the type of cells in colony isolates can only be obtained if the initial growth is trypsinized and subcultured.

The whole cell growth from an agar suspension culture can be harvested by pipetting off the top layer and agitating this in medium to free the colonies from the agar. The colonies may then be cultured directly on glass or trypsinized.

III. Comments

The proportion of cells transformed by oncogenic viruses is often low even following their infection with high multiplicities of virus.

Agar suspension culture provides a method for the selective cultivation of virus-transformed cells. In some cases the method provides the only satisfactory way of detecting scarce transformed cells.

Some of the applications of the method are listed in Table I.

Since cells infected with mycoplasma may be capable of growing in agar suspension (Macpherson and Russell, 1966) it is important to ensure that cells used in the study of virus transformation are free of such contamination.

TABLE I
CELLS CAPABLE OF GROWTH IN AGAR SUSPENSION CULTURE

Transforming virus	Cells	References
–	HeLa, Hep2, L, BHK 21/13 suspension culture variant	Macpherson and Montagnier (1964)
–	Epithelioid BHK 21/13 variant	Montagnier *et al.* (1966)
Polyoma	(i) Hamster embryo	(i)(ii) Macpherson and Montagnier (1964)
	(ii) BHK 21/13	Montagnier and Macpherson (1964)
	(iii) NIL 2/E (Diamond, 1967)	(iii) Macpherson (1965)
	(iv) Rat embryo	(iv) Williams (1968)
Rous sarcoma virus		
Bryan strain	(i) BHK 21/13	(i) Macpherson (1966)
Bryan strain	(ii) Chick embryo fibroblasts	(ii) Rubin (1966)
Schmidt-Ruppin strain	(iii) BHK 21/13	(iii) Macpherson (1965)
Schmidt-Ruppin strain	(iv) NIL 2/E	(iv) Macpherson (1965)
SV40	3T3 mouse	Black (1966)
Adenovirus 12	NIL 2/E	McAllister and Macpherson (1969)

REFERENCES

Black, P. H. (1966). *Virology* **28**, 760.
Diamond, L. (1967). *Intern. J. Cancer* **2**, 143.
McAllister, R. M., and Macpherson, I. (1969). *J. Gen. Virol.* **4**, 29.
Macpherson, I. (1965). Unpublished data.
Macpherson, I. (1965). *Science* **148**, 1731.

Macpherson, I. (1966). *In* "Recent Results in Cancer Research," Vol. 6, pp. 1-8. Springer, Berlin.
Macpherson, I., and Montagnier, L. (1964). *Virology* **23**, 291.
Macpherson, I., and Russell, W. (1966). *Nature* **210**, 1343.
Montagnier, L., and Macpherson, I. (1964). *Compt. Rend.* **258**, 4171.
Montagnier, L., Macpherson, I., and Jarrett, O. (1966). *J. Natl. Cancer Inst.* **36**, 503.
Rubin, H. (1966). *Exptl. Cell Res.* **41**, 138.
Williams, J. (1968). Unpublished data.

21. Transformation Assay Using Cell Line 3T3

George J. Todaro

Viral Carcinogenesis Branch
National Cancer Institute
National Institutes of Health
Public Health Service
Department of Health, Education, and Welfare
Bethesda, Maryland

I. Introduction

The mouse cell line 3T3 is highly sensitive to contact inhibition of cell division and under standard conditions ceases dividing when a monolayer is reached. The cells may be transformed either by polyoma virus or by simian virus 40 (SV40). In both cases, infection with the tumor virus leads to the production of cells that are much better able to grow, and these cells form discrete colonies that can be seen against the background monolayer of untransformed cells (Todaro *et al.*, 1964). Since SV40 does not grow vegetatively in 3T3 cells, it is possible to measure the transforming activity of the virus by infecting the cells and then inoculating them at dilutions sufficient to permit the formation of discrete colonies. The transformed colonies are recognized both on the basis of their morphology and their ability to form multiple cell layers under conditions in which nontransformed cells do not. When high multiplicities of infection are used (1000:1 or greater) up to 50% of the cells can be transformed as the result of a single exposure to SV40 (Todaro and Green, 1966a; Black, 1966).

Most biological assays using viruses are based on their ability to cause cell death with subsequent degeneration and a visible cytopathic effect in tissue culture. The principal and important feature of tumor viruses, however, is that infection does not necessarily lead to the destruction of the cell. Rather, a number of heritable changes are produced involving certain of the normal processes of cell regulation. The viruses that are capable of permanently altering the properties of cells in tissue culture are also able to induce malignancies in the appropriate host. It is assumed that the fundamental change that the virus induces in the cell is the same both *in vivo* and *in vitro*.

II. Handling the Cells

The most critical requirement for the transformation assay probably is the quality of the 3T3 stock that is used. Cells may be obtained from one of the laboratories using the 3T3 line for transformation assays. Repeated subculturing of the cells or handling them under different conditions than those used during their evolution will lead to alteration in properties and very likely to altered susceptibility to transformation. The cells must be maintained under conditions that do not allow the selection of variants which are somewhat less susceptible to contact inhibition of cell division. These cells will have a pronounced selective advantage. The culture conditions determine whether or not such cells will be selected.

The medium used is Dulbecco's modification of Eagle's medium containing a fourfold higher concentration of amino acids and glucose and also some nonessential amino acids that are not present in Eagle's basal medium (Table I). This medium contains a high concentration of bicarbonate and therefore to be properly buffered requires an atmosphere of 10% CO_2 and 90% air.

The medium is supplemented with 10% unheated calf serum. Serum obtained from Colorado Serum Co., Denver, Colorado has been found to be preferable both to calf serum from other sources and to fetal calf serum for the growth of 3T3 cells. Individual lots, however, should be tested on cells inoculated at 100 cells/plate and should not be used if there is a significant reduction in colony-forming ability. Under the proper conditions, the colony-forming ability of 3T3 cells should be between 30 and 60%.

The cells are grown on 50 mm Falcon plastic petri dishes. The medium is changed three times weekly. When the cell density reaches roughly $8\text{-}10 \times 10^5$ cells/plate, a confluent monolayer is formed and cell division stops. The cells will remain in the stationary phase for many weeks with little reduction in plating efficiency.

To preserve the properties essential for transformation studies, the

TABLE I
MEDIUM COMPOSITION
USED FOR 3T3 TRANSFORMATION ASSAY (DULBECCO'S MEDIUM)[a]

Medium	gm/liter
NaCl (biological grade)	6.4
KCl	0.4
$CaCl_2$	0.2
Na HCO_3	3.7
$NaH_2PO_4H_2O$	0.125
$MgSO_4 \cdot 7H_2O$	0.20
Ferric nitrate	0.0001
Glucose	4.5
Penicillin	0.10
Streptomycin	0.10
Phenol red	0.015
L-arginine	0.0840
L-histidine HCl · H_2O	0.0420
L-isoleucine	0.1048
L-leucine	0.1048
L-lysine	0.1462
L-methionine	0.030
L-phenylalanine	0.066
L-threonine	0.0952
L-tryptophane	0.016
L-valine	0.0936
Glycine	0.030
L-serine	0.042
L-tyrosine	0.072
L-cystine	0.048
L-glutamine	0.584
Choline	0.004
D-pantothenic acid	0.004
Pyridoxal HCl	0.004
Thiamine	0.004
Riboflavin	0.0004
Nicotinamide	0.004
Inositol	0.007
Folic acid	0.004

[a]This medium may be obtained from Grand Island Biological Co.

line should either be continually recloned, i.e., inoculated at 100 cells/plate and rapidly growing, flat colonies selected or, alternatively, the line should be passaged at a 1:1,000 or 1:10,000 dilution. The latter method allows 2–3 weeks for the cultures to grow back to confluence. The stock cultures then may be maintained at confluence with media changes twice weekly for an additional period of up to

4 weeks. In spite of these precautions, it would be advisable to have frozen down a large enough stock of the cells having the desired properties and to expect to go back every 3–6 months to this stock.

III. Assay Method

Two to four days after subculturing 5×10^4 cells, logarithmically growing cultures containing roughly $2–4 \times 10^5$ cells/plate are infected as follows: The medium is removed; the plates are washed twice with serum-free medium and then infected with 0.5 ml of virus preparation in medium. During the adsorption period the plates are maintained in a 37°C incubator in an atmosphere with 10% CO_2 and are tilted back and forth every 15 minutes for 3 hours. Gentle agitation of the plates during this period is necessary to prevent areas of the cell layer from drying out and appears to increase the rate of viral adsorption. The adsorption of SV40 to 3T3 cells is relatively slow and is not completed until 3 hours in monolayer cultures. After the adsorption period, the culture is washed twice with serum-free medium and fresh medium is added. Either later that day or the following day the cells are removed from the dishes with 2.0 ml of 0.1% trypsin solution in phosphate-buffered saline (PBS), counted in a hemocytometer, and inoculated with fresh medium in petri plates at cell densities ranging from 50 to 10,000 cells/plate. At least six plates should be prepared at each dilution.

Great care should be taken in order to obtain the highest possible cloning efficiency of the cells, and for this purpose the following method is used: If the cells are to be plated at the end of the adsorption period, they should be washed with serum-containing medium, then fresh medium added, and an hour later the cells trypsinized and inoculated onto new plates. Prewarmed medium is added to the plates into which the cells will be inoculated at the time that the cells are first seen to be detaching. It is best to pipette the trypsin solution gently over the monolayer at a time when the cells are beginning to detach rather than to wait for complete detachment. The cells should be diluted in serum-containing medium and should not be centrifuged after trypsinization. Centrifugation lowers the colony-forming ability and is not necessary since the serum contains sufficient trypsin inhibitory activity. The medium is generally changed on the third, seventh, ninth, eleventh, and thirteenth days. It is advisable to change the medium on the day before the cells are fixed and stained.

Plates inoculated with 50 or 100 cells are fixed and stained after 10 days to determine the plating efficiency. The cells on these plates are fixed by decanting the medium, washing once with PBS, then adding 10% formalin in PBS [1 part stock formaldehyde solution (37% HCHO), 1 part 10 times normal strength PBS, and 8 parts water] for at least 10 minutes. The formalin is poured off and the plates are stained by pouring on 1% Harris' hematoxylin (Fisher Scientific Co.). After 1 hour the stain is poured off and the plates are washed with water and dilute ammonium hydroxide is added briefly (5–10 seconds). Colonies containing more than 64 cells—the equivalent of 6 cell doublings—should be counted.

The cells on the plates used for the transformation assays are fixed and stained 14–16 days after inoculation although in most cases transformed colonies can be recognized by the ninth day. Leaving the cells more than 16 days does not result in any increase in the number of transformed colonies that are scored. The cells in the transformed colonies grow readily over one another and form multiple cell layers. These are easily recognized, even in unstained preparations, against the background of untransformed cells (Fig. 1). Transformation frequencies obtained from plates inoculated with 50 or 100 cells agree very well with data derived from plates inoculated with 1,000 cells or with 10,000 cells. At inoculation densities greater than 2×10^4, however, there is some apparent decrease in transformation frequency because the cells are not allowed a sufficient number of generations for the expression of the transformed property (see below).

The frequency of transformation may be expressed as that fraction of cells plated which give transformed colonies (*T* cell, %) or the fraction of total colonies obtained which are transformed colonies (*T* colony, %). The colony-forming ability of virus-infected cultures is not significantly different from that of control cultures.

To score for transformed colonies we use the following procedure: Control-uninfected or mock-infected plates are first examined carefully to see the range of colony morphology and monolayer morphology present in the control cells. Then, control and infected plates are coded and scored under a low-powered dissecting microscope. In practice, it is most convenient when there are between 5 and 50 transformed colonies per plate. More than 50 transformed colonies per plate are difficult to count because of the overlapping of adjacent colonies.

IV. Comments

Various factors influence the probability of transformation. Log phase cells are transformed with greater efficiency than stationary phase cells (Todaro and Green, 1966a); cells that have been treated with the thymidine analogs, bromodeoxyuridine and iododeoxyuridine, have an increased transformation frequency (Todaro and Green, 1964b) as do cells that have been treated with sublethal doses of X-irradiation (Pollack and Todaro, 1968). The efficiency of transformation per infectious unit is somewhat greater if cells are infected in suspension culture. This is done as follows: The cells are removed from the petri dish with 0.1% trypsin and then centrifuged at 800 rpm for 5 minutes in medium containing 2% calf serum. The cells are then resuspended in 1 ml of the virus preparation, and incubated in a gently shaking water bath set at 37°C. After a 1 hour adsorption period, the cells are diluted and inoculated onto petri dishes as described previously. Using this method, the efficiency of transformation is increased about threefold; however, there is a small reduction in the colony-forming ability of the cells as compared to cells maintained in monolayer culture.

Transformation of 3T3 cells also occurs with DNA extracted from SV40 virus. In this case, the DNA preparation is allowed to adsorb using the technique described by Pagano (see Chapter 17). The efficiency of transformation with DNA, however, is low as compared to that obtained using whole virus.

It is important to recognize that several cell divisions subsequent to infection are needed for the expression of transformation (Todaro and Green, 1966b). For this reason, it is not possible to infect confluent or near confluent cultures and simply observe them over a period of weeks. These cultures will very rarely if ever give discrete transformed foci. Four to six cell generations are needed for complete expression of transformation. Starting with a confluent monolayer culture, full expression of transformation does not occur unless the cells are diluted at least 1:64. Therefore, the infected cells must be inoculated at cell densities of 1.5×10^4 cells/plate or less.

The agar suspension culture technique described elsewhere in this volume by Macpherson can also be used to study transformation of 3T3 cells, but when compared to the monolayer transformation method, the agar technique is less efficient (Black, 1966). Apparently a large fraction of the cells recognizable as transformed in monolayer culture still is not capable of forming progressively growing colonies in the agar medium. However, the method does have the advantage of allowing the inoculation of large numbers of cells to detect extremely rare transformants.

Recently a cell line has been developed from Balb/c mouse embryo cells that has properties that are very similar to 3T3 (Aaronson and Todaro, 1968a). This line (Balb/3T3) is also susceptible to SV40

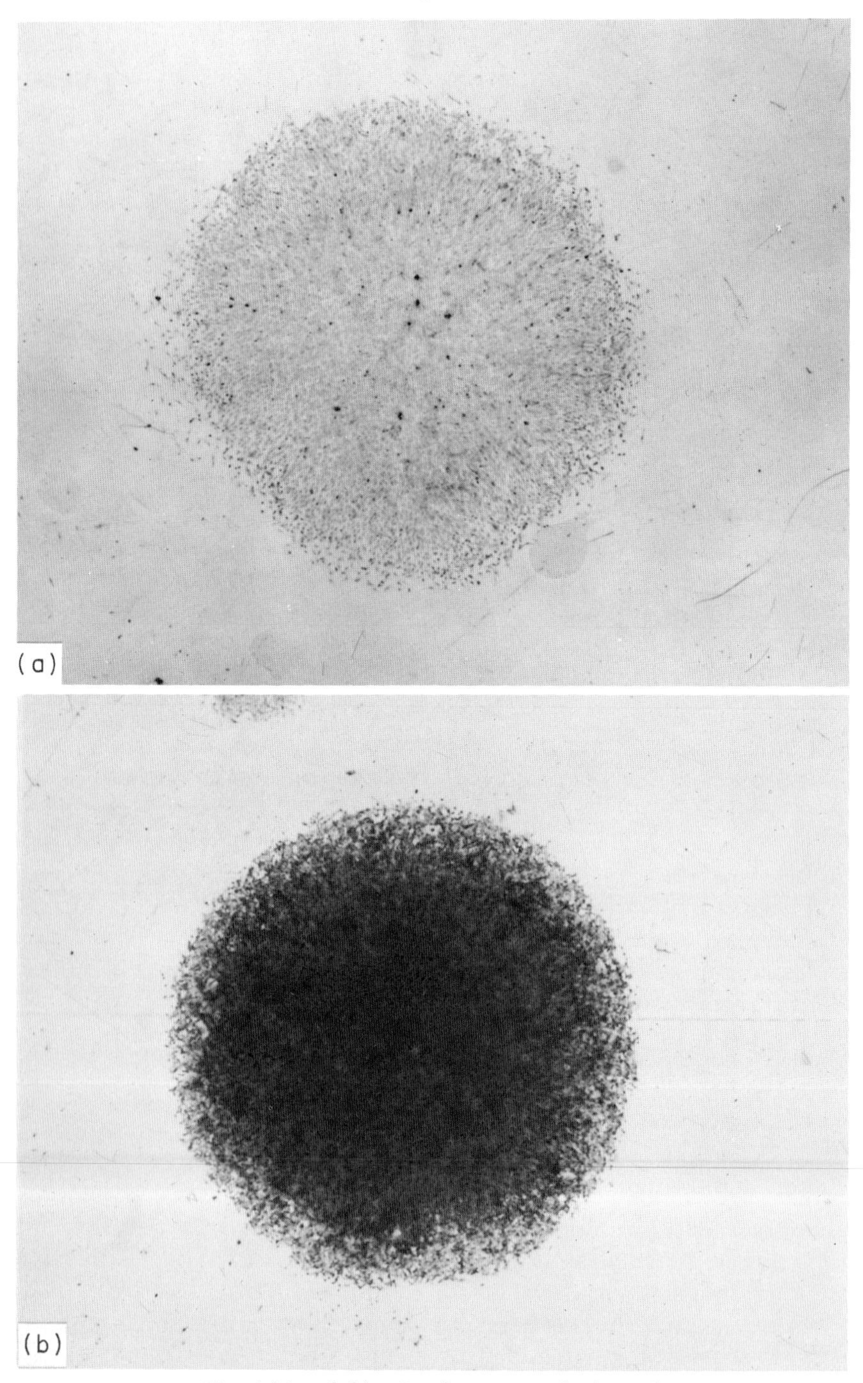

Fig. 1 (a) and (b). See facing page for legend.

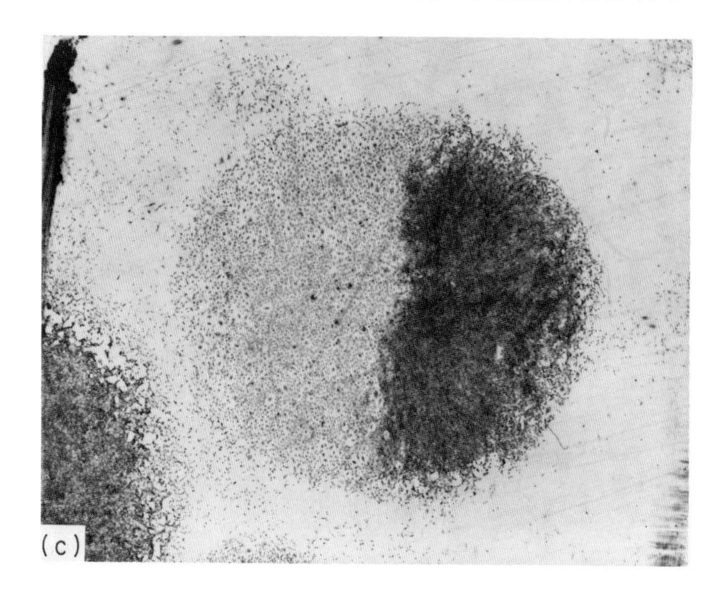

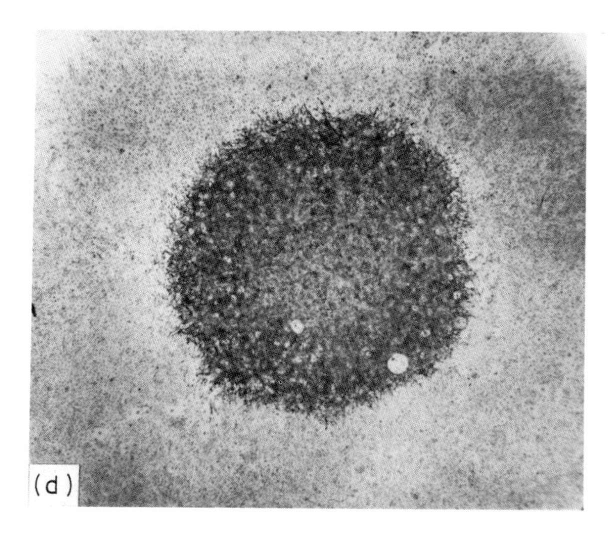

FIG. 1. Morphology of SV40 transformed 3T3 colonies: (a) Untransformed 3T3 colony (from Todaro and Green, 1965). (b) A typical SV40 transformed colony (from Todaro and Green, 1965). (c) "Mixed" colony, containing a normal and transformed half, presumably resulting from transformation of one of the two progeny of the originally infected cell. These colonies are scored as transformed in the assay (from Todaro and Green, 1966a). (d) A colony of transformed cells against a background of untransformed cells (from Todaro and Green, 1964a). All cells are fixed and stained 14-16 days after infection.

transformation and can be used in the transformation assay along with or instead of 3T3. Since it was derived from an inbred mouse strain the cells can be tested for tumorigenicity in newborn or irradiated weanling Balb/c mice. Balb/3T3 is not tumorigenic while the SV40 transformed Balb/3T3 cells produce tumors (Aaronson and Todaro, 1968b).

REFERENCES

Aaronson, S. A., and Todaro, G. J. (1968a). *J. Cell. Physiol.* **72**, 141.
Aaronson, S. A., and Todaro, G. J. (1968b). *Science* **162**, 1024.
Black, P. H. (1966). *Virology* **28**, 758.
Pollack, E. J., and Todaro, G. J. (1968). *Nature* **219**, 520.
Todaro, G. J., and Green, H. (1964a). *Virology* **23**, 117.
Todaro, G. J., and Green, H. (1964b). *Virology* **24**, 393.
Todaro, G. J., and Green, H. (1965). *Virology* **27**, 179.
Todaro, G. J., and Green, H. (1966a). *Virology* **28**, 756.
Todaro, G. J., and Green, H. (1966b). *Proc. Natl. Acad. Sci. U.S.* **55**, 302.
Todaro, G. J., Green, H., and Goldberg, B. D. (1964). *Proc. Natl. Acad. Sci. U.S.* **51**, 66.

V. Quantitative Procedures for Assay of RNA, DNA, and Protein

22. Colorimetric Reactions for DNA, RNA, and Protein Determinations

Aaron J. Shatkin[*]

Laboratory of Biology of Viruses
National Institute of Allergy and Infectious Diseases
National Institutes of Health
Bethesda, Maryland

I. Introduction

A large number of color reactions have been developed for the quantitative estimation of nucleic acids (Dische, 1955) and proteins (Bailey, 1962). Among the most widely used are the diphenylamine reaction for determining DNA, the orcinol test for RNA, and the Lowry method for proteins. With these three relatively simple procedures, microgram amounts of biological material can be accurately and reproducibly measured.

II. DNA

Dische (1930) first reported that a stable blue color developed when 50–500 μg of DNA in 1 ml was mixed with 2 ml of diphenylamine reagent (1 gm of diphenylamine, 100 ml of glacial acetic acid, and 2.75 ml of H_2SO_4) and heated at 100°C for 10 minutes. The procedure was subsequently modified by Burton (1956). He increased the sensitivity of the method several-fold by adding acetaldehyde to the reagent and changing the reaction time and temperature to 17 hours and 30°C. The

[*]Present address: Roche Institute of Molecular Biology, Nutley, New Jersey.

milder conditions also had the effect of reducing the number of interfering substances.

A. Materials

1. *Standard DNA Solutions*

A stock solution is prepared by dissolving purified DNA at a concentration of 0.5–1.0 mg/ml in 5 m*M* NaOH. Both calf thymus DNA (Worthington Corp.) and salmon sperm DNA (Calbiochem) have been used interchangeably in this laboratory. The solution is stable for at least 6 months at 5°C. At monthly intervals a series of standard solutions is made by mixing equal amounts of stock DNA solution and 1 *N* $HClO_4$, heating for 15 minutes at 70°C, and diluting with 0.5 *N* $HClO_4$ to obtain appropriate concentrations.

2. *Diphenylamine Reagent*

One and one-half grams of diphenylamine (Fisher Scientific Co.) which has been recrystallized from ligroin are dissolved in 100 ml of glacial acetic acid and 1.5 ml of concentrated H_2SO_4 are added. The reagent may be stored in the dark. An aqueous solution containing 16 mg of fresh or redistilled acetaldehyde per milliliter is prepared and stored at 5°C. Before use, 0.1 ml of aqueous acetaldehyde is added for each 20 ml of reagent.

B. Procedure

To 1 ml of a standard solution or an acid extract (0.5 *N* $HClO_4$) of biological material is added 2 ml reagent. The samples are covered with parafilm and incubated for about 20 hours at 25–30°C. The optical density is read against an incubated blank which contains 0.5 *N* $HClO_4$ but no DNA. Typical standard curves are shown in Fig. 1.

C. Notes

(1) The formation of the blue color depends upon an interaction between the diphenylamine and 2-deoxypentoses, more specifically in the case of DNA, 2-deoxyribose. Deoxyribose may also be used as a standard. However, only the purine nucleotides in DNA react with diphenylamine since the pyrimidine-sugar linkage is not hydrolyzed under the conditions of the test. Therefore the color intensity obtained with 2-deoxyribose as a standard will be twice that seen with DNA containing an equivalent amount of 2-deoxyribose. RNA does not interfere in the reaction.

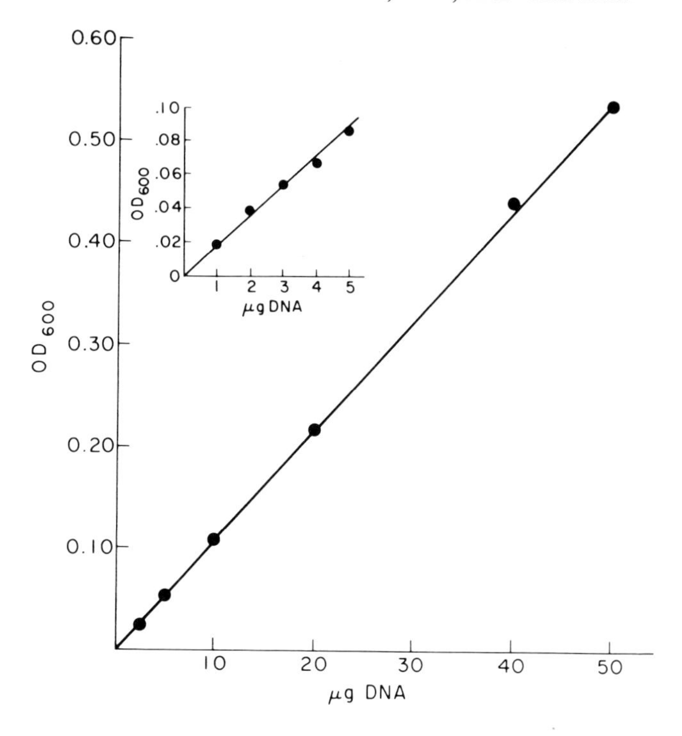

FIG. 1. Typical standard curves for DNA.

(2) Some preparations of acetic acid promote color development in the reagent and cause high blank values. The interfering material can be removed by distilling the acid.

(3) The final color intensity does not vary when the concentration of $HClO_4$ is between 0.25 and 0.65 *N*. Trichloroacetic acid at a concentration of 10% or less does not interfere with the reaction when 0.5 *N* $HClO_4$ is present.

(4) The temperature and duration of the reaction may be varied from 25 to 35°C and 16 to 21 hours provided all the samples are maintained under the same conditions.

III. RNA

When pentoses are heated with orcinol in the presence of HCl and $FeCl_3$ as catalyst an intense green color develops. The reaction of Bial has been modified for measuring RNA by many investigators but the procedure of Mejbaum (1939) is generally used.

A. MATERIALS

1. Standard RNA Solution

An aqueous solution of 0.5 mg/ml of yeast RNA (Miles Laboratories Inc.) is prepared and diluted as necessary.

2. Orcinol Reagent

In 100 ml of concentrated HCl dissolve 100 mg of $FeCl_3 \cdot 6H_2O$ and 100 mg of orcinol (Fisher Scientific Co.) which has been recrystallized from benzene.

B. PROCEDURE

Add 1 ml of freshly prepared reagent to 1 ml of standard RNA solution or unknown material. Place in boiling water bath for 45 minutes (Albaum and Umbreit, 1947), cool, and read the optical density at 670 mμ vs. a water blank. A standard curve is shown in Fig. 2.

C. NOTES

(1) In addition to pentoses, 2-deoxyribose and DNA as well as hexuronic acids and some aldoheptoses react to give a green color (Dische, 1955). The intensity obtained with 100 mg of DNA is equivalent to that with 25–30 mg of RNA. An accurate RNA estimate for a preparation containing both types of nucleic acid depends upon an adjustment for DNA content.

(2) Certain cellular polysaccharides, proteins, and lipids may promote the formation of a red or brown color which interferes with the RNA determination.

(3) As noted for the diphenylamine reaction, only the purine nucleotides in RNA react in the orcinol test. It follows that the purine content of the unknown sample and the RNA standard should be similar. Adenylic acid may also be employed as a standard. Yeast RNA gives only 40% of the green color obtained with a comparable weight of adenylic acid (Cori and Cori, 1945).

IV. Proteins

Although the Folin-Ciocalteu phenol reagent was used for the determination of proteins in the 1920's, it found general acceptance only after the publication of a detailed study by Lowry *et al.* (1951). The

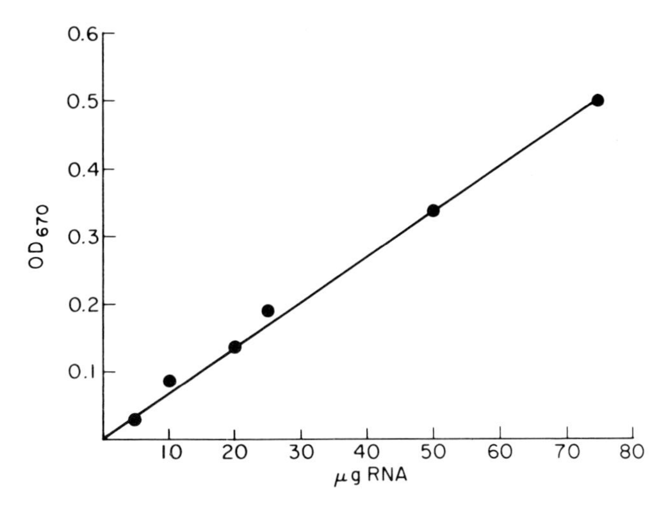

FIG. 2. Standard curve for RNA.

two-step Lowry procedure depends upon the formation in the presence of alkali of a protein-copper complex which reduces the phosphomolybdic-phosphotungstic reagent. The intensity of the resulting blue color is a measure of the protein content.

A. MATERIALS

1. Standard Protein Solution

Crystalline bovine serum albumin (Armour and Co.) is dissolved in H_2O at a concentration of 0.5 mg/ml and diluted as necessary.

2. Reagent solutions

Reagent solutions are as follows:

A. 2% Na_2CO_3 together with 0.02% NaK tartrate in 0.1 *N* NaOH.
B. 0.5% aqueous Cu $SO_4 \cdot 5H_2O$.
C. Prepared fresh by mixing 50 parts A and 1 part of B.
D. Same as C but alkali omitted from A.
E. Folin-Ciocalteu reagent (Fisher Scientific Co.): The reagent is titrated with NaOH and phenolphthalein as indicator and diluted with H_2O to make it 1 *N* in acid (about 1:1 v/v). When measurements are to be made during long intervals with different batches of reagent, greater reproducibility is achieved if a standard dilution is determined experimentally for each batch. A series of dilutions are reacted with a known quantity of protein, and the dilution which gives the

maximum stable color within the 30 minute reaction time is selected for subsequent analyses (Oyama and Eagle, 1956).

B. Procedure

To 0.2 ml of unknown or albumin solution containing 5–100 μg of protein add 1 ml of reagent C and mix. After 10 minutes at room temperature, rapidly add 0.1 ml of diluted phenol reagent and mix immediately. Read the optical density at 660 mμ 30–120 minutes later against a sample containing no protein. A standard curve for crystalline bovine serum albumin is shown in Fig. 3.

C. Notes

(1) In the original procedure the tartrate was present in the Cu SO_4 solution at a concentration of 1%. To avoid the precipitate which developed under these conditions, the procedure was modified to in-

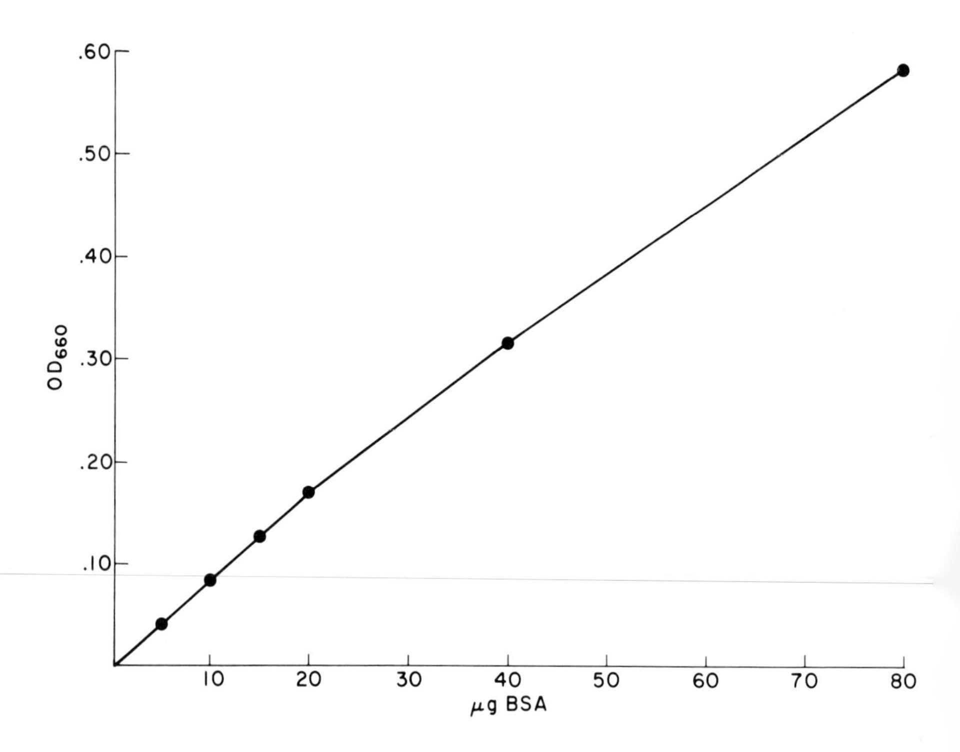

FIG. 3. Standard curve for crystalline bovine serum albumin.

clude the tartrate in the alkaline Na_2CO_3 solution (Oyama and Eagle, 1956). An alternative is to replace the tartrate in solution B with 1% sodium citrate which gives a more stable reagent (Eggstein and Kreutz, 1955).

(2) The absorption peak of the final color is 750 mμ. Lowry *et al.* (1951) recommended that reaction mixtures containing 5-25 μg protein/ml be read at $\lambda = 750$ mμ and those with greater protein levels at $\lambda = 500$ mμ. Optical density readings at the intermediate wavelength of 660 mμ are approximately 90% of those obtained at 750 mμ.

(3) Precipitation of proteins with $HClO_4$ or trichloroacetic acid makes them difficult to dissolve in 0.1 *N* NaOH (solution C). Acid-treated samples can be more easily solubilized in 1 *N* NaOH. An aliquot of alkali-solubilized protein (5-100 μg in 0.1 ml) can then be mixed with 1 ml of solution D and assayed with 0.1 ml of diluted Folin reagent in the usual manner.

(4) The relation between protein concentration and color intensity deviates slightly from linearity.

(5) The color intensity obtained with equivalent amounts of different pure proteins varies, but the variation is not a major drawback for protein mixtures.

REFERENCES

Albaum, H. G., and Umbreit, W. W. (1947). *J. Biol. Chem.* **167**, 369.

Bailey, J. L. (1962). "Techniques in Protein Chemistry," pp. 293-304. Elsevier, Amsterdam.

Burton, K. (1956). *Biochem. J.* **62**, 315.

Cori, G. T., and Cori, C. F. (1945). *J. Biol. Chem.* **158**, 321.

Dische, Z. (1930). *Mikrochemie* **8**, 4.

Dische, Z. (1955). *In* "The Nucleic Acids" (E. Chargaff and J. N. Davidson, eds.), Vol. 1, pp. 285-305. Academic Press, New York.

Eggstein, M., and Kreutz, F. H. (1955). *Klin. Wochschr.* **33**, 879.

Lowry, O. H., Rosebrough, N. J., Farr, A. L., and Randall, R. J. (1951). *J. Biol. Chem.* **193**, 265.

Mejbaum, W. Z. (1939). *Z. Physiol. Chem.* **258**, 117.

Oyama, V. I., and Eagle, H. (1956). *Proc. Soc. Exptl. Biol. Med.* **91**, 305.

23. Estimation of RNA, DNA, and Protein by the Use of Isotopic Precursors Followed by Chemical Fractionation

Aaron J. Shatkin[*]

Laboratory of Biology of Viruses
National Institute of Allergy and Infectious Diseases
National Institutes of Health
Bethesda, Maryland

I. Introduction

The colorimetric procedures described in the previous section are useful for measuring microgram quantities of nucleic acids and proteins. In addition, it is often necessary to analyze smaller amounts of material, as, for example, in studies of the rates of synthesis in cells during short intervals in their growth cycle or after virus infection. Radiolabeled precursors of biological macromolecules are indispensable for such studies. In some cases the isotopic precursor is incorporated specifically, i.e., thymidine into DNA. However, most precursors appear in more than one product, and chemical methods are used to separate them before radioassay.

II. Procedure

A convenient technique for the successive analysis of RNA, DNA, and protein is as follows. At the end of an incubation in the presence of one or more labeled precursors, incorporation is terminated by

[*]Present address: Roche Institute of Molecular Biology, Nutley, New Jersey.

chilling rapidly to 0–4°C. For suspended tissue culture cells this is best accomplished by pouring the culture onto frozen, crushed media. The cells are centrifuged and washed by resuspending them in the same volume of cold isotonic buffer (phosphate-buffered saline; Dulbecco and Vogt, 1954) or a medium such as Eagle's medium (Eagle, 1959) lacking glutamine and serum. The washed cells are suspended in about 20 times their volume of 5% perchloric acid (PCA) and allowed to stand for 30 minutes in an ice bath to extract the acid-soluble materials. The extracted cells are sedimented by centrifugation at 2000 rpm for 10 minutes (International PR-2 centrifuge). The supernatant fluid is discarded, and the cell pellet is washed with a similar volume of acid. Although not essential, the sample is usually defatted to yield a dry residue by treatment with cold ethanol followed by ethanol-ether (3:1, v/v) and ether (Schmidt and Thannhauser, 1945; Schneider, 1945).

The RNA in the residue is hydrolyzed to ribonucleotides by incubation for 16–20 hours at 37°C in 0.3 *N* KOH. A longer incubation (48 hours) at room temperature in 1 *N* alkali will also suffice. The digest is chilled, and the pH is adjusted to 5–6 by the addition of 2.5 *N* PCA. After 30 minutes at 0–4°C, the precipitated cellular DNA and protein and the insoluble $KClO_4$ are removed by centrifugation. The pellet is washed with a small volume of dilute acid. The wash fluid is combined with the soluble fraction and assayed for radioactivity and RNA digestion products (Mejbaum, 1939). Since alkaline digestion quantitatively liberates inorganic phosphorus from phosphoproteins, radioactivity from ^{32}P-labeled proteins will also be present in the soluble phase at this stage (Schmidt and Thannhauser, 1945; Davidson and Smellie, 1952).

For the hydrolysis of DNA to its constituent bases, the pellet is next resuspended in a small volume of 5% PCA and heated for 15 minutes at 70°C. The sample is chilled, and the precipitated protein and $KClO_4$ are sedimented and washed with 5% PCA. The combined soluble materials are analyzed for radioactivity and deoxyribose (Burton, 1956). The pellet is solubilized in a small volume of 1 *N* NaOH and diluted for measuring radioactive and total protein (Lowry *et al.*, 1951).

III. Discussion

The choice of precursor as well as the concentration, specific activity, and incubation conditions employed will be dictated by the purpose of the experiment and the system under study. To prepare RNA or DNA for base composition analysis, all nucleotides must be labeled to the same high specific radioactivity and phosphate-^{32}P is required. In most instances ^{3}H or ^{14}C-labeled uridine, thymidine, and one or more amino acids are the preferred precursors of RNA, DNA, and protein, respectively, since they are more specific and convenient to use. The level and activity of exogenous isotope should be adjusted to insure that (a) it is nonlimiting throughout the exposure period, (b) a sufficient number of counts are incorporated, and (c) irradiation effects do not damage the cells, especially with high specific activity tritiated thymidine (Hell *et al.*, 1960). A concentration of 4.4×10^{-5} μg of uridine per cell is adequate to support a maximum rate of uptake into RNA for 24 hours when the initial population density of growing mouse L cells is 3.4×10^{5}/ml (Rake and Graham, 1964).

Care should also be taken that the specific activity of the exogenous precursor is not progressively decreased owing to the release into the medium of degraded cellular components, especially during long exposure intervals or in virus-infected cells (Newton *et al.*, 1962). Another source of precursor dilution is the intracellular content or "pool" of nonradioactive precursor. An increase in the pool size will result in a lower rate of incorporation of radioactivity which is not necessarily indicative of a decreased rate of formation of the macromolecule under study. In some instances an inhibitor can be added to the cell culture to block endogenous synthesis of the precursor causing an increase in uptake of the radioactive compound from the medium. For example, thymidine-^{14}C is incorporated into DNA in HeLa S3 cells at a higher rate in the presence of 5-fluorodeoxyuridine than in its absence.

When labeled uridine is employed as an RNA precursor, radioactivity will also appear in DNA since it is converted to dCMP and dUMP. In HeLa cells uridine is incorporated into RNA at a tenfold greater rate than into DNA. Uridine-5-^{3}H can be employed to avoid the labeling of thymidine in DNA since the conversion from dUMP to dTMP by reductive methylation at the 5 position eliminates the tritium.

The procedure outlined above can be modified in several ways. It is not necessary to separate DNA and RNA when thymidine incorporation is measured since the precursor is specific and RNA does not contribute to the Burton colorimetric test for DNA. In this case the nucleic acids in the dried residue are hydrolyzed to bases directly by treatment with hot acid. Similarly, incorporation of amino acids into proteins can be assayed in samples treated with cold acid and solubilized in alkali. If the incubation period with radioactive amino acids is very brief (ca. 1 minute), the amino acids and short peptides which are bound to tRNA and consequently are precipitated in cold acid will comprise a significant proportion of the total counts. As a result, the synthetic rates will be falsely high. To prevent this, the acid-treated samples are hydrolyzed with 1 *N* NaOH for 15 minutes at room temperature, reprecipitated with acid, and solubilized in alkali for assay.

The PCA may be replaced with 5% trichloroacetic acid (TCA) and the digestion performed at 90°C for 15 minutes (Schneider, 1945). Trichloroacetic acid decomposes at higher temperatures, and the hydrolysis should be controlled. In contrast to the precipitation of PCA as the potassium salt, TCA is removed from the hydrolysate by extracting several times with two volumes of ether. To avoid a decrease in hydrolysate volume, the ether should be saturated with H_2O. If the digest is to be assayed by absorbancy measurements, PCA is preferred. The ultraviolet absorption spectrum of TCA rises sharply between 260 and 230 mμ; PCA absorbs only slightly in the same range (Ogur and Rosen, 1950). Trichloroacetic acid (but not PCA) also precipitates Nonidet P-40, a detergent used to prepare mammalian cell polyribosomes (Borun *et al.*, 1967). In order to dry samples on planchets for gas flow counting, it is essential to extract the hygroscopic TCA. If unhydrolyzed, acid-precipitated samples are assayed by collecting them on nitrocellulose filters, TCA should be used when possible. Perchloric acid washed filters are sometimes degraded when dried by heating before counting. They can be rinsed with 95% ethanol to reduce the amount of PCA on the filters and to facilitate drying.

REFERENCES

Borun, T. W., Scharff, M. D., and Robbins, E. (1967). *Biochim. Biophys. Acta* **149**, 302.

Burton, K. (1956). *Biochem. J.* **62**, 315.

Davidson, J. N., and Smellie, R. M. S. (1952). *Biochem. J.* **52**, 599.

Dulbecco, R., and Vogt, M. (1954). *J. Exptl. Med.* **99**, 167.

Eagle, H. (1959). *Science* **130**, 432.

Hell, E., Berry, R. J., and Lajtha, L. G. (1960). *Nature* **185**, 47.

Lowry, O. H., Rosebrough, N. J., Farr, A. L., and Randall, R. J. (1951). *J. Biol. Chem.* **193**, 265.

Mejbaum, W. (1939). *Z. Physiol. Chem.* **258**, 117.

Newton, A., Dendy, P. P., Smith, C. L., and Wildy, P. (1962). *Nature* **194**, 886.

Ogur, M., and Rosen, G. (1950). *Arch. Biochem.* **25**, 262.

Rake, A. V., and Graham, A. F. (1964). *Biophys. J.* **4**, 267.

Schmidt, G., and Thannhauser, S. J. (1945). *J. Biol. Chem.* **161**, 83.

Schneider, W. C. (1945). *J. Biol. Chem.* **161**, 293.

24. Autoradiography of Cultured Cells*

Robert P. Perry

The Institute for Cancer Research
Philadelphia, Pennsylvania

I. Introduction

Autoradiography is a valuable and comparatively economical technique for studies of cellular phenomena in which it is necessary to determine—either qualitatively or quantitatively—the incorporation of a radioactively labeled metabolite. In some instances it may be the only practical method for assaying radioactivity, for example, when the available quantities of biological material are too small for chemical analysis, or when incorporation must be correlated with microscopically observable events. In others it may be an important adjunct, for example, as a check on the uniformity of incorporation from cell to cell in a population, or for an accurate determination of the cellular sites where the metabolite is incorporated.

II. Methods

The techniques described here are those used in my laboratory for the study of RNA and protein synthesis in cell cultures. They were adapted for cultured cells from the liquid emulsion method described by Adrienne Ficq of the Université Libre de Bruxelles (Ficq, 1959).

*This work supported by the National Science Foundation (GB 4137), the National Institutes of Health (CA 06927 and FR 05539), and an appropriation from the Commonwealth of Pennsylvania.

Details for the preparation of autoradiographs from both monolayer and suspension cultures will be given. For other information concerning alternative methods, quantitative aspects, and modification for electron microscope autoradiography the reader should consult Baserga (1967), Perry (1964), and Caro (1964), respectively.

A. Preparation of Slides from Monolayer Cultures

Cells are grown on cover slips in stoppered Leighton tubes (Bellco Glass Co., Vineland, New Jersey, Cat. No. 1951) or in petri dishes in a CO_2 incubator. After an appropriate incubation period in the presence of radioactive metabolite, the cover slips are rinsed by brief immersion in buffered balanced salt solution and fixed for 15 minutes in ice-cold acetic acid-ethanol (1:3). This fixative is suitable for preserving nucleic acids and acid insoluble proteins. Fixation and subsequent processing of cover slips may be conveniently performed in Columbia staining dishes (A. H. Thomas, Philadelphia, Cat. No. 9201). After fixation, cover slips are immersed for about 10 minutes in cold 70% ethanol and then either air dried for later processing or submitted to one of the treatments described below. If desired, a cover slip may be divided into several parts for different treatments by gently bending at scribe lines made with a diamond pencil.

At this point the type of treatment employed will depend on the information desired and the kind of molecule which has been labeled. The following have been used in my laboratory:

(a) Twenty minutes in ice-cold solution of 1% perchloric acid followed by a 30–60 minute rinse in running tap water. Routinely used in RNA and protein-labeling studies to insure complete removal of acid soluble precursors and intermediates.

(b) One hour incubation at 37°C with 0.25 mg/ml of electrophoretically pure deoxyribonuclease (Worthington Biochemical Corp., Freehold, New Jersey, code DPFF) in 0.01 *M* phosphate buffer, pH 7.1, containing 3 m*M* $MgSO_4$.

(c) One hour incubation at 37°C with 0.5 mg/ml of ribonuclease in 0.01 *M* phosphate buffer, pH 7.1.

Both of the above enzyme treatments are followed by a 20 minute wash in cold 1% perchloric acid and a 30–60 minute rinse in running tap water.

After the cover slips are dry, they are cemented, cell side up, in appropriate groupings onto 1 by 3 inch glass microscope slides. An excellent cement for this purpose can be made from Gelva V7 resin (Shawinigan Resins Corp., Springfield, Massachusetts) which is dissolved to an appropriate consistency in acetone. Care should be taken to avoid getting cement on the cells. It is advisable to leave about 1 inch at one end of the slide free of cover slips. This end can be used for labeling the slide and as a handle for dipping in the liquid emulsion. After the acetone has evaporated the slides are rinsed briefly in distilled water and air dried. They are now ready for coating with emulsion.

B. Preparation of Slides from Suspension Cultures

Upon completion of a radioactive labeling experiment a volume of medium containing 4-6 million cells is chilled and centrifuged for 3 minutes at 300 g. The cell pellet is washed with 5 ml of a chilled mixture of 50% calf serum-50% growth medium, and recentrifuged for 5 minutes at 600 g in a conical centrifuge tube of reasonably sharp taper (for example, Corning No. 8100, 15 ml tubes). After the wash medium is carefully aspirated off, the cells are fixed by covering the pellet with about 5 ml of ice-cold acetic acid-ethanol (1:3). The cell pellet is not disturbed during the 15-30 minute fixation period. The serum in the wash helps the pellet to form a cohesive mass, usually about 3 mm^3, which does not easily disintegrate upon subsequent handling.

The fixative is aspirated off and the pellet is infused with 5 ml of cold 70% ethanol for at least 15 minutes. (Pellets may be conveniently stored in this form at 5°C for later handling.) The pellet in 70% ethanol is then dislodged from the bottom of the centrifuge tube with the aid of a fine spatula and/or momentary pulsing on a vortex mixer. Slight disintegration of the pellet is tolerable as long as the fragments are sufficiently large for embedding and sectioning.

The pellet is then dehydrated in absolute alcohol, cleared in toluene, and embedded in Paraplast using standard histological procedures. If some difficulty is encountered in handling the pellets, they can be conveniently carried from one solution to the next in small cuvettes with sieve bottoms. Such a cuvette can be made with a piece of lens paper covering one end of a 1 inch length of 1 cm glass tubing and held in place by a concentric glass ring.

Paraffin blocks are trimmed and sectioned at 2 μ. The sections are mounted on "subbed" glass slides (cf. Appendix), deparaffinized in toluene, and passed through an alcohol series to distilled water. If desired, either of the enzyme treatments described earlier may be performed at this time. The slides are then treated with ice-cold 1% perchloric acid for 20 minutes, rinsed for about 30 minutes in running tap water, dipped in distilled water, and dried. They are now ready for coating with emulsion.

Although the sectioning procedure just described is more lengthy than a simple squash preparation, it has the distinct advantage of yielding material with a well-defined geometry. Under these conditions all parts of the cell have an equal probability of being contiguous with the photographic emulsion, and thus when a sufficient number of cells are averaged, the serious errors connected with the tissue self-absorption of weak (e.g., ^{3}H) β particles are minimized. This becomes extremely important when trying to make quantitative comparisons between autoradiographic and biochemical extraction data on the same cell population (Perry *et al.*, 1964).

C. Coating with Emulsion, Exposure, Developing and Staining

All handling of the emulsion is done in a dark room under *indirect* illumination by a dim ruby red safelight. The L4 emulsion is delivered in the form of small noodles (cf. Appendix). A 25–30 ml portion is transferred to a beaker, melted in a 50°C water bath for about 30 minutes, and filtered through two layers of cheesecloth into a "dipper." The filtration effectively removes trapped air bubbles. The dipper, a cylindrical vessel with oval cross section, is made by flattening a 50 ml nitrocellulose centrifuge tube which has been made maleable by soaking in boiling water. The dipper, containing emulsion, is kept in a 50°C water bath during use. Afterward it is stored at 5°C in a tightly capped jar in a light-tight can. for subsequent use the emulsion may be remelted in the dipper without necessity of refiltration. This can usually be done three or four times without any appreciable increase in background.

The slides are warmed on a temperature-controlled plate set at 50°C, and dipped in pairs, back-to-back, with the cells facing outward. Upon withdrawal from the emulsion the two slides are pulled apart with a minimum of sliding motion—sliding can generate static electricity which produces grain streaks in the autoradiograph—and shaken vigorously with a wrist-snapping action. The shaking can be omitted when a thick film is desired, for example, when one is interested in viewing tracks produced by ^{14}C disintegrations.

The slides are then placed on a tray, horizontally, cell side up, and stored in a light-tight box containing drying agent. The horizontal position is preferred over the vertical for drying because it results in a film of more uniform thickness. To avoid having the slides stick to the trays after the emulsion is dried we place them across pairs of parallel glass rods mounted about 2 inches apart on the tray. After drying (8 hours or more) the slides are easily picked up from the trays and placed in light-tight, microscope boxes containing drying agent. During the exposure period the autoradiographs are stored in a refrigerator as a precaution against thermal "fogging."

Exposure times vary from 1 day to 6 months depending on the amount of radioactive isotope incorporated per unit area. For exposures longer than 3 weeks we transfer the slide boxes to a vacuum desiccator which is then evacuated and filled with nitrogen. Nitrogen atmospheres tend to reduce the latent image fading that is encountered with long exposures.

Upon completion of the exposure period the autoradiographs are developed in complete darkness for 20 minutes at 16°C in amidol developer (cf. Appendix), immersed in water for a few moments, and fixed for 40 minutes at 16°C in a one-third saturated solution of sodium thiosulfate. Two hundred and fifty milliliter staining dishes (A. H. Thomas, Cat. #9190) make convenient receptacles for the developer and fixer. After thorough washing under cold running tap water (45-60 minutes) the slides are soaked overnight in 70% ethanol which hardens the film and improves its permeability to stain. The slides are placed vertically in a rack to dry and are then stained for 20 minutes in Unna's methyl green pyronine (cf. Appendix). This stain colors the nucleoli and cytoplasm bright pink and the nucleoplasm pale blue. The slides are rinsed *briefly* with distilled water and dried thoroughly. They are now ready for observation. No cover slip on top of the film is needed. Oil immersion can be performed directly on the film.

D. Examples

Figure 1 illustrates some examples of autoradiographs made by the techniques described above. The autoradiographic film thickness for the ^{3}H experiments (Fig. 1A-C) is about 1-2 μ; for the ^{14}C experiment (Fig. 1D-G) it is about 6-8 μ. The ease with which one can ascertain

---

FIG. 1. Autoradiographs of cultured cells. (A) and (B) show cells of *monolayer cultures* of the WISH line which were incubated with cytidine-^{3}H: (A) 30 minute pulse; (B) 30 minute pulse followed by 5.5 hour chase. Note that the activity is confined to the nucleoli and the nucleoplasm in (A) but is also in the cytoplasm in (B). (C) A 2 μ section cut through a pellet from a *suspension culture* of L cells which was incubated for 15 minutes with guanine-^{3}H and chased with excess guanine for 30 minutes. Note the intense activity associated with the nucleoli. (D)-(G) A series of photographs taken at focal planes 0, 2, 4, and 6 μ, respectively, above a HeLa cell that was labeled with 8-azaguanine-2^{14}C for 2.5 hours. Magnification: (A), (B) 800×; (C) 1280×; and (D)-(G) 640×.

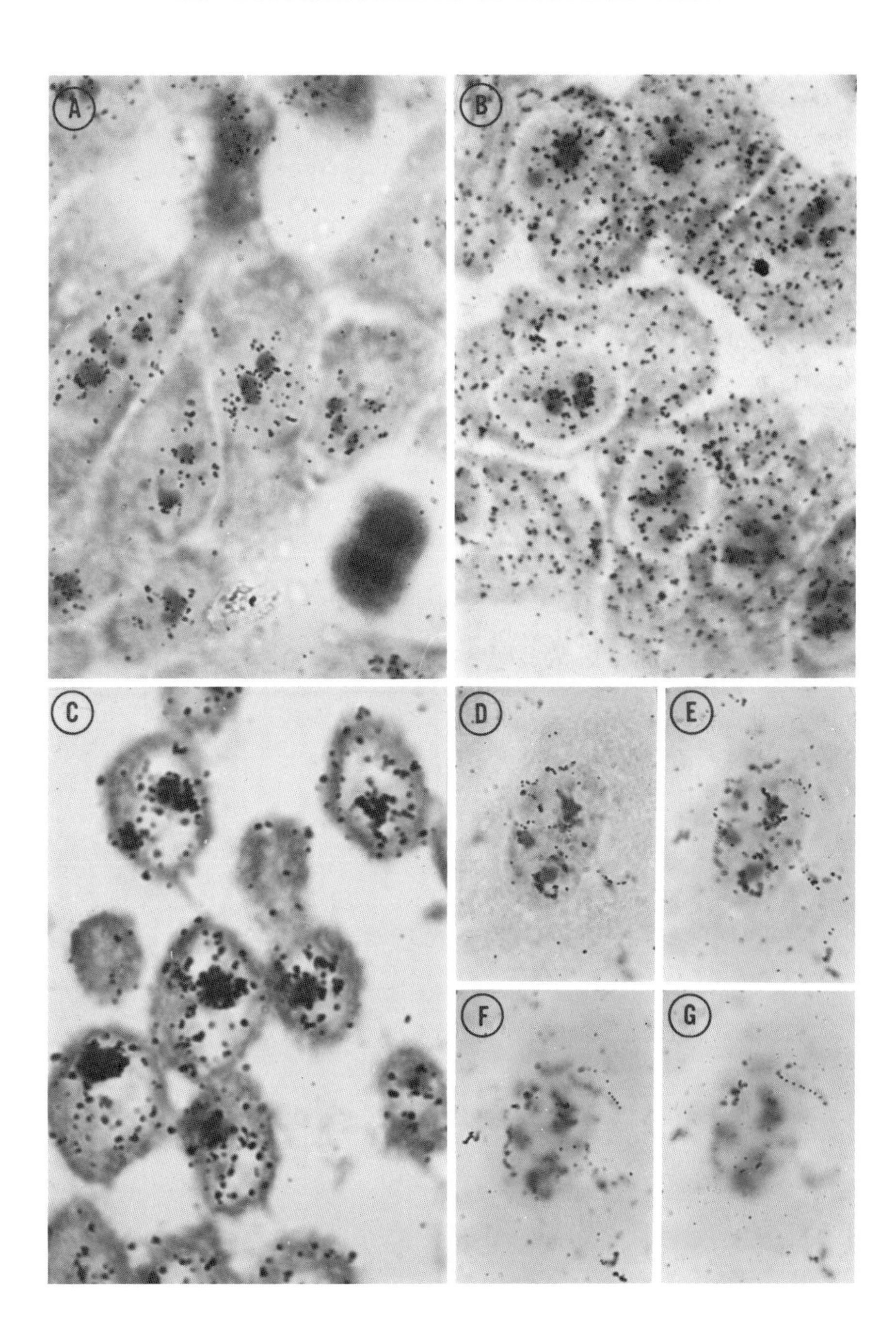
A
B
C
D
E
F
G

the location of incorporation is demonstrated in Fig. 1A and 1B which show the sites of newly synthesized RNA in a monolayer culture of WISH cells at different times after incubation with cytidine-^{3}H. Figure 1C shows a section through a pellet of L cells which were grown in suspension, labeled for 15 minutes in guanine-^{3}H, and chased for 30 minutes with excess unlabeled guanine. Zonal ultracentrifuge analysis of the RNA extracted from the same population of cells which was used for the autoradiograph showed that most of the intense nucleolar activity seen in this figure represents the 32 S RNA intermediate in ribosomal RNA synthesis.

The tracks produced by the incorporation of 8-azaguanine-2^{14}C into the nucleoli and nucleoplasm of a HeLa cell are illustrated in the series Fig. 1D–G which shows focal planes 0, 2, 4, and 6 μ above the plane of the cell. The origin of a track can sometimes be distinguished from the terminus on the basis of a slightly larger spacing of the grains nearest the origin.

Appendix

A. Developer

Amidol (2,4-diaminophenol dihydrochloride from Matheson, Coleman, and Bell)	0.9 gm
Na_2SO_3 (anhydrous)	3.6 gm
KBr (10% solution)	1.6 ml
Distilled water	200 ml

Prepared fresh before use. First dissolve sodium sulfite, then add KBr, then dissolve Amidol, and filter through Whatman No. 1 paper.

B. Preparation of "Subbed" Slides

Clean microscope slides are immersed in a solution containing 5 gm/liter of gelatin and 0.5 gm/liter of Chrom-Alum ($CrK(SO_4)_2 \cdot 12H_2O$), then placed vertically in a rack to drain and dry.

C. Shipment of Liquid Emulsion

In my laboratory we routinely use the liquid emulsion L4 supplied by Ilford, Ltd., Essex, England. This emulsion has the desirable characteristics of small grain size and relatively good sensitivity. For use in the United States it is advisable to request that the emulsion be packed in ice and shipped via Air Express. Shipped in this manner the emulsion has adequately low background characteristics which are usually retained after storage in the refrigerator for up to 6 months. The L4 emulsion should arrive in the form of small noodles unless it has been inadvertantly heated or mishandled during shipment. Kodak NTB_3, an emulsion of similar type, but which is supplied in a bulk phase rather than as noodles, is also used by several investigators.

D. Stain (Unna)

Methyl green (Anachemia, Ltd., Montreal, Canada)	0.30	gm
Pyronine (A. G. Fluka, Buchs, SG, Switzerland)	0.50	gm
0.05 *M* acetate buffer, pH 4.7	200	ml
95% ethyl alcohol	5	ml
Chloroform		

Dissolve methyl green in buffer and shake with an equal volume of chloroform in a separatory funnel. Decant and repeat with fresh chloroform until chloroform is colorless. After final decantation, dissolve the pyronine in the methyl green solution and add the ethyl alcohol. Filter through Whatman No. 1 paper and allow to stand about 24 hours to evaporate residual chloroform. Stain is stable for at least 2 months when stored at room temperature in dim illumination.

ACKNOWLEDGMENTS

The author would like to thank Misses H. Dürwald and D. E. Kelley for their part in developing some of the procedures described in this chapter.

REFERENCES

Baserga, R. (1967). *In* "Methods in Cancer Research" (H. Busch, ed.), Vol. 1, pp. 45-116. Academic Press, New York.

Caro, L. (1964). *Methods Cell Physiol.* **1**, 327-363.

Ficq, A. (1959). *In* "The Cell" (J. Brachet and A. E. Mirskey, eds.), Vol. 1, pp. 67-90. Academic Press, New York.

Perry, R. P. (1964). *Methods Cell Physiol.* **1**, 305-326.

Perry, R. P., Srinivasan, P. R., and Kelley, D. E. (1946). *Science* **145**, 504.

VI. Protein Analysis

25. The Production of Antiserum Against Viral Antigens*

M. S. Horwitz and M. D. Scharff

Departments of Cell Biology and Medicine
Albert Einstein College of Medicine
Bronx, New York

I. Introduction

Antisera from naturally infected subjects have played an important role in the classification of viruses and in the diagnosis and epidemiology of viral diseases. As interest has increased in the biochemical aspects of viral replication, immunological techniques have also been used to investigate (1) the presence of virus-related proteins in transformed cells (Ginsberg *et al.*, 1969), (2) the rate of synthesis of individual viral proteins (Scharff and Levintow, 1963), (3) the relationship of soluble proteins of the infected cell to the structural proteins of the virion (Wilcox *et al.*, 1963; Valentine and Pereira, 1965), and (4) differences in the tertiary structure of the virion and its substructures (Anderer, 1963).

While potent and specific antisera have been successfully prepared by a variety of techniques (Schmidt and Lennette, 1967), the aim of this chapter will be to present an approach which is based on well-known immunological principles and has been successfully applied to a number of virus systems.

*This work supported by grants from the NIH (AI-4153 and AI-5231), American Cancer Society (E-379B), and National Science Foundation (GB 4751 and GB 6364Y). Dr. Horwitz is an ACS postdoctoral fellow (PF-416) and Dr. Scharff is the recipient of an NIH Career Development Award.

II. Preparation of Antigen

Methods for the purification of a variety of viruses are described elsewhere in this volume and by Schmidt and Lennette (1967). Immunization with virions which have been purified by chromatography and then by buoyant density centrifugation usually results in virus specific antisera uncontaminated with antibody against host cell protein. This is not only because of the efficacy of the purification procedure but also the fact that the immunogenicity of intact virus particles is much greater than that of most host cell or soluble viral proteins.

Soluble viral proteins can be prepared from cell lysates and purified from host cell proteins and other viral antigens by standard methods of protein purification as described elsewhere in this volume. Since soluble viral proteins are not as immunogenic as whole virus and are more likely to be contaminated with significant amounts of cell protein, it is useful to propagate the virus in cells derived from different species than those to be used in the actual experiment. Since exceedingly small amounts of a highly immunogenic impurity can induce large amounts of undesired antibody, the specificity of all antisera must be thoroughly validated (cf. Horwitz and Scharff, Chapter 29, this volume).

III. Choice of Animal

Antisera against viral proteins are usually produced in rabbits since (1) they are large enough to produce adequate amounts of serum and yet easy to handle, (2) they have readily available ear veins for bleeding and injection, (3) there is a great deal of information about the optimum conditions for immunization of this species, and (4) they produce high titers of antibody which is primarily precipitating in type and can be assayed by standard precipitin techniques.

If liter amounts of antisera must be obtained, sheep or goats appear to provide the most useful alternative. Mice, rats, and guinea pigs can be immunized but the result is often a small amount of low titer serum containing significant amounts of nonprecipitating antibody. In mice the use of ascitic fluid as a source of antibody is an easy and useful technique (Munoz, 1957). The choice of animal may be limited by the susceptibility of a particular species to rapidly lethal infection.

IV. Immunization – General Considerations of Route and Use of Adjuvant

A. Whole Virus Particles

If antibodies against the surface structural proteins of the virion are desired, immunization is best started by the intravenous injection of freshly prepared intact virions. Because of their excellent immunogenicity, microgram amounts of virions injected intravenously will rapidly elicit amounts of precipitating antibody specific for the quantitatively major antigens. Serum obtained 2–7 days after such immunization often contains antibody against surface antigens and may be specific for the fully assembled virions (Scharff, 1962). Since the virion is presumably degraded in the animal, later bleedings often contain antibody against additional antigenic determinants. This is especially evident when immunizing with poliovirus which changes its antigenicity from D (or N) to C (or H) even upon standing at 37°C (LeBouvier, 1955; Hummeler and Hamparian, 1958). Antibody against D antigen, which is the neutralizing antibody in this system, predominates in the first 2–3 days after immunization while subsequent bleedings contain more nonneutralizing antibody directed against the C antigenic determinant (Hummeler and Tumilowicz, 1960). The use of these early bleedings is complicated by the fact that initially large amounts of 19 S antibody are produced (Svehag and Mandel, 1964) and this antibody has different biological properties (Robbins *et al.*, 1965) than the 7 S antibody which predominates within a few days after immunization.

B. Degraded Virus Particles

If antiserum against more of the structural proteins is desired, the virions should be dissociated under mild conditions (such as heating at 56°C in the case of poliovirus (LeBouvier, 1955), dialysis against high pH buffer in the case of adenovirus type 5 (Wilcox and Ginsberg, 1963), or treatment with detergents for lipid containing viruses (Brown *et al.*, 1967). It is sometimes possible, as has been done with adenovirus, to select a treatment which degrades the virus into subviral components such as aggregates of subunits or cores (Smith *et al.*, 1965; Laver *et al.*, 1967; Maizel *et al.*, 1968). When attempting to elicit antisera which will react with individual polypeptide chains or the nascent chains on ribosomes, immunization should be carried out with material which has been derived from extensively dissociated virions (Scharff *et al.*, 1963, 1964; Kleczkowski, 1961). This can usually be done by treating the virions with 0.15 *M* 2-mercaptoethanol (ME), and either 8–10 *M* urea, 6 *M* guanidine, or 2% sodium dodecyl sulfate (SDS). The exact dissociating conditions must be worked out for each situation and each virus. Poliovirus, for example, is resistant to SDS at neutral pH values (Mandel, 1962). Since even partially degraded virus is not as immunogenic as the whole particle, dissociated proteins are best injected in the footpads of rabbits in complete Freund's adjuvant (see Section V).

C. Soluble Viral Proteins

Because soluble viral proteins can be easily separated from each other, they have often been used to make antiserum specific for individual viral antigens (Klemperer and Pereira, 1959). After purification, these proteins may be injected intravenously but multiple large doses are necessary if this route is to be used without the aid of adjuvants.

If milligram amounts of protein of questionable purity are to be used, they may be alum precipitated (see Section V) and then injected intravenously or in the footpad. The use of alum will significantly increase the immunogenicity but is less likely than Freund's adjuvant to result in antibodies against quantitatively minor proteins. Since it appears that polyacrylamide gels have an adjuvant action (Weintraub and Raymond, 1963), proteins which have been purified by this method may be injected without removing the polyacrylamide. In many cases, however, appropriate levels of antibody will not be obtained with either alum or polyacrylamide alone. Immunization with antigen emulsified in complete Freund's adjuvant is then necessary, even though this is more likely to result in antibody against small amounts of impurities.

Some of the important aspects of immunization with Freund's adjuvant have been delineated in studies in which rabbits have been immunized with serum proteins. Farr and Dixon (1960) have presented evidence that the concentration of bovine serum albumin (BSA) in the adjuvant–antigen mixture is more important than the total amount of antigen injected. For example, the injection of 0.125 μg of BSA in 0.1 ml or 1.25 μg in 1.0 ml results in a similar response, suggesting that the concentration of an antigen is more important than the absolute amount injected.

One study with multiple injections of bovine serum albumin has shown that the subcutaneous, intraperitoneal and intramuscular routes were not as effective as the footpad injection of antigen-adjuvant emulsion (Leskowitz and Waksman, 1960). The injection of 0.1 ml of emulsified antigen into the muscle of the thigh and shoulder produced a maximum response within 8–10 weeks. Injection of a similar amount of antigen into the footpads resulted in a more rapid but quantitatively smaller response. Reimmunization of intramuscularly or subcutaneously primed animals did not significantly increase the level of antibody. However, reinjection of animals immunized in the footpads did result in an increase of antibody to levels significantly higher than those obtained by any other route.

V. Immunization – Detailed Methods

A. Preparation of Adjuvants

1. Alum

Methods for absorbing proteins to alum have recently been reviewed by Chase (1967). We have found it convenient to use the method of Holt (1950): 0.5 ml of 0.2 *M* $AlCl_3$ and 0.5 ml of 0.2 *M* Na_3PO_4 are mixed, adjusted to pH 5 with HCl, and the concentration of aluminum phosphate adjusted to 10 mg/ml by bringing the mixture to a final volume of 1.22 ml. An equal volume of protein solution is incubated with the aluminum phosphate at room temperature for 1 hour and then injected. It is useful to determine whether the protein has been absorbed by examining the supernate after the aluminum phosphate precipitate has been spun off. This is most easily done if radioactive proteins are used.

2. Freund's Adjuvant

Freund's adjuvant is a mixture of a lanolin derivative (Bayol F) and mannide monooleate (Arlacel A). If the mixture contains tubercle bacilli (usually *Mycobacterium butyricum*) it is called "complete" while it is termed "incomplete" if the mycobacterium is absent. Both complete and incomplete Freund's adjuvant are commercially available from Difco in 10 ml vials and the *Mycobacterium butyricum* can be purchased from the same supplier in 100 mg vials. If the incomplete adjuvant is purchased, it is possible to adjust the concentration of mycobacterium to prepare material for footpad injection containing a final concentration of 0.5–1.0 mg/ml and for intramuscular injections containing a final concentration of 2 mg/ml.

Since it is necessary to convert the antigen–adjuvant mixture into a water-in-oil emulsion, antigen must be free of detergents before emulsification. Sodium dodecyl sulfate can be removed by dialysis for approximately 5 days with repeated changes of buffer or chromatography through Dowex (Cebra, 1964). Since aggregates are more highly immunogenic than soluble proteins (Gill and Kunz, 1966; Nossal, 1967) and provide a wide variety of antigenic determinants, any precipitate formed following removal of SDS, urea, or guanidine should be included in the emulsion. If antigen has been purified by electrophoresis on acrylamide gels, the appropriate slice of gel may be used without eluting the protein (see Horwitz and Scharff, Chapter 29, this volume).

The antigen-adjuvant emulsion is prepared by resuspending the antigen in isotonic saline (0.14 *M* NaCl) and mixing it with complete Freund's adjuvant by vigorous shearing. This can be accomplished by a variety of methods (Chase, 1967), but with viruses or viral proteins which are usually available in only small amounts, emulsification is best carried out in 2 ml Luer-Lok syringes connected with a double hub needle. Such needles are commercially available (Chase, 1967) or can be made in any machine shop. We have found that size 20 needle hubs are most useful. One-half to one milliliter of the antigen in saline is placed in one syringe and an equal volume of adjuvant in the other. As the mixture is blended by rapidly forcing it back and forth between the two syringes it will immediately turn white and progressively become more viscous. After about 20–40 strokes, all of the emulsion is forced into one syringe which is removed from the hub and attached to a size 26 needle. A small drop of the adjuvant emulsion is then ejected onto a water surface. If the drop remains intact, a water-in-oil emulsion has been achieved; if it spreads over the surface, further emulsification is necessary. More rapid emulsification may sometimes be achieved by cooling the material at 4°C for 20–60 minutes before emulsification.

B. Injection of Antigen

Soluble or alum-precipitated antigen can be easily injected into the marginal ear vein of a rabbit, especially if a breed, such as New Zealand White, having long white ears is used. The hair over the vein is shaved with a single edge razor, and the injection is made with either a 23 or 26 needle. It is usually not necessary to dilate the vein, but if needed this can be done by placing a drop of xylene on the tip of the ear. The xylene must be removed by washing with an alcohol sponge after the injection is made.

The footpad injection is somewhat more difficult since the animal must be completely immobilized. Although an experienced handler can immobilize the animal, this is more easily done by using a rabbit board on which the limbs of the animal are stretched out and held firmly by strings attached to the board. The middle two toes are spread apart, the area between the toes wiped with 70% alcohol, and a number 20 needle inserted into the soft tissue between the toes in the same plane as the digits. If significant resistance is met upon inserting the needle it has not been properly placed. If one places one's thumb and forefinger on either side of the foot, it is possible to feel the needle moving freely within the space between the fingers. The antigen is injected into all four limbs of the rabbit.

C. Bleeding of Rabbits

Cardiac puncture and bleeding from the artery of the ear (Chase, 1967) require a considerable amount of practice and skill. Bleeding from the ear vein however is simple and poses no threat to the life of the animal. After the animal is immobilized in a rabbit box,* a few drops of xylene are placed on the tip of the ear, and an area over the vein shaved with a single edge razor. A 3-5 mm incision is then made along the line of flow with a fresh razor blade. If the incision has been made properly, the blood will immediately begin to flow rapidly and 30-50 ml can be collected within 5-10 minutes. Clotting on the skin around the incision can be prevented by applying Vaseline before the incision is made, but this is usually not necessary. The flow of blood can sometimes be increased by clamping the ear vein central to the incision either with the fingers or with a paper clip. If a clot forms inside or around the vein during the bleeding, it can be removed by gently rubbing with a clean piece of gauze or probing the incision with the tip of the razor blade. Once bleeding stops, the remaining xylene should be removed from the tip of the ear with an alcohol sponge and any residual bleeding stopped by applying direct pressure to the vein with a clean piece of gauze. If the xylene is not completely removed, necrosis of the ear will occur. A longitudinal incision will heal within a few days and the same site may be used again within a week. If the incision is made across the vein, healing is less rapid and subsequent bleedings more difficult. Bleedings may be repeated every 3 or 4 days, alternating ears. If the original incision has not healed, a new incision is made closer to the head. In this way at least 100 ml of

*Brett and Co., P.O. Box 42, 570 Cedar Lane, Teaneck, New Jersey.

serum can be collected within a short time. After each bleeding, the blood is allowed to clot in a tube, then rimmed and allowed to retract in the refrigerator overnight. Serum and red blood cells are decanted from the clot, the red blood cells removed by centrifugation, and the serum frozen. Centrifugation of the whole clot does not produce significantly more serum and often results in hemolysis. We have generally avoided the addition of preservatives since some have been known to affect viral antigens [the D antigen of poliovirus is converted to C when treated with Merthiolate (LeBouvier, 1959)]. The serum may, however, be sterilized with a sintered glass filter or with one of the commercially available disposable filters. When frequent use is anticipated the serum should be frozen in a number of small aliquots. If there is a strong indication for the addition of preservatives, sodium azide may be used.

VI. Evaluation of Antisera

At each stage of immunization, sera should be obtained and tested to determine whether there is sufficient antibody of the right specificity to make additional bleedings worthwhile. While antisera must ultimately be thoroughly evaluated (see Horwitz and Scharff, this volume), preliminary testing is most effectively carried out using the method of double agar diffusion (Ouchterlony, see Salzman and Moss, Chapter 31, this volume). In some situations, however, double diffusion in tubes using the method of Preer (see Horwitz and Scharff, Chapter 29, this volume) provides valuable additional information because it is more sensitive than the Ouchterlony plate and employs dilute agar which allows the diffusion of even large virus particles. It is important to remember that CsCl inhibits antigen-antibody reactions (Edelman and Bryan, 1960).

VII. An Outline for the Production of Antisera against Structural Viral Proteins

When making antibody against soluble viral proteins, one omits steps (b) and (c).

(a) Thirty to fifty milliliters of blood is removed from each animal as a preimmunization control serum.

(b) Purified virions are prepared, dialyzed free of cesium chloride if present, and 30–150 μg injected intravenously into each of 2–4 New Zealand White rabbits (4–5 kg in size).

(c) Bleedings are taken 3, 6, and 12 days after immunization and the sera are frozen separately and tested later for antibodies specific for the whole virion and subviral structures.

(d) Two weeks later 30–150 μg of intact virus is emulsified in an equal volume of complete Freund's adjuvant containing 1–2 mg/ml of *Mycobacterium butyricum* and 0.2 ml is injected into each of the four footpads.

(e) Three to four weeks later a trial bleeding is taken and if antibody is present the animal is bled at 3–4 day intervals until 100–200 ml of serum has been obtained. These bleedings should contain antibody against all of the outer coat proteins.

(f) Virions are degraded both by mild and vigorous techniques, dialyzed free of the denaturing reagents, pooled, and emulsified with an equal volume of Freund's adjuvant containing 4 mg/ml of *Mycobacterium butyricum* and 0.2 ml injected intramuscularly into all four legs.

(g) Trial bleedings are taken 4 weeks after immunization and 100–200 ml of serum accumulated. These bleedings should contain antibody which will react both with the internal and external proteins as well as with nascent polypeptide chains.

(h) After 2–4 months the rabbit may be boosted intramuscularly [as in step (f)] with dissociated peptides, cores, or individual virus proteins against which sufficient amounts of antisera were not present initially.

VIII. Conclusion

The procedures described above have been used to produce potent and highly specific antisera which may be used in a variety of immunological investigations. It is most important, however, to remember that no matter how logical the immunization procedure, the antibody elicited may have unexpected specificities and the injection of a number of animals with a single antigenic preparation often results in a variety of different antisera. The exact specificity of a given antisera cannot, therefore, be predicted but must be evaluated experimentally (see Horwitz and Scharff, Chapter 29, this volume).

REFERENCES

Anderer, F. A. (1963). *Advan. Protein Chem.* **18**, 1.
Brown, F., Cartwright, B., and Small, C. J. (1967). *J. Immunol.* **99**, 176.
Cebra, J. J. (1964). *J. Immunol.* **92**, 977.
Chase, M. W. (1967). *In* "Methods in Immunology and Immunochemistry," (C. A. Williams and M. W. Chase, eds.), Vol. I, p. 127. Academic Press, New York.
Edelman, I. S., and Bryan, W. P. (1960). *J. Am. Chem. Soc.* **82**, 1491.
Farr, R. S., and Dixon, F. J. (1960). *J. Immunol.* **85**, 250.
Gill, T. J., III, and Kunz, H. W. (1966). *Biochim. Biophys. Acta* **124**, 374.
Ginsberg, H. S., Defendi, V., and Gilead, Z. (1969). *Federation Proc.* (in press).
Holt, L. B. (1950). "Developments in Diphtheria Prophylaxis." Heinemann, London.
Hummeler, K., and Hamparian, V. V. (1958). *J. Immunol.* **81**, 499.
Hummeler, K., and Tumilowicz, J. J. (1960). *J. Immunol.* **84**, 630.
Kleczkowski, A. (1961). *Immunology* **4**, 130.
Klemperer, H. G., and Pereira, H. G. (1959). *Virology* **9**, 536.
Laver, W. G., Suriano, J. R., and Green, M. (1967). *J. Virolo.* **1**, 723.
LeBouvier, G. L. (1955). *Lancet* **269**, 1013.
LeBouvier, G. L. (1959). *Brit. J. Exptl. Pathol.* **40**, 605.
Leskowitz, S., and Waksman, B. H. (1960). *J. Immunol.* **84**, 58.
Maizel, J. V., Jr., White, D. O., and Scharff, M. D. (1968). *Virology* **36**, 126.
Mandel, B. (1962). *Virology* **17**, 288.
Munoz, J. (1957), Proc. Soc. Exptl. Biol. Med. **95**, 757.
Nossal, G. J. V. (1967). *Ann. Rev. Med.* **18**, 81.
Robbins, J. B., Kenny, K., and Suter, E. (1965). *J. Exptl. Med.* **122**, 385.
Scharff, M. O. (1962). Unpublished data.
Scharff, M. D., and Levintow, L. (1963). *Virology* **19**, 491.
Scharff, M. D., Shatkin, A. J., and Levintow, L. (1963). *Proc. Natl. Acad. Sci. U.S.* **50**, 686.
Scharff, M. D., Maizel, J. V., Jr., and Levintow, L. (1964). *Proc. Natl. Acad. Sci. U.S.* **51**, 329.
Schmidt, N. J., and Lennette, E. H. (1967). *In* "Methods in Immunology and Immunochemistry" (C. A. Williams and M. W. Chase, eds.), Vol. I p. 87. Academic Press, New York.
Smith, K. O., Gehle, W. D., and Trousdale, M. D. (1965). *J. Bacteriol.* **90**, 254.
Svehag, S.-E., and Mandel, B. (1964). *J. Exptl. Med.* **119**, 1.
Valentine, R. C., and Pereira, H. G. (1965). *J. Mol. Biol.* **13**, 13.
Weintraub, M., and Raymond, S. (1963). *Science* **142**, 1677.
Wilcox, W. C., and Ginsberg, H. S. (1963). *J. Exptl. Med.* **118**, 295.
Wilcox, W. C., Ginsberg, H. S., and Anderson, T. F. (1963). *J. Exptl. Med.* **118**, 307.

26. Complement Fixation Technique for Assay of Viral Antigens and Antibodies

Nathalie J. Schmidt

Viral and Rickettsial Disease Laboratory
California State Department of Public Health
Berkeley, California

I. Introduction

The complement fixation (CF) test is one of the most valuable serological procedures available to the virologist. Although generally less sensitive than neutralization, hemagglutination inhibition or fluorescent antibody techniques, it possesses the advantage of greater simplicity. Further, the CF test can be utilized for assay of certain viral antigens which do not possess infectivity or hemagglutinating activity, e.g., the so-called "soluble" antigens of the myxoviruses, the coreless capsids of the enteroviruses, and the "neoantigens" produced by certain oncogenic viruses.

Assay of CF antibodies is one of the most useful procedures for diagnosis of viral infections. Some viruses possess CF antigens with broad group reactivity, for example, the soluble antigens of influenza viruses, which are specific for influenza groups A and B but not for various strains within each group. The adenoviruses also share a group CF antigen, and certain arboviruses produce CF antigens with broad group reactivity. While the presence of group-reactive antigens may prevent type-specific diagnosis of infection with these viruses, the CF test may be used to advantage in screening for infections within the group and, if desired, type-specific diagnosis can then be made by more specific serological methods. With certain other viruses, such as the Coxsackie viruses and the ECHO viruses, heterotypic CF antibody responses may occur in natural infections but not with sufficient regularity to permit group-specific diagnosis; for these agents the diagnostic value of the CF test is greatly limited.

Complement fixation tests may be particularly valuable for delineating antigenic relationships between viruses since differences which might be detected between strains by neutralization or hemagglutination inhibition tests are not so apparent in CF reactions.

II. Antigens

Primary considerations in the preparation of viral CF antigens are potency, freedom from host materials which might fix complement with the test serum, and freedom from anticomplementary activity.

Antigenic potency may be increased by harvesting only those tissues or organs of infected animals or eggs which are richest in viral antigen (Smadel *et al.*, 1939; Sosa-Martinez and Lennette, 1955; Fazekas de St. Groth *et al.*, 1958) by employing cell culture techniques which give rise to the largest yields of antigen (Schmidt *et al.*, 1957, 1964; Westwood *et al.*, 1960) or by various physical and chemical concentration procedures (Schmidt and Lennette, 1967).

Since viral antigens must be prepared in living host systems, they contain relatively large proportions of animal, egg, or tissue culture material, and these may fix complement with certain animal or human sera. In every CF test an uninfected control antigen prepared from the same host tissue and in the same manner as the infected antigen must be tested against the sera to establish that any reactivity with the particular viral antigen is not because of the presence of host material. If an animal immune serum is to be assayed by the CF reaction, the test antigen should be derived from a host system different from the one employed for preparation of the immunizing antigen. The amount of host material present in viral CF antigens may be reduced by purification procedures such as density gradient centrifugation, column chromatography or fluorocarbon treatment.

Antigens may exert an anticomplementary effect, i.e., they may by themselves bind or destroy certain components of complement and thus prevent hemolysis of the sensitized cells in the indicator system. Fluorocarbon treatment has been recommended for removal of anticomplementary activity from viral antigens (Halonen *et al.*, 1958; Hamparian *et al.*, 1958) as has treatment with heated guinea pig complement (von Zeipel, 1958). For the latter procedure normal guinea pig serum, inactivated by heating at 56°C for 30 minutes, is added to the antigen to give a final concentration of 5%; the mixture is then incubated at 37°C for 30–60 minutes. Complement-treated antigens are generally stored at −20°C or lower.

The potency of viral antigens is best determined by "block" titrations in which dilutions of the antigen are tested against dilutions of immune serum (see example in Section VI,A,4) rather than by a "straight line" titration in which the dilutions of antigen are assayed against a single, low dilution of immune serum. The unit of antigen obtained by the "block" titration represents the optimal proportion between antigen and antibody. It is considered good practice first to confirm the identity of an antigen by titrating it against a specific animal immune serum and, if it is intended for use with sera from natural human or animal infections, to then determine the optimal dilution for use in these tests by titrating the antigen against convalescent-phase serum from a natural infection. This is done because antigens may show a higher titer with serum from hyperimmune animals than with sera from natural infections.

III. Sera

All sera are heated at 56° or 60°C for 30 minutes to inactivate native complement prior to examination for viral CF antibodies. Because of the tendency of higher concentrations of serum to fix complement nonspecifically, a starting dilution of 1:4 or 1:8 is usually employed for assay of viral CF antibodies.

The anticomplementary activity of certain sera may make them unsuitable for examination. Sera of some individuals may be inherently anticomplementary, or the activity may be owing to exogenous factors such as bacterial or chemical contamination or the presence of anticoagulants or preservatives. Also, prolonged storage of sera, even in the frozen state, tends to render them anticomplementary. Several methods have been described for removal of anticomplementary activity from sera (Taran, 1946; Rapp *et al.*, 1955; Modified Sachs Method, 1959), but the following modification of the method described by Taran (1946) has been the most satisfactory in the experience of this laboratory. One volume of guinea pig complement is added to 3 volumes of serum, and the mixture is held at 4°C overnight and then at

37°C for 30 minutes. Sufficient physiological saline is added to give a 1:4 or 1:8 dilution of the test serum and inactivation is carried out at 60°C for 30 minutes.

IV. Complement

Lyophylized guinea pig complement, which is available commercially, is generally employed for viral CF tests. However, it has been found that guinea pig sera employed for complement may contain antibodies to certain myxoviruses (Chanock *et al.*, 1958), the reoviruses (Rosen, 1960) and the agents of the psittacosis-lymphogranuloma venereum group (Ellis *et al.*, 1961). The use of complement containing such antibodies makes the homologous antigen appear to be strongly anticomplementary. Thus, it is essential to pretest each lot of complement for antibodies to the test virus antigen. (Some of the commercially available guinea pig complement is pretested for the most commonly occurring viral antibodies.)

Since viral antigens may vary widely in their anticomplementary or procomplementary tendencies, it is important to titrate complement in the presence of each antigen (see complement titration in Section VI,A,3) to determine the optimal dilution of complement to use with each antigen.

V. General Conditions for Viral CF Tests

Modifications of the Kolmer technique are generally employed for viral CF tests since they occupy an intermediate position between sensitivity and specificity. Fixation of complement is usually allowed to proceed at 4°C overnight, since the sensitivity (amount of complement fixed by antigen-antibody complexes) is greater under these conditions than with shorter incubation at 37°C. Also, deterioration of complement is minimized at 4°C.

The microtiter procedure, developed by Takatsy (1950) and modified by Sever (1962), has greatly increased the practicability of the CF test for assay of viral antigens and antibodies. Since viral antigens are generally low in titer and frequently require concentration, the use of macromethods may be prohibitive. Also, the use of the microtiter system increases the number of viral antigens against which a given serum can feasibly be assayed. The procedure is also advantageous from the standpoint of space required for performing and incubating tests and the ease of performance.

The following microtechnique is the standard CF procedure of this laboratory and is employed for serological diagnosis of viral infections in humans and animals and also for assay of viral antigens produced by oncogenic and nononcogenic viruses. The test is performed in microtiter U plates. If a highly quantitative method is required, the microcomplement fixation technique developed by Wasserman and Levine (1961) may be utilized.

VI. Microtiter Complement Fixation Test

A. Reagents

1. *Diluent*

Kolmer saline (0.85% saline containing 1.0 ml/liter of the following magnesium-calcium solution) is employed as a diluent for all of the reagents in the test.

Magnesium-calcium solution: $MgCl_2 \cdot 6H_2O$, 10.0 gm; $CaCl_2 \cdot 2H_2O$, 4.0 gm; distilled water to 100.0 ml. Store solution at 4°C.

2. *Sensitized Erythrocyte Suspension*

a. Sheep erythrocytes. Defibrinated or citrated sheep red blood cells are washed in saline three successive times by centrifuging for 8 minutes at 2000 rpm and made to a 2% suspension in sufficient volume for the entire test. This 2% cell suspension may be used directly, or it may be standardized colorimetrically as follows: 0.8 ml of the suspension is lysed in 3.2 ml of distilled water and the optical density of the resulting hemoglobin solution is determined at 550 mμ in a Coleman Jr. spectrophotometer using a 12 by 75 mm cuvette. The concentration of the cell suspension is adjusted to give an OD (optical density) of 0.47.

b. Hemolysin (antibody to sheep erythrocytes)

(1) Preparation of a 1:100 stock solution of hemolysin: Saline diluent, 94.0 ml; 5% phenol in saline, 4.0 ml; mix and add hemolysin, 50% in glycerin (stored at 4°C), 2.0 ml.

(2) Titration of hemolysin (performed in 13 by 100 mm tubes)

(i) Hemolysin dilutions are prepared as follows:

0.5 ml of 1:100 hemolysin	+ 4.5 ml saline = 1:1,000 dilution
1.0 ml of 1:1,000 hemolysin	+ 5.0 ml saline = 1:6,000 dilution
1.0 ml of 1:1,000 hemolysin	+ 7.0 ml saline = 1:8,000 dilution
1.0 ml of 1:1,000 hemolysin	+ 9.0 ml saline = 1:10,000 dilution
1.0 ml of 1:10,000 hemolysin	+ 0.5 ml saline = 1:15,000 dilution

1.0 ml of 1:10,000 hemolysin + 1.0 ml saline = 1:20,000 dilution
1.0 ml of 1:10,000 hemolysin + 1.5 ml saline = 1:25,000 dilution

(ii) Each dilution of hemolysin (from 1:6,000 through 1:25,000) is dispensed into a tube in a volume of 0.2 ml. To each tube is added 0.1 ml of a 1:30 dilution of complement, 0.2 ml of the 2% sheep cell suspension and 0.5 ml of saline. A cell control consisting of 0.2 ml of the sheep cell suspension and 0.8 ml of saline is incubated with the titration.

(iii) The contents of the tubes are mixed by shaking and the titration is incubated in a water bath at 37°C for 30 minutes. The highest dilution of hemolysin which shows *complete* hemolysis represents 1 unit. A dilution containing 2 units of hemolysin is used in the test. Example: if the 1:10,000 dilution shows complete hemolysis, and the 1:15,000 partial hemolysis, one unit would be represented by a 1:10,000 dilution. Therefore, 2 units would be contained in a 1:5,000 dilution of hemolysin.

The volume of hemolysin required for the entire test is diluted to the proper concentration at one time.

Sensitized cells are prepared in sufficient volume for the complement titration (see Section VI,A,3) by pouring diluted hemolysin into an equal volume of the cell suspension and rapidly pouring the mixture back and forth several times. The sensitized cells are held at room temperature for 10 minutes before use.

The remaining cell suspension and diluted hemolysin are held at 4°C and mixed together the following day for completion of the test.

3. *Complement*

Lyophylized guinea pig complement is restored to its original volume in the diluent supplied by the producer and titrated *in the presence of each antigen* used in the test. (For antigen titrations the complement is titrated in the presence of 2 units of a previous lot of antigen prepared in the same manner as the test antigen.)

COMPLEMENT TITRATION (performed in 13 by 75 mm tubes)

Reagent	Volume (ml) of reagent to be added to tube number: 1	2	3	4	5	6	7	8
Antigen (diluted to 2 units)	0.10	0.10	0.10	0.10	0.10	0.10	0.10	0.10
Complement (1:60)	0.12	0.11	0.10	0.09	0.08	0.07	0.06	0.05
Saline	0.08	0.09	0.10	0.11	0.12	0.13	0.14	0.15

Tubes are shaken and incubated in a 37°C water bath for 30 minutes, after which 0.2 ml of sensitized cells are added to all tubes. The mixtures are shaken and incubated at 37°C for an additional 30 minutes.

The tube containing the least amount of complement giving complete hemolysis represents 1 unit. Two *exact* units of complement are employed in the test. The dilution of complement containing 2 units of complement is determined as follows:

If 0.09 ml of a 1:60 dilution of complement equals 1 exact unit, then 0.18 ml of the 1:60 dilution equals 2 exact units. $60/0.18 \times 0.1$ = 1:33 dilution of complement (2 units).

The appropriate dilution of complement for use in the test should be prepared and held at 4°C for 1–2 hours prior to addition to the test; equilibration of complement in this manner enhances the reproducibility of the test results.

4. Antigen

Antigens are assayed in a "block" titration by testing 2-fold dilutions of the antigen against serial 2-fold dilutions of immune serum. This gives an indication of the full range of antigenic reactivity of a viral antigen and also indicates the optimal dilution of antigen to be employed in viral antibody assays. The procedure is illustrated in Table I.

Immune serum dilutions are prepared using 0.025 ml microtiter diluting loops. Antigen dilutions are prepared in master tubes and, starting with the highest dilution, 0.025 ml of each dilution is added to the appropriate row of wells. Complement controls are included to assay possible anticomplementary activity of each antigen dilution (testing antigen dilutions against 2.0, 1.5, 1.0, and 0.5 units of complement).

A 1:8 dilution of negative serum is dispensed into appropriate wells in a volume of 0.025 ml, and 0.025 ml of each antigen dilution is added.

Saline in a volume of 0.025 ml is added to the serum control wells in lieu of antigen; this set of controls detects possible anticomplementary activity on the part of the immune serum or negative serum.

The immune serum dilutions and the negative serum dilution are assayed against 0.025 ml of an uninfected control antigen diluted to the same degree as the previous lot of specific antigen; this control detects possible host reactivity of the sera. The uninfected antigen is also assayed for anticomplementary activity against the four concentrations of complement.

TABLE I
ANTIGEN TITRATION

Antigen dilution	Immune serum dilution					Negative serum	Complement controls – Antigen dilutions + Complement diluted to:			
	1:8	1:16	1:32	1:64	1:128	1:8	2 U	1-1/2 U	1 U	1/2 U
1:2	4[a]	4	4	0	0	0	0	0	1	4
1:4	4	4	4	1	0	0	0	0	0	4
1:8	4	4	4	2	0	0	0	0	0	4
1:16	4	4	4	2	0	0	0	0	0	4
1:32	4	4	2	0	0	0	0	0	0	4
1:64	1	0	0	0	0	0	0	0	0	4
Serum control (serum and saline)	0	0	0	0	0	0				
Uninfected antigen	0	0	0	0	0	0	0	0	0	4
Previous lot of specific-antigen	4	4	4	1	0	0	0	0	0	4

[a] Degree of complement fixation: 4+ = no hemolysis; 3+ = 25% hemolysis; 2+ = 50% hemolysis; 1+ = 75% hemolysis, and 0 = 100% hemolysis.

A previously titrated lot of specific antigen is tested at a dilution containing 2 units (in a volume of 0.025 ml) against the immune serum dilutions, the negative serum, and for possible anticomplementary activity.

Saline is added to all of the complement control wells (in lieu of serum) in a volume of 0.025 ml.

To the test proper and the 2 unit complement control wells is added 0.025 ml of complement diluted to contain 2 units; 0.025 ml of the appropriate complement dilutions is added to the complement controls containing 1.5, 1.0, and 0.5 units of complement. (The preparation of these complement dilutions is described in Section VI,B,3).

The contents of the wells are mixed by rubbing the bottom of the plate gently, and the titration is incubated at 4°C overnight.

The plates are then warmed at room temperature for 15 minutes, and 0.05 ml of the sensitized cell suspension is added to each well. The plates are agitated on a vibrating shaker and then held in a 37°C incubator for 15–30 minutes or until the complement controls show the proper degree of hemolysis (see Section VI,B,5).

The highest antigen dilution giving 3+ or 4+ fixation with the highest dilution of immune serum is considered to represent 1 unit. In the example, this would be a 1:16 dilution of the antigen, and therefore the antigen would be diluted 1:8 to contain 2 units for use in antibody assays. The complement controls indicate that this dilution of antigen is not anticomplementary in the presence of 2.0, 1.5, and 1.0 units of complement.

5. *Sera*

Sera to be examined for the presence of viral CF antibodies are diluted 1:4 or 1:8, depending upon the test virus, and inactivated at 60°C for 30 minutes prior to examination in the CF test. If they are found to be anticomplementary they may be treated with guinea pig complement as described above. A positive control serum for each antigen should be included in every run.

B. Test Proper

Table II shows the protocol for a CF antibody assay on a serum specimen. (For serologic diagnosis of a viral infection, acute- and convalescent-phase serum specimens must be examined in parallel in the same run, and a 4-fold or greater increase in CF antibody titer is considered diagnostically significant.)

Twofold dilutions of serum are tested against one or more specific

TABLE II
SCHEME FOR PERFORMANCE OF THE MICROTITER COMPLEMENT FIXATION TEST

Part of test	Test serum (ml)	Saline (ml)	Specific antigen (ml)	Uninfected antigen (ml)	Complement (ml)		Sensitized cells (ml)	
Serum antibody assay	0.025[a]	–	0.025	–	0.025	Overnight incubation at 4°C followed by 15 minutes at room temperature	0.050	15–30 minutes at 37°C
Serum anticomplementary control	0.025[b]	0.025	–	–	0.025		0.050	
Serum nonspecific control	0.025[b]	–	–	0.025	0.025		0.050	
Complement controls for each specific and uninfected antigen	Complement units							
	2.0	0.025	0.025	–[c]	0.025		0.050	
	1.5	0.025	0.025	–	0.025 (1:1.5)		0.050	
	1.0	0.025	0.025	–	0.025 (1:2)		0.050	
	0.5	0.025	0.025	–	0.025 (1:4)		0.050	
Hemolytic system control	–	0.050	–	–	0.025		0.050	
Sensitized sheep cell control	–	0.075	–	–	–		0.050	

[a] Series of wells, each containing 0.025 ml of a serial dilution of serum.
[b] Initial serum dilution of 1:4 or 1:8.
[c] Complement controls should also be run on uninfected antigen.

antigens, and the initial serum dilution is tested against the appropriate uninfected host antigens and for anticomplementary activity. Each run includes four dilution complement controls on the specific and uninfected antigens employed in the test. Other controls are the hemolytic control containing (in addition to saline diluent) only complement and sensitized cells, and the sheep cell control containing only diluent and sensitized cells; the former should show hemolysis while the latter should not.

(1) Serial dilutions of serum are prepared for assay against the specific antigen by adding 0.05 ml of the initial serum dilution (1:4 or 1:8) to the first well in a row and then preparing successive 2-fold dilutions using 0.025 ml loops. A 0.025 ml volume of the initial serum dilution is added to a well for the uninfected control antigen and to a well for the serum anticomplementary control.

(2) Specific antigen diluted to contain 2 units is added to the serum dilutions in a volume of 0.025 ml. The uninfected control antigen, diluted to the same degree as the specific antigen, is added to the initial serum dilution in a volume of 0.025 ml, and 0.025 ml of saline is added to the initial serum dilution for the anticomplementary control.

(3) Complement is diluted appropriately and added to the test.

(a) Complement is diluted in cold saline to contain 2 exact units (and held at 4°C for 1–2 hours).

(b) Dilutions of complement are prepared for the complement controls as shown in the accompanying tabulation.

	Final dilution of complement:		
	1.5 units	1.0 unit	0.5 unit
Complement (2 units)	1.0 ml	1.0 ml	0.5 ml
Saline	0.5 ml	1.0 ml	1.5 ml

(c) Two units of complement are added to the test proper and to the 2 unit complement controls in a volume of 0.025 ml, and the dilutions of complement containing 1.5, 1.0, and 0.5 units are added to the appropriate wells in a volume of 0.025 ml.

(4) The contents of the wells are mixed by rubbing the bottom of the plates gently, and the plates are incubated at 4°C overnight.

(5) On the following day the plates are held at room temperature for 15 minutes, 0.05 ml of sensitized cells is added to each well, and the contents of the wells are mixed by placing the plates on a vibrating

shaker. The plates are then incubated at 37°C for 15 or 30 minutes or until the complement controls show the proper degree of hemolysis.

The wells containing 2.0 and 1.5 units of complement should show complete hemolysis, and those containing 1.0 unit complete or nearly complete hemolysis. The wells containing 0.5 unit of complement should show no hemolysis. If the wells containing 0.5 units show hemolysis, an excess of complement was used in the test, and if those containing 2.0 and 1.5 units do not show *complete* hemolysis, insufficient complement was used.

(6) When the complement controls show the proper degree of clearing the plates are removed from the incubator. They are then held at 4°C until the unlysed cells have settled and the tests are ready to read. Settling of the cells may be expedited by centrifuging the plates in special carriers.

C. Antigen Titration

The same procedure as outlined above may be used to measure the complement-fixing activity of antigens against a standard immune serum except that serial dilutions of the test antigen are mixed with 2–4 units of antiserum including the corresponding controls.

REFERENCES

Chanock, R. M., Parrott, R. H., Cook, K., Andrews, B. E., Bell, J. A., Reichelderfer, T., Kapikian, A. Z., Mastrota, F. M., and Huebner, R. J. (1958). *New Engl. J. Med.* **258**, 207–213.

Ellis, R. J., Falcone, R. G., and Winn, J. F. (1961). *Public Health Lab.* **19**, 34–46.

Fazekas de St. Groth, S., Graham, D. M., and Jack, I. (1958) *J. Lab. Clin. Med.* **51**, 883-896.

Halonen, P., Huebner, R. J., and Turner, H. C. (1958). *Proc. Soc. Exptl. Biol. Med.* **97**, 530–534.

Hamparian, V. V., Muller, F., and Hummeler, K. (1958). *J. Immunol.* **80**, 468–475.

Modified Sachs Method. (1959). "Manual of Serologic Tests for Syphilis," Public Health Serv. Publ. No. 411. U.S. Dept. of Health, Education and Welfare, Communicable Disease Center, Venereal Disease Branch, Atlanta, Georgia.

Rapp, F., Gnesh, G. M., and Gordon, I. (1955). *Proc. Soc. Exptl. Biol. Med.* **90**, 335-339.

Rosen, L. (1960). *Am. J. Hyg.* **71**, 242–249.

Schmidt, N. J., and Lennette, E. H. (1967). *In* "Methods in Immunology and Immunochemistry" (M. W. Chase and C. A. Williams, eds.), Vol. 1, pp. 87–102. Academic Press, New York.

Schmidt, N. J., Lennette, E. H., Doleman, J. H., and Hagens, S. J. (1957). *Am. J. Hyg.* **66**, 1-19.

Schmidt, N. J., Lennette, E. H., Shon, C. W., and Shinomoto, T. T. (1964). *Proc. Soc. Exptl. Biol. Med.* **116**, 144-149.
Sever, J. L. (1962). *J. Immunol.* **88**, 320-329.
Smadel, J. E., Baird, R. D., and Wall, M. J. (1939). *Proc. Soc. Exptl. Biol. Med.* **40**, 71-73.
Sosa-Martinez, J., and Lennette, E. H. (1955). *J. Bacteriol.* **70**, 205-215.
Takatsy, G. (1950). *Kiserl. Orvostud.* **2**, 393-396.
Taran, A. (1946). *J. Lab. Clin. Med.* **31**, 1037-1039.
von Zeipel, G. (1958). *Arch. Ges Virusforsch.* **8**, 246-258,
Wasserman, E., and Levine, L. (1961). *J. Immunol.* **87**, 290-295.
Westwood, J. C. N., Appleyard, G., Taylor-Robinson, D., and Zwartouw, H. T. (1960). *Brit. J. Exptl. Pathol.* **41**, 105-111.

27. Hemagglutination with Animal Viruses

Leon Rosen

Pacific Research Section
National Institute of Allergy and Infectious Diseases
National Institutes of Health
Honolulu, Hawaii

I. Applications of the Technique

The knowledge that viruses can cause the agglutination of erythrocytes *in vitro* dates from 1941 when this phenomenon was reported for influenza virus and red blood cells from the domestic chicken. Since then, hemagglutination has been demonstrated for some, or all, members of most of the presently recognized groups of animal viruses. It has also been found that certain viruses have the capacity to cause erythrocytes to be adsorbed to the surface of infected cells in monolayer cultures. This phenomenon is termed "hemadsorption."

Viral hemagglutination and hemadsorption have proved to be useful tools in many kinds of virologic investigation. Some current uses are as follows.

A. Virus Isolation

Hemagglutination and hemadsorption have been widely used for the detection of myxoviruses, either for testing fluids from inoculated embryonated eggs (hemagglutination) or for testing inoculated cell cultures (hemadsorption). Hemagglutination and hemadsorption are the only practical ways of detecting some myxoviruses and the existence of several of these agents was first discovered by the application of these techniques. Hemadsorption also has been used to detect viruses of other families (e.g., variola).

B. Virus Identification

When available, hemagglutination and hemadsorption are usually the techniques of choice for determining the family and serotype of an unknown virus. Most definitive identifications are based on hemagglutination- or hemadsorption-inhibition tests, but other hemagglutination "markers" are sometimes available for preliminary grouping and tentative identification. These include the species of erythrocytes agglutinated, the titer of hemagglutinin, and the optimum temperature (4 or 37°C) and pH for the reaction.

C. Virus Classification

The hemagglutinating properties of viruses also have proved useful in delineating virus groups and subgroups. For example, the recognition that the viruses of such diverse diseases as influenza, mumps, and Newcastle disease belonged in the same group was largely the result of the study of their hemagglutinating properties. Cross hemagglutination-inhibition tests and the types of "markers" mentioned above are used for this purpose.

D. Detection of Antibodies

Because of the simplicity of the technique, the hemagglutination-inhibition test for detecting (and titrating) antibodies against viruses is the most widely employed application of viral hemagglutination. The nature of the antibodies measured by this technique varies among the different groups of viruses. For example, group-specific antibodies occur in poxvirus infections, whereas type-specific responses are commonly observed with adenoviruses. The hemagglutination-inhibition responses which occur in artificially immunized animals are sometimes more specific than those encountered in naturally infected hosts. Viruses which hemagglutinate usually can be employed in hemagglutination-inhibition tests—but this is not always the case because of the presence of irremovable nonspecific inhibitors in sera.

E. Virus Purification and Concentration

Since some hemagglutinating viruses elute from erythrocytes under conditions which are not optimal for adsorption, it is frequently possible to purify and concentrate virus suspensions by relatively simple techniques. A number of viruses are adsorbed to erythrocytes at 4°C and elute at 37°C and vice versa. Thus, a virus suspension can be mixed with erythrocytes at the optimum temperature for adsorption and the erythrocytes then sedimented and washed. The temperature is subsequently changed and the virus recovered relatively free of extraneous material. If desired, a volume of diluent smaller than the original volume can be used in the recovery phase. Theoretically, similar techniques based on other conditions which affect the adsorption and elution of viruses can be used.

F. Studies of the Structure and Function of Virions

When correlated with electron microscopy and biochemical techniques, hemagglutination has proved useful in clarifying the structure and function of virions. It is now clear, for example, that in the case of measles virus and adenoviruses, hemagglutination can result from the action of particles much smaller than the intact virion—as well as from the virions themselves.

II. Factors Which Influence Viral Hemagglutination

A. Virus

1. Strain

The influence of strain on the hemagglutinating properties of a virus varies from one virus group to another and also within a single group. Thus, while all known strains of certain enterovirus serotypes hemagglutinate, hemagglutinating strains of other serotypes are only rarely encountered.

2. Titer

It is obvious that a certain minimum number of particles must be present in order to detect hemagglutination by the usual techniques. The magnitude of this minimum number, however, is not known in most instances. Since the hemagglutinating properties of many viruses are more resistant to adverse conditions than the infective properties, it is not uncommon to encounter hemagglutinating titers higher than infectivity titers, or to be able to demonstrate hemagglutination in the absence of infectivity. On the other hand, for reasons discussed elsewhere, it is possible to have very high infectivity titers without being able to detect hemagglutination.

3. *Passage Level*

The passage level of a particular virus strain sometimes determines whether or not it will hemagglutinate. In some instances freshly isolated strains hemagglutinate better than those with a long passage history, in some cases the reverse is true. It is likely that titer changes and the selection of hemagglutinating or nonhemagglutinating particles with passage account, at least in part, for this phenomenon.

4. *Host Cell*

The type of host cell in which a virus propagates is also known to influence its hemagglutinating properties in some instances. This effect can be independent of titer changes and the production of inhibitors, although the latter factors obviously also can play a role.

5. *Other Factors*

Other factors which are known to affect the production of viral hemagglutinins include the size of the virus dose used to infect cell cultures or animals, the temperature at which cell cultures are incubated, and, in the case of intact animals, the route of inoculation. The mechanisms by which these effects are mediated are not known in most instances.

B. Erythrocyte

1. *Species of Donor*

The species of animal from which erythrocytes are obtained for hemagglutination studies is of the utmost importance. Some viruses agglutinate erythrocytes from a wide variety of animals, and others are known to agglutinate the erythrocytes of only a single species. In some instances a virus agglutinates only the erythrocytes of animals which are susceptible to infection with the virus or whose cells can be infected *in vitro*. In others, no correlation is known. In general, and with many exceptions, viruses in the same group tend to agglutinate the same types of erythrocytes. For obvious reasons, the erythrocytes of domestic mammals and birds are the most widely used. The type of erythrocyte commonly employed with various kinds of viruses is shown in Table I. In seeking to demonstrate hemagglutination by viruses not known to have this property, there is as yet no substitute for empiricism in the choice of erythrocytes.

2. *Age of Donor*

The age of the animal from which erythrocytes are obtained has been shown to be of importance for hemagglutination by certain viruses. For example, erythrocytes of adult chickens are more readily agglutinated by the poxviruses than those of newborn chickens. Exactly the reverse is true for many of the arthropod-borne viruses.

3. *Differences in Individual Donors*

Another factor which is known to influence the suitability of erythrocytes for viral hemagglutination is variation in the sensitivity of erythrocytes from different individuals of the same species. This variation is usually one of degree, but in the case of poxviruses and chicken erythrocytes, the phenomenon is "all or none."

4. *Other Factors*

The suitability of erythrocytes for viral hemagglutination is sometimes influenced by the sex of the donor animal. Also, it is known that, in general, erythrocytes tend to lose their reactivity with storage at refrigeration temperatures. It is common practice to use human group O erythrocytes for viral hemagglutination. This is not because erythrocytes of this blood group are more readily agglutinated, but rather because their use eliminates the need to adsorb isoagglutinins from human sera when the latter are employed in hemagglutination-inhibition tests.

C. Milieu

1. *Temperature*

Temperature is an important consideration in viral hemagglutination. Some viruses hemagglutinate only, or best, at 4°C, others only, or best, at 37°C, and others equally well at either temperature. Although room temperatures (20 to 25°C) are often employed for the sake of convenience, no virus has been reported to hemagglutinate better at these temperatures than at either 4 or 37°C.

2. *Hydrogen Ion Concentration*

Hydrogen ion concentration affects hemagglutination by many viruses, particularly those known loosely as arboviruses. Since some viruses in this group are unstable at the pH which is optimum for hemagglutination, it is necessary to dilute the virus at a pH at which it is stable and then adjust the pH for hemagglutination by using a suitable diluent for the erythrocytes.

3. *Presence or Absence of Other Ions*

The hemagglutination of certain viruses is known to be influenced by the presence or absence of certain ions, such as Na, Ca, and Mg.

TABLE I
CONDITIONS COMMONLY EMPLOYED FOR HEMAGGLUTINATION BY ANIMAL VIRUSES

Virus	Species of erythrocyte	Milieu
Myxoviruses		
Influenza	Chicken, human, or guinea pig	4°C, pH not important
Parainfluenza	Chicken, human, or guinea pig	4°C, pH not important
Mumps	Chicken, human, or guinea pig	4°C, pH not important
Measles	*Macaca* or *Cercopithecus* monkey	37°C, pH not important
Enteroviruses	Human	Temperature of 4 or 37°C and pH important for some serotypes
Reoviruses	Human	Temperature and pH not important
Arboviruses	Goose	37°C, pH very important
Rubella	Goose	4°C, pH important
Rabies	Goose	0°C and low pH very important
Poxviruses	Chicken	37°C, pH not important
Adenoviruses	*Macaca* monkey and rat	37°C, pH not important
Polyoma virus	Guinea pig	4°C, pH not important

4. *Inhibitors*

The presence of viral hemagglutinins is sometimes masked by the presence of "inhibitors" of complex composition derived from the cells in which the virus replicates. In most cases, the nature of these inhibiting substances is unknown. Among the methods which have been used to remove them from virus-containing material are treatment with heat, acetone, ether, fluorocarbon, receptor-destroying enzyme (RDE), trypsin, and high-speed centrifugation. Inhibitors are more often encountered in preparations derived from tissues of intact animals than in those derived from cell cultures.

5. *Heterotypic Antisera*

An unusual factor which can sometimes influence viral hemagglutination is antiserum to a related virus. For example, the presence of heterotypic antisera in the reaction mixture has been shown to enhance the hemagglutinating properties of certain adenoviruses.

III. Notes on Technique

A. METHODS OF DETECTING HEMAGGLUTINATION

1. *Pattern of Sedimentation*

Although several methods for detecting viral hemagglutination are available, the pattern method is almost universally employed. In this procedure, the presence or absence of hemagglutination is indicated by the distribution of erythrocytes after they have settled to the bottom of glass tubes or hemispherical wells in plastic plates. Agglutinated cells are more or less evenly distributed in a thin layer over the entire bottom of the tube or well in the form of a "shield." In the absence of agglutination, cells are present only in the center in the form of a compact "button." Partial agglutination is indicated by intermediate types of patterns. For successful use of the pattern method, it is necessary that the number of erythrocytes added to each tube be adjusted within relatively narrow limits. The number varies with the diameter of the tube or well and the species of erythrocyte. It is also important that the erythrocytes be allowed to settle with the tubes in a perpendicular position. The time required for the sedimentation varies with the volume of the reaction mixture, the species of erythrocyte, and the temperature (erythrocytes settle faster at higher temperatures).

2. *Hemadsorption*

Hemadsorption is detected by microscopic observation of cell monolayers on which erythrocytes have been allowed to settle. In the presence of a hemadsorbing virus the erythrocytes attach to the cell sheet; in the negative cultures they float freely over the monolayer. The distribution of adsorbed erythrocytes varies with different viruses and may be useful for tentative identification.

B. Erythrocytes

1. *Choice of Donor Species*

The species of erythrocyte employed is often dictated by the properties of the virus and the availability of various kinds of animals. When a choice is possible, certain principles can be followed. Some species of erythrocytes agglutinate spontaneously more readily than others (see below) and should be avoided if possible. Some species of erythrocytes sediment faster than others (e.g., chicken) and should be used if possible. Finally, certain species of erythrocytes are agglutinated by sera employed in hemagglutination-inhibition tests more often than others and should be avoided if possible.

2. *Quantity of Erythrocytes*

Since the activity of viral hemagglutinins varies inversely with the number of erythrocytes used, in most instances it is obviously desirable to employ as few erythrocytes as possible. The minimum number which can be used is that necessary to form a good "button" in the control tubes. This quantity can be determined first by trial and error and reproduced thereafter by preparing a suspension of the same percentage from erythrocytes sedimented in a calibrated centrifuge tube. A more accurate method is to prepare a suspension of the same density with a spectrophotometer. It should be noted that it is the total number of erythrocytes which is of importance and not the concentration in the particular volume added to the reaction mixture (e.g., using 0.2 ml of a 0.5% erythrocyte suspension is the same as using 0.1 ml of a 1.0% suspension).

C. Volume of the Reaction Mixture

The total volume of the reaction mixture is dictated to a certain extent by the quantities necessary for accurate measurement and preparation of serial dilutions. Aside from these considerations, it should be as small as possible to ensure adequate contact between virus and erythrocyte and to give the shortest possible sedimentation time.

D. Hemagglutination-Inhibition

1. *Serum*

a. Agglutinins. Sera often contain agglutinins for the erythrocytes of heterologous, and sometimes homologous, species. Unless the sera are diluted beyond their range of activity, these agglutinins must be removed before the sera can be used in hemagglutination-inhibition tests. This is usually accomplished by adsorbing the sera with a concentrated suspension of the appropriate erythrocytes at 4°C.

b. Nonspecific inhibitors. Sera often contain nonspecific inhibitors for viral hemagglutinins, and various methods have been devised to eliminate these. The methods include the use of heat, trypsin, periodate, RDE, acetone, bentonite, and kaolin. The latter material has been widely employed and is used in hemagglutination-inhibition tests with arboviruses, myxoviruses, adenoviruses, reoviruses, and enteroviruses.

c. "Slippage." "Shield" patterns in tubes containing low dilutions of serum in hemagglutination-inhibition tests are often unstable and tend to "slip" into patterns resembling "buttons." Adsorption of sera with kaolin often prevents this "slippage."

2. *Hemagglutinin*

a. Quantity. The quantity of hemagglutinin which should be used in a hemagglutination-inhibition test will depend on the desired sensitivity of the test and on the particular virus used. Small amounts of hemagglutinin of some viruses are apt to be inhibited nonspecifically by most sera. It is necessary therefore to employ a sufficient amount of antigen to avoid this pitfall and yet avoid an excess which would unduly decrease the sensitivity of the test. In practice, from 4 to 16 units of hemagglutinin are commonly used.

b. Avidity and sensitivity to nonspecific inhibition. Various strains and passage levels of some viruses differ in the ease with which they are inhibited by antisera and also in their sensitivity to nonspecific inhibition. It is obviously important to consider these factors when choosing a virus for hemagglutination-inhibition tests.

3. *Virus-Serum Incubation*

The duration and temperature of virus-serum incubation are sometimes significant factors in determining the hemagglutination-inhibition titer of a serum. For some viruses the conditions which can be used are limited by the stability of the hemagglutinin.

E. Common Sources of Error

1. *"Spontaneous" Agglutination of Erythrocytes*

As noted above, certain species of erythrocytes have a tendency to agglutinate spontaneously. This is particularly true of the erythrocytes of rabbits and rats and the phenomenon has been found to be a characteristic of individual animals in the case of the latter species. "Spontaneous" agglutination can also result from contact of the erythrocytes with a variety of known and unknown chemical substances and it is not uncommonly the result of employing dirty glassware. "Spontaneous" agglutination can sometimes be eliminated by adding low concentrations of protein-containing material (such as bovine serum albumin) to the erythrocyte diluent. This is not always a satisfactory procedure since the amount of protein-containing material necessary may affect the stability of the "shield" type of sedimentation patterns.

2. *Agglutination by Serum in Cell Culture Media*

Agglutination of erythrocytes by sera present in cell culture media is a very common finding. Although this type of agglutination can be recognized by the use of suitable controls, it often cannot be eliminated. It is possible that low-titered viral agglutinins might thus be masked.

3. *Agglutination by Unrecognized Contaminating Viruses*

It is now well known that experimental animals and cell cultures often harbor viruses other than those under study. Since these contaminating viruses may hemagglutinate or hemadsorb, it is not surprising that they are sometimes a source of error. The SV5 virus commonly found in rhesus kidney cultures is a notorious offender in this regard. This type of error can be recognized by the employment of suitable controls and by testing the hemagglutinins for specific inhibition. Obviously, antisera used in these tests should not have been prepared by immunizing animals with the material in question.

F. AN EXAMPLE OF A HEMAGGLUTINATION AND A HEMAGGLUTINATION-INHIBITION TEST

Detailed directions for performing a hemagglutination and a hemagglutination-inhibition test with a reovirus are given below as an illustration of the way in which such tests are carried out in practice. It should be noted that unlike some viruses reoviruses do not require very specific conditions of temperature and pH.

1. *Hemagglutinin*

Hemagglutinin is prepared in tube or bottle cultures of rhesus kidney cells maintained on a serum-free medium. Both fluid and cell debris are harvested from infected cultures after complete destruction of the culture has occurred. This material is used as the hemagglutinin, either immediately, or after storage in the frozen state.

2. *Erythrocytes*

Human type O erythrocytes are collected and stored in Alsever's solution (dextrose, 2.05 gm; sodium citrate, 0.8 gm; citric acid, 0.055 gm; NaCl, 0.42 gm/100 ml of distilled water, autoclave at 10 pounds pressure for 10 minutes) adding about 10 ml of blood to 50 ml of that solution. Before use, the cells are washed three times in 0.85% NaCl (saline) and made up for use as a 0.75% suspension in saline.

3. *Titration of Hemagglutinin*

Titration of the hemagglutinin and the hemagglutination-inhbition test are carried out in glass tubes (12 by 75 mm) with hemispherical bottoms. For titration of the hemagglutinin, 0.2 ml of the erythrocyte suspension is added to serial twofold dilutions of cell culture material in saline. The tubes are then shaken and allowed to stand at room temperature. The first tube showing a "one-plus" pattern of sedimentation (Chanock and Sabin, 1953) is taken as the end point of the titration and considered to contain 1 unit of hemagglutinin.

4. *Treatment of Sera*

Before use in a hemagglutination-inhibition test sera are adsorbed as follows with kaolin. A 1 in 5 dilution of serum in saline is mixed with an equal volume of 25% suspension of acid-washed kaolin in saline (25 gm of kaolin plus 100 ml of saline) and allowed to stand for 20 minutes at room temperature. The mixture is then centrifuged briefly to sediment the kaolin and the supernatant fluid decanted. The latter is considered as a 1 in 10 dilution of serum and, in the case of human sera, need not be treated further. Animal sera are further adsorbed with human erythrocytes to remove any agglutinins for this type of cell which might be present. This is done by adding 0.1 ml of a 50% suspension of erythrocytes in saline for each 1.0 ml of the 1 in 10 dilution of serum. After allowing the mixture to stand for 1 hour at approximately 4°C, the supernatant fluid is decanted and is ready for use. Sera are not inactivated.

5. *Hemagglutination-Inhibition Test*

The hemagglutination-inhibition test is carried out by adding 0.2 ml of hemagglutinin, so diluted in saline as to contain 4 units (*in 0.2 ml*), to 0.2 ml amounts of serial twofold dilutions of serum in saline. The mixtures are shaken briefly and then allowed to stand for 1 hour at room temperature. Erythrocyte suspension is then added in 0.2 ml amounts. Finally, the tubes are again shaken and allowed to stand at room temperature. The titer of a serum is taken as that dilution which completely inhibits agglutination. The lowest dilution of each serum is also tested for the presence of erythrocyte agglutinins by substituting 0.2 ml of saline for the hemagglutinin. A titration of hemagglutinin is also included with the test.

IV. A Note on References

The literature on viral hemagglutination is now very extensive. Detailed citations to original work published through 1961 and to older reviews are given by Rosen (1964). The most significant recent work on viral hemagglutination has been done with measles virus and with the adenoviruses. Data on the former virus have been summarized by Waterson (1965) and citations to that on the latter group can be found in the recent papers of Bauer and Wigand (1967) and Norrby and co-workers (Norrby and Skaaret, 1967; Wadell *et al.*, 1967).

REFERENCES

Bauer, W., and Wigand, R. (1967). *Arch. Ges. Virusforsch.* **21**, 11.

Chanock, R. M., and Sabin, A. B. (1953). *J. Immunol.* **70**, 271.

Norrby, E., and Skaaret, P. (1967). *Virology* **32**, 489.

Rosen, L. (1964). *In* "Techniques in Experimental Virology" (R. J. C. Harris, ed.), pp. 257-276. Academic Press, New York.

Wadell, G., Norrby, E., and Schönning, U. (1967). *Arch. Ges. Virusforsch.* **21**, 234.

Waterson, A. P. (1965). *Arch. Ges. Virusforsch.* **16**, 57.

28. Virus Neutralization Test

Karl Habel

Department of Experimental Pathology
Scripps Clinic and Research Foundation
La Jolla, California

I. Introduction

When viruses are mixed with antisera containing specific antibodies directed against the viral coat or envelope antigens, the two usually combine in such a way as to render the virus noninfectious (Dulbecco *et al.*, 1956). In general the neutralization test is the most specific of all virus-antibody reactions and other types of serological tests are usually evaluated in relation to it. With known standardized reagents the neutralization test can be used to identify virus or antibody and to quantitate both elements (Schmidt, 1964). The virus-inhibiting properties of specific antisera are very useful for eliminating infectious extracellular virus in virus-tissue culture systems in the course of basic studies of virus-cell relationships.

Neutralization tests are qualitative or quantitative in nature depending upon the information sought from them, but the principles and methods are common to both types. Since quantitative results are more meaningful and useful, the detailed procedure described here will be that to quantitate the neutralizing antibody titer of a given serum. Although tests may be carried out in any test system including animals and *in ovo* chick embryos in which a given virus may be quantitated, the method to be described will be that carried out in cell monolayers using the plaque technique for quantitation and is usually referred to as the "plaque reduction method."

II. Preliminary Procedures

Before carrying out a quantitative neutralization test the known elements in the test must be standardized. If the relative susceptibility of a given virus is being tested against a known antiviral serum then the antiserum must have been tested against the known homologous virus used to prepare it. If antiserum is being titrated for its ability to neutralize a known virus then the virus used in the test should be from a standardized and previously quantitated pool of stock virus.

A. Virus

1. Virus Stock Pools

In order to use a given number of plaque-forming units (pfu) in a test a working pool should be kept frozen. This working pool should have been prepared preferably from plaque-purified virus and demonstrated to be free of bacterial, fungal, and mycoplasma contamination. It should be stored diluted in a diluent and at a temperature known to maintain the pfu titer over a prolonged period of time. The diluent is usually the tissue culture maintenance medium with its 2–5% heat-inactivated normal serum component, and −70°C is the usual storage temperature.

2. Titration of Virus Pool

Titration of the stock virus pool for use in the neutralization test requires that it be done under the conditions of that test. Therefore, serial tenfold dilutions of virus are made in the tissue culture maintenance medium and are mixed with equal amounts of heat-inactivated normal serum of the same species at the most concentrated dilution to be used in the antiserum test. These mixtures are incubated at the same temperature and for the same time as to be used in the test, then plated in a plaquing system. From repeated tests on a single virus pool it should be possible to know within a 20% variation the number of pfu in a given dilution of the stock virus.

B. Antiserum

1. Preparation of Antiserum

The source of antiserum will vary depending on the purpose of the neutralization test. In general, standard sera will be used and the technique of their preparation has been given in Chapter 25 of this volume. For definitive work the virus used to produce the antiserum should be plaque purified, free of contaminants, and preferably separated from all other tissue culture elements by one of the purification procedures given in Chapters 9-13. To be sure that the antiserum contains no antibodies against cellular antigens from the tissue culture in which it was grown, the serum can be absorbed several times by mixing with packed uninfected cells of the type to be used in the tissue culture system employed in the final neutralization test. The cells are suspended at 20% in undiluted or one-fifth dilution of inactivated antiserum, incubated overnight at 4°C, then centrifuged at 20,000 rpm for 30 minutes.

2. *Inactivation of Antiserum*

To remove variable heat-labile nonspecific factors from the serum it should be heated at 56°C for 30 minutes. In some special situations where a heat-labile accessory factor is required for optimum neutralization, this should be added in the form of unheated normal serum from a standard frozen pool at the time of making the virus-serum mixture in the neutralization test. Standard antisera should be kept frozen at −20°C or lower temperatures.

3. *Control Serum*

In order to detect any nonspecific inhibition of plaque formation by the test antiserum, it is necessary to include a normal control serum. Preferably this should be serum obtained before immunization from the same animal in which the antiserum was prepared. In using the plaque reduction neutralization test for diagnostic purposes an acute phase, early serum sample should be tested along with a late, convalescent sample and a normal, antibody-free serum of the same species used as the control serum.

C. Test System

Obviously the monolayer cell culture to be used must be capable of producing distinct, countable plaques with the virus being neutralized. For standardized reproducible results preliminary experiments should determine the type of cell, the age of the culture, the growth medium as well as the agar overlay medium, the temperature of incubation, and time of observation to get the highest and most uniform plaque counts (see Chapters 14-18 on plaque assay).

III. Test Procedure

A. Virus Dilution

The final inoculum should contain 50 pfu/0.2 ml of the virus-serum mixture. Therefore, the standard stock pool virus is diluted in cold maintenance culture medium to contain 100 pfu/0.2 ml, based on previous titrations.

B. Antiserum Dilution

The dilution factor in setting up the serial dilutions will vary depending upon the accuracy of the antibody titration required, but in general fivefold or half log 10 dilutions are used. The diluent should be the same as that for the virus. The span of the dilution levels to be tested will vary with the potency of the serum but should extend from a dilution giving complete suppression of plaque formation to a dilution in which there is no reduction in the number of plaques. This usually requires three to five fivefold dilutions.

C. Control Serum

The inactivated normal control serum should be diluted to the same degree as the most concentrated dilution of the antiserum in the test.

Where possible a positive control serum should be included at a dilution known from previous standardization to give an 80% reduction in the pfu as compared to the normal serum controls.

D. Mixing of Virus and Serum Dilutions

One-half milliliter of the virus dilution containing 100 pfu/0.2 ml should be pipetted into a series of small test tubes, the number depending on how many serial dilutions of antiserum are to be tested. To these is added 0.5 ml of the various dilutions of antiserum and the single dilutions of the normal control and the positive control sera. A further control tube should contain 0.5 ml of diluent only. Mixing is done by shaking and the stoppered tubes are then placed at room temperature, 37°C, or 4°C, depending on the temperature sensitivity of the virus. Where room temperatures are relatively constant this is usually used. The time of incubation is usually 30–60 minutes, but with some viruses longer periods may be required.

E. Inoculation of Cell Cultures

Previously grown confluent cell monolayers in 60 mm plastic or glass petri dishes have their growth medium removed and are washed once with BSS. After pouring off the BSS wash, 0.2 ml from each of the virus-serum and control mixture tubes is dropped onto the center of each of two culture dishes. The dishes are rotated a few times to spread the inoculum and are then placed in a CO_2 incubator set at the proper temperature, humidity, and gas mixture for the cell-virus system. Where CO_2 incubators are not available, plaquing may be carried out in cultures grown in stoppered small bottles.

The length of time of incubation will depend upon the absorption characteristics of the virus involved, usually 30 minutes to 3 hours. At the end of this time the inoculum should be pipetted off and the cultures washed once with balanced salt solution (BSS) before adding the overlay medium.

F. Overlay Medium

The technique for this is the same as described in Chapters 14-18 for plaque assay and the ingredients of the overlay depend upon the virus-cell system involved. This likewise determines the conditions of incubation, the question of whether additional feeding overlays must be applied, and the incubation time before adding the final overlay containing the vital stain for developing the plaques.

G. Reading Results of Test

The next day after the cell-staining overlay the plaques are counted. The plaque reduction test is based only on plaque count although frequently there will be a reduction of plaque size in the antiserum-treated cultures. In some systems where the reproducibility of plaque counts from culture to culture is at a high level, 50% reduction of pfu may be taken as the end point but a safer cut off level is 80% reduction. For a test to be valid the variation of pfu per plate in the two similar cultures should be no more than 20% and the positive serum control should show between 50 and 95% reduction.

H. Calculation of Neutralizing Index

A simple mathematical use of the twofold dilution of antiserum occurring at the time of mixture with virus times the dilution factor of the highest dilution giving at least 80% reduction of pfu represents the 80% plaque reduction index in 0.2 ml of the original antiserum.

IV. Limitations of Neutralization Test

An important limitation is variability in virus susceptibility from one batch of cell cultures to another. Where possible the use of an established, cloned line of cells should reduce the variability. Obviously, this type of test is limited to virus-cell systems where definite countable plaques are produced.

Nonspecific inhibition of plaque production owing to factors in the antiserum can normally be eliminated if the serum has been previously absorbed with normal cells.

A common phenomenon in virus neutralization is the presence of a persistent nonneutralizable fraction of virus where increasing amounts of antibody do not reduce the infectivity below a certain minimal level. This may result from agglutination of virus particles making some of them unavailable to antibody (Wallis and Melnick, 1967) or to the formation of infectious virus-antibody complexes (see below).

V. Modification of the Test

In certain virus-cell systems plaques cannot be produced or at least not visualized by the standard cell-staining procedure. The foci of infected cells may be quantitated by developing them with fluorescent antibody staining (see Chapter 30), hemadsorption with red blood cells (RBC) that are agglutinable by the virus (see Chapter 27), or by interference with the growth and cell destruction of a second challenge virus (see Chapter 16).

Less quantitative tests using cell culture tubes with liquid medium into which the virus-antiserum mixtures are inoculated depend on visible cell destruction[cytopathic effect (CPE)] or reduction of cell metabolic activity as indicated by a change in the pH of the culture medium (metabolic-inhibition neutralization test).

With viruses for which only low antibody responses can be produced, enhancement of the plaque reduction may be obtained by incorporating the antiserum in the agar overlay medium in addition to the incubation of the virus-antiserum mixture.

For showing small antigenic differences between different viruses or strains of the same virus, the kinetic neutralization test is probably the most sensitive.

VI. Kinetic Neutralization Test

This test is based on the rate of neutralization of relatively large amounts of different viruses by a fixed amount of a given antibody. The number of pfu of infectious virus remaining after the reaction of virus-antiserum mixtures is measured at increasing times of incubation of the mixture (McBride, 1959).

A. Virus Preparation

Stock virus previously titrated for pfu titer is diluted in BSS to contain between 5×10^5 and 5×10^6 pfu/ml.

B. Antiserum Preparation

The antiserum is diluted to that concentration found by preliminary tests to allow survival of 10^{-1}–10^{-2} of the homologous virus preparation after 15 minutes incubation at 37°C.

C. Virus and Antiserum Mixture

One-half milliliter of the diluted virus and the properly diluted antiserum both prewarmed to 37°C are mixed in a 13 by 100 mm test tube and placed in a 37°C water bath.

D. Sampling and Plating

At 0, 2, 5, 10, and 15 minutes 0.1 ml is removed and immediately blown into 100 ml of cold BSS. This dilution after mixing and a 1–10 dilution of it are each plated on two cell monolayer petri dish cultures with 0.2 ml inoculum. The dishes are rotated to evenly spread the inoculum, incubated at the proper temperature for the proper adsorption time, and then overlayed with agar medium, incubated, stained with a final vital stain overlay after the proper incubation period, and the plaques then counted.

E. Calculation of *K* Values

Plot the results showing the amount of surviving pfu of each sample on a logarithmic scale against time on a linear scale. A straight line is drawn through the points and the K value is determined by the slope of the line using the following equation:

$$K = \frac{D}{t} 2.3 \log \frac{V_0}{V_t}$$

where V_0 and V_t = active virus at times zero and t, and $D = 1/C$ = the dilution of antiserum.

F. Comments

For more complete comparisons of two strains of virus, reciprocal tests should be made using antisera to both viruses.

In general, it has been found that sharper differences between closely related strains of virus can be shown if the antiserum has been obtained early after the course of immunization of the serum-producing animal. Small differences tend to disappear when serum is obtained after many immunizing booster doses of antigen.

VII. Immune Precipitation Test

In some virus-antibody systems such as with herpes simplex, lactic dehydrogenase, Aleutian mink disease, and lymphocytic choriomeningitis viruses, there is evidence that antiviral antibody may form complexes with the virus particle without destroying its infectivity. In fact, the persistent nonneutralizable fraction noted previously may be this type of complex. In the case of the lactic dehydrogenase virus and Aleutian mink disease virus it is difficult, if not impossible, to demonstrate neutralizing type of antibody by standard procedures. However, the infectious virus-antibody complexes can be demonstrated by their immune precipitation in the presence of anti-γ-globulin antibody. On removal of the resulting precipitate the infectivity of the preparation is reduced (Notkins *et al.*, 1966).

Virus-antibody complexes may already be preformed in the serum of an animal exhibiting a persistent carrier type of infection. Otherwise a virus suspension having an infectious titer of 10^5 can be mixed with the antiserum suspected of containing antiviral antibody and the mixture incubated as in the neutralization test. Normal serum from the same species is mixed with virus as a control. At the end of the incubation period the virus-antibody mixture is divided into two parts. To one is added an antibody produced against the γ-globulin of the species of serum which is the source of the antibody in sufficient quantity to precipitate all the γ-globulin contained in the antiserum (see Chapter 29 for technical details). An antibody against the albumin of the same species serum is likewise added to the second sample. The anti-γ-globulin is also added to the control virus-normal serum mixture. After incubation at 37°C for 1 hour the tubes are centrifuged to pellet the precipitates and the supernatants are titered for infectious virus by the best available quantitative technique (plaque assay if possible). Reduction of greater than tenfold with the test serum as compared to the normal serum control is significant evidence of the presence of virus-antibody complexes. The virus-antiserum mixture precipitated with antialbumin antibody should show no reduction in infectivity because of nonspecific trapping of virus.

This procedure is very similar to the radioactive coprecipitation technique described in Chapter 29 by Horwitz and Scharff.

REFERENCES

Dulbecco, R., Vogt, M., and Strickland, A. (1956). *Virology* **2**, 162.
McBride, W. (1959). *Virology* **7**, 45.
Notkins, A. L., Mahar, S., Scheele, C., and Goffman, J. (1966). *J. Exptl. Med.* **124**, 81.
Schmidt, N. (1964). *In* "Diagnostic Procedures for Viral and Rickettsial Diseases" (E. H. Lennette and N. J. Schmidt, eds.), 3rd ed., pp. 119–129. Am. Public Health Assoc., New York.
Wallis, C., and Melnick, J. L. (1967). *J. Virol.* **1**, 478.

29. Immunological Precipitation of Radioactively Labeled Viral Proteins*

M. S. Horwitz and M. D. Scharff

Departments of Cell Biology and Medicine
Albert Einstein College of Medicine
Bronx, New York

I. General Introduction

The immunological precipitation of radioactively labeled viral antigens provides a useful technique for studying the synthesis of viral proteins (Scharff and Levintow, 1963; Scharff *et al.*, 1964). By analyzing cells after brief incubations with radioactive precursors, it is possible to determine the rate of synthesis of an individual viral protein at any time in the replicative cycle. While complement fixation and hemagglutination also allow the recognition and quantitation of viral antigens, they measure amounts of antigen rather than rates of synthesis. The precipitin techniques described below may also be used to identify viral antigens in column effluents and sucrose gradient fractions. The immunologically precipitated protein may be recovered and further characterized chemically (see below). Finally, the indirect technique may be used to detect small amounts of antiviral antibodies (Gerloff *et al.*, 1962).

The immunological precipitation of labeled virus protein may be carried out either by indirect precipitation, which requires only small

*This work was supported by grants from the National Institutes of Health (AI-4153 and AI-5231), American Cancer Society (E-379B), and National Science Foundation (GB 4751 and GB 6364Y). Dr. Horwitz is an ACS postdoctoral fellow (PF-416) and Dr. Scharff is the recipient of an NIH Career Development Award.

amounts of antiviral antibody, or by direct coprecipitation which requires large amounts of purified antigen and antiviral antibody. In the indirect technique, small amounts of highly specific antibody (usually rabbit hyperimmune antiserum) are reacted with infected cell lysates, sucrose gradient fractions, or column effluents which contain radioactively labeled viral antigen. Since both the antigen and the antibody are present in small amounts, immune complexes form but do not precipitate. These soluble complexes are then precipitated with antibody (usually sheep or goat) made against rabbit γ-globulin (RγG) (Fig. 1a). In the direct technique, sufficient amounts of antibody and purified unlabeled viral antigen are added to labeled cell lysates (or other anti-

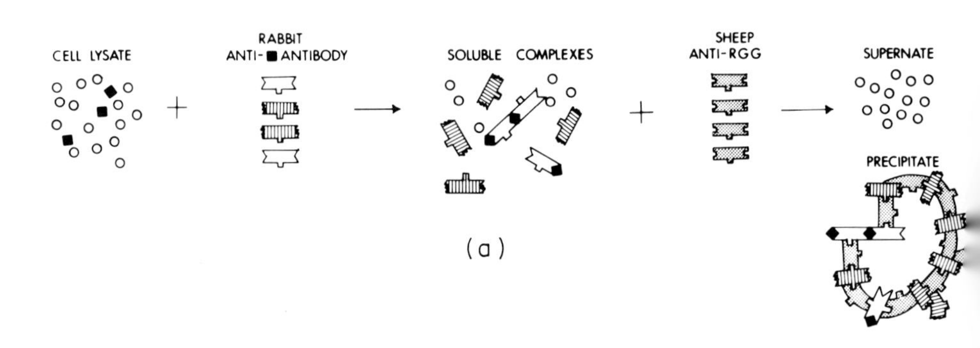

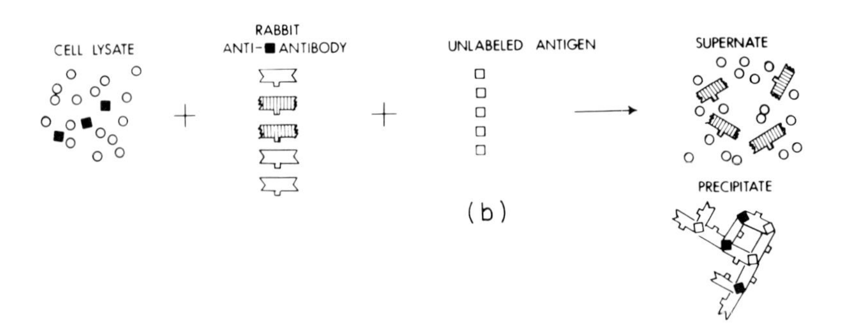

FIG. 1. Schematic representation of the (a) indirect and (b) direct precipitation techniques: The radioactively labeled antigen being investigated is representated by the filled squares (■), and other cellular and viral proteins by the open circle (○). The rabbit antiserum contains both antibody against the viral antigen, represented by the open symbol and rabbit γ-globulin which is not directed against that antigen (striped symbol). The sheep anti-rabbit γ-globulin is stippled.

gen-containing samples) to form an immunological precipitate. The small amount of labeled viral antigen is then specifically coprecipitated along with the unlabeled added viral antigen (Fig. 1b).

The indirect technique requires highly purified antigen only for immunization, and small amounts of rabbit antibody are used for each determination. The antibody, however, must be highly specific for the antigen being examined. Even small amounts of antibody against cell protein or other viral antigens will form soluble complexes and subsequently be precipitated by the sheep anti-rabbit γ-globulin. The direct technique is less sensitive to small amounts of antibody against other antigens since only those antigen–antibody systems present in large enough amounts to precipitate will be counted; small amounts of antibody against cell proteins will remain as soluble complexes. If valid data are to be obtained with either technique, adequate controls must be provided for the nonspecific precipitation of radioactivity.

II. Indirect Technique

A. Introduction

An example of the use of the indirect technique to examine adenovirus infected cells is presented in Table I. Cells which had been infected with adenovirus type 2 were incubated with radioactive amino acids. A cell lysate was prepared and was centrifuged at 100,000 *g* just prior to immunological analysis. It was then divided into eight aliquots which were reacted in duplicate with: (1) rabbit antiserum which was made against purified adenovirions and which reacted with all three of the major structural viral antigens (hexon, penton, and fiber); (2) a rabbit antiserum which was specific for the hexon antigen; (3) a rabbit antiserum made against lambda bacteriophage which would act as a control for the nonspecific precipitation of radioactivity; and (4) trichloroacetic acid (TCA) to determine the total acid precipitable radioactivity in the lysate. After 30 minutes at 37°C, sheep anti-rabbit γ-globulin was added to 1, 2, and 3 and the samples incubated for an additional 2 hours at 37°C (see Fig. 1a). The immunological precipitates which formed were sedimented at 2000 rpm in a refrigerated centrifuge, washed three times in phosphate-buffered saline, dissolved in 0.5 ml of 0.25 *N* acetic acid, and after being dried on planchets counted for radioactivity.

The radioactivity precipitated by the antiphage antiserum was subtracted from 1 and 2 to determine the amount of specifically

TABLE I
INDIRECT IMMUNOLOGICAL ANALYSIS OF ADENOVIRUS-INFECTED CELLS

Rabbit antiserums	Total immunologically precipitated counts/minute (±10%)	Specifically precipitated counts/minute (total − no. 3)	Acid precipitable counts/minute (TCA)	Percent specifically precipitated
1. Anti-whole virus	1656	1434	4650	31
2. Anti-hexon	920	698	4650	15
3. Anti-bacteriophage	222	0	4650	0

precipitated counts in the three major structural antigens and in the hexon antigen. By comparison with the total acid precipitable radioactivity, it was determined that 31% of the soluble labeled proteins consisted of hexon, penton, and fiber and half of this, or 15% of the total, was hexon.

These results can be considered valid, however, only if all of the following requirements were fulfilled: (1) the rabbit antiviral antibody must have been proved to be specific under the conditions of the experiment—proof of specificity by some less sensitive method such as Ouchterlony agar diffusion is not sufficient, (2) there must have been enough rabbit antibody present to bind all of the available viral antigen, (3) there must have been sufficient sheep anti-rabbit γ-globulin present to precipitate all of the rabbit γ-globulin, and (4) each determination must have been properly controlled for the nonspecific precipitation of radioactivity. The preparation and quantitation of the immunological reagents to fulfill these requirements will be described in the subsequent sections.

B. PREPARATION OF ANTIBODY AGAINST RABBIT γ-GLOBULIN

It is desirable that the sheep or goat antibody against rabbit γ-globulin be specific since contaminating antibody against other serum proteins (such as albumin) may result in an increase in the nonspecifically precipitated radioactivity. Sheep or goat anti-rabbit γ-globulin can be obtained commercially but it is quite expensive, sometimes of low titer, and often slow to precipitate if it comes from very hyperimmunized animals. For these reasons we have routinely made our own antisera.

The rabbit γ-globulin used for immunization is purified first by column chromatography and then by acrylamide gel electrophoresis. The electrophoretic step is optional. One milliliter of rabbit serum is dialyzed against 0.01 *M* phosphate buffer pH 6.6, then chromatographed on a diethylaminoethyl (DEAE) column with the same buffer. Rabbit γ G globulin is the first protein eluted from the column under these conditions.

If subsequent purification on acrylamide gels is to be carried out, the technique of Davis (1964) may be used. Two gels are run simultaneously, a marker gel containing 10–25 μg and a second gel containing 0.5–1 mg. After the broad γ-globulin peak has been located near the top of the marker gel by staining, the corresponding area of the second gel is cut out with a scalpel or a razor blade and introduced into the barrel of a 2 ml Luer-Lok syringe. Phosphate-buffered saline (PBS) is added to bring the solution to the desired volume, and the gel crushed by forcing it between the two syringes (Horwitz and Scharff, Chapter 26 this volume). An equal volume of complete Freund's adjuvant containing 12 mg/ml of *M. butyricum* (this large amount of mycobacteria is not toxic for the sheep, and results in elevated levels of antibody) is added and the mixture emulsified as described (Horwitz and Scharff, Chapter 26, this volume). If the γ-globulin eluted from DEAE is to be used without additional purification, between 0.5 and 5 mg of RγG is emulsified in the same way. Sheep or goats are immunized by injecting 0.2–0.5 ml of the adjuvant mixture intramuscularly into the upper part of each leg.

After 4 weeks the animals are bled of small quantities of blood for determination of antibody titers. An initial estimate of the amount of antibody against rabbit γ-globulin, and of its specificity, can be obtained using the Ouchterlony technique of agar gel diffusion (Salzman and Moss, Chapter 32, this volume). The undiluted sheep or goat antiserum is tested against serial dilutions of the rabbit serum. The sheep or goat antiserum is placed in the center well, and the rabbit serum in the peripheral wells at dilutions of 1:5, 1:10, 1:20, 1:40, 1:80, and 1:160 (Fig. 2). An additional Ouchterlony plate is set up comparing whole rabbit serum and the DEAE purified RγG to be sure that the sheep antibody is directed against RγG. Since both the antigen (RγG) and the antibody (sheep or goat anti-RγG) are γ-globulins with approximately equal mobilities in agar, the dilution at which the line of precipitation is equidistant from the antigen and antibody wells represents "equivalence" (a more exact definition of equivalence will be given below, but for the purpose of the discussion here it may be considered the highest dilution of sheep antisera which will completely precipitate all of the RγG). If equivalence is found at the dilutions between 1:5 and 1:20, the sheep antiserum is of sufficient potency for use in the indirect precipitin test, and the animal may then be exsanguinated.

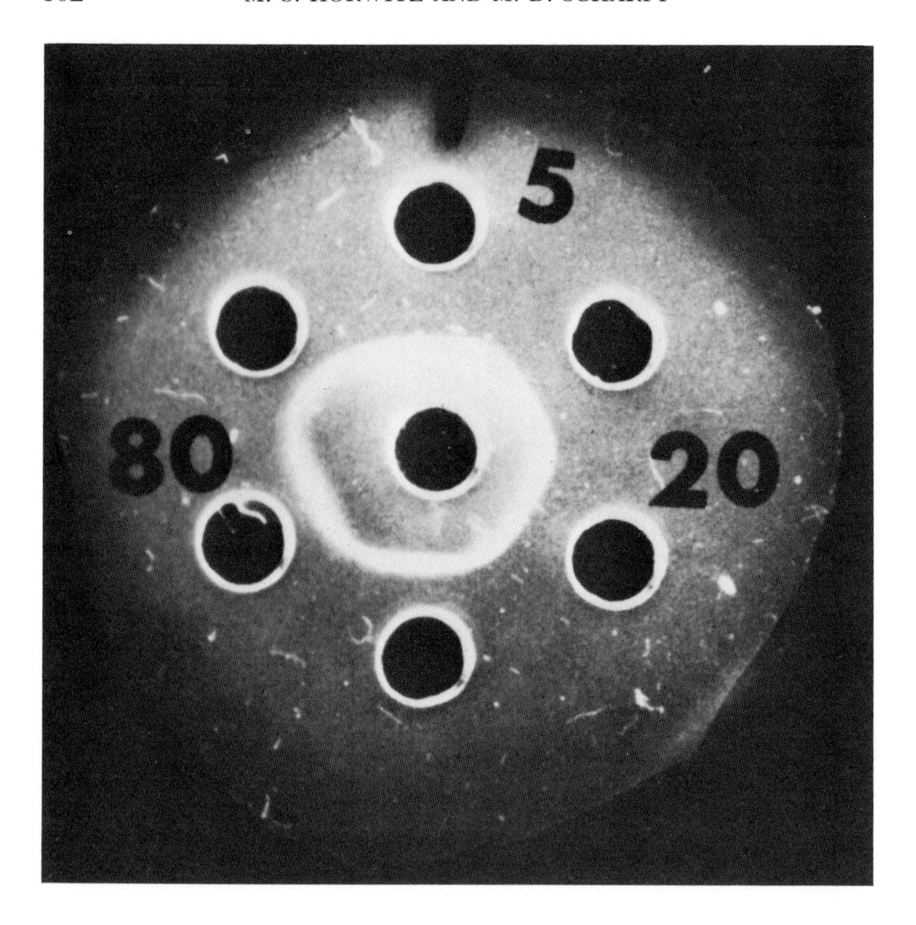

FIG. 2. Ouchterlony agar diffusion analysis of sheep anti-rabbit γ-globulin. Undiluted sheep anti-rabbit antiserum has been placed in the center well and twofold dilutions ranging between 1:5 and 1:160 of rabbit antiserum (containing antibody against the hexon antigen of adenovirus type 2) have been placed in the peripheral wells (the reciprocal of the dilution is shown on the figure). The precipitin line is approximately equidistant between the antibody and the antigen wells at both the 1:20 and 1:40 dilutions.

C. Preparation of Rabbit Antiviral Antibody

Antiviral antiserum is obtained from rabbits which have been immunized with viral antigens as described by Horwitz and Scharff, Chapter 26. Additional rabbits should also have been immunized against an unrelated antigen to provide a comparable hyperimmune serum to serve as a control for the nonspecific precipitation of radioactivity. The presence of the desired antibody against viral antigens can be determined by the use of the Ouchterlony technique of agar diffusion. However, even if repeated immunization does not result in levels of antibody sufficient to be detected by this relatively insensitive technique, the rabbit antiserum may still be adequate for the indirect precipitin technique, and should be processed and tested as described below.

Rabbit antisera may be partially purified to obtain an enriched γ-globulin fraction, thereby reducing some of the extraneous proteins that might nonspecifically add to the precipitate. The γ-globulin from 10 ml of rabbit serum is precipitated by dropwise addition of 5 ml of saturated ammonium sulfate (51.5 gm/100 ml). The precipitate is allowed to form overnight at 4°C, centrifuged at 2500 rpm for 15 minutes in a refrigerated centrifuge, the supernatant decanted, and the precipitate dissolved in 10 ml of 0.145 *M* sodium chloride. The γ-globulin is then dialyzed in the cold against several changes of the isotonic sodium chloride solution until sulfate ions can no longer be detected in an aliquot of dialysate by precipitation with a few drops of 10% barium chloride. Residual undissolved protein is removed by centrifugation. The γ-globulin solution is diluted with phosphate buffered saline to 40 ml (four times the original volume of serum) and frozen in small aliquots. This dilution is suggested since in our experience it has provided a convenient starting point for the quantitative precipitin curves which constitute the next step in the procedure.

D. Quantitation of the Sheep Anti-Rabbit γ-Globulin System

In order to determine the amount of sheep anti-rabbit γ-globulin and of rabbit γ-globulin (containing the antibody against viral antigens), which must be used in the indirect precipitin technique, quantitative precipitin curves must be carried out. The precipitin reaction between antigen and antibody conforms to a well-defined pattern (Kabat and Mayer, 1961) which is illustrated by the idealized representation shown in Fig. 3. The amount of antigen–antibody complex precipitated increases as increasing amounts of antigen are added to a constant amount of antibody. After a point of maximum precipitation is reached, the further addition of antigen results in a reduction in the amount of antigen–antibody complex precipitated. In the rising part of the curve, called the "region of antibody excess," sufficient antigen has not been added to precipitate all of the available antibody. In a narrow region, called the "zone of equivalence," around the point of maximal precipitation, all of the antibody and all of the antigen are

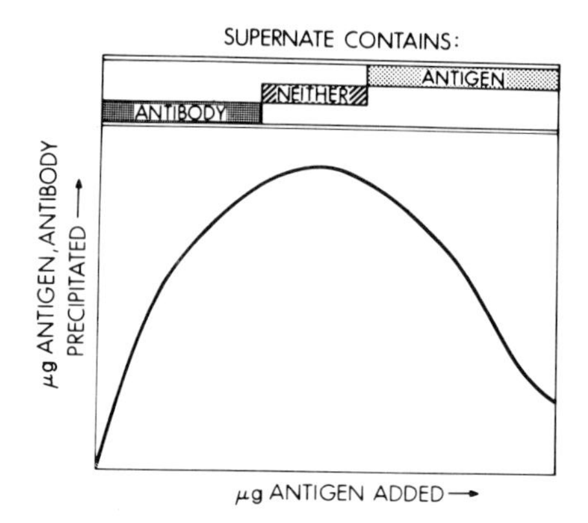

FIG. 3. Idealized quantitative precipitin curve. Varying amounts of antigen are added to a constant amount of antibody. The amount of protein in the precipitate is shown by the solid line. The supernate is tested for both antigen and antibody. Neither is present in the zone of equivalence. A detailed presentation of this subject can be found in Kabat and Mayer (1961).

precipitated; neither can be found in excess in the supernatant. With the continued addition of antigen, soluble antigen–antibody complexes are formed, and all of the antigen is no longer precipitated.

Since in the indirect technique, the purpose of the sheep anti-rabbit γ-globulin is to precipitate all of the labeled viral antigen which has complexed with rabbit antibody (see Fig. 1a), it is necessary that sufficient amounts of sheep antisera be added to precipitate all of the rabbit γ-globulin.

As described above, the preliminary quantitation of the rabbit γ-globulin and sheep anti-rabbit γ-globulin is carried out by agar diffusion. The following example demonstrates how the results of Ouchterlony analysis may be used to set up the quantitative precipitin curves. In the indirect precipitin technique, it is desirable to work with immunological precipitates containing between 300 and 500 μg of protein since larger precipitates result in increased nonspecific precipitation of radioactivity and smaller precipitates cannot be thoroughly washed without the loss of antigen (Kabat and Mayer, 1961). Since at equivalence, the ratio of sheep γ-globulin (antibody) to rabbit γ-globulin (antigen) is usually between 3 and 5 to one, the desired precipitate should contain 100 μg of RγG. If it is assumed that rabbit serum contains approximately 10 mg/ml of γ-globulin, the desired amount of RγG will be contained in 0.01 ml of whole serum. By Ouchterlony analysis undiluted sheep serum was equivalent to approximately a

1:20 dilution of rabbit serum (Fig. 2). Therefore, 20 times as much sheep anti-rabbit γ-globulin, or 0.20 ml, should be added to the 0.01 ml of rabbit serum to achieve the proper amount of precipitate in the general area of equivalence. In this case, ammonium sulfate precipitated γ-globulin had been prepared and after the initial dilution of 1:4 (see above) a further one-half dilution was carried out so that the predicted point of equivalence would be in the tube containing 0.2 ml of sheep anti-rabbit γ-globulin and 0.08 ml of RγG. While each of these calculations is based on certain assumptions which represent only broad approximations, they provide an estimate of how much reagent should be used in the initial quantitative precipitin curve. As a result of the calculations, points were picked on either side of the predicted equivalence so that the regions of antibody excess, equivalence, and antigen excess could be clearly defined (Table II). All dilutions were carried out with phosphate-buffered saline since its pH of 7.2 is in the middle of the optimum range for immunological precipitation and the concentration of sodium chloride is also optimal (Kabat and Mayer, 1961). If chicken sera are being used, the optimum salt concentration is 0.9 *M* NaCl rather than 0.145 *M* NaCl (Kabat and Mayer, 1961).

Each of the points in the precipitin curve was carried out in duplicate in conical centrifuge tubes. After the contents are added in the order shown in Table II, they were thoroughly mixed in a Vortex mixer, and the tubes incubated at 37°C for 2 hours. These conditions have been selected because in our experience nearly complete precipitation may be achieved in this time at 37°C and the amount of radioactivity nonspecifically precipitated is less than if the reaction is carried out more slowly at 4°C. At the end of the incubation, the tubes were centrifuged for 10 minutes at 2000 rpm in a refrigerated centrifuge at 4°C. The supernate was decanted and the tubes drained by inversion in a paper-lined test-tube rack (Kabat and Mayer, 1961). One drop of chilled phosphate-buffered saline is then added to each tube, and the

TABLE II
QUANTITATIVE PRECIPITIN CURVE WITH SHEEP ANTI-RγG AND RγG

Tube no.:	1	2	3	4	5	6	7	8	9	10
Anti-hexon RγG (ml)	0.020	0.040	0.060	0.080	0.100	0.120	0.140	0.160	0.180	0.200
PBS (ml)	0.280	0.260	0.240	0.220	0.200	0.180	0.160	0.140	0.120	0.100
Sheep anti-RγG (ml)	0.200	0.200	0.200	0.200	0.200	0.200	0.200	0.200	0.200	0.200

precipitates resuspended with a Vortex mixer, diluted to 0.5 ml with additional PBS, and centrifuged as described above. After three such washes, the precipitates were dissolved in 3 ml of 0.25 *M* acetic acid (1.43 ml of glacial acetic acid/100 ml of water) and the optical density at 279 mμ was read in a spectrophotometer (Gitlin, 1949).

The precipitin curve presented in Table II and Figure 4a, uses the reagents tested on the Ouchterlony plate (Fig. 2). The rabbit γ-

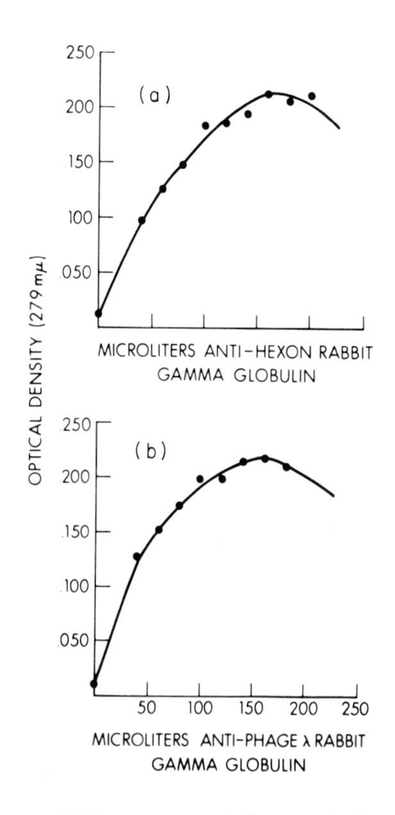

FIG. 4. Quantitative precipitin curves carried out with sheep anti-rabbit γ-globulin and partially purified rabbit γ-globulin containing either antibody against hexon antigen or lambda bacteriophage. The anti-hexon γ-globulin had been prepared by ammonium sulfate precipitation and represents a 1:8 dilution of the original antiserum. The anti-bacteriophage antiserum was prepared similarly but represents a 1:16 dilution of the original antiserum. The indicated amounts of rabbit γ-globulin (microliter of the diluted rabbit γ-globulin) were added to 0.2 ml of sheep anti-rabbit γ-globulin, incubated at 37°C for 2 hours, the precipitates washed as described in the text, dissolved in 0.25 *N* HAc, and absorbance determined at 279 mμ (Gitlin, 1949). The absorbance can be converted into micrograms of protein and the amount of antigen and antibody in each precipitate determined using the formulas presented by Gitlin.

globulin contained antibody against hexon, one of the structural proteins of adenovirus. Figure 4b also shows the quantitative precipitin curve of the serum (containing antibody against lambda bacteriophage) which will be used as a control for the nonspecific precipitation of radioactivity (see Table I).

Once equivalence has been determined, five dilutions in the region of slight antibody excess were examined to determine the number of counts nonspecifically precipitated. (Points in slight antibody excess for the sheep anti-rabbit γ-globulin system have been chosen so that maximum amounts of rabbit antibody can be used.) In the case presented here, uninfected HeLa cells were labeled with valine-^{14}C and threonine under identical conditions to those which would later be used in experiments on the synthesis of adenovirus protein. After centrifugation at 100,000 *g* for 30 minutes, 0.1 ml volumes of the concentrated labeled cytoplasm were mixed with the five dilutions of anti-hexon RγG and anti-bacteriophage RγG, the volume brought to 0.3 ml with phosphate-buffered saline, incubated for 30 minutes at 37°C, and then 0.2 ml of sheep anti-rabbit γ-globulin added. After additional incubation for 2 hours, the precipitates which formed were washed as described above, dissolved in 1 ml 0.25 *M* acetic acid, dried on planchets and counted in a low background counter. Table III shows the number of nonspecific counts precipitated from uninfected HeLa cell cytoplasm by both anti-hexon and anti-bacteriophage systems. Based on the experimental results, 0.1 ml of each of the rabbit antisera was used. Although the amount of radioactivity nonspecifically precipitated did not vary with the dilution of rabbit γ-globulin and was the same for both systems, this is not always true. Therefore, each set of reagents must be tested individually.

Since considerable effort is made in this technique to provide proper controls for the nonspecific precipitation of radioactivity, it is useful to mention some of the characteristics of this nonspecifically precipitated radioactivity. A significant portion of the nonspecifically precipitated radioactivity has nothing to do with the antigen–antibody precipitate but is caused by material which pellets on centrifugation of cell lysates after incubation for 2½–3 hours at 37°C. This material is present even though the cell lysate was centrifuged just prior to the addition of the immunological reagents and presumably results from continued aggregation of cellular material. This finding suggests that preliminary high speed centrifugation would appreciably reduce the nonspecific precipitation of radioactivity, and this in fact is so. When soluble viral proteins are being assayed, cell lysates are routinely sedimented at 100,000 *g* immediately prior to immunological precipita-

TABLE III
NONSPECIFIC PRECIPITATION OF RADIOACTIVITY

RγG (ml):	0.060	0.080	0.100	0.120	0.140
Sheep anti-RγG (ml):	0.20	0.20	0.20	0.20	0.20
Counts/minute (±10%) precipitated with anti-hexon RγG and sheep anti-RγG	298	313	292	260	297
Counts/minute (±10%) precipitated with anti-bacteriophage RγG and sheep anti-RγG	364	331	314	317	306

tion. However, if either whole virus, or large aggregates of viral subunits, are being investigated, such high speed sedimentation is not possible. In our hands, a variety of attempts to reduce the residual nonspecific precipitation have not been fully successful. Immunological precipitation can be carried out in the presence of 0.5% deoxycholate, and this results in a small but significant reduction in the amount of nonspecifically precipitated radioactivity. The amount of radioactivity nonspecifically precipitated when the reaction is carried out in the presence of sucrose, as when sucrose gradient fractions are being assayed, is much lower than with crude cell lysates; however, quantitative precipitin curves carried out in the presence of 10–20% sucrose have shown that only 80% precipitation occurs. Some investigators do a preliminary immunological precipitation with an unrelated system prior to specific precipitation with the hope that this will reduce the number of counts nonspecifically precipitated. While some reduction is gained by this maneuver, in our hands it has not been sufficiently helpful to use routinely. Based on analogy with the fixation of complement by antigen–antibody precipitates, it seemed possible that the addition of large amounts of unlabeled cell lysates from uninfected cells might reduce the amount of radioactivity nonspecifically precipitated. However, a number of experiments revealed the opposite to be true, and it appears that the addition of unlabeled cell lysates provided more material for aggregation. In conclusion, 3-5% of the radioactivity in crude cell lysates is almost always nonspecifically precipitated, and it is this which makes careful quantitation and preparation of adequate controls absolutely necessary.

E. QUANTITATION OF THE RABBIT ANTIVIRAL ANTIBODY

In order to obtain quantitative information from the indirect precipitin technique, it is necessary to establish that there is sufficient antiviral antibody to bind all of the labeled viral antigen. This is most easily determined by adding a constant amount of rabbit antiviral antibody to serial 2-fold dilutions of radioactively labeled sample containing the maximum virus antigen expected in the experiment (Fig. 5). The previously determined amounts of rabbit γ-globulin (anti-hexon antiserum) and sheep anti-rabbit γ-globulin were used. For purposes of graphic representation, both the abscissa and the ordinate are logarithms of the actual values. It can be seen that this particular hexon preparation must be diluted eight times before a parallel linear relationship was established between the counts specifically immunologically precipitated and those precipitated by TCA. It is clear that at the higher concentrations of hexon too much antigen is present to be bound by the available antibody and immunological analysis could be performed only if the samples were first diluted.

F. Examination of the Specificity of the Antiviral Antisera

Valid results will be obtained only if the antiviral antiserum used is specific for the antigen being assayed. Determination of specificity by

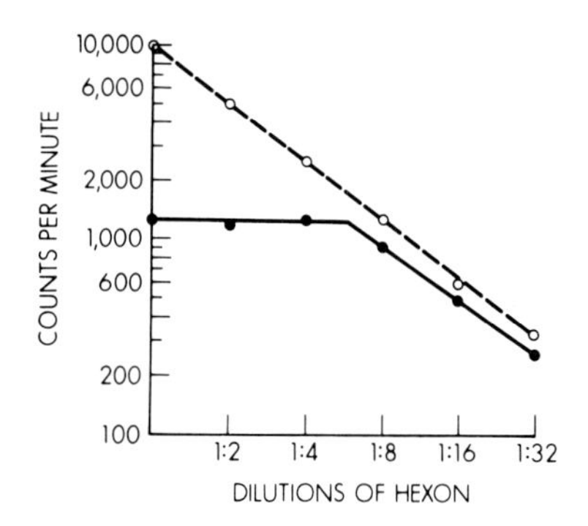

FIG. 5. Determination of antigen and antibody excess for the rabbit anti-hexon antiserum. Radioactively labeled hexon purified by one cycle of DEAE column chromatography was serially diluted and reacted for 30 minutes at 37°C with 0.1 ml of a 1:8 dilution of rabbit anti-hexon antibody. Sheep anti-rabbit γ-globulin (0.2 ml) was then added and incubated for 2 hours at 37°C. The precipitates were washed, dissolved in 0.25 *N* HAc, and counted as described in the text. At each dilution equal aliquots were examined for acid precipitable radioactivity with TCA. Where multiple antigens are being precipitated, the region of antigen excess is usually represented by a curved line (rather than the flat plateau seen here) representing successive breaks in the curve as antibody excess is achieved for each antigen. (○) Trichloracetic acid precipitable counts and (●) immunoprecipitable counts.

techniques such as agar diffusion, which are considerably less sensitive than the indirect precipitin technique, are not sufficient; it is necessary to establish specificity by indirect precipitation. This may easily be done by electrophoresis of the labeled precipitated antigen on SDS-containing acrylamide gels (Fig. 6) (Maizel, Chapter 33, this volume). Both specific and nonspecific precipitates were formed in the presence of radioactively labeled adenovirus-infected HeLa cells (see Table I), washed three times with phosphate-buffered saline, and dissolved in 2% sodium dodecyl sulfate, 1% mercaptoethanol, and 0.5 *M* urea. After heating the sample to 100° for 1 minute, dialysis was carried out against 0.01 *M* phosphate buffer, 0.1% SDS, and 0.1% mercaptoethanol as has been described by Maizel. Figure 6B shows an acrylamide gel of adenovirus 2 infected HeLa cells which have not

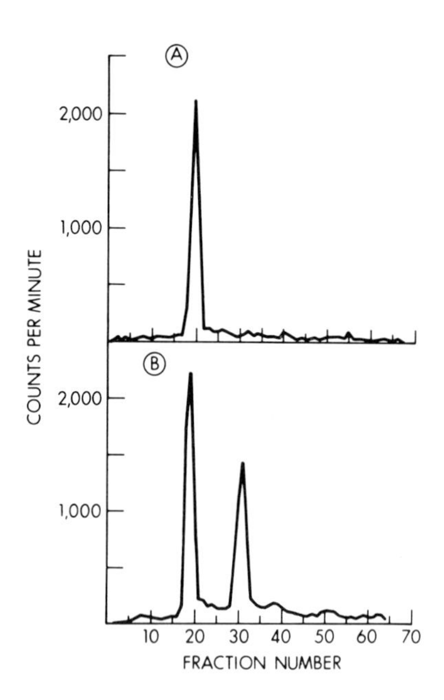

FIG. 6. Acrylamide gel analysis of labeled antigen precipitated with anti-hexon antiserum from adenovirus infected cells. (B) The gel electropherogram of the soluble proteins of an adenovirus-infected cell. (A) The gel electropherogram of the immunological precipitate resulting from incubation of first rabbit anti-hexon antiserum and then sheep anti-RγG with the infected cell lysate shown in B. Conditions of gel electrophoresis on neutral SDS-containing acrylamide gels are briefly described in the text and detailed by Maizel elsewhere in this volume. The nonspecifically precipitated radioactivity also run on gels, has not been subtracted from A. If it had been subtracted, the nonhexon radioactivity would be reduced to background levels.

been immunologically precipitated. Peak 1 has previously been identified as the hexon peptide which forms the major soluble protein of the adenovirus infected cell. Peak 2 is a combination of the penton and fiber peptides (Maizel *et al.*, 1968) which comprise other major soluble viral proteins. When the cell lysate was treated with antiserum made against hexon (Fig. 6A), only the hexon peptide could be identified in the immunological precipitate. One can conclude that under the conditions of the indirect precipitin technique (see Table I), this rabbit antiserum did not contain antibody against the penton and fiber. If this sort of examination had revealed small amounts of antibody against proteins other than the hexon, the antiserum could have been absorbed by the serial addition of unlabeled antigen as described in Kabat and Mayer (1961) until no further contaminating antibody remained. Immunological precipitation and subsequent acrylamide gel electrophoresis can also be used to identify the peptide structure of an uncharacterized antigen.

III. Direct Coprecipitation

A. Quantitation of the Rabbit Antiviral Antigen System

As mentioned in the introduction, the technique of direct coprecipitation (Fig. 1b) does not require antiviral antibody of as high a specificity as does the indirect technique. Since an immunological precipitate containing approximately 400 μg of protein must be formed in each determination, large amounts of antiviral antibody and purified viral antigen are required. This technique is almost impossible to use if one is examining proteins which are made in very small amounts, or proteins which are either not easily available in soluble form or difficult to separate from other viral proteins, for example, nascent polypeptide chains or internal proteins which in most cases have not been purified from cell lysates in reasonable quantities. If the direct coprecipitation technique is to be used in examining proteins which are available in large amounts, quantitation of the rabbit antibody and the antigen in question is carried out in much the same way as has been described above for the sheep anti-rabbit γ-globulin and rabbit γ-globulin. Initial estimates of equivalence are derived from agar diffusion in Ouchterlony plates, and quantitative precipitin curves are then carried out to determine the relative amounts of antigen and antibody which must be added to provide immunological precipitates in the region of antibody excess containing between 300 and 500 μg of protein. However, if only small amounts of protein are available or large virions poorly diffusable in 0.85% agar are to be examined, preliminary quantitative precipitin curves may be carried out using the method of agar diffusion in tubes originally described by Preer. Details of the Preer technique of double diffusion are presented both in the original articles (Preer, 1956), and in Kabat and Mayer (1961). This technique provides sufficiently accurate information on the approximate equivalence zone so that it needs verification by quantitative precipitation in solution with only selected points. We will present a brief description of the method here since it is extremely useful in a variety of studies.

Glass tubing with an inside diameter of 1.7 mm and outside diameter of 3.0 mm is cut into 1 foot lengths, cleaned, and rinsed with distilled water. It is internally coated by drawing a 0.1% solution of agarose cooled to 50–55°C into the glass tubing, blowing it out and then withdrawing all the excess agarose by gentle suction. After the glass tubing has been cut into 5 cm lengths, the agarose is allowed to dry thoroughly at room temperature. Each tube is sealed in an oxygen flame. A very hot, fine flame is necessary so that the agar will not melt. The tubes are then placed in a rack and antisera placed in the lower third of the tube. A 0.3% agarose solution at 50–55°C is gently layered over the serum using either a finely drawn Pasteur pipette or a fine syringe. (If dilutions of antisera are to be used, they must be made either in normal serum or 0.5% agar to be of sufficient density to allow an interface to form between the lower layer and the 0.3% agar.) The height of the agar column may be between 5 and 10 mm, but it must be the same in each of the tubes. After the agarose has gelled, antigen is placed over it, and the tube is sealed by layering some heavy mineral oil over the antigen solution. The tubes are incubated on their side so that any proteins which come out of solution will not fall into the agar and give the appearance of a precipitin band. This technique is approximately 20 times more sensitive than the Ouchterlony plate (Kabat and Mayer, 1961), and because of the low concentration of agarose in the agar column, large particles may migrate through it. A precipitin curve done by this technique with purified poliovirus and rabbit antisera is shown in Fig. 7. Plots of the migration of the bands in each of the tubes are presented in Fig. 8. The tubes may be observed daily, or more often, and the positions of bands which appear measured with magnification. In the region of antibody excess, the immunoprecipitin line will broaden toward the antigen (tubes 7 and 8),

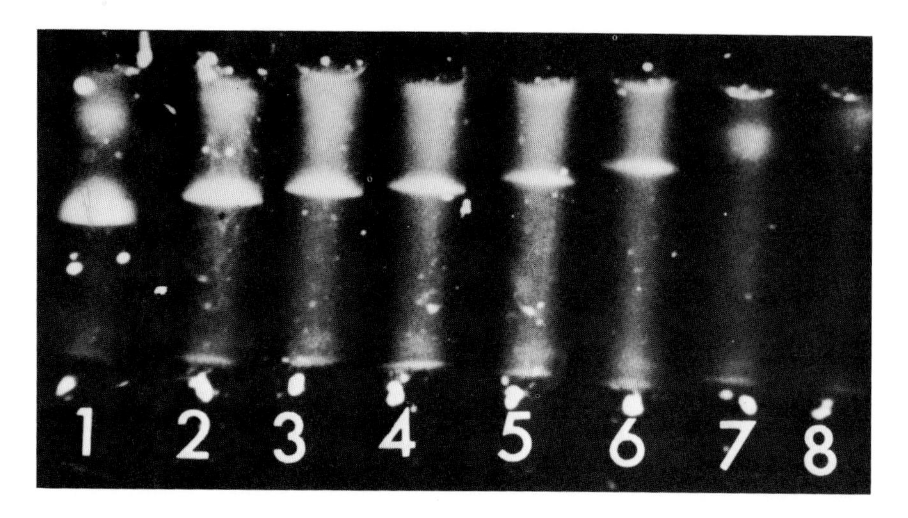

FIG. 7. Photograph of the agar columns of Preer tubes in which ECTEOLA purified poliovirus and antisera made against purified poliovirions have been examined. Only the agar column (enlarged by photography) is shown. Poliovirus was placed above the column and undiluted antiserum below. Tube 1 contained 650 μg/ml of poliovirus; tube 2, 325 μg/ml; tube 3, 260 μg/ml; tube 4, 195 μg/ml; tube 5, 130 μg/ml; tube 6, 97.5 μg/ml; tube 7, 48.7 μg/ml; and tube 8, 24 μg/ml. The major precipitin line represents the reaction between D antigen (infectious virions) and antibody. Since these preparations contain small amounts of C antigen (top component) a second line is seen at the higher concentrations of antigen.

while in the region of antigen excess (tubes 1-5), the precipitin line will be progressively dissolved and move in the direction of the antibody. Since the virus or virus antigens are usually much larger than γ-globulin, at equivalence the band is usually found closer to the antigen than to the antibody column. However, there should be no movement in either direction at the point of equivalence.

Direct coprecipitation could then be carried out by adding sufficient amounts of purified poliovirus and of rabbit antiserum to produce an immunological precipitate containing approximately 400 μg of protein in the range of antibody excess. As with the indirect technique, a proper control for the nonspecific precipitation of radioactivity must be provided. This may be done by quantitating an unrelated antigen-antibody system either using reagents produced against an unrelated virus or a large protein such as hemocyanin. As described for the indirect technique, quantitative precipitin curves are carried out and then a number of points of both the specific and nonspecific

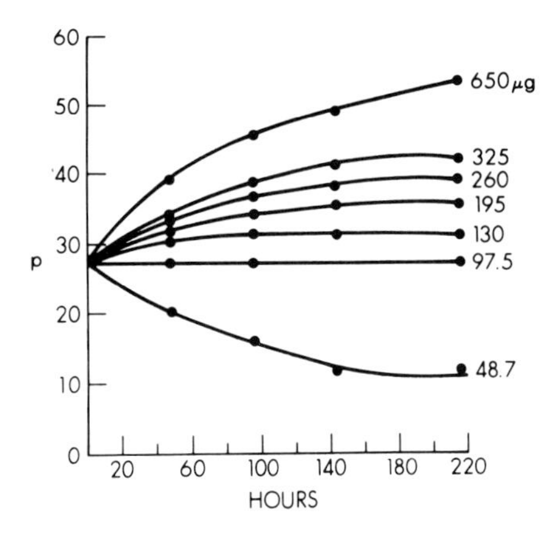

FIG. 8. Plot of the migration of the immunoprecipitin lines seen in Fig. 7. The location of the leading edge of each of the precipitin lines seen in Fig. 7 was measured at the time indicated and its location plotted as a percentage of height of each agar column (p). At higher antigen concentrations, the line moved toward the antibody, at lower antigen concentrations, toward the antigen, while at 97.5 μg/ml the line did not move at all. This is taken as equivalence.

system are taken in the region of antibody excess and compared in uninfected cells to be certain that the control nonspecifically precipitates the same amount of radioactivity as the virus antivirus precipitate.

IV. Conclusions

In our experience, the indirect technique is more useful because of its greater flexibility and its lack of requirement for large amounts of purified viral proteins or virions. Once properly set up, the reagents for the indirect technique may be conveniently frozen away in small aliquots, and multiple determinations carried out on short notice with great ease. However, it is important to emphasize that valid results may only be obtained if the specificity and quantitation of all the reagents have been carried out as described, and if the ratio of specific to nonspecific counts is at least 3:1 and preferably more than 10:1. In some systems, such ratios are hard to achieve when crude cell lysates are being examined, and the technique becomes unreliable unless the labeled antigen is recovered and subsequently characterized by some other method such as electrophoresis.

REFERENCES

Davis, B. J. (1964). *Ann. N.Y. Acad. Sci.* **121**, 404.
Gerloff, R. K., Hoyer, B. H., and McLaren, L. C. (1962). *J. Immunol.* **89**, 559.
Gitlin, D. (1949). *J. Immunol.* **62**, 437.
Kabat, E. A., and Mayer, M. M. (1961). "Experimental Immunochemistry," 2nd ed., Chapter 2, Thomas, Springfield, Illinois.
Maizel, J. V., Jr., Scharff, M. D., and White, D. O. (1968). *Virology* **36**, 115.
Preer, J. R., Jr. (1956). *J. Immunol.* **77**, 52.
Scharff, M. D., and Levintow, L. (1963). *Virology* **19**, 491.
Scharff, M. D., Maizel, J. V., Jr., and Levintow, L. (1964). *Proc. Natl. Acad. Sci. U.S.* **51**, 329.

30. Immunofluorescent Detection of Viral Antigens*

Peter K. Vogt

Department of Microbiology
University of Washington Medical School
Seattle, Washington

I. Introduction

Fluorescent antibody techniques have gained wide acceptance in virology, and have proved especially useful in the study of animal viruses. Fluorescent antibody staining serves four main purposes:

(1) The cellular localization of viral antigens can be determined at the light microscope level (Watson and Coons, 1954; Spendlove *et al.*, 1963).

(2) The temporal sequence of appearance after infection can be established for different viral antigens (Breitenfeld and Schäfer, 1957).

(3) In the case of noncytopathic viruses fluorescent antibody staining may be used to identify infected cells, and can thus serve as the basis for quantitative infectivity assays (Rapp *et al.*, 1959, 1963; Vogt and Rubin, 1963).

(4) Virus-infected cells which fail to produce viral progeny often still synthesize virus-coded antigens. Immunofluorescent staining permits the identification of such cells which continue to harbor viral genetic material (Pope and Rowe, 1964; Tevethia *et al.*, 1965).

Coons' original technique (Coons and Kaplan, 1950; Coons, 1958) has been modified numerous times and is now used as a routine tool

*Work supported by U.S. Public Health Service Research Grant CA 10569 from the National Cancer Institute and by Grant E 302 from the American Cancer Society.

in many laboratories (Nairn, 1962). Several review papers have appeared on the subject of fluorescent antibody techniques in virology (Löffler, 1962; Liu, 1960; Mims, 1964; Poetschke, 1961; Spendlove, 1968). An excellent, comprehensive volume on fluorescent antibody methods has appeared recently and is highly recommended (Goldman, 1968). The following instructions cover the main variants of fluorescent antibody staining.

II. Reagents, Buffers, Solutions

Analytical grade reagents and glass distilled water are used. All pH values should be checked with a pH meter.

Sodium chloride, 0.15 *M*. NaCl, 8.8 gm/liter.

Saturated ammonium sulfate solution. $(NH_4)_2SO_4$, in excess of 750 gm/liter.

Diethylaminoethyl (DEAE) cellulose, Selectacel, type 40, 0.9 meq/gm, Schleicher and Schuell, Keene, New Hampshire. The ion exchanger is washed with 0.5 *N* NaOH and thereafter with water until neutral. It is then suspended in 0.01 *M* phosphate buffer, pH 7.5, and is poured into a 2.5 cm i.d. Sephadex or Pyrex column. The material is allowed to settle to form a bed of about 10 cm and is washed with 500 ml 0.01 *M* phosphate buffer pH 7.5.

Phosphate buffer, pH 7.5, 0.01 *M*. Na_2HPO_4, 1.02 gm/liter; KH_2PO_4 0.38 gm/liter.

Phosphate-buffered saline is 0.01 *M* phosphate buffer pH 7.5 plus 8.8 gm/liter of NaCl.

Carbonate-bicarbonate buffer, pH 9.5, 0.5 *M*. $NaHCO_3$, 26.5 gm/liter; Na_2CO_3, 19.5 gm/liter.

Fluorescein isothiocyanate (FITC): Several biological and biochemical supply houses offer this reagent. Good results have been consistently achieved with material purchased from Baltimore Biological Laboratories, Baltimore, Maryland.

Sodium phosphate dibasic, 0.1 *M*. Na_2HPO_4, 14.2 gm/liter.

Sodium hydroxide, 0.04 *M*. NaOH, 1.6 gm/liter.

Carbonate-bicarbonate buffer, pH 9.5, 0.025 *M*. $NaHCO_3$, 1.8 gm/liter; Na_2CO_3, 0.36 gm/liter.

Sephadex G-50 (Pharmacia Fine Chemicals, Piscataway, New Jersey) is allowed to swell in phosphate-buffered saline for 1 hour in a boiling water bath. The slurry is poured in the column and allowed to settle uniformly, avoiding the formation of air bubbles. Flow at an operating pressure of about 100 mm water is maintained during this process.

Tris-buffered saline contains NaCl, 8 gm/liter; KCl, 0.37 gm/liter; Na_2HPO_4, 0.1 gm/liter; glucose, 1 gm/liter; tris hydroxy methylaminomethane (Trizma, Sigma Chem. Co.), 3 gm/liter; 10 *N* HCl, 1.8 ml/liter.

Buffered glycerol is a 9:1 mixture of glycerol and phosphate-buffered or tris-buffered saline.

Acetone and ethanol are used for fixation of cells.

Versenate buffer contains ethylenediaminetetraacetic acid disodium 0.2 gm/liter; NaCl, 8.0 gm/liter; KCl, 0.2 gm/liter; Na_2HPO_4, 1.15 gm/liter; KH_2PO_4, 0.2 gm/liter.

Trypsin may be obtained from tissue culture supply houses as a 0.25 or 2.5% stock solution. It is diluted with tris-buffered saline.

Fluorescein isothiocyanate conjugated anti-γ-globulins are available from several tissue culture supply houses (Hyland Laboratories, Los Angeles, California; Baltimore Biological Laboratories, Baltimore, Maryland; and Microbiological Associates, Bethesda, Maryland), as well as from companies specializing in immunological reagents (Immunology, Inc., Glen Ellyn, Illinois; Antibodies, Inc., Davis, California; and Pentex, Inc., Kankakee, Illinois). The potency and specificity of these conjugates should ideally be tested, e.g., in complement fixation with the γ-globulin against which they are prepared.

Acetone-dried tissue powder (Coons, 1958). The tissue (usually liver) is homogenized in an electric blendor with an equal volume of 0.15 *M* NaCl, and the homogenate is mixed with 4 volumes of acetone and allowed to settle. The acetone is decanted and the precipitate washed by centrifugation and resuspension in several changes of 0.15 *M* NaCl until the supernatant remains free of hemoglobin. The precipitate is then suspended in an equal amount of 0.15 *M* NaCl to which 4 volumes of acetone are added and is allowed to settle. The supernatant is again discarded. The precipitate is now suspended in 4 volumes of acetone and harvested on filter paper in a Buchner funnel. Before removing the material from the funnel for drying it is advisable to rinse it with additional 4 volumes of fresh acetone. The powder may be dried at 37°C and is stable in the refrigerator indefinitely. Acetone-dried tissue powders are also available commercially (Pentex, Inc., Kankakee, Illinois).

III. Equipment

Magnetic stirrers with separate rheostat to avoid heating of the stirrer (A. H. Thomas Co., Philadelphia, Pennsylvania, Model 14).

Refrigerated centrifuge, medium speed: A Sorvall SS-1 placed in a cold room is satisfactory (I. Sorvall, Norwalk, Connecticut).

For gel filtration with Sephadex G-50 a Sephadex K-9 column is satisfactory, for chromatography with DEAE-cellulose a Sephadex K-25 column is recommended (Pharmacia Fine Chemicals, Inc., Piscataway, New Jersey).

Pressure dialysis: A glass suction apparatus with collodion bags (Schleicher and Schuell, Keene, New Hampshire) is used for concentration of small volumes (6 ml maximum). Larger volumes are concentrated with a Diaflo cell (Amicon Corp., Lexington, Massachusetts).

Millipore filtration of small serum samples is conveniently carried out with a Swinny filter holder equipped with a type HA filter and type AP 25 prefilter (Millipore Corp., Bedford, Massachusetts).

Moist chamber for fluorescent antibody staining: A clear styrene box (No. F 16621, Bel Art Plastics, Pequannock, New Jersey) may be used. Cover glasses are placed in the box on top of sturdy nylon brushes 4½ by 1½ inches (Anchor Brush Co., Aurora, Illinois) (Fig. 1).

Cover glasses are Corning No. 1 (18 by 18 mm or other sizes). They are heat sterilized and placed in tissue culture vessels without prior cleaning.

Microscope slides should have a thickness between 0.97 and 1.07 mm (e.g., Precleaned Gold Seal Micro Slides, Clay Adams, Inc., New York, New York).

Washing of stained cover slip cultures is carried out in Columbia staining jars (A. H. Thomas Co., Philadelphia, Pennsylvania).

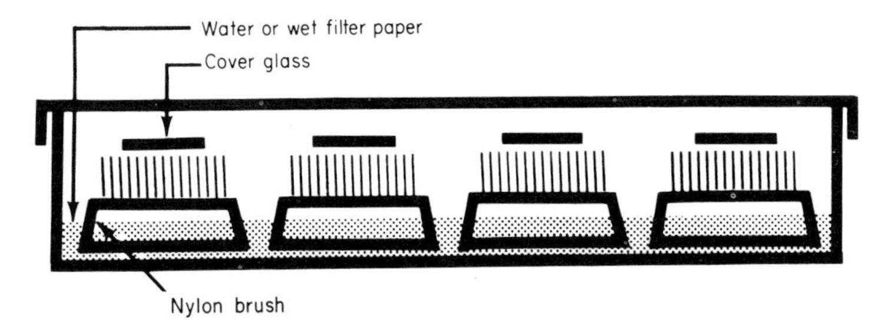

FIG. 1. Moist chamber for fluorescent antibody staining.

Microscope. Optics: High aperture objectives are important. For a 25× objective the aperture should be greater than 0.60, for 40× it should be greater than 0.95. A dark field, oil immersion condenser is recommended to reduce background fluorescence. An Osram HBO 200 mercury burner serves as light source. The most useful exciter filter is Schott BG 12; UG 1 or UG 5 filters may be used with brightly fluorescing preparations. A heat absorbing filter, Schott KG 1, is mounted between light source and exciter filters. Barrier filters inserted in the microscope tube should cut off light with wavelengths below 470 to 530 mμ. Complete optical equipment for fluorescent antibody work is offered by several companies. The unit marketed by C. Zeiss, Inc., New York, New York appears to be most widely used.

IV. Procedures

A. Preparation of γ-Globulin

1. *Method 1*

The serum sample (at least 5 ml) is diluted with an equal volume of 0.15 *M* NaCl, placed in an ice bath, and stirred with a magnetic stirrer. Ammonium sulfate solution, saturated at 4°C is added dropwise under stirring to the diluted serum until the mixture is half-saturated with respect to $(NH_4)_2SO_4$. Stirring at ice bath temperature is continued for ½ hour. The precipitated globulins are then sedimented in a refrigerated centrifuge, 5000 rpm, 20 minutes. The sediment is washed once by suspension in cold, half-saturated $(NH_4)_2SO_4$, and after a second centrifugation the globulins are dissolved in 0.15 *M* NaCl at a final volume of half that of the original serum sample. Remaining $(NH_4)_2SO_4$ is removed by dialysis against 0.15 *M* NaCl. The protein concentration of the γ-globulin preparation is determined by optical density measurements at 280 mμ using an extinction coefficient of 1.24/mg/ml/cm. The protein precipitated by half-saturated $(NH_4)_2SO_4$ contains, besides γ-globulins, also α and β-globulins. An alternative technique designed for chicken sera uses Na_2SO_4 to precipitate γ-globulins (Deutsch, 1967).

2. *Method 2*

A purer γ-globulin preparation can be obtained by chromatography on DEAE-cellulose (Fahey and Horbett, 1959). The serum sample is dialyzed overnight against 0.01 *M* phosphate buffer, pH 7.5. For 5 ml of serum a column of approximately 2.5 by 10 cm is poured with

DEAE-cellulose equilibrated with 0.01 *M* phosphate buffer, pH 7.5. The dialyzed serum is applied to the column followed by 0.01 *M* phosphate buffer pH 7.5. γ-Globulin is not retained by the column under these conditions and eluted after the void volume. The eluate containing most of the γ-globulin is about 3–5 times the volume of the original serum sample. It should be dialyzed against 0.15 *M* NaCl. Before conjugation the γ-globulin is concentrated by pressure dialysis to one-half the initial serum volume.

B. Conjugation of γ-Globulin to FITC

1. *Method 1*

For Method 1 (Marshall *et al.*, 1958) the globulin fraction is diluted with 0.15 *M* NaCl to a protein concentration of 1.1% and is mixed with one-tenth of its volume carbonate-bicarbonate buffer (0.5 *M*, pH 9.5) (Klugerman, 1965). Fluorescein isothiocyanate (0.02 mg/liter mg protein) is added and carefully dissolved by stirring on a magnetic stirrer. Conjugation is completed by stirring the mixture overnight in a cold room.

2. *Method 2*

For Method 2 (McKinney *et al.*, 1964; Spendlove, 1966) a 0.125% solution of FITC in 0.1 *M* Na_2HPO_4 is prepared. For conjugation a globulin solution in 0.15 *M* NaCl is adjusted to 5% protein and mixed with the FITC solution at a ratio of 1:0.8 (v/v). The pH is adjusted to 9.5 by addition of 0.04 *M* NaOH. Conjugation is complete after 30 minute stirring at room temperature.

3. *Method 3*

For Method 3 (Clark and Shepard, 1963) the globulin solution is adjusted to a protein concentration of 1% and dialyzed overnight against 0.025 *M* carbonate-bicarbonate buffer, pH 9.5. Conjugation is achieved by dialysis for 24 hours against 10 volumes of the same buffer containing 0.1 mg/ml FITC.

C. Removal of Free FITC and Storage of Conjugates

Unreacted FITC is a source of nonspecific staining of proteins and must be removed after the conjugation process. In many systems dialysis against phosphate-buffered saline is satisfactory. This may require several days and should be continued until the dialyzate is free of fluorescent material when viewed under uv light. A more rapid separation of conjugated globulin and unreacted FITC may be achieved by passing the mixture through a column (approximately 2.5 by 10 cm for 5 ml conjugate) of Sephadex G-50 equilibrated with phosphate-buffered saline and using this buffer for elution. The conjugate may also be rechromatographed following method 2 of the γ-globulin fractionation. In this case overnight dialysis against 0.01 *M* phosphate buffer, pH 7.5, is necessary before the mixture is applied to the DEAE-cellulose column equilibrated with the same buffer. After chromatography concentration of the conjugate by pressure dialysis may be indicated.

Conjugates may be stored frozen (–20°C or below) or may be filtered through a Millipore filter with an average pore size of 0.45 μ and can then be kept in the refrigerator for several months.

D. Direct Staining Techniques

In this procedure the viral antibody is conjugated to FITC and serves as a highly specific stain which combines with antigens in virus-infected cells.

1. *Staining of Nonfixed Cells*

Since antibody does not penetrate the intact plasma membrane the staining of live cells reveals only those antigens present at the outer cell surface. Cells are seeded in culture vessels containing cover slips. The cell population should be sparse to allow complete spreading of individual cells and to prevent detachment of confluent cell sheets from the cover slip during staining manipulations ($1.5\text{–}3 \times 10^4$ cells/cm^2 culture area). The cells may be infected before or after seeding. For immunofluorescent staining cover slips are removed from the culture vessel and rinsed in tris-buffered saline. Their cell-free side is wiped with absorbent paper. They are placed in the humid chamber and covered with a drop of fluorescent antibody. Staining is usually rapid, requiring only 3–5 minutes to complete. Excess antibody is removed by leaving the cover slips in Columbia jars containing tris-buffered saline for 5 minutes, then draining and immersing them in fresh jars with tris-buffered saline for two additional 5 minute washes. Gentleness during this procedure is important, otherwise many cells will be lost. The backs of the cover slips are then wiped dry with absorbent paper, and the stained cells are mounted in a drop of buffered glycerol. Microscopic inspection should be carried out as early as possible after mounting; the preparations cannot be kept overnight. Controls should include noninfected cells as well as FITC-conjugated normal γ-globulin from the same species as the immune globulin. The staining reaction should also be blocked by nonconjugated antiserum against the viral antigens under study but not by normal serum.

2. *Staining of Fixed Cells*

Seeding and infection of cells follow the instructions given above for the staining of nonfixed cells except that higher initial cell concentrations are permissible.

a. Fixation. Method 1—The cover glass is rinsed in tris-buffered saline, drained and air dried. Fixation is for 5 minutes at room temperature in acetone. After drying the cover glass is dipped into tris-buffered saline. Excess fluid is wiped off the back with absorbent paper and the cells are ready for staining.

Method 2—The cover glass is rinsed in tris-buffered saline, drained, and fixed in precooled acetone or ethanol at −60°C for 10 minutes. The preparation is then air dried. At this point many viral antigens are stable during storage at 60°C or below for several months. Before staining the cover slip is dipped in tris-buffered saline and drained.

b. Staining. The cover glass is placed in a humid chamber and the cell sheet is flooded with a drop of fluorescent antibody. Staining may be accomplished in as little as 10 minutes, but in some cases extension of the staining period up to 24 hours may prove advantageous. Staining may be carried out at room temperature or 37°C. After staining the cells are washed as described above for nonfixed preparations and are mounted in buffered glycerol. Controls are the same as for the staining of nonfixed cells.

E. Indirect Staining Techniques

The indirect procedure includes two immunological reactions. In the first, viral antigens present in infected cells combine with specific, nonconjugated antibody. In the second, the cellular sites binding viral antibody are visualized by staining with FITC-conjugated anti-γ-globulin. This immunochemical reagent is prepared specifically against the γ-globulin of the animal species from which viral antibody is obtained. The indirect staining is more flexible because the same fluorescent anti-γ-globulin can be used to detect the γ-globulin of a given species in a large variety of reactions with different antigens and to screen many antisera of the same species without having to conjugate all of them to FITC. The indirect staining technique is also more sensitive than the direct one because the fluorochrome-binding surface is enlarged by the primary antigen–antibody reaction. However, nonspecific staining is more of a problem in the indirect technique and may outweigh the advantage of higher sensitivity.

1. Preparation of anti-γ-Globulin Conjugates

Although most investigators obtain FITC-conjugated anti-γ-globulins from commercial sources, larger quantities of such reagents may be prepared more economically in the laboratory. Immunization should be carried out with γ-globulin prepared according to method 2 in Section IV, D, 2a. For immunization the γ-globulin is given intramuscularly in complete Freund's adjuvant, approximately 1 mg protein per kilogram of body weight, and a booster injection of the same amount is administered 4–6 weeks after the primary stimulus. Serum is obtained 2–3 weeks after the second injection. Fractionation of this antiserum and conjugation to FITC follows the procedures described under Section IV, D.

2. Staining of Nonfixed Cells in Suspension

The staining of nonfixed cells in suspension (Möller, 1961) is a sensitive technique for the detection of viral antigens at the outer cell surface. It is ideally suited for cells cultured in suspension or cells suspendible without enzymatic treatment. Cells growing attached to the surface of a culture vessel may be detached with 0.02% ethylenediaminetetraacetate although this often results in cell damage which leads to an increase of nonspecific staining. Suspension with dilute trypsin (0.01% in tris-buffered saline) may be tolerable in certain systems; however, some viral antigens are removed from the cell surface by this procedure.

For staining 2–5 × 10^6 cells are suspended in tris-buffered saline and sedimented in a small centrifuge tube at low speeds (2000 rpm, 2 minutes). They are gently resuspended in a drop of nonconjugated antiserum and incubated at 37°C for 20 minutes. Excess serum is washed off the cells with three cycles of centrifugation and suspension in tris-buffered saline. The packed cell–antibody complexes are then suspended in a drop of FITC-conjugated anti-γ-globulin directed against the antibodies used in the primary reaction and incubated again for 20 minutes at 37°C. Noncombined conjugate is removed by 2–3 cycles of washing in tris-buffered saline. A drop of the washed cell suspension is placed under a cover glass and inspected within a short time after mounting for the presence of the characteristic fluorescence at the periphery of the cell. Controls of staining specificity are prepared with the same reagents but noninfected cells, with normal serum instead of viral antiserum, and with an FITC conjugate of unrelated specificity instead of the anti-γ-globulin.

3. Staining of Fixed Cells

For fixation of the cells one of the two methods given under Section IV, D may be used. The cover glass is then put in a humid chamber, and the cell sheet is covered with a drop of nonconjugated antiviral serum for 30 minutes. After washing in three changes of tris-buffered saline the cover glass is returned to the humid chamber and the cells are flooded with FITC-conjugated anti-γ-globulin. The staining reaction is allowed to take place for 30 minutes. The cover glass is then washed as above and mounted in buffered glycerol. The controls are the same as for staining in suspension.

V. Nonspecific Staining

Nonspecific reactions between cellular components and the globulin preparations may present serious problems in the immunofluorescent detection of viral antigens. There are no universally applicable remedies for nonspecific staining, but a few general guidelines should be discussed.

Most of the nonspecific fluorescence appears to be caused by globulins which are too heavily conjugated with FITC (Goldstein *et al.*, 1961; Herbert *et al.*, 1967). Reducing the dye to protein ratio in the conjugation mixture alleviates this situation.

The problem of nonspecific staining is also substantially reduced by using a pure γ-globulin fraction for conjugation or by rechromatography of the conjugate on DEAE-cellulose (see Section IV, A, 2) (Wood *et al.*, 1965).

Absorption of the conjugate with acetone-tissue powders also removes nonspecifically staining molecules. To this end 150 mg of tissue powder are suspended in phosphate-buffered saline and centrifuged at 5000 rpm for 10 minutes. The packed sediment is mixed with 1 ml of fluorescent serum and left at room temperature for 1 hour. The tissue powder is removed by centrifugation, and the serum is filtered through a Millipore filter of 0.45 μ pore size. Since 30–50% of the conjugate remains in the tissue powder sediment, this absorption procedure should not be applied routinely but only if tests indicate its usefulness. High titered sera can often be diluted sufficiently to eliminate all nonspecific staining which may be prevalent at low serum dilutions. During staining in suspension many cells may die. The result is a nonspecific uptake of the immunofluorescent stain. Addition of calf serum to the tris-buffered saline at a concentration of 10% often substantially improves cell survival and reduces cell clumping.

REFERENCES

Breitenfeld, P., and Schäfer, W. (1957). *Virology* **4**, 328.

Clark, H. F., and Shepard, C. C. (1963). *Virology* **20**, 643.

Coons, A. H. (1958). *Gen. Cytochem. Methods* **1**, 399–422.

Coons, A. H., and Kaplan, M. H. (1950). *J. Exptl. Med.* **91**, 1.

Deutsch, H. F. (1967). *In* "Methods in Immunology and Immunochemistry" (C. A. Williams and M. W. Chase, eds.), Vol. I, p. 315. Academic Press, New York and London.

Fahey, J. L., and Horbett, A. P. (1959). *J. Biol. Chem.* **234**, 2645.

Goldstein, G., Slizyz, I. S., and Chase, M. W. (1961). *J. Exptl. Med.* **114**, 89.

Goldman, M. (1968). "Fluorescent Antibody Methods." Academic Press, New York.

Herbert, G. A., Pittman, B., and Cherry, W. B. (1967). *J. Immunol.* **98**, 1205.

Klugerman, M. R. (1965). *J. Immunol.* **95**, 1165.

Liu, C. (1960). *Ergeb. Mikrobiol.* **33**, 242.

Löffler, H. (1962). *Ergeb. Mikrobiol.* **35**, 240.

McKinney, R. M., Spillane, J. T., and Pearce, G. W. (1964). *J. Immunol.* **93**, 232.

Marshall, J. D., Eveland, W. C., and Smith, C. W. (1958). *Proc. Soc. Exptl. Biol. Med.* **98**, 898.

Mims, C. A. (1964). *Bacteriol. Rev.* **28**, 30.

Möller, G. (1961). *J. Exptl. Med.* **114**, 415.

Nairn, R. C. (1962). "Fluorescent Protein Tracing." Livingstone, Edinburgh and London.

Poetschke, G. (1961). *Progr. Med. Virol.* **3**, 79.

Pope, J. H., and Rowe, W. P. (1964). *J. Exptl. Med.* **120**, 121.

Rapp, F., Seligman, S. J., Jaross, L. B., and Gordon, I. (1959). *Proc. Soc. Exptl. Biol. Med.* **101**, 289.

Rapp, F., Rasmussen, L. E., and Benyesh-Melnick, M. (1963). *J. Immunol.* **91**, 709.

Spendlove, R. S. (1966). *Proc. Soc. Exptl. Biol. Med.* **122**, 580.

Spendlove, R. S. (1968). *In* "Methods in Virology" (K. Maramorosch and H. Koprowski, eds.), Vol. 3 p. 475. Academic Press, New York.

Spendlove, R. S., Lennette, E. H., and John, A. C. (1963). *J. Immunol.* **90**, 554.

Tevethia, S. S., Katz, M., and Rapp, F. (1965). *Proc. Soc. Exptl. Biol. Med.* **119**, 896.

Vogt, P. K., and Rubin, H. (1963). *Virology* **19**, 92.

Watson, B. K., and Coons, A. H. (1954). *J. Exptl. Med.* **99**, 419.

Wood, B. T., Thompson, S. H., and Goldstein, G. (1965). *J. Immunol.* **95**, 225.

31. Analysis of Radioactively Labeled Proteins by Immunodiffusion

N. P. Salzmann and Bernard Moss

Laboratory of Biology of Viruses
National Institute of Allergy and Infectious Diseases
National Institutes of Health
Bethesda, Maryland

I. Introduction

Immunological procedures are useful for the detection of specific antigens in the presence of large quantities of unrelated protein. Multiple antigens may be resolved by allowing immunoprecipitation to occur in a semisolid medium. A technically simple procedure consists of placing the antigen and antibody in separate wells and allowing precipitin lines to form during diffusion. The sensitivity of detection is greatly enhanced by the use of radioactively labeled antigens and radioautography. In virological studies additional information may be obtained by labeling the antigen at different times during the growth cycle.

Alternatively the antigens may first be separated into individual components by electrophoresis and then immunodiffusion carried out in the second dimension (Hunneeus-Cox, 1964). The immunological identification is a particularly useful adjunct to high resolution polyacrylamide gel electrophoresis. Longitudinal slices from the same polyacrylamide gel may be stained, used for enzyme analysis, dried directly for radioautography, and embedded in agar for immunodiffusion.

In this laboratory, these procedures have been found useful in studying temporal control of vaccinia viral protein synthesis and in measuring the rate with which virus-infected animal cells lose the capacity to synthesize particular proteins after inhibition of messenger RNA synthesis (Salzman and Sebring, 1967; Sebring and Salzman, 1967; Moss and Salzman, 1968). The technique should also prove useful in monitoring the purity of viral proteins during purification and in the examination and classification of the defects in a series of mutant viruses.

The procedure for immunodiffusion outlined in this chapter is that described by Wadsworth (1957) and Crowle (1958).

II. Materials and Solutions

(a) Precleaned miscroscope slides (25 by 75 mm) with one frosted end.

(b) Plastic mold: The mold is made from ⅛ inch thick Plexiglas—dimensions 25 by 25 mm. Each well is first drilled through with a $\frac{1}{16}$ inch drill and then with a $\frac{9}{64}$ inch drill in the manner shown in Fig. 1a. In the mold shown in Fig. 1b, the centers of the peripheral holes are 4 mm from that of the central hole.

(c) Special agar (Noble, Difco Laboratories, Detroit, Michigan).

(d) Ponceau S staining solution: The concentrated solution is obtained from Consolidated Labs., Inc., P.O. Box 234, Chicago Heights, Illinois. To 1 ml of this concentrate, add 124 ml of 3% trichloroacetic acid.

(e) Ansco high speed X-ray film (General Aniline and Film Corp., New York, New York). The film is processed according to the manufacturer's directions.

(f) X-Ray casettes (Halsey X-Ray Products, Inc., New York, New York).

(g) Vinyl plastic electrical tape, No. 33, $\frac{3}{4}$ inch wide, (Minnesota Mining and Manufacturing, St. Paul, Minnesota).

(h) One percent solution of Merthiolate (thimerosal, N.F.). The powder is obtained from Eli Lilly and Co., Indianapolis, Indiana.

(i) Antiserum (see Horwitz and Scharff, Chapter 25).

(j) Antigen (see legends to Figs. 3 and 4).

(k) Chemicals and equipment for polyacrylamide gel electrophoresis (Maizel, Chapter 32).

(l) Two single edge razor blades, preferably $2\frac{1}{4}$ inch "prep" size,

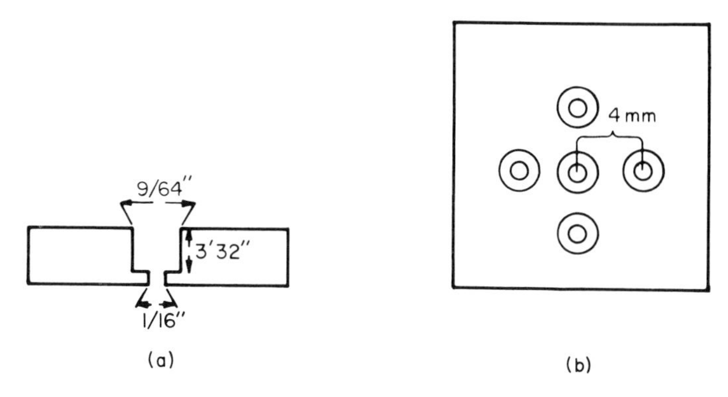

FIG. 1. Plastic molds (a) (b).

clamped together to form a double cutting edge with a 1 mm separation.

(m) Clean $3\frac{1}{4}$ by 4 inch lantern slide cover glasses.

III. Procedure

A. IMMUNODIFFUSION

One or more days prior to the start of the actual experiment, the microscope slides are coated with agar. A solution of 0.3% special agar Noble in water is prepared and held near 100°C. Each slide is dipped in this solution and then drained and air dried while held in horizontal position. After the slides are dried, two thicknesses of black electrical tape are placed on each slide at two positions as illustrated in Fig. 2.

At the start of the actual experiment, a 1% agar solution is made up in 0.85% saline and 1 ml of a 1% Merthiolate solution is then added to each 100 ml of agar solution. The agar solution is held at a temperature between 60 and 65°C while the slides are prepared. Agar (0.3 ml) is added to the area on the microscope slide between the two double thicknesses of tape, and the plastic mold is immediately placed so that it is supported on each side by the electrical tape. It is important to avoid entrapment of air in the agar when the mold is lowered. This can generally be avoided if the mold is held at an angle and the upper edge of the mold is first placed against the upper edge of the slide. When the mold is then lowered, entrapped air can escape. It is also

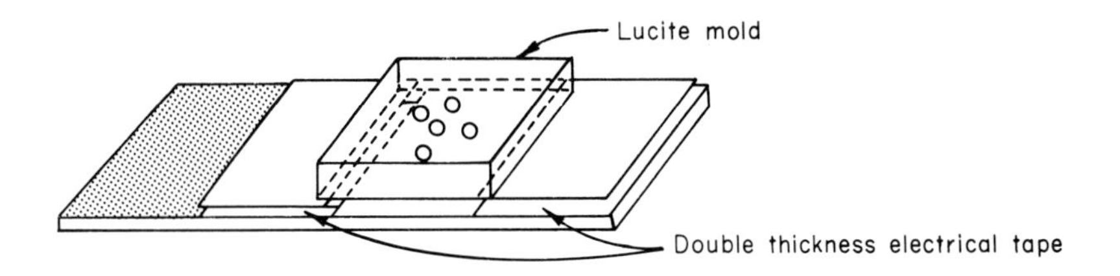

FIG. 2. Microscope slide.

important to remove agar which enters the wells since this will produce irregularity in the precipitin pattern. This can be most easily achieved if the slide is placed on absorbent paper tissue prior to the addition of the agar and placement of the mold. When the mold is lowered, excess agar is drawn from the slide onto the tissue, the agar first draining from the wells. At that point when air just begins to enter the area between the slide and the mold, the slide is lifted from the tissue for a few seconds to break the capillary action. A series of 6–12 slides is prepared in this manner. The samples are then added with finely drawn out capillary pipettes and each well is completely filled. The mold cannot be moved when the samples are added, since this will break the seal between the mold and the agar surface. It is also important to avoid entrapment of air between the sample and the agar. Diffusion is carried out at room temperature in a desiccator jar. The atmosphere is kept humid by lining the sides of the desiccator with Whatman No. 3 paper, the bottom of which is immersed in water contained in the bottom of the desiccator. Precipitin patterns are usually examined after 48–72 hours. At this time the Lucite mold is carefully pried from the slide. The slide is placed horizontally in a petri dish containing 0.85% NaCl. It is desirable to *gently* rub the submerged agar surface with your finger to remove insoluble material that has precipitated at each well position. Slides are washed for 48 hours in saline solution which is changed once after 24 hours. The tape is most conveniently removed when the slides are in the saline wash solution. Following the two saline washes, slides are washed for 1 hour in distilled water and air dried.

The dried slides are stained by immersion in a Ponceau S solution for 7 minutes and then washed three times in 5% acetic acid, each wash of 5 minute duration. The stained patterns can be examined directly, or the slide can be used as a negative in order to prepare a photographic enlargement of it.

Radioautographs are prepared by placing the stained slides in a cassette, where they are held by cellophane tape. A piece of X-ray film is placed in contact with the slides for a period of time which varies depending on the nature of the experiment. We have usually examined the film after 2–8 days. The negative that is obtained can be examined directly or can be used to prepare a photographic enlargement.

Results of one type of experiment are illustrated in Fig. 3.

B. Immunodiffusion following Polyacrylamide Gel Electrophoresis

Cytoplasmic extracts or other soluble proteins are centrifuged at high speed to remove particulate material. Polyacrylamide gel electrophoresis is carried out as described by Maizel (Chapter 32) for native proteins. Care should be taken to avoid protein denaturation. Dissociating agents such as urea or SDS have been avoided in order to preserve immunological reactivity. It is better but may not be essential to use recrystallized acrylamide and perform the electrophoresis at low temperature. Following electrophoresis the polyacrylamide gel cylinders or longitudinal slices (Fairbanks *et al.*, 1965) are placed on $3\frac{1}{4}$ by 4 inch glass plates, precoated with 0.3% agar (Section III, A). The glass plates are placed on a level surface and 15 ml of 1.2% agar in buffered saline, pH 7.2, containing 0.01% Merthiolate at 45°C, is rapidly delivered from a pipette in order to cover the entire glass surface and partially embed the polyacrylamide gel. Buffered saline has been used because the high pH of disc gel electrophoresis buffers may not be optimal for formation of the antigen–antibody complex. Channels, cut parallel to the long axis of the gel with two razor blades fastened together, are filled with antiserum. The plates are placed in a humid chamber and immunoprecipitin lines are allowed to form for 5–6 days. In order to obtain a sufficient separation of the immunoprecipitin lines from the polyacrylamide gel, the distance between the trough and gel should be empirically varied according to the concentration of polyacrylamide, concentration and molecular weight of the antigens, and potency of the antisera. Initially a distance of 1 cm may be used. It may also be useful to allow proteins to begin diffusing from the polyacrylamide several hours before the antiserum is added. After removal of the polyacrylamide gel, the agar is washed for three days with multiple changes of buffered saline. A sheet of Whatman No. 50 paper moistened with distilled water is placed on the surface and the agar is dried overnight at 37°C. Staining is carried out as described in Section III, A. Radioautography (Section III, A), greatly enhances the sensitivity of the procedure if labeled antigen or antiserum has been used. Results from one experiment are illustrated in Fig. 4.

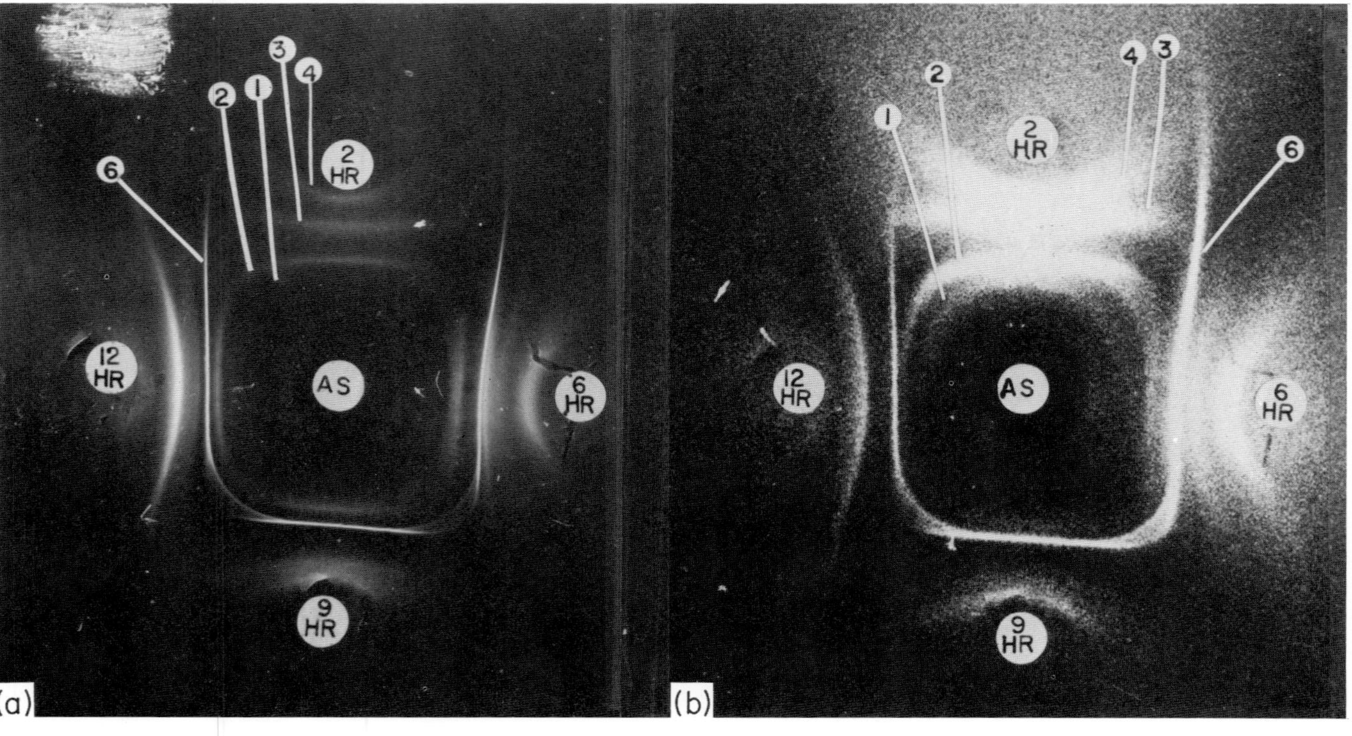

FIG. 3. Vaccinia virus-infected HeLa cells in suspension culture were exposed to L-phenylalanine-^{14}C(0.01 mM, 0.1 μc/ml) for 1 hour periods at different times during the infectious cycle. Cells were collected by centrifugation at the end of the 1 hour labeling period. The cell pellet containing 4×10^7 cells was resuspended in 1 ml of 0.85% saline. The cells were disrupted by four 30 second cycles of sonic vibration using a Mullard TC vibrator. The samples are held in an ice bath during this procedure. The disrupted cell suspension was then centrifuged at 900 rpm for 10 minutes and the supernatant fluid was used as the source of antigens. This type of experiment provides information concerning temporal synthesis of viral proteins. (a) Stained slide. (b) Radioautograph. From Salzman and Sebring (1967).

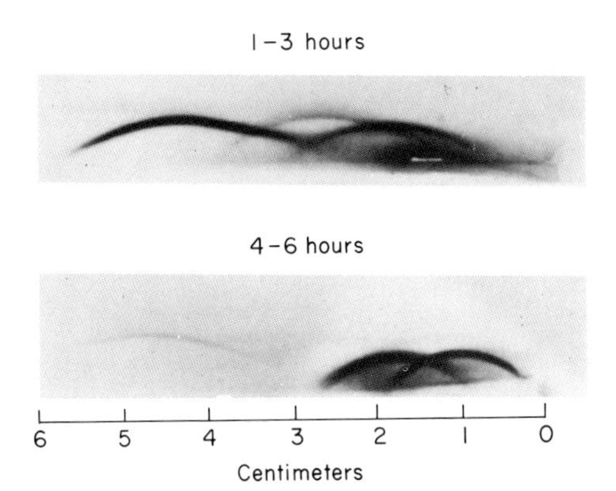

FIG. 4. Radioautographs of immunoprecipitin lines formed in agar following polyacrylamide gel electrophoresis. HeLa cells were incubated with L-phenylalanine ^{14}C (0.01 m*M*, 0.2 μc/ml) from 1 to 3 hours and 4 to 6 hours after infection with vaccinia virus. The washed cells suspended in 10 m*M* KCl, 1.5 m*M* $MgCl_2$, 10 m*M* tris, pH 7.8, were broken with a Dounce homogenizer and the cytoplasmic extract centrifuged for 2 hours at 100,000 g. Polyacrylamide gel electrophoresis was carried out according to the original method of Davis (1963) using 100 μg of protein and 7.5% polyacrylamide gels. The gels were embedded in agar and immunodiffusion carried out as described in the text. The radioautographs indicate that different viral proteins are synthesized during the two time intervals. From Moss and Salzman (1968).

ACKNOWLEDGMENT

The authors wish to thank Dr. L. Chessin for describing the method of immunoelectrophoresis.

REFERENCES

Crowle, A. J. (1958). *J. Lab. Clin. Med.* **52**, 784.

Davis, B. J. (1963). "Disc Electrophoresis," Vol. II. Distillation Prod. Ind., Rochester, New York.

Fairbanks, G., Jr., Levinthal, C., and Reeder, R. H. (1965). *Biochem. Biophys. Res. Commun.* **20**, 393.

Hunneeus-Cox, F. (1964). *Science* **143**, 1036.

Moss, B., and Salzman, N. P. (1968). *J. Virol.* **2**, 1016.

Salzman, N. P., and Sebring, E. D. (1967). *J. Virol.* **1**, 16.

Sebring, E. D., and Salzman, N. P. (1967). *J. Virol.* **1**, 550.

Wadsworth, C. (1957). *Intern. Arch. Allergy Appl. Immunol.* **10**, 355.

32. Acrylamide Gel Electrophoresis of Proteins and Nucleic Acids*

Jacob V. Maizel, Jr.†

Department of Cell Biology
Albert Einstein College of Medicine
Bronx, New York

I. Introduction

Acrylamide gel electrophoresis provides a relatively simple and inexpensive, but very versatile, way to analyze the proteins and nucleic acids of viruses, virus-infected cells, and other biological systems. The method has been applied to a variety of problems for both analytical and preparative purposes and promises to be increasingly useful (cf. Frederick, 1964).

Acrylamide is not the first gelling agent to be employed in electrophoresis experiments, but certain of its properties are especially favorable and have led to its widespread use. It is a simple organic substance commercially available in sufficiently pure form to be used directly. This relative purity is an advantage over such other gelling agents as agar, agarose, and partially hydrolyzed starch, which are all of biological origin, and which are contaminated to various degrees with such natural impurities as degradative enzymes (e.g., ribonuclease), or substances leading to irreversible sample adsorption and other problems. An example of one such impurity-caused problem is encountered when electrophoresis is performed in gels made from agar, which ordinarily contains sulfated polysaccharides. A phe-

*This work was supported by National Institutes of Health grant AI 4153, National Science Foundation grant 4751, and American Cancer Society grant E 379.

†The author is a recipient of a U.S. Public Health Service Career Development Award.

nomenon known as "electroendosmosis" occurs which results in a flow of liquid when current is passed through an electrolyte solution in contact with an immobile, charged substrate. This effect can cause slowly migrating substances to be carried in the opposite direction to their true mobility. The use of agarose instead of agar eliminates this property only to the degree that traces of immobile, charged polymers have been removed, but properly made acrylamide gels are free of this and other serious difficulties.

The purpose for gels is twofold. First, in zonal separations the gel matrix provides a homogeneous support to eliminate gravity-induced disturbances arising from density differences owing either to local concentration changes or to ohmic heating from the passage of current. Second, as clearly pointed out for hydrolyzed-starch gels by Smithies (1955, 1959), gels of the appropriate concentration have effective spacings in their matrices (pore sizes) on the same order of size as macromolecules, and they thereby act as molecular sieves in which smaller molecules can move more freely than larger ones. In gel electrophoresis this effect on mobility is superimposed on that of an electric field on charged molecules to obtain remarkable resolving power.

Acrylamide readily forms gels over a wide range of concentrations from approximately 2% (useful for macromolecules on the order of one to two million daltons) up to greater than 20% (which may provide sieving effects for molecules as small as 1000 daltons). None of the biological gelling materials covers as wide a range. Further, since acrylamide gels form through covalent bond formation, strong hydrogen bonding agents (e.g., high concentrations of urea), which interfere with agar, agarose, and starch gel formation, can be included. This is not to imply that other gelling materials are useless. Agarose, for example, forms gels at concentrations of less than 0.5% and therefore is useful for higher molecular weight molecules than can be handled by 2% acrylamide. Indeed, gels made with combinations of agarose and low concentrations of acrylamide have been used successfully for separating nucleic acids (Peacock and Dingman, 1968).

The rationale for the selection of the systems described in this chapter are based on two approaches at opposite extremes. In one case it is often desirable to fractionate samples that have been exposed to the least possible denaturing conditions; for example, when a delicate biological property must be preserved. In general the requirements for the specific applications of this approach are highly individualized and while a variety of such systems can be conceived, only two of the most useful systems are described here.

Another tactic is employed when, as frequently occurs, information on the primary polypeptide composition of a system is desired. When such is the case buffers that exert strong dissociating effects on polypeptide aggregates are used. One commonly employed, nonionic agent is concentrated urea (5–10 *M*) added to normally nondenaturing systems. An even more potent agent is the anionic detergent sodium dodecyl sulfate (SDS). It is capable of dissociating a wide variety, if not all proteins or protein mixtures under mild conditions of neutral pH (cf. Section IV). Not only protein–protein interactions are eliminated by SDS but protein–nucleic acid and protein–lipid interactions as well so that mixtures as crude as total solublized cells may be resolved without interaction between the macromolecules in the system.

II. Materials and Methods

In the following, reference is made to certain specific items with the understanding that substitutes, if equal in characteristics, can be used.

A. Preparation and Storage of Reagents

The designation "stable" means that a solution can be kept indefinitely in the cold and dark (e.g., in a closed refrigerator). Other storage conditons are specified.

(1) Acrylamide-bis acrylamide (30:0.8): This solution is used for forming gels in the range of 3–20% acrylamide. It consists of 30 gm of acrylamide (Eastman 5521) and 0.8 gm of *N,N'*-bis-methylylene acrylamide (Eastman 8383) distilled water (stable).

(2) Acrylamide-bis acrylamide (20:1): This solution is the same as (1) above except in the concentrations of solutes. It is used for preparation of gels from 2–3% acrylamide (stable).

(3) Acrylamide-bis acrylamide (10:2.5): This solution is used for the preparation of "spacer" and "sample" gels in "disc" buffer systems (stable).

(4) Sodium dodecyl sulfate (10%): This solution is prepared from 10.0 gm of 95% SDS (Matheson, Coleman and Bell DX 2490) dissolved and diluted to 100 ml with distilled water. It should be clear and colorless (stable at room temperature).

(5) TEMED—*N,N,N',N'*-tetramethylethylenediamine (Matheson, Coleman and Bell TX 405): It is added in the appropriate amount (see Section II, D) just before casting the gels (stable as undiluted liquid).

(6) Ammonium persulfate (10%): 1.0 gm of solid ammonium persul-

fate (Fisher A-682) is dissolved in 9.0 ml of distilled water. This solution is preferably made fresh every 2 weeks and stored under refrigeration.

(7) Riboflavin: 4.0 mg of riboflavin (Nutritional Biochemicals Corp.) in 100 ml of distilled water (stable in the cold but light sensitive).

(8) 2-Mercaptoethanol (Matheson, Coleman and Bell 6377): The liquid is stable in a tightly closed container. It is used for reduction of the disulfide bonds of proteins.

(9) 2-Hydroxyethyl disulfide (Aldrich Chemical Corp. H2640): This reagent is used with 2-mercaptoethanol to produce stable, mixed disulfides of proteins (stable).

(10) Sodium phosphate (1 *M*): Prepared by dissolving 81.0 gm of Na_2HPO_4 and 59.3 gm $NaH_2PO_4 \cdot H_2O$ in a final volume of 1.0 liter of solution in distilled water (stable at room temperature).

(11a) Discontinuous gel buffer sytem (acidic substances): 48 ml of *N*-hydrochloric acid and 36.3 gm of tris (hydroxymethylaminomethane – Fisher T-395) are dissolved and diluted to 100 ml with distilled water (Davis, 1964) (stable).

(11b) Spacer gel buffer (acidic substances): 25.6 ml 1 *M* phosphoric acid and 5.7 gm tris are dissolved and diluted to 100 ml with distilled water (stable).

(11c) Electrode buffer (acidic substances) (10X): 6.0 gm tris and 28.8 gm of glycine (Fisher G-46) are dissolved and diluted to 1 liter with distilled water. In use it is diluted tenfold (stable).

(12a) Discontinuous gel buffer (basic substances): 48 ml of *N*-potassium hydroxide and 17.2 ml of glacial acetic acid (Fisher A-38) are mixed and diluted to 100 ml with distilled water (Reisfeld *et al.*, 1962) (stable).

(12b) Spacer gel buffer (basic substances): 48 ml of *N*-potassium hydroxide and 2.87 ml of glacial acetic acid are mixed and diluted to 100 ml with distilled water (stable).

(12c) Electrode buffer (basic substances) (5X):31.2 gm of β-alanine (Matheson, Coleman and Bell AX 425) and 8 ml of glacial acetic acid are dissolved and diluted to 1 liter with distilled water (stable). It is diluted 5-fold with distilled water for use.

(13) Amido black stain: 0.3 gm of amido black (also called Amidoschwarz, Naphthol Blue Black, or Buffalo Black NBR – Allied Chemical) per 100 ml of 7% acetic acid (stable at room temperature).

(14) Fixative (for Coomassie Blue procedure): 20 gm of sulfosalicylic acid (Fisher A-297) dissolved and diluted to 100 ml with distilled water (stable at room temperature).

(15) Coomassie Blue stain: 0.25 gm of Coomassie Brilliant Blue R 250 (Consolidated Laboratories) is dissolved in 100 ml distilled water (stable at room temperature).

(16) Destaining solution: 70 ml of glacial acetic acid to 1 liter with distilled water (stable at room temperature).

(17) Agarose: Available from Bausch & Lomb or Mann Chemicals.

(18) 0.2 *M* EDTA: 74.4 gm of disodium ethylenediaminetetraacetate (Na_2EDTA) (Baker 8993) to 1 liter with distilled water (stable at room temperature).

B. Apparatus

1. *Electrode Vessels and Fittings*

Satisfactory results may be obtained with a very simple and inexpensive homemade apparatus. The design for the electrophoresis chambers used here has been modified from that described by Davis (1964). Equipment patterned along the same lines is available from a number of manufacturers. Science and Analytical Chemistry publish extensive and well indexed annual lists of such manufacturers.

In this laboratory apparatus has been made from a wide variety of plastic vessels. Figure 1 and the accompanying legend describes a satisfactory and easily duplicated design. Refinements may be readily introduced to satisfy particular user's tastes. For example, one useful improvement, if a single diameter of glass gel tube is always used, is to install polypropylene tubing connectors (bulkhead union 5/16 inch i.d., Nalge Co., Inc., P.O. Box 365, Rochester, New York) in the upper electrode vessel instead of the one hole, silicone rubber stoppers. They provide ease of attachment of the gel tubes, and their rigidity eliminates the need for the bottom cover with spaced holes whose function is to align the tubes vertically.

Three different sizes of glass tubes are commonly used for preparing gels in this laboratory. If the intended purpose of the gels is for fractionation after electrophoresis they are formed in straight lengths of Pyrex tubing of outside diameter 8 mm (inside diameter approximately 6 mm). Lengths 16.5 and 26.5 centimeters long are cut for gels 10 and 20 cm long, respectively. If the gels are for staining only or if they are to be first stained and then fractionated, tubing with an outside diameter of 7 mm is used to allow for the swelling that occurs during staining. Tubing should be cut by breaking after first scoring at the desired breakage point with a file. Sharp edges should be removed by rubbing with medium grit emory cloth (available from hardware stores). Fire polishing is unsatisfactory because it tends to restrict the end of the tubing and makes gel removal difficult.

2. *Buffer Recirculation*

In any electrophoresis experiment electrolysis of the buffer occurs during the passage of current. A variety of electrolytic decomposition products may be produced depending on the chemical properties of the buffer ions, but there is always an accumulation of acid at the anode and alkali at the cathode. In long electrophoresis experiments or with large numbers of gels the electrolysis products may exceed the buffer capacity of the reservoirs. Very large buffer reservoirs or continuous replacement of the buffers can eliminate this problem or, in single buffer systems, it can be prevented by continuously exchanging the buffers between the anode and cathode reservoirs. In a vertically disposed apparatus this is very simply accomplished by pumping buffer from the lower electrode chamber into the upper electrode chamber where it mixes and overflows into the lower chamber through a tube with an opening at the desired height (see Fig. 1, *J*). Since the liquid path may have the full electric potential applied to it the metallic parts of the pump should be isolated from the buffer stream. Various peristaltic pumps, plastic impeller pumps, and vibrating pumps are suitable. In this laboratory a vibrating pump (Cole, Parmer) has been used. (cf. Fig. 1).

3. *Power Supplies*

Again simple and inexpensive equipment can be readily built (e.g., Davis, 1964) and can provide excellent results. There are also many commercial power supplies available. The requirements vary from one gel system to another but generally not more than approximately 1000 V of direct current (dc) and 200 mA is needed. For most work in this laboratory, an inexpensive supply that produces 400 V dc and 100 mA has been satisfactory (Heathkit IP-17, Heathkit Co., Benton Harbor, Michigan). The choice of either regulated constant voltage or constant current is not of overriding significance even though in certain cases arguments can be raised for one or the other.

Caution—Almost any source of current is potentially dangerous. Lethal shock can occur at potentials of even a few volts, but its danger is heightened by high voltages. Care should be taken to prevent contact with any part of the apparatus or solutions when the power is applied.

4. *Analytical Apparatus*

A variety of forms of analysis can be performed once the electrophoresis experiment has been completed. For fractionation of gels manual slicers have been described (Heidemann, 1964; Chrambach, 1966)

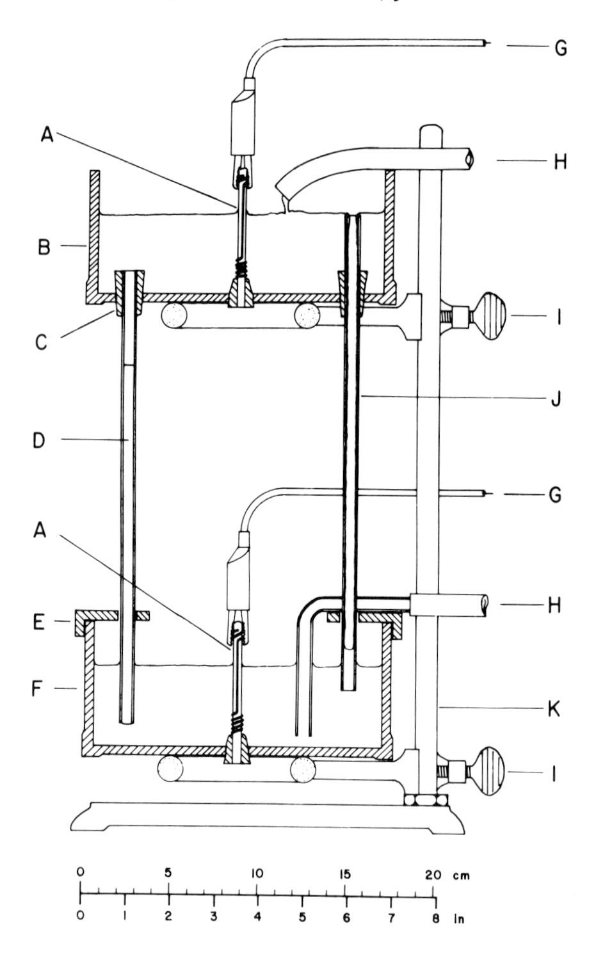

FIG. 1. An apparatus for cylindrical gel electrophoresis. The various parts are as follows: *A*, Electrodes fashioned from 6 inches of No. 22 gage platinum wire wrapped around a 4 inch length of (4 mm o.d.) glass rod inserted into a No. 0 silicone rubber stopper. *B*, Upper electrode vessel, made by cutting a polycarbonate jar (6$\frac{5}{16}$ inch i.d. by 9$\frac{3}{8}$ inch height, Nalge Co., Inc., Box 365, Rochester, New York) to a height of 3 inches and drilling 12 holes in the bottom (0.5 inch i.d.) equally spaced, at a radius of 2$\frac{3}{8}$ inch from a similar hole in the center. *C*, Silicone rubber stopper (No. 1) with a hole (8 mm o.d.) for attachment of gel tubes. *D*, Gel tube (8 mm o.d. by 26.5 cm in length) with 20 cm gel. *E*, Guide for spacing and aligning the gel tubes, fashioned from one cover for the above jar by cutting 12 holes ($\frac{3}{8}$ inch diam) spaced equally the same radius as the holes of the upper electrode vessel, and a large central hole (4 inch i.d.) for access to the lower elec-

but the most convenient approach in this laboratory has been the use of a semiautomated, extrusion-type fractionator (Maizel, 1966) in conjunction with a specially designed fraction collector that permits direct collection into counting dishes, vials, or test tubes (the fractionator and fraction collector are available from Savant Instrument, Inc., 221 Park Ave., Hicksville, New York). Equipment for radioautography has also been described (Fairbanks *et al.*, 1965, available from Canal Ind., Bethesda, Maryland). For ultraviolet photometric scanning of gels a variety of devices are available. Gilford Instruments, Oberlin, Ohio provide an attachment for their spectrophotometers which will accommodate gels up to approximately 10 cm in length. The Joyce Chromoscan (National Instrument Labs., Rockville, Maryland) accommodates gels up to approximately 20 cm in length. Attachments for the automatic gel fractionator have been devised (Maizel, 1969) that permit simultaneous photometry and fractionation, or nondestructive photometry, using standard spectrophotometers. All of the above instruments can perform scanning with visible and ultraviolet light. In addition there are numerous photometers that work exclusively in the visible region with stained gels or colored proteins.

Other instrumentation may be found in the previously mentioned guides to scientific equipment (see Section II, B, 1).

C. Choice of a Buffer System and Sample Preparation

The exact choice of sample preparation and gel-buffer system, as mentioned above, will depend on whether it is desired to maintain the sample in as "native" condition as possible (e.g., if a biological activity is to be retained) or if it is desired to dissociate all macromolecular aggregates into their individual polymeric subunits by means of a "dissociating" buffer system (e.g., dissociation and separation of the

---

trode. *F*, Lower electrode vessel, made from the same type jar as *B* but with a single, central hole for the electrode. *G*, Electrode leads with alligator clips (from electronic supply houses) at one end and terminals compatible with the power supply at the other. *H*, Recirculation lines of plastic tubing leading to and from an oscillating pump (Model 7103-1, Cole-Parmer Instrument and Equipment Co., 7330 North Clark Street, Chicago, Illinois), and recirculating buffer at a rate of approximately 50 ml/minute. It is not used for discontinuous buffer systems. *I*, Support rings, for the upper and lower electrode chambers. *J*, Overflow tube, consisting of an empty gel tube extended upward so that when the upper electrode buffer depth reaches approximately 2 inches, the excess will overflow into the lower electrode. It provides a part of the path for buffer recirculation. *K*, Support stand.

polypeptide and polynucleotide of virus particles or ribosomes or the separation of the dissociated subunits of multimeric enzymes). Generally both systems should be used. Table I lists buffer systems commonly used for these purposes. Tables II and III give abbreviated protocols for nondenaturing and denaturing systems respectively.

1. *Native Proteins*

For "native" proteins one of the most generally applicable buffer systems is the so-called high pH system (Table 1; Davis, 1964). Although it was originally designed for serum proteins there are apparently many cellular proteins which move as anions at pH 8.3, a pH suitable for the preservation of many enzymes and antigens. A complementary buffer system for basic proteins that do not migrate in the high pH system is the pH 4.3 system (Table 1; Reisfeld *et al.*, 1962). Samples are best prepared for either of these methods by extraction or solution in dilute buffers (e.g., 0.01 *M* tris or phosphate buffers at neutral pH) or if they are obtained in higher salt concentration by dilution or dialysis to less than 0.01 *M* salts. The amount of sample to be applied will be governed by the detectability of a given component after separation. Typically, by Coomassie Brilliant Blue staining, a few micrograms in a given protein component of a mixture is detectable, but, for most cases, 100 μg in a single band can be handled easily and will permit detection of possible minor contaminants. On the other hand, with a mixture of many proteins, it is generally desirable to limit the total load to about 200 μg of protein in order that most components will be detected but that the gel not be overloaded. The application of large amounts of crude, and of some purified, samples may lead to precipitation of a part of the protein. Each protein behaves differently in this regard but generally soluble, stable, low molecular weight proteins behave best. This generalization is strengthened by the observation that the behavior of crude extracts can be improved by using the supernatant fraction after centrifugation at high speeds (e.g., 50,000 rpm, 1 hour in a Spinco No. 50 rotor) to remove large macromolecular aggregates.

2. *Dissociating or Denaturing Systems*

a. Concentrated urea. For the electrophoresis of dissociated proteins a simple and sometimes satisfactory approach is to modify the native systems through the inclusion of 8 *M* urea. This is most safely done in the low pH system in which the ammonium cyanate that accumulates during the storage of urea, and which reacts with amino groups of proteins, is decomposed. Small amounts of cyanate may also be eliminated from high pH systems by inclusion of 0.01 *M* methylamine with which the cyanate reacts in preference to proteins. The effectiveness of the urea-modified buffer systems, like the parent systems, is greatest for partially purified or pure proteins and not completely effective for crude mixtures.

b. SDS The most powerful and effective dissociating systems are those employing SDS. In this system biological activity is usually abolished but the resultant solubilization of difficult samples in part compensates this loss. Some very sturdy, disulfide-stabilized enzymes may retain activity (e.g., ribonuclease in the absence of reducing agents) or certain structures may be metastable (cf. below) but most enzymes, protein antigens, and all antibodies are denatured. The reversibility of denaturation varies, but limited experience in this laboratory suggests that some proteins can recover antigenicity when SDS is removed. Usually greater than 90% of the protein of crude extracts (e.g., whole HeLa cells) migrates cleanly into gels containing this reagent. For the buffer systems described in Tables I and III samples are prepared or equilibrated with 0.01 *M* sodium phosphate, pH7, and should be especially free of divalent metal and potassium ions, which precipitate SDS. The sample is mixed with 10% SDS to contain a final concentration of 1–2% SDS, or if a very concentrated protein sample is used, dry SDS is added to at least five times the protein concentration. The mixture should then be heated to 100°C for 1 minute, if determined necessary by trial, to achieve complete dissociation. Dissociation of purified virions or turbid suspensions can be easily observed by the decrease or disappearance of opalescence. The requirements of individual samples vary widely, so it is best to treat an unknown sample various ways. Partial stability in SDS sometimes occurs with viruses. For example, the poliovirion is resistant to neutral SDS at room temperature but is readily and permanently dissociated in SDS either by lowering the pH, by heating to 45°C, or by the addition of 8 *M* urea at room temperature. Other viruses require different conditions for dissociation, but in all cases examined, the proteins remain dissociated in SDS alone after the additional dissociating factor is withdrawn.

Samples in SDS are stable for long periods of time. Most, if not all, degradative enzymes are apparently destroyed by rigorous SDS treatment. Bacterial contamination, however, frequently occurs in dilute SDS solutions (0.1% or less) stored at room temperature. Storage in the presence of 0.001 *M* sodium azide in the cold eliminates this prob-

TABLE I
BUFFER SYSTEMS FOR ACRYLAMIDE GEL ELECTROPHORESIS

Formula	Sample gel	Spacer gel	Resolving gel	Electrode buffer
Neutral-SDS (for all proteins)	10% sucrose[a] or 1% agarose[a]	Not used	For 10 ml of 5% gel[b]: 1.67 ml reagent (1) 1.00 ml reagent (10) 0.10 ml reagent (4) 0.005 ml reagent (5) 7.10 ml distilled water 0.10 ml reagent (6)	For 1.0 liter: 100 ml reagent (10) 10 ml reagent (4) 890 ml distilled water
Neutral-SDS- EDTA (for nucleic acids)	Not used	Not used	For 10 ml of 2.4% gel[b]: 1.20 ml reagent (2) 1.00 ml reagent (10) 0.10 ml reagent (4) 0.005 ml reagent (5) 0.50 ml reagent (18) 7.10 ml distilled water 0.10 ml reagent (6)	100 ml reagent (10) 10 ml reagent (4) 50 ml reagent (18) 840 ml distilled water

High pH discontinuous (for acidic proteins)[c]	Gelled sample: 1 part reagent (11b) 2 parts reagent (3) 1 part reagent (7) 4 parts sample in water or dilute buffer plus 0.005 ml of 0.1% bromphenol blue[c]	1 part reagent (11b) 2 parts reagent (3) 1 part reagent (7) 4 parts of distilled water[c]	For 8 ml of 7.5% gel[b,c]: 1.00 ml reagent (11a) 2.00 ml. reagent (1) 0.005 ml reagent (5) 4.90 ml distilled water 0.10 ml reagent (6)	100 ml reagent (11c) 900 ml distilled water
	Direct layer: sample in 10% sucrose and 8-fold dilution of reagent (11b)	Same as above	Same as above	Same as above
Low pH discontinuous (for basic proteins)[c]	Gelled sample: 1 part reagent (12b) 2 parts reagent (3) 1 part reagent (7) 4 parts sample in water or dilute buffer plus 0.005 ml of 0.1% methyl green	1 part reagent (12b) 2 parts reagent (3) 1 part reagent (7) 4 parts distilled water	For 8 ml of 7.5% gel[b,c]: 1.00 ml reagent (12a) 2.00 ml reagent (1) 0.005 ml reagent (5) 4.90 ml distilled water 0.10 ml reagent (6)	200 ml reagent (12c) 800 ml distilled water
	Direct layer: sample in 10% sucrose and 8-fold dilution of reagent (12b)	Same as above	Same as above	Same as above

[a] See text, Section II, E.

[b] For other gel concentrations the proportion of reagent (1) and added water are varied.

[c] As discussed in the text dissociating buffer systems can be made from nondenatured systems by addition of 8 *M* urea (4.8 gm/10 ml final solution).

lem. The SDS precipitated in the cold dissolves instantly on rewarming the sample.

c. Reduction of disulfide bonds. If it is desired to reduce disulfide linkages 0.1 *M* 2-mercaptoethanol can be added during the dissociating step. Alkylation of the reduced proteins is usually not necessary in the SDS system but if it is desired 0.3 *M* iodacetic acid or iodacetamide is added after the sample has been reduced for 30 minutes. The alkylation reaction is then stopped after an additional 30 minutes of incubation by further addition of 0.6 *M* 2-mercaptoethanol. Dialysis of the sample against 0.01 *M* sodium phosphate and 0.1% SDS, or other sample buffers, before electrophoresis is necessary to eliminate salts produced in the reaction. A convenient alternative procedure to reduction and alkylation is the reaction of dissociated or denatured protein with 0.1 *M* 2-hydroxyethyl disulfide (Aldrich Chemical Co., reagent 6) containing 0.001–0.002 *M* 2-mercaptoethanol to catalyze the exchange of all protein sulfhydryls and disulfide bonds into the stable, mixed disulfide of mercaptoethanol as described by Smithies (1965). A detailed discussion of reductive alkylation is given by Hirs (1967).

3. *Nucleic Acids*

Nucleic acids can be readily separated by acrylamide gel electrophoresis if polyvalent metal ions and ionic strength are controlled and if sufficiently low concentration gels are used to accommodate high molecular weight nucleic acids. Gels with 2.2–2.4% acrylamide are the lowest concentration acrylamide gels that can be formed and handled conveniently. They permit migration of nucleic acids with sizes on the order of 2×10^6 daltons or less. Slightly larger molecules may be handled by dilute gels formed with a combination of agarose and acrylamide (Peacock and Dingman, 1967). The SDS-phosphate dissociating buffer system described above for proteins can be modified to give a simple buffer for separation of nucleic acids by the addition of 0.01 *M* Na_2EDTA in the sample, gel, and electrode buffers (Bellamy *et al.*, 1967). Bishop *et al.* (1967) have likewise added SDS to Loening's (1967) buffers to give an analogous system.

Since SDS eliminates the interaction of proteins with nucleic acids, either protein-containing or deproteinized samples can be used. The SDS-phosphate buffer is best used if the gel is to be analyzed either by fractionation for radioactivity or by uv photometry, but it is less satisfactory if staining is intended because both SDS and phosphate precipitate with many of the cationic dyes and some fixatives in nucleic acid stains. It is therefore necessary that the gels be washed free of these ions by soaking in a suitable fixative (e.g., trichloroacetic acid) if staining is to be used. Other buffer systems not containing phosphate or SDS (see Loening, 1967; Peacock and Dingman, 1967) are more convenient if staining is the sole purpose, but use of deproteinized nucleic acids is then recommended.

4. Concentration of Dilute Samples

If a sample is too dilute for direct analysis but is available in large volume it can be concentrated for any electrophoresis system by placing it in dialysis tubing and sprinkling a small quantity of dry Sephadex G-200 or G-100 on it. The water absorption is approximately 20 gm per dry gram of G-200 powder and a tenfold concentration of a dilute sample can be obtained in approximately an hour. Other, dry, hydrophilic, high molecular weight substances can also be used (e.g., Carbowax 20 *M* made by Union Carbide and Aquacide sold by Calbiochem).

The sample and stacking gels in the "native," discontinuous systems (but not the SDS system) provide another convenient and powerful concentration process for very dilute samples. It is possible to gelify any volume of sample having the desired amount of material and to concentrate it electrophoretically into as sharp a starting zone as obtained from a concentrated sample. It is essential for successful application of this stacking process that the spacer gel be of approximately the same dimensions as the gelled samples. The time for electrophoresis will be increased as a result of the lengthening of the gels.

In the SDS system described here, some initial concentration of the starting sample occurs, but unlike the discontinuous buffer systems the SDS buffers cannot deal satisfactorily with unlimited volumes of samples. The concentrating effect involved is well known in free boundary electrophoresis and results from introducing the sample in a lower conductivity (more dilute) buffer than the adjoining buffer. The resulting higher potential gradient (volts/cm) across the sample at the start of electrophoresis causes faster migration in the sample region than in the adjoining, more conductive, lower potential gradient, buffer regions. Thus concentration of the sample occurs as fast-moving molecules join those that have slowed upon entering the lower potential gradient of the gel buffer. In the usual acrylamide gels this effect is accentuated by the additional slowing of molecules as they go from the free solution, or the open gel, of the sample region into a resolving gel offering some restriction of migration. These combined effects are sufficient to concentrate a sample 1 cm high into an effective starting region of approximately 1 mm or less.

The great solvent power of SDS buffers permits other concentration procedures that would be unthinkable in the "native" systems. For example, it is often convenient, especially when dealing with large numbers of samples, to precipitate the proteins and nucleic acids with cold trichloracetic acid (TCA), acetone, or alcohol, or to lyophilize them and then to solubilize them in SDS. If excess acid is removed and the sample has neutral pH, samples precipitated with TCA behave identically to those taken up directly in SDS. If there is a question of the presence of excess electrolytes in the sample it is always advisable to dialyze it against 0.01 *M* sodium phosphate and 0.1% SDS.

D. Choice of Gel Concentration and Preparation of Gels

The choice of a resolving gel concentration depends mainly on the size range of the components of interest. Generally, higher gel concentrations (i.e., smaller "pore" sizes) give wider separation between two different sized molecules, but a practical upper limit on concentration will be reached when the molecules of interest cannot enter the gel or, even before that, when migration times become impractically long. Most proteins migrate satisfactorily in a 7.5% acrylamide gel, but for an unknown sample it is advisable to try a range of concentrations from 4 to 10% acrylamide.

When the choice has been made the desired gels are formed by mixing the appropriate reagents in solution and allowing them to polymerize directly in the tubes in which the electrophoresis will occur. A convenient cap for the lower end of the gel tube is a rubber stopper from a 13 mm serum collection tube (Vacutainer, Becton-Dickenson Co., Baltimore, Maryland). The tubes should then be placed in a vertical position. In this laboratory racks for this purpose have been made from baskets used in laboratory glassware washing machines (Heinecke Corp., New York) in which holes on one side are enlarged to 0.5 inch (12.7 mm). Tubes 6.5 inches (16.5 cm) or longer extend through to matching holes on the opposite side of the basket when the rubber end caps are snugly engaged and the whole assemblage of rack and tubes can be handled easily.

The reagents for the various systems of spacer and resolving gels should be mixed in the order given in Table I including the additions of water. Since the initiation process for the polymerization step depends on the reaction between TEMED and ammonium persulfate (or riboflavin and light as the case may be) the rate of which in turn depends on their concentrations it is essential that the persulfate be added at the final step before filling the tubes and then quickly mixed to dilute it to the correct concentration. The mixed reagents will gel in a time ranging from a few minutes to hours depending on the buffer system, temperature, and other conditions. If premature gelling occurs before all the desired tubes have been filled, the mixed reagents may be cooled before and during the filling operation to slow the polymerization reaction.

As soon as the gel tubes are filled to the desired height they should be overlayered with distilled water (or buffer without acrylamide) to a height of 0.5–1.0 cm. This operation can be done conveniently with a fine-tipped Pasteur pipette. Ensure that the pipette is filled to the tip with no pendant drop, then touch the tip against the meniscus and allow the overlayer liquid to flow slowly onto the denser gel solution. At the same time slowly withdraw the pipette to keep the tip approximately even with the overlayer meniscus. If there is a pendant drop on the pipette tip, or if the tip is inserted below the meniscus, the surface of the gel solution will be disturbed resulting in a diffuse gel boundary and possibly diffuse bands. When gels longer than 10 cm, such as those used in automatic gel fractionation, and greater than 5% acrylamide are to be formed, additional precautions are necessary to eliminate internal ruptures which tend to develop during polymerization. The considerable heat produced expands the gel solution at the same time as the gel becomes solid and adherent to the glass tube. When the rigid gel cools the resulting internal tension can produce ruptures. This problem is solved by evacuating the gel solution to remove dissolved gases before filling the tubes and by incubating the filled tubes in a bath at 25°C (a bucket of water is satisfactory) during polymerization. In special cases (e.g., 20% gels in the SDS system) it is further essential to halve the concentration of ammonium persulfate.

In most systems the gels form in approximately 30 minutes, as evidenced by the reappearance of a sharp, flat interface on top of the gel. The overlayer can then be shaken off, and the gels may be used.

If a spacer gel is to be used it is formed at this time by a repetition of the process for resolving gels including the water overlayering step except that polymerization is usually initiated by photoxidation of riboflavin. Irradiation of the tubes can be done with light boxes made for that purpose (cf. Canal Industries) or by a fluorescent desk lamp. The tubes should be in a single row in front of the lamp so that all tubes receive similar illumination. Tubes with both resolving gel and spacer gel cannot be stored but should be used as soon as possible after the spacer gel is polymerized. Resolving gels alone can be stored. The limit of useful lifetime may vary with gel system, but experience has shown that gels made in the SDS-phosphate system can be used after storage for as long as several months in a moist atmosphere at room temperature.

E. Electrophoresis

Samples (see Section II, B for preparation of samples) may be introduced either by gelling them into dilute acrylamide or agarose (sample gel) or by direct layering with a sufficient amount of an inert nonelectrolyte to make the sample denser than the overlying buffer. Gelling is the most desirable approach, if convenient and feasible, since it totally eliminates any convective stirring of the sample region. The addition of an inert solute (e.g., 10–20% glycerol or sucrose) to permit layering also minimizes convection. High concentrations of sucrose (30–50%) withdraw water osmotically from the top of the gel. This is to be avoided since it may lead to some trapping or trailing as the sample enters the gel. Addition of an inert solid matrix such as Sephadex beads or polyvinyl chloride or starch powder can further improve the anticonvection action of directly layered samples.

There are certain restrictions on the use of each of the various ways of sample introduction. For the discontinuous gel buffers, dilute acrylamide spacer and sample gels are usually preferred. If, however, the sample contains an inhibitor of acrylamide polymerization (e.g., sulfhydryl reagents or colored components) direct layering should be used. Commercial agarose is not acceptable in the high pH discontinuous buffers because it contains traces of sulfated polysaccharide which are entrained by the stacking process, cause the gel to collapse, and distort the electrophoretic pattern. Agarose (0.5–1%) can be used in the neutral-SDS system, although the usual, more convenient method, for sample volumes not greater than 0.4 ml is direct layering with 10% sucrose mixed into the sample.

When the samples have been introduced they should be carefully overlayered with the appropriate electrode buffer and inserted into the electrophoresis apparatus without delay.

The exact current, voltage, and polarity to be used depends on the system employed, but for the discontinuous buffers the voltage is generally several hundred volts or higher and the current is 2–5 mA/gel. In the neutral-SDS system, with its higher conductivity buffers, the voltages are usually less than 100 V and currents vary from 5 to

15 mA/gel depending on the length of gel and time of run. Tables II and III give suggested settings for various conditions. The limiting factor in choosing voltages is the temperature that the sample and gel can tolerate. The heat produced is proportional to the product of the current squared and the resistance per unit length of the gel (or the current times the voltage per unit length). The actual temperature will depend on both this rate of heat production and its rate of dissipation. Usually the native systems have low conductivities (high resistance), draw low currents, and do not heat excessively. The temperature can be further controlled by refrigeration.

Neutral-SDS gels with their higher conductivities may become quite warm, but high temperature does not necessarily have a harmful effect in this system unless it goes above the boiling point of the buffer in the gel. Cooling can be employed, but the temperature must stay above the point at which SDS precipitates.

The choice of constant current or constant voltage need not be a critical decision. Unlike hanging paper electrophoresis in which regulated current operation is advantageous in preventing catastrophic heating either mode of operation can be used for gels. If both options are available the constant current mode is slightly preferrable for the discontinuous buffer systems and constant voltage for the homogeneous buffers such as the neutral-SDS system.

Running times for various buffers, gel concentrations, and distances vary widely but gels for staining or radioautography can usually be run in a few hours, while the longer gels for fractionation and subsequent analysis are most conveniently run overnight. It is sometimes useful to follow the course of electrophoresis by the migration of a small amount of a marker or "tracking" dye introduced with the sample, especially if new conditions are being tried. Bromphenol blue serves for the high pH-discontinuous and neutral-SDS systems and methyl green is satisfactory for the low pH-discontinuous system. In the discontinuous systems the respective dyes migrate as very sharp bands at the boundary between the different kinds of buffers. This band does not broaden with time and is an example of the kind of concentration that occurs with suitably charged molecules, including proteins, in these systems. Were it not for the sieving effect of the resolving gel on large molecules they too would migrate at the buffer discontinuity as the bromphenol blue does. In contrast to the discontinuous systems, homogeneously buffered systems do not exhibit this stacking effect. For example, bromphenol blue in the neutral-SDS system, although still migrating faster than most macromolecules, is not retained in a hyper-sharp zone.

TABLE II

ABBREVIATED PROTOCOL FOR HIGH pH (ACIDIC PROTEIN) OR LOW pH (BASIC PROTEINS) DISCONTINUOUS GEL ELECTROPHORESIS[a]

1. Prepare samples having 100–200 μg of protein in spacer gel buffer diluted eightfold with 5 μg of tracking dye added (bromphenol blue for high pH; methyl green for low pH).
2. Layer the sample directly in 10% sucrose or gel it in spacer gel on top of a previously made resolving gel with a spacer gel on top of it.
3. Fill remaining empty portion of tube with electrode buffer, attach to electrode vessels, and fill the vessels with electrode buffer.
4. Apply a voltage such that excessive heating does not occur (200–400 V and 1–5 mA/gel).
5. Observe the tracking dye and stop when it nears the end of the gel (usually within 3–4 hours for a 10 cm gel).
6. Remove gels (see Section II, F, 1).

7a. Stain gels as in 8a of Table III.

b. Fractionate or radioautograph.

[a]See Table I for formulations.

TABLE III

ABBREVIATED PROTOCOL FOR NEUTRAL-SDS GEL ELECTROPHORESIS[a]

1. Dialyze sample against 0.01 *M* sodium phosphate pH 7.1.
2. Bring sample to 1% SDS, 0.01 *M* sodium phosphate, 1% (v/v) 2-mercaptoethanol, and 10% sucrose or glycerol.
3. Heat to 100°C for minute (if necessary).

4a. For samples to be stained apply 100–200 μg of protein in 0.2–0.3 ml on a gel 10 cm long having the desired acrylamide concentration.

b. For radioactive analysis or recovery apply up to 1 mg of protein in 0.2–0.3 ml on a gel 20 cm long.

5. Carefully fill the tube to the top with electrode buffer, attach gels to the electrode vessels, and fill with buffer.
6. Apply voltage.
   a. For 10 cm gels having 5% acrylamide apply 90 V (with a current initially of 10 mA/gel and finally of approximately 15 mA/gel) for 2 hours. For 7.5% gels run 3 hours, and for 10% gels run 4 hours.
   b. For 20 cm gels having 5% acrylamide apply 50 V (5 mA/gel initial) for 16 hours. For 7.5% gels apply 70 V for 16 hours. For 10% gels apply 90 V for 16 hours.
7. Remove gels (see Section II, F, 1).

8a. Stain gels by fixing 16–24 hours in 10 volumes of 20% sulfosalycilic acid, followed by 0.25% Coomassie Brilliant Blue R250 (2.0 hours for 5% gels, 3.0 hours for 7.5% gels, or 4.0 hours for 10% gels), followed by repeated washes with 7% acetic acid.

b. Perform radioautography or fractionate.

[a]*Note:* This system is primarily for proteins but can be used for nucleic acids (see Table I for formulations).

F. Analysis of Gels Following Electrophoresis

1. *Removal of Gels*

An effective technique for removing gels containing from 2.4 to 10% acrylamide is to hold the gel tube nearly horizontally in one hand while rotating it slowly back and forth through one turn (about one cycle every 2-5 seconds) and rimming between the gel and the glass tube with a blunt-tipped, 20 gage, 4 inch needle. A jerky, to-and-fro lengthwise motion of the needle (amplitude not more than 1/16 to 1/8 inch) with slow but steady ejection of water from a syringe through the needle lubricates the entire gel surface and loosens the bond between the gel and the glass permitting the intact gel to slide from the tube.

Gels with greater than 10% acrylamide are very rigid and difficult to remove by rimming, and a different procedure is required. Two strips of wood 1/4 inch thick are laid on each side of the gel tube, lying flat on a sheet of aluminum foil on a sturdy work bench. A sheet of Plexiglass approximately 1/2 inch thick, 2 inches wide, and 1 foot long is placed on top of the gel tube and hit, lightly but numerous times, along its length with a hammer to shatter the tube completely. The gel, usually with only superficial marks, is then lifted from the broken glass tubing, rinsed free of any small glass fragments, and treated as desired.

2. *Staining*

Staining is accomplished in one of several ways. The original methods of acrylamide gel electrophoresis used amido black staining as described by Davis (1964). This procedure works well with systems free of SDS but is less sensitive than Coomassie Blue staining (Fazekas de St. Groth *et al.*, 1963; Maizel, 1966), especially for SDS-containing systems.

Coomassie Blue staining is accomplished by first fixing the gel overnight in at least 10 volumes of 20% sulfosalicylic acid followed by staining in 0.25% Coomassie Brilliant Blue in water for a time dependent upon the gel concentration. Five percent gels are stained for 2 hours and 10% gels are stained 4 hours. Longer staining may lead to retention of background stain between bands. After staining, the gels are washed with repeated changes of 7% acetic acid to remove unbound dye. Three to five washes of 10-20 volumes are sufficient to reduce the background stain to negligible levels. The entire procedure is usually carried out in 18 by 150 mm test tubes partially immersed in a 37°C water bath to produce convective stirring of the solutions. Quantities of protein as small as a microgram of protein in a single band may be detected by this method.

An alternative method using Coomassie Blue has been described by Chrambach *et al.* (1967) using 0.05% Coomassie Blue in 10% TCA. Coomassie Blue is relatively insoluble in TCA, and resultantly partitions into dye-protein complexes preferentially. In some cases it is possible to view the protein pattern immediately after staining and before destaining. For maximum sensitivity, however, prolonged staining and subsequent destaining is required.

3. *Fractionation*

Fractionation of gels for subsequent analysis can be accomplished by hand cutting, either free-hand or using a template (Heideman, 1964; Chrambach, 1966), or by an automated fractionator (Maizel, 1966) and fraction collector.

Automated fractionation is accomplished simply by extrusion of the gel through either an adjustable oriface (for 2.4–4% gels) or a fine screen (for 4–20% gels) to give a stream of crushed, diluted particles that accurately reflects the sequential arrangement of successive zones in the gel and which can be automatically collected. Separated components readily elute from the gel particles permitting recovery or analysis. Radioactivity can be determined on the fractions either by direct collection and drying on dishes for thin-window, gas-flow counting or by collection in vials followed by scintillation counting. Gas-flow counting is especially suitable for carbon-14 or phosphorus-32 determination, for which there is less than 10% self-absorption because of the gel particles. The usual procedure for gas-flow counting is to collect gel particles equivalent to 1.2–5 mm of gel length in 1 ml of 0.05% SDS to ensure even spreading of the mixture on flat-bottomed aluminum planchets ⅛ inch deep by 1¼ inch diam. For liquid scintillation counting crushed gel corresponding to 2 mm length is collected directly into scintillation vials in 1 ml of water and then either stored overnight or frozen and thawed to enhance elution of radioactive sample into solution. Ten milliliters of a dioxane-naphthalene-PPO scintillant (Bray, 1960; or Bray's solution omitting methanol, ethylene glycol, and POPOP for scintillation counters equipped with phototubes sensitive to short wavelengths) is then added and the samples counted. There is a small (10–20%), gradual change in the efficiency and energy distributions which stabilizes after about 1 day. For most qualitative comparisons this effect is trivial. Quantitative measurements can be related by counting all samples after they have stabilized. The problem is not inherently related to acrylamide gel samples and may arise from the slow coalescence of macromolecules insoluble in dioxane. If in special cases the effect presents serious problems it may be eliminated by treating the sample with one of several alkaline solubilizers (available from scintillation equipment suppliers) before adding the scintillation solvent.

4. *Recovery*

For recovery, the samples from fractionated gels are simply allowed to diffuse into water, or any desired buffer, and then decanted from the gel particles. Recovery of samples is essentially complete in the neutral-SDS buffer system but varies with individual samples and buffers in the "native" systems.

5. *Radioautography*

When highly radioactive samples are available they can be analyzed by radioautography as described by Fairbanks *et al.* (1965). In this method gels are sliced longitudinally in a special template and the thin slices are immobilized and dried *in vacuo* onto a sheet of filter paper. This latter step, which serves to maintain the linear dimensions of the gel, is the innovative key of this method. Simple drying of the gel without the filter paper backing results in shrunken, curled, and very irregular products unsuitable for radioautography. The dried slices on paper are then exposed to medical X-ray film (e.g., Kodak Blue brand) for a period of exposure best determined by trial. (As a very rough guide, 50,000 disintegrations/minute in a band gives a reasonable exposure in 1 day.) The film is then developed in regular X-ray film processing chemicals. This method is theoretically very sensitive but for short exposure times (i.e., a few days) it is less sensitive than fractionation and counting. This method can be used to perform a kind of double labeling experiment by mixing very small amounts of a radioactive material with a stainable amount of nonradioactive sample. Then radioautography of the stained gel will reveal the two samples separately. Quantitation of radioautographs can be achieved by densitometry of the developed film. Controls standardizing the exposure, development, and densitometric steps should be included.

6. *Immunotechniques*

Immunotechniques are widely recognized as being especially sensitive for certain problems and it is possible to employ them in conjunction with acrylamide gel electrophoresis. Since immunoglobulins are rather large proteins (M_w 150,000) they diffuse poorly in the 5–10% acrylamide gels most useful for protein electrophoresis and thus direct double diffusion experiments are unsuccessful. One way of combining the techniques is to perform the usual cylindrical gel electrophoresis, then to lay the gel on a flat plate and embed it (or slices of it) in a thin layer (2 mm thick) of a soft gel (e.g., 1-2% agarose) suitable for immunodiffusion (Hunneeus-Cox, 1964). After allowing the electrophoretically separated proteins to diffuse into the surrounding soft gel, troughs about 2-3 mm wide are cut parallel to the acrylamide cylinder and about 0.5-1 cm away. Antiserum is then placed in them and precipitation arcs are observed to develop in the soft gel between the acrylamide cylinder and the trough. This technique is described in detail in Chapter 31 by Salzman and Moss.

With materials recovered from fractionated gels it is also possible to apply most of the other standard immunological techniques as well as double diffusion. A potentially very useful technique for resolving radioactively labeled antigens employs the solvent power of the neutral-SDS buffer to solubize and permit the electrophoresis of specific immune precipitates (see Horwitz and Scharff, Chapter 29).

III. Interpretation of Results

A. Significance of Single and Multiple Zones

There is an inclination to regard a sample having a single well-defined zone by acrylamide gel electrophoresis as a homogeneous material; however, regardless of the sensitivity of the method, true homogeneity is only indicated, and then tentatively, if all other tests agree. While, by the above criterion, it is difficult to prove homogeneity gel electrophoresis can prove the heterogeneity of a protein or nucleic acid preparation better than many methods.

Usually the observed multiple components of a sample are discovered to have great significance and, indeed, prove highly informative about the biological system being studied. It is desirable, however, to establish this significance in each case. One of the most general ways of doing so is to examine the covariation of the appearance or disappearance of a given electrophoretic zone with some biological aspect, as, for example, developmental sequence, replicative stage, or genetic mutation. For instance, if a given zone varies independently from other zones but in correlation with the mutation of a particular gene it is clearly a unique component.

There are also simple biochemical tests that can be applied to acrylamide gel patterns to prove the uniqueness (or show relatedness) between different components. One such test can be done by labeling a protein mixture with two chemically different radioactive amino acids, one having carbon-14 and the other tritium. If the compositions of the various components are different, the ratios of tritium to carbon-14 will vary systematically through the electrophoretic pattern. This experiment has been used to show that the multiple proteins of the adenovirion differ from each other (Maizel *et al.*, 1968a). Controls with two different isotopes in the same amino acid show a constant tritium to carbon-14 ratio.

Another way to show compositional differences is by the preparation and electrophoresis of a protein mixture labeled with a number of amino acids, followed by recovery of the resolved components from the gel, and analysis of the radioactivity in various chromatographically separated amino acids. This technique was used to show differences among the virion and nonvirion proteins of poliovirus-infected cells (Maizel and Summers, 1968). Since the actual chemical analysis of the proteins is not determined, heavy contamination with nonradioactive material does not interfere.

Perhaps the most sensitive technique for comparing proteins is through peptide mapping. This procedure can be applied to samples obtained from gels. It involves digestion with specific proteolytic enzymes or reagents followed by separation of the resulting peptides on ion exchange columns. When coupled with the specific incorporation of individual-labeled amino acids, similarities and differences not only of composition but of sequence as well can be readily detected. In addition, if amino acid compositional data are available, size estimations obtained from gels or other physical measurements can be confirmed independently (Horwitz and Maizel, 1969).

B. Estimations of Size

As pointed out previously, size is an important determinant in gel electrophoresis experiments, and it is therefore possible to obtain information about size from such experiments. One very versatile way for molecular weight (M_w) estimation has been described by Shapiro *et al.* (1967) who found that in the neutral-SDS buffer system the logarithm of the M_w of a protein and its distance of migration were inversely related over a M_w range of 15,500–165,000 with an accuracy of about 10% or better. Proteins of widely different isoelectric points conformed to this relationship. A similar relationship has been observed for nucleic acids by McPhie *et al.* (1966). Presumably in the cases both of nucleic acids and SDS-protein complexes the molecules behave as polyanions and small charge differences are obscured. In practice the molecular weight of an unknown polypeptide is estimated by comparison of its mobility with that of proteins of known M_w; preferably with as many examples and as nearly the same M_w as practical. This may be done either in parallel experiments or, more satisfactorily, by double isotopic labeling. A line is then drawn through the plot of the logarithm of the known molecular weights and their migration distances. The distances migrated by the unknowns are used with this plot to estimate the unknown M_w's. It is advisable to perform such an experiment in several gel concentrations both as a repeated determination and as a way of detecting anomalous behavior. Such anomalous behavior may arise if measurements are made too near the gel origin, where the gel concentration is not uniform, or with small proteins in low concentration gels, where their migration may not be sensitive to sieving effects by the gel. This same test has also detected an as-yet unexplained anomalous behavior in a single protein running in the midst of a number of normally behaving components (Studier and Maizel, 1969). Such behavior might be expected if the protein had either an unusual configuration, or SDS-binding, properties.

Other methods of size estimation have also been developed using nondenaturing buffers. They likewise depend on the previously stated property that the mobilities of large molecules are affected relatively more by changes in gel concentration than are those of small proteins. Zwaan (1967) has characterized this relationship in a useful way by showing that the logarithm of the M_w of a protein is proportional to the relative mobilities of a protein in any arbitrary higher concentration gel to that in a lower concentration gel. Once again the method is used by comparing an unknown with several proteins of known M_w. This system is independent of the type of buffer used and can be employed with any gel electrophoretic system.

It should be noted that these methods of M_w estimation are empirical, and that although they work well with a number of known, characterized proteins there may be proteins that do not behave as expected. Unusual configurations and interactions, for example, may occur which do not fit these empirical relationships.

IV. Discussion

The techniques described here were developed mainly to study problems of animal virus molecular biology. They have turned out to be applicable to a number of other kinds of biological samples as well.

The characterization and understanding of any molecular biological system is usually based on a description of the primary protein and nucleic acid molecules comprising it. The first stage in gathering this information is the determination of their numbers and size. The neutral-SDS electrophoretic procedure is among the most useful of available methods for these problems. Figure 2 shows the results of applying this method to a wide variety of viruses and animal cell fractions. It clearly demonstrates, without going into detail on the specific examples, that the method reveals unique protein compositions for the individual samples shown. These results are not meant to be taken as definitive descriptions of these biological systems. Some have been studied in great detail and references to them appear in the figure legend. The complexity of most of the samples, with the exception of the minor component appearing with the single major protein of tobacco mosaic virus (Fig. 2, gel 12), is real and significant. In fact, the presentation of such data in a photograph does not reveal all of the true complexity that is usually seen on direct visual examination of the stained gels. Visual examination of photographs also does not permit reliable quantitative estimation of various components. Attempts to compare different patterns side by side are sometimes uncertain. Such problems of quantitation and identification can be handled very satisfactorily using isotopic double labeling experiments and fractionation of the gel. The experiment shown in Fig. 3 illustrates the usefulness of this approach for detecting and measuring the proteins produced in poliovirus-infected cells and identifying certain of them as the virion structural proteins (Summers *et al.*, 1965; Summers and Maizel, 1968; Maizel and Summers, 1968). Similar kinds of studies have been done on adenoviruses (Maizel *et al.*, 1968a,b) and vaccinia (Holowczak and Joklik, 1967a,b).

It is reasonable from the present growth of gel electrophoretic methodology to anticipate significant development in the future. Certainly the basic equipment is simple, far less expensive and capable of handling larger numbers of samples than many other techniques of analysis, for example, ultracentrifugation. Output, ease of operation, reproducibility, and precision may be expected to improve as more experience is gained. In particular, further efforts to control such variables as physical parameters and gel chemistry and further automation of the methods should be rewarding. The development of a theoretical basis for behavior of macromolecules in gel matrices, which is now lacking, would be of considerable value. Then the now largely empirical but obviously powerful results obtainable by these methods could be used for more complete interpretations and predictions than is now possible.

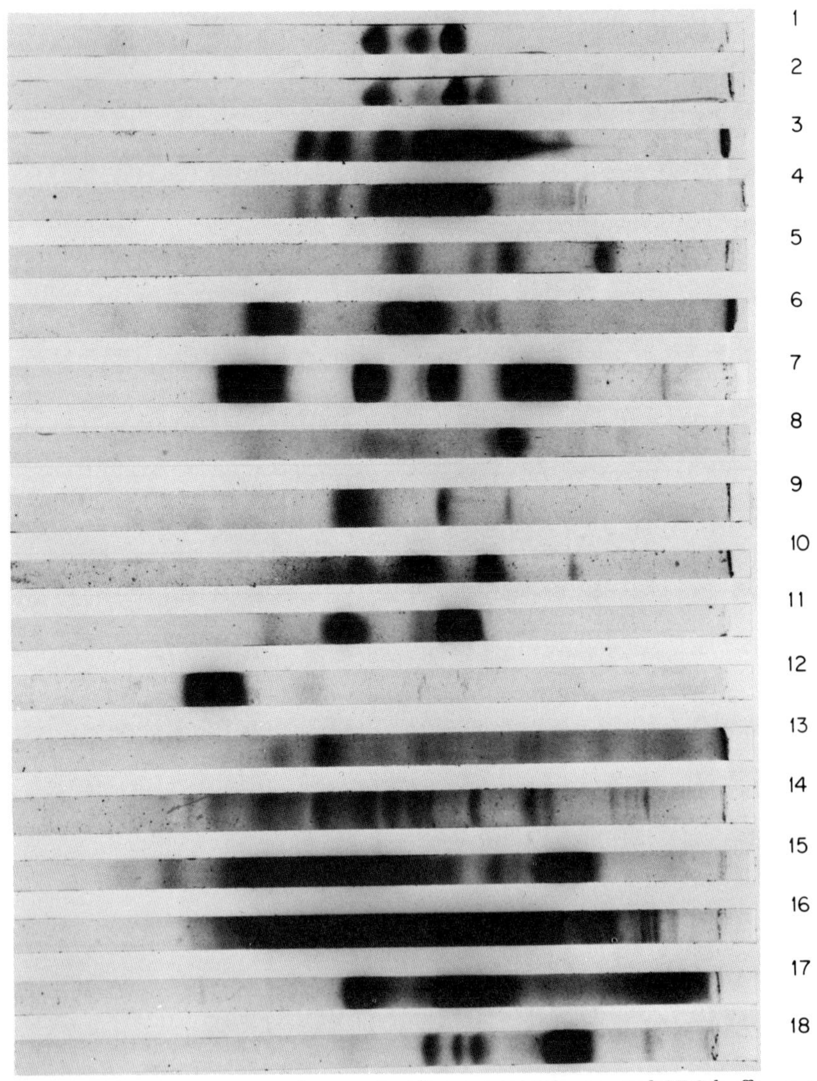

FIG. 2. Electrophoresis of a variety of proteins in the neutral-SDS buffer system. Samples are listed below along with certain of the conditions. All were stained with Coomassie Brilliant Blue (see Section II, F, 2). No attempt was made to remove nucleic acids which do not stain in this procedure. Patterns 1, 2, 13, and 14 were on 10% acrylamide gels, and the others were on 5% acrylamide gels. Patterns 1 and 2 are poliovirions and empty capsids, respectively, isolated from cesium chloride gradients (Maizel *et al.*, 1967). Patterns 3 and 4 are virions and presumed empty capsids of SV40 (kindly provided by D. Axelrod, National Institute of Allergy and Infectious Diseases). Pattern

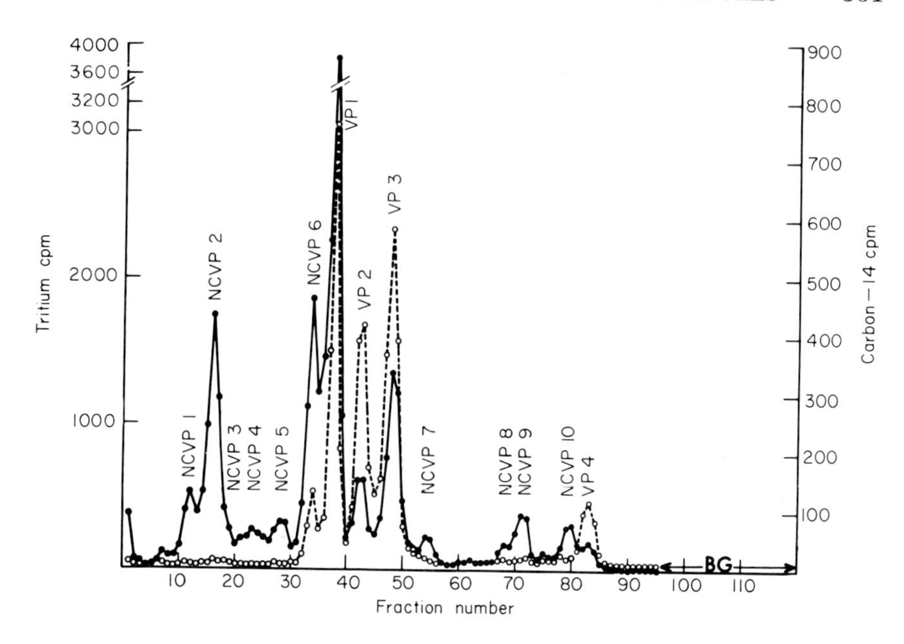

FIG. 3. Poliovirus-induced proteins in the cytoplasm of infected HeLa cells and identification of the virion proteins. The regions labeled VP 1 through VP 4 are virion proteins. Regions labeled NCVP 1 through 10 are noncapsid viral proteins whose functions are currently under study. (○) Distribution of tritium-containing proteins from cells infected and then labeled under conditions where only virus-specified proteins are made. (●) Distribution of the label of ^{14}C-labeled purified virions (see Summers *et al.*, 1965; Summers and Maizel, 1968).

---

5 is reovirion (kindly provided by A. R. Bellamy and W. K. Joklik, Albert Einstein College of Medicine, New York). Pattern 6 is influenza (kindly provided by W. G. Laver, Australian National University, Canberra, Australia). Pattern 7 is adenovirions (see Maizel *et al.*, 1968a,b). Pattern 8 is vaccinia virions (kindly provided by J. Holowczak and W. K. Joklik, see Holowczak and Joklik, 1967a,b). Pattern 9 is the *E. coli* bacteriophage T7 (Studier and Maizel, unpublished). Pattern 10 is a *B. subtilis* bacteriophage (kindly provided by T. Subbaiah and J. Marmur, Albert Einstein College of Medicine, New York). Pattern 11 is *E. coli* bacteriophage ϕ×174 (kindly provided by A. Burton, Brookhaven National Laboratory, Upton, New York). Pattern 12 is tobacco mosaic virus (kindly provided by R. E. F. Matthews, University of Auckland, Auckland, New Zealand). Pattern 13 is HeLa cell histones (kindly provided by E. Robbins, see Robbins and Borun, 1967). Pattern 14 is HeLa cell 50 S ribosomal subunits (kindly provided by J. Warner, see Warner, 1966). Pattern 15 is rat heart mitochondria (kindly provided by W. Levine, Albert Einstein College of Medicine, New York). Pattern 16 is cytoplasmic extract of HeLa cells. Patterns 17 and 18 are 2-mercaptoethanol – reduced and unreduced human γ-globulin (Pentex).

REFERENCES

Bellamy, A. R., Shapiro, L., August, J. T., and Joklik, W. K. (1967). *J. Mol. Biol.* **29**, 1.
Bishop, D. H. L., Claybrook, J. R., and Spiegelman, S. (1967). *J. Mol. Biol.* **26**, 373.
Bray, G. A. (1960). *Anal. Biochem.* **1**, 279.
Chrambach, A. (1966). *Anal. Biochem.* **15**, 544.
Chrambach, A., Reisfeld, R. A., Wyckoff, M., and Zaccari, J. (1967). *Anal. Biochem.* **20**, 150.
Davis, B. J. (1964). *Ann. N. Y. Acad. Sci.* **121**, 404.
Fairbanks, G., Jr., Levinthal, C., and Reeder, R. H. (1965). *Biochem. Biophys. Res. Commun.* **20**, 343.
Fazekas de St. Groth, S., Webster, R. G., and Datyner, A. (1963). *Biochim. Biophys. Acta* **71**, 377.
Frederick, J. F. (1964). *Ann. N. Y. Acad. Sci.* **121**, 307.
Heideman, M. L. (1964). *Ann. N. Y. Acad. Sci.* **121**, 501.
Hirs, C. H. W. (1967). *Methods Enzymol.* **11**, 199–203.
Holowczak, J. A., and Joklik, W. K. (1967a). *Virology* **33**, 717.
Holowczak, J. A., and Joklik, W. K. (1967b). *Virology* **33**, 726.
Horwitz, M. S., and Maizel, J. V., Jr. (1969). In preparation.
Huneeus-Cox, F. (1964). *Science* **143**, 1036.
Loening, U. F. (1967). *Biochem. J.* **102**, 251.
McPhie, P., Hounsell, J., and Gratzer, W. B. (1966). *Biochemistry* **5**, 988.
Maizel, J. V., Jr. (1966). *Science* **151**, 988.
Maizel, J. V., Jr. (1969). In preparation.
Maizel, J. V., Jr., and Summers, D. F. (1968). *Virology* **36**, 48.
Maizel, J. V., Jr., Phillips, B. A., and Summers, D. F. (1967). *Virology* **32**, 692.
Maizel, J. V., Jr., White, D. O., and Scharff, M. D. (1968a). *Virology* **36**, 115.
Maizel, J. V., Jr., White, D. O., and Scharff, M. D. (1968b). *Virology* **36**, 126.
Peacock, A. C., and Dingman, C. W. (1967). *Biochemistry* **6**, 1818.
Peacock, A. C., and Dingman, C. W. (1968). *Biochemistry* **7**, 668.
Reisfeld, R. A., Lewis, U. J., and Williams, D. E. (1962). *Nature* **195**, 281.
Robbins, E., and Borun, T. W. (1967). *Proc. Natl. Acad. Sci. U.S.* **57**, 409.
Shapiro, A. L., Viñuela, E., and Maizel, J. V. Jr. (1967). *Biochem. Biophys. Res. Commun.* **28**, 815.
Smithies, O. (1955). *Biochem. J.* **61**, 629.
Smithies, O. (1959). *Advan. Protein Chem.* **14**, 65.
Smithies, O. (1965). *Science* **150**, 1595.
Studier, F. W., and Maizel, J. V., Jr. (1969). Unpublished data.
Summers, D. F., and Maizel, J. V., Jr. (1968). *Proc. Natl. Acad. Sci. U.S.* **59**, 966.
Summers, D. F., Maizel, J. V., Jr., and Darnell, J. E., Jr. (1965). *Proc. Natl. Acad. Sci. U.S.* **54**, 505.
Warner, J. R. (1966). *J. Mol. Biol.* **19**, 383.
Zwaan, J. (1967). *Anal. Biochem.* **21**, 155.

33. Protein Analysis with Molecular Sieve Chromatography*

Thomas C. Merigan

Division of Infectious Diseases
Department of Medicine
Stanford University
Stanford, California

I. Introduction

In 1959, gel filtration techniques were introduced by Porath and Flodin as a laboratory aid both in analytical and preparative problems. This paper is written to summarize our results with this technique as employed with vertebrate interferons. This allows a discussion of some of the special problems encountered with the use of this method with biologically active materials to be studied with tissue culture and virological techniques. Viral antibodies, nonspecific serum inhibitors (Hanna and Styk, 1963), viruses (Bell and Engler, 1964; Bengtsson and Philipson, 1964; Inglot *et al.*, 1964), viral polynucleotides (Strohmaier, 1963; Erikson and Gordon, 1966; Kingsbury, 1966; Bishop *et al.*, 1967), viral receptors (Brishammar and Philipson, 1966), viral enzymes (Karasek and Schramm, 1962), and other materials of interest to the virologist (Delihas and Evans, 1963) have been studied with this technique.

Basically, the method described herein employs difference in molecular size to separate molecules. Those molecules larger than the largest pores of the gel particle cannot penetrate the particle and so pass through the bed in the liquid phase outside the particle and are thus eluted first. Smaller molecules penetrate the gel particles to a

*Work described in this article was supported by U.S. Public Health Service Grant (AI-05629).

varying extent depending on their molecular size; hence, they are slowed down. Therefore molecules are eluted in order of decreasing molecular size. If the gel column has been calibrated with standard proteins of known molecular size, one can extrapolate the size of unknowns from their behavior. The work of Ackers (1964) points up a more complex analysis of the behavior of macromolecules on the gels which takes into account the steric and frictional interactions of the soluble molecule with the gel matrix as well as exclusion effects resulting from dimensional heterogeneity of the gel interstices. The former effects become of importance with the more loosely cross-linked G-200 or agar gels.

II. Material and Methods

A. Preparation of Gel

The Sephadex G-100 (Pharmacia, Piscataway, New Jersey) is swelled in 5–10 fold excesses of the chromatography buffer which contains 0.1 *M* sodium phosphate (pH 6.0) for at least 5 hours. The gel slurry is shaken and repeatedly allowed to partially sediment in a two liter graduated cylinder before decanting the slowly sedimenting portions of gel particle ("fines"), which would increase the column resistance if they were included.

B. Pouring the Column

A 1.2 by 100 cm glass column with porous polyethylene disc or nylon net support is employed, and the gel column is poured at 4°C after buffer and gel have been equilibrated to this temperature to avoid the formation of bubbles in the final gel column. A small amount of buffer is placed in the bottom of the column. Then the thick gel suspension is poured down the side of the glass column allowing the excess buffer to drain out the bottom of the column without letting the top of the gel become dry. Then more gel slurry is carefully added to the top repeatedly until the column is packed. A small head of buffer is left above the gel to prevent the buffer flowing into the top of the column from disturbing the gel packing when the column is used in chromatography. Alternatively, a column flow adapter is available* which will do away with the buffer head, pressing on the top of the gel column to which the sample is applied directly.

*Pharmacia, Piscataway, New Jersey.

C. Chromatography Equipment Arrangement

The buffer column and fraction collector is set up in a 4°C room where the fractions are stored to decrease growth of bacterial contaminants. A peristaltic pump is used to supply the chromatography buffer to the top of the column with a flow rate of 25 ml/hour. The effluent from the column is led to a covered fraction collector with volume collection (Beckman-Spinco Model 132, Palo Alto, California) (to avoid changes in volume owing to changes in viscosity of the stream) employed to collect 5 ml fractions in sterile 3.5 by 18.5 cm collection tubes. In certain experiments where tubes may be held for long periods of time before assay, the tubes were preloaded with 0.5 ml of antibiotic solution (penicillin 10,000 units/ml and streptomycin 10 mg/ml) as well as 0.5 ml of a 5% solution of bovine serum albumin to stabilize the biological activity of partially purified interferon. A bacteriostatic agent should be added to gel columns or slurries if they are to be stored for long periods. These include 0.02% sodium azide or 0.002% chlorohexadine or 0.1% 1,1,1-trichloro-*tert*-butanol.

D. Applying the Sample and Performing Chromatography

Here, 0.03 ml of an 80% sucrose and 0.1 ml of 5% phenol red are added to the 2.5 ml sample before it is carefully applied to the top of the gel column, layering under the head of buffer with a needle and syringe after removing 2.5 ml of the buffer head. The sucrose is not used with samples of high protein content such as animal sera. If two materials which can be independently assayed in the same fraction are to be precisely compared, they can be in the same sample. This was possible with mouse and chick interferons (Merigan, 1964) since there was no crossover in their antiviral activity and each could be assayed in its own cell species of origin in each fraction independent of one another. After chromatography has been performed tubes containing fractions are covered. Fractions are analyzed for protein and the position of the phenol red marker by reading absorption at 280 mμ in a spectrophotometer. They are assayed for antiviral activity in a plaque inhibition assay with bovine vesicular stomatitis virus as the challenge and 4 ml volumes applied to plates (Merigan, 1964). If the activity of the starting sample is very high and titrations carried out at dilutions of 1/30 or greater, it can be done directly. But if the activity in starting samples is low, all fractions are individually dialyzed against two changes of 5-fold excess minimal Eagle's media. The units of interferon present in a fraction are calculated by interpolation from the degree of inhibition seen in 2-fold dilution of the fraction as the reciprocal of that dilution which would half inhibit the number of plaques. This calculation is discussed in detail by Ke and Ho (1967).

E. Calibration of the Column and Determination of Molecular Weight

In order to determine the molecular weight of the unknown, each column must be run with a series of known standard proteins, e.g., bovine serum albumin, bovine ribonuclease, and bovine γ-globulin. Each protein is run individually together with a phenol red internal marker. Approximately 25 mg of protein are put up in each 2.5 ml sample, and the resulting chromatographic position determined spectrophotometrically. The tube in the middle of each peak of the standard proteins was used to calculate the standard curve by plotting the log of the molecular weight against the tube number. This semilogarithmic plot is based upon the finding of Whitaker (1963) that with these proteins a linear relationship exists between the logarithm of the molecular weight and the peak of the elution volume of proteins on any individual column.

III. Results

A typical group of standard curves obtained with a G-100 column is shown in Fig. 1, and the results with a chick interferon preparation prepared in chick embryo fibroblasts with *Rickettsia tsutsugamushi* is shown in Fig. 2. The phenol red peak on columns to be compared appears within 2–3 tubes. It is likely that small differences in results between laboratories studying similar materials reflect the error or variability of the method rather than real differences. The work of Smith and Wagner (1967) employing columns with much larger gel beds than we employ demonstrates the high degree of resolution one can obtain with slightly larger samples and collection of the column effluent in greater number of fractions. Fantes (1968) has recently reported charge heterogeneity as measured by either elution from CM Sephadex or isoelectric focusing associated with the molecular size heterogeneity in material eluted in a peak on gradient chromatographs from CM Sephadex. This suggests an even greater range of molecular heterogeneity in "purified" preparations than heretofore recognized. However, there is no question that there are several discrete molecular weight species of vertebrate interferons.

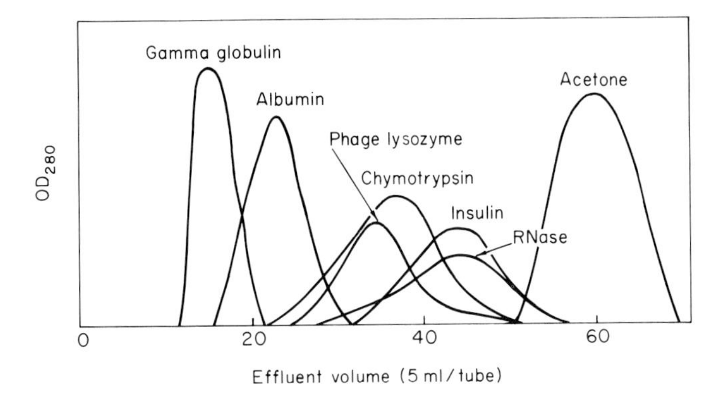

FIG. 1. Chromatography of purified proteinson G-100 Sephadex. All proteins were run individually together with their phenol red internal standard and the data superimposed for this figure. The behavior of acetone is similar to that of phenol red.

IV. Discussion

The techniques described in this section are useful in purification or characterization of macromolecules. The principle of separation according to size can either be applied grossly to separate large molecules from salts as in dialysis or more finely to separate various large molecules from one another. The resolving power of this method is decreased by diffusion of molecular species or band spreading during chromatography. Diffusion is dependent upon time on the column, which is dependent in turn upon viscosity of the sample and packing of the column. Optimum flow rates for gel columns have been determined by Flodin (1962). Upward flow column chromatography (Rothstein, 1965) may decrease packing and in turn resistance and thereby improve resolution. The column can be used repeatedly until packing increases resistance and significantly decreases flow rate. The diameter of the column is selected on the basis of the sample volume and its length determined on the basis of the resolution required, and it is agreed that the diameter-to-length ratio of 1-10 or greater is optimal. Recycling chromatography allows separation of molecules with only slightly different behavior on these columns (Porath and Bennich, 1962).

The method is useful in interferon purification (Merigan *et al.*, 1965) when larger diameter columns are employed, but the results are limited because of the presence of other contaminating proteins with

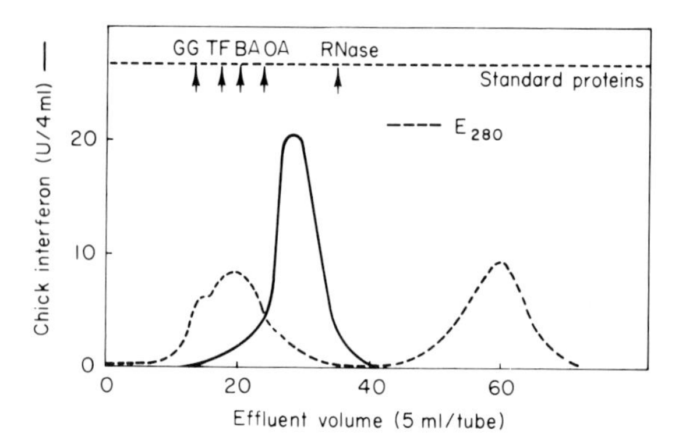

FIG. 2. Molecular weight determination of the rickettsial-induced chick interferon on G-100 Sephadex. The interferon was generously donated by Dr. Hope Hopps, Division of Biologic Standards, National Institutes of Health, Bethesda, Maryland, and was produced by the method of Hopps *et al.* (1964). The second 280 mμ absorbing peak results from the phenol red internal standard added to the sample. Emergence positions of the peak concentration of various standard proteins chromatographed on the same column are indicated at the top of the figure (GG stands for bovine γ-globulin; TF, human transferrin; BA, bovine serum albumin; OA, ovalbumin; and RNase, bovine pancreatic ribonuclease).

similar molecular weights in most preparations. When it is used in purification and the resulting peaks are to be lyophilized, it is often useful to perform the chromatography in a volatile buffer such as 0.2 *M* ammonium bicarbonate which can be removed by lyophilization.

The porous gels employed for this technique have been selected for their lack of charged or other reactive groups, to allow theoretical behavior of macromolecules. Those commonly employed include dextran gels (cross-linked dextrans), polyacrylamide gels, and agarose (linear polysaccharides of D-galactose and 3,6-anhydro-L-galactose). The generally excellent results with dextran gels for protein characterization and purification have limited the information available about acrylamides for protein gel filtration, and it is possible they might not have as favorable properties. Agarose is very effective in the high molecular weight ranges. It allows high flow rates and probably is the most useful material presently available for gel filtration of viruses. Presence of a salt concentration of 0.02 *M* or greater in the column buffer will help block any weak interactions between dextran gels and sample components. The lack of reactivity of these same materials has allowed their use as supporting media for ion exchange and thin-layer chromatography and electrophoresis. Extremely high resolving power with minimal diffusion of sample components has led to widespread use of polyacrylamide in zone electrophoresis under conditions (e.g., 7½ and 15% gels) where both molecular size and charge are important in separation (Ornstein and Davis, 1962). Many different pore sizes are available in each of the three materials at present (Table I) with different optimum resolving powers.

These techniques also offer great potential for the study of interaction between large and small molecules (e.g., drug and/or dye binding as in equilibrium dialysis; Hummel and Dreyer, 1962), or between large molecules (protein-protein or protein-polynucleotide interaction, etc.). If the interaction is dependent upon the concentration of

TABLE I
VARIOUS COMMERCIALLY AVAILABLE MOLECULAR SIEVE GELS

	Type of material	Optimum range (M_w)
A. Dextran gels – Sephadex[a]	G-10	<700
	G-15	<1,500
	G-25	1,000-5,000
	G-50	1,000-30,000
	G-75	3,000-70,000
	G-100	4,000-150,000
	G-150	5,000-400,000
	G-200	5,000-800,000
B. Polyacrylamides – Bio-Gel P[b]	P-4[c]	500-4,000
	P-300[c]	100-400,000
C. Agarose – Sepharose[a]	2B	300,000-3,000,000
(beads)	4B	2,000-25,000,000
Sagarose[d] or		
Agogel[e] (granules)	10	10,000-250,000
	8	25,000-700,000
	6	50,000-2,000,000
	4	200,000-15,000,000
	2	500,000-150,000,000
Biogel A[b]	0.5 *M*	<10,000-500,000
(beads)	1.5 *M*	<10,000-1,500,000
	5 *M*	10,000-5,000,000
	15 *M*	40,000-15,000,000
	50 *M*	100,000-50,000,000
	150 *M*	1,000,000->150,000,000

[a]Available from Pharmacia, Piscataway, New Jersey.
[b]Available from Bio-rad Laboratories, Richmond, California.
[c]These represent the extremes of a large series of gels made up with this material.
[d]Available from Gallard-Schlesinger Corp., Long Island, New York.
[e]Available from Mann Research Laboratories Inc., New York, New York.

the reactants and reversible, then sophisticated analysis may be applied to the system as described by Ackers (1967). If such interactions are undesirable, then various denaturants such as urea, organic acids, and sodium dodecyl sulfate can be included in the column buffer to decrease them (Bennett and Haber, 1963), but it must be remembered that they also can affect the gels and their porosity. For example, a 3% acetic acid buffer decreases the optimum resolving range of G-100 to one like that of G-75.

REFERENCES

Ackers, G. K. (1964). *Biochemistry* **3**, 723.
Ackers, G. K. (1967). *J. Biol. Chem.* **242**, 3026.
Bell, W. C., and Engler, R. C. (1964). *Arch. Ges. Virusforsch.* **15**, 109.
Bengtsson, S., and Philipson, L. (1964). *Biochim. Biophys. Acta* **79**, 399.
Bennett, J. C., and Haber, E. J. (1963). *J. Biol. Chem.* **238**, 1362.
Bishop, D. H., Claybrook, J. R., and Spiegelman, S. (1967). *J. Mol. Biol.* **26**, 373.
Brishammar, S., and Philipson, L. (1966). *Biochim. Biophys. Acta* **127**, 140.
Delihas, N., and Evans, E. (1963). *Nature* **199**, 488.
Erikson, R. L., and Gordon, J. A. (1966). *Biochem. Biophys. Res. Commun.* **23**, 422.
Fantes, K. (1968). *In* "Interferons" (G. Rita, ed.). Academic Press, New York.
Flodin, P. (1962). *In* "Dextran Gels and Their Application in Gel Filtration," p. 32. Pharmacia, Uppsala.
Hana, L., and Styk, B. (1963). *Acta Virol* **6**, 479.
Hopps, H. E., Kohno, M., and Smadel, J. E. (1964). *Bacteriol. Proc.* p. 115.
Hummel, J. P., and Dreyer, W. J. (1962). *Biochim. Biophys. Acta* **63**, 530.
Inglot, A. D., Lisowski, J., and Niedzwiedzka, E. (1964). *Acta Virol.* (*Prague*) **8**, 541.
Karasek, M., and Schramm, G. (1962). *Biochem. Biophys. Res. Commun.* **9**, 63.
Ke, Y. H., and Ho, M. (1967). *J. Virol.* **1**, 883.
Kingsbury, D. W. (1966). *J. Mol. Biol.* **18**, 195.
Merigan, T. C. (1964). *Science* **145**, 811.
Merigan, T. C., Winget, C. D., and Dixon, C. B. (1965). *J. Mol. Biol* **13**, 679.
Ornstein, L., and Davis, B. L. (1962). *In* "Disc Electrophoresis." Distillation Prod. Ind., New York.
Porath, J., and Bennich, H. (1962). *Arch. Biochem. Biophys.* Suppl. 1.
Porath, J., and Flodin, P. (1959). *Nature* **183**, 1657.
Rothstein, F. (1965). *J. Chromatog.* **18**, 36.
Smith, T. J., and Wagner, R. R. (1967). *J. Exptl. Med.* **125**, 579.
Strohmaier, K. Z. (1963). *Z. Naturforschg.* **18b**, 788.
Whitaker, J. R. (1963). *Anal. Chem.* **35**, 1950.

34. Peptide Mapping of Viral Proteins

W. G. Laver

Department of Microbiology
John Curtin School of Medical Research
Australian National University
Canberra, Australia

I. Introduction

Trypsin hydrolyzes proteins, splitting only those peptide bonds involving the carboxyl groups of lysine and arginine residues. The resulting peptides may be separated by two-dimensional electrophoresis and chromatography and form a map which is characteristic for each protein. (These maps are sometimes referred to as "fingerprints.") Two proteins which differ by as little as a single amino acid may give quite obviously different maps. On the other hand, because the position of each peptide depends more on its amino acid composition than on the sequence, two proteins differing considerably in amino acid sequence nevertheless may give apparently identical maps. The technique may therefore be used, with reservations, to compare the primary structures of two closely related proteins such as may be obtained from wild type and mutant viruses; it may also be used to estimate the molecular weight of proteins and to assess to some extent the purity of protein preparations.

II. Apparatus

A. High Voltage Paper Electrophoresis and Paper Chromatography Equipment

Tank: The Lucite tank described by Katz *et al.* (1959) is excellent. Various modifications of this, where the cooling coils were located on the sides of the tank rather than under the lid, or where the tank was made of fibre glass instead of Lucite, were found to be less satisfactory. Systems where the filter paper, soaked in buffer, is sandwiched between glass plates are also said to be less satisfactory than those where the paper is immersed in an organic solvent.

Power supply: A constant voltage dc power supply capable of delivering up to 3000 V and 250 mA is suitable.

Equilibration box: A Lucite box 65 cm wide, 60 cm high, and 18 cm deep with a well-fitting lid.

Paper: Whatman No. 3MM filter paper, 70 by 45 cm.

Chromatography jars: Round glass jars 46 cm high and 27 cm in diameter are suitable for ascending chromatography. These should have ground glass tops and plate glass lids.

Drying oven: Well ventilated, for drying chromatograms.

X-Ray viewing screen and camera: For photographing peptide maps.

III. Reagents

Trypsin: Twice crystallized. Obtained from the Sigma Chemical Co., St. Louis, Missouri. Ammonium hydroxide, calcium chloride, phenol red, acetic acid, pyridine, isoamyl alcohol, ninhydrin, and acetone should all be analytical grade reagents. Some batches of pyridine have been found to contain impurities giving an intense blue color with ninhydrin. Therefore all reagents which are used to make buffers for electrophoresis or solvents for chromatography are routinely tested before use to ensure that they are ninhydrin negative.

IV. Procedure

A. Tryptic Digestion

Proteins to be compared should be digested and mapped at the same time and under the same conditions. If enough is available, approximately 0.05 μmole of protein should be used (this corresponds to 2 mg of a protein with a molecular weight of 40,000) but satisfactory maps may be obtained with lesser amounts of material. The protein samples, free from salt and suspended or dissolved in water (0.4 ml), are denatured by heating in a boiling water bath for 2–3 minutes. Then, 0.01 *N* NH_4OH (0.2 ml) is added to bring the mixture to approximately pH 10. The crystalline trypsin is dissolved in 0.001 *M* $CaCl_2$ at a concentration of 0.5 mg/ml, and 0.02 ml of this trypsin solution is added to each 2 mg sample of denatured protein. The mixtures are incubated at 37°C for 2 hours after which time the insoluble denatured protein should be completely dissolved. More trypsin (0.02 ml) is then added and the digestion is continued for a further 4 hours. If more protein is available, the digestion may be carried out in a pH-stat and the uptake of alkali followed. For those working with animal virus proteins however, this will rarely be possible. At the end of the digestion a drop of phenol red solution (0.1% w/v phenol red in 0.01 N NH_4OH) is added to each sample to serve as a visible marker in the subsequent operations.

B. Separation of Diffusible from Nondiffusible Peptides

The digested protein is dialyzed, in a small dialysis bag, against distilled water (10 ml) at 4°C for 48 hours in a 15 ml test tube. The dialysis tubing should be tied with gloved hands. If not, the bag must be well washed before use to remove peptides and amino acids coming from the fingers. After dialysis, the bag is removed and the nondiffusible peptides remaining inside the bag are stored frozen for subsequent analysis. The diffusible peptides in the solution outside the bag are then dried. This is best done by immersing the tube in a hot water bath (50–60°C) and blowing a stream of dry nitrogen onto the surface of the solution. Approximately 1.5 hours are needed to dry 10 ml of solution in this way. The dried mixture of peptides and phenol red is dissolved in 0.01 N NH_4OH (0.1 ml, followed by two washings each 0.1 ml) and transferred to a micro test tube. The peptides are again dried in a current of nitrogen and finally dissolved in 0.02 ml of pH 6.5 buffer (pyridine:acetic acid:water, volume ratio 10:0.4:90) for electrophoresis. If less than 2 mg of protein is digested the peptides should be finally dissolved in a correspondingly smaller volume of buffer.

Alternatively, the whole tryptic digest may be dried in a current of nitrogen. In this case, the dried peptides are dissolved in the pH 6.5 electrophoresis buffer (0.2 ml), centrifuged to remove any material insoluble at this pH, and the supernatant again dried in a current of nitrogen. The peptides finally are dissolved in 0.02 ml of pH 6.5 buffer for electrophoresis.

C. High Voltage Paper Electrophoresis

The size of the filter paper used for mapping the peptides will depend on the dimensions of both the electrophoresis equipment and the chromatography jars available, but satisfactory maps have been obtained with sheets of Whatman No. 3MM filter paper measuring 70 by 46 cm. Thick (3MM) paper should be used; thinner (No. 1) paper gives satisfactory maps but is much harder to handle when wet. The papers should be handled with gloved hands to avoid contamination by peptides and amino acids from the fingers.

The filter paper sheet is hung on the glass or Lucite electrophoresis rack and this is then placed in the Lucite equilibration box. The sides and bottom of the box are drenched with the pH 6.5 electrophoresis buffer and enough of this buffer is pipetted onto the paper to just wet the whole sheet. This is allowed to equilibrate in the closed box for about 10 minutes. The rack is then removed from the box and the solution of peptides in buffer (20 μl) is drawn up into a short piece of capillary tubing having a flame-polished tip and rapidly spotted onto the wet paper. (The position of the origin is shown in Fig. 1.) The rack is then immersed in the electrophoresis tank and electrophoresis started without delay.

The voltage used and the time for the run will depend on the equipment used. In the apparatus described above, good separation of peptides was obtained following electrophoresis at 2000 V (34 V/cm) for 2 hours. The current drawn was approximately 150 mA.

After electrophoresis the rack is placed in a drying oven and the paper is dried in a current of warm air for 3–4 hours. Alternatively, the paper can be removed from the rack by picking up one end in a long spring clamp and hung by this in the oven to dry.

D. Chromatography

Ascending chromatography is carried out in cylindrical glass jars 27 cm diam and 46 cm high with close-fitting plate glass lids. The single phase solvent (isoamyl alcohol:pyridine:water, volume ratio 35:35:30) is placed in the bottom of the tank to a depth of about 1 cm. A crystallizing dish 12 cm diam is placed in the center of the jar and half-filled with the same solvent. A cylinder of filter paper 12 cm in diameter and 40 cm high is placed in this dish and soaked in the solvent. This helps to keep the atmosphere in the jar saturated with solvent vapor. Chromatography should be carried out in a constant temperature (20°C) room. If this is not available, the jar should be covered with some insulating material.

The dried sheet of paper, containing the peptides and the phenol red marker separated by electrophoresis, is curled into a cylinder 22 cm in diameter and 45 cm high and the overlapping ends are fastened together with paper clips. A small square (2 by 2 cm) is cut from each lower corner of the paper before fastening to prevent the overlap from

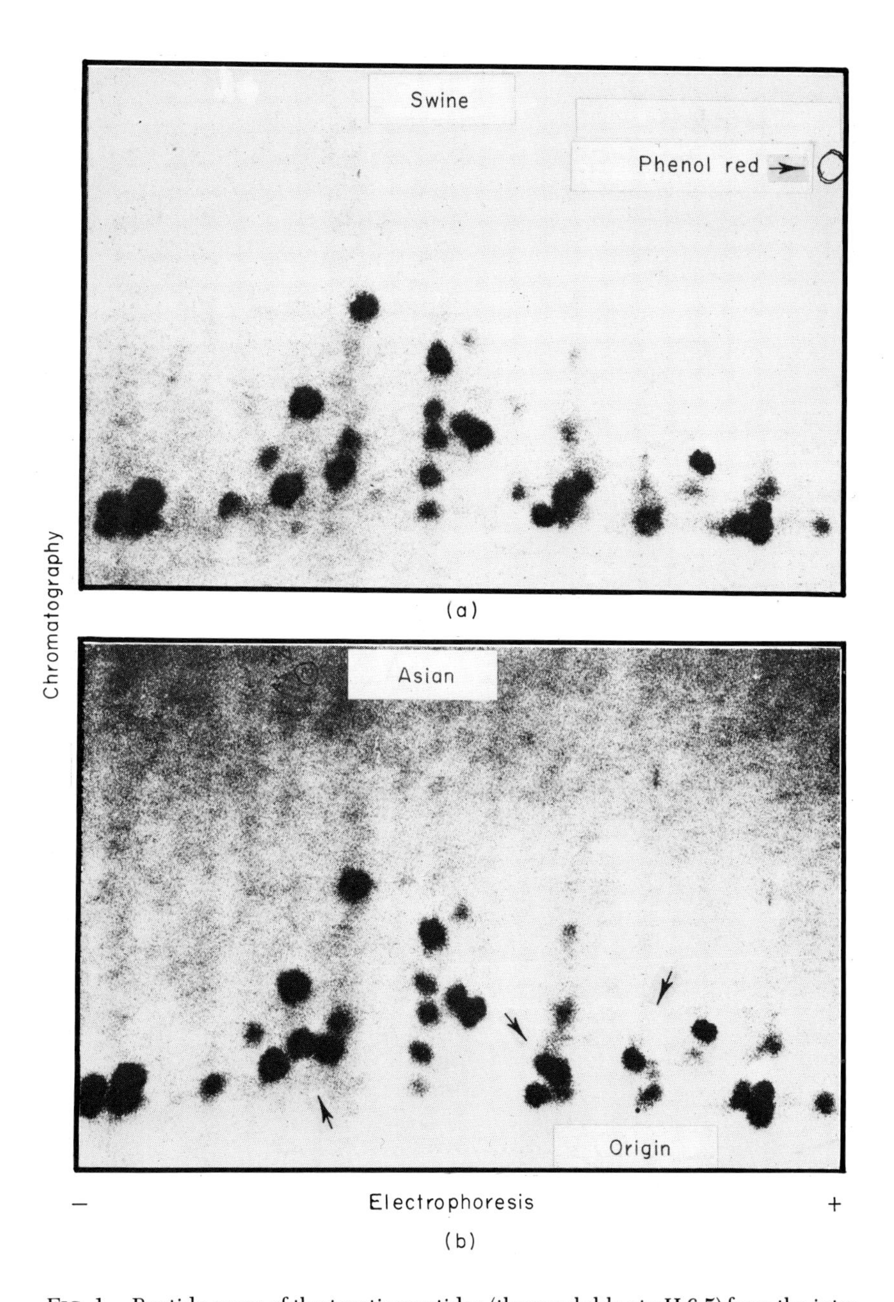

FIG. 1. Peptide maps of the tryptic peptides (those soluble at pH 6.5) from the internal antigens of the (a) swine and (b) Asian (A_2/AA 23/57) strains of influenza virus. Approximately 1.5 mg of each antigen was digested with trypsin (15 μg) for 3 hours at 37°C and pH 10, and the peptides were mapped, stained with ninhydrin, and photographed as described. Peptides which differ obviously between the two maps are indicated by arrows. The position of the origin in this case was 6 cm from the edge of the paper sheet and 18 cm from the positive end. The solvent front is situated just off the top of the diagram (phenol red = R_f 0.7).

reaching to the bottom of the cylinder, thus preventing the solvent from rising preferentially at the join and distorting the chromatographic front. This paper cylinder, with the peptides lying along a line around the circumference, 6 cm from the bottom, is then placed upright in the chromatography jar and the solvent is allowed to rise immediately without any period for equilibration. After about 20 hours, when the solvent has reached the top of the paper cylinder, the paper is removed, hung in an oven and dried for 3–4 hours in a current of warm air.

E. Location of Peptides

The peptides are located by staining with ninhydrin. A freshly prepared solution of ninhydrin in acetone (1% w/v) is poured over the dried paper sheet (approximately 250 ml is required for each sheet); excess solution is allowed to drain off and the paper is held in a current of warm air for a few minutes until the acetone has completely evaporated. The paper is then placed in a glass jar containing a dish of concentrated sulfuric acid (to keep the atmosphere free from ammonia) and the colors are allowed to develop in the dark at room temperature for about 40 hours. The maps should then be photographed. This is best done by transmitted light, using a large X-ray viewing screen, a fast panchromatic film (e.g., Kodak Plus-X Pan), and a green filter. The maps will keep for several weeks if stored in a cold, dark, dry, ammonia-free atmosphere.

V. Application to the Peptide Mapping of Viral Proteins

Figure 1 shows examples of peptide maps obtained by this method. These maps are of the tryptic peptides (those soluble at pH 6.5) from the internal antigens of the swine and Asian (AA 23/1957) strains of influenza A virus. Some are poorly resolved, but it can be seen that most of the peptides (and the well-separated phenol red marker) travel as almost circular spots with little trailing. A small number of very clear-cut differences can also be seen between the two maps (these are marked with arrows); otherwise the two proteins appear to have the same sequence. The internal antigens of these two viruses differ slightly immunologically (Davenport *et al.*, 1960), but it is not known whether the differences seen in amino acid sequence are related to the antigenic differences.

VI. Molecular Weight Determinations from Peptide Maps

A. PRINCIPLES

The molecular weight of a protein may be estimated from a knowledge of its lysine and arginine content and the total number of peptides produced by digestion with trypsin. This method is particularly useful for establishing the existence and molecular weight of identical subunits in protein macromolecules which possess masked or unreactive N-terminal and C-terminal amino acids (for example, see Harrison and Hofmann, 1962), but the calculation of molecular weight depends on the ability to obtain a reliable estimate of the number of unique tryptic peptides, and this is often difficult to do. The following alternative method, which does not require knowledge of the total number of peptides, may also be used. Since trypsin splits proteins specifically at the carboxyl groups of lysine and arginine residues, each peptide released by this enzyme (except the C-terminal peptide) should contain one, and only one, of these amino acids. Provided that the release of any unique peptide from a known weight of a protein is complete, and that this peptide can be isolated quantitatively and in pure form, then its analysis for arginine or lysine will provide a direct measure of the molecular weight of the polypeptide chain from which it is derived. The size of the peptide analyzed is irrelevant. In practice a number of peptides are analyzed and the molecular weight of the protein is calculated from the average basic amino acid content of the peptides. This calculation is similar to that used to estimate the molecular weight of a protein from a knowledge of its N-terminal or C-terminal amino acid content. Thus, if the peptides from 1 mg of a protein each contain on the average 0.04 μmole of arginine or lysine, then it follows that 1 μmole of arginine or lysine would have been obtained from each tryptic peptide from 25 mg (or 1 μmole) of this protein. Therefore the polypeptide chains of the protein have a molecular weight of 25,000. Of course, if the protein is composed of equimolar amounts of different polypeptide chains, then the estimated molecular weight will be the sum of the molecular weights of the individual chains.

B. PROCEDURE

The weight of the protein taken for analysis must be accurately known. Digestion of the protein and mapping of the tryptic peptides is carried out as described above except that the Whatman No. 3MM paper is well washed by irrigation with 0.01 N NH_4OH and dried before use, and the peptides are located by very light staining with ninhydrin (0.01% w/v in acetone). As many as possible of the better separated spots are cut out and the peptides eluted from the paper with 0.01 N NH_4OH. Blank areas of paper of similar size and standard amounts of lysine and arginine applied to the paper are also eluted. The eluates are centrifuged to remove filter paper fibers and the supernatants are transferred to Pyrex glass hydrolysis tubes and dried in a current of nitrogen. The dried peptides are taken up in 6 N HCl (0.5 ml), the tubes are evacuated, sealed, and heated to 102°C for 18 hours.

Analysis of the hydrolyzed peptides for basic amino acids may then be carried out by standard methods. The hydrolysates from blank areas of paper will probably contain some neutral amino acids, but the basic amino acid content of well-washed paper has been found to be very low. Losses of basic amino acids during elution and hydrolysis of the peptides can be estimated from the recovery (usually about 80%) of the arginine and lysine standards. Some peptides may contain two to three times the average content of basic amino acids (overlapping peptides) or no basic amino acids at all (C-terminal peptides) and these values are discarded. The molecular weight of the protein is then calculated from the average basic amino acid content of the peptides as described. In making this calculation, losses occurring during tryptic digestion and peptide mapping have not been allowed for (these losses have been found to amount to approximately 20–30%). Therefore, the recovery of basic amino acids from tryptic peptides from proteins which contain polypeptide chains of known molecular weight (e.g., bovine serum albumin, lysozyme) should be assessed before using the method to estimate the molecular weight of an unknown protein.

REFERENCES

Davenport, F. M., Rott, R., and Schäffer, W. (1960). *J. Exptl. Med.* **112**, 765.
Harrison, P. M., and Hofmann, T. (1962). *J. Mol. Biol.* **4**, 239.
Katz, A. M., Dreyer, W. J., and Anfinsen, C. B. (1959). *J. Biol. Chem.* **234**, 2897.

35. N-Terminal Amino Acid Analysis of Viral Proteins

W. G. Laver

Department of Microbiology
John Curtin School of Medical Research
Australian National University
Canberra, Australia

I. Introduction

A number of methods are available for the N-terminal amino acid analysis of proteins, but only one will be described in detail here. This is a micromodification of the Edman method using ^{35}S phenyl isothiocyanate of high specific radioactivity and is sufficiently sensitive to detect and measure accurately as little as 10^{-5} μmole of N-terminal amino acid. The chemical reactions involved in this method have been described by Edman (1956) and are outlined below:

$$C_6H_5—NCS+H_2N—CHR'—CO—NH—CHR''—COOH \xrightarrow{pH\,9} C_6H_5—NH—CS—NH—CHR'—CO—NH—CHR''—COOH \quad (1)$$

$$C_6H_5—NH—CS—NH—CHR'—CO—NH—CHR''—COOH \xrightarrow{H+} C_6H_5—NH—C{=}N—CHR'—CO \text{ (ring closed via S between C and CO)} + H_2N—CHR''—COOH \quad (2)$$

$$C_6H_5—NH—C{=}N—CHR'—CO \text{ (ring closed via S)} + H_2O \xrightarrow{H+} C_6H_5—NH—CS—NH—CHR'—COOH \quad (3)$$

$$C_6H_5—NH—CS—NH—CHR'—COOH \xrightarrow{H+} C_6H_5—N—CS—NH—CHR'—CO \text{ (ring closed between N and CO)} + H_2O \quad (4)$$

The protein is coupled with phenyl isothiocyanate at pH 9 [Eq. (1)], to form a phenylthiocarbamyl protein, then the N-terminal amino acid is split off as the 2-anilino-5-thiazolinone derivative by treatment with acid [Eq (2)]. The thiazolinone is separated from the rest of the protein and converted, by treatment with aqueous acid, firstly to the free phenylthiocarbamyl amino acid [Eq (3)], and then to the corresponding phenylthiohydantoin (PTH) [Eq (4)]. This method may also be used for sequence determinations in proteins and peptides and has been automated (Edman and Begg, 1967). Sequential analysis on a microscale using radioactive phenyl isothiocyanate has not been reported.

II. Apparatus

Small, ground-glass stoppered test tubes. These are obtained from Quickfit and Quartz Ltd., Staffordshire, England or from Quickfit Reeve Angel Inc., New Jersey. The tubes are 10 cm long and of 5 ml capacity with socket size B10 and stopper SB10. Tubes and stoppers are best cleaned after use by heating them in a bath of concentrated sulfuric acid containing 1% of concentrated nitric acid.

Apparatus for descending paper chromatography. Radioactive counting equipment—An automatic chromatogram scanner, or a liquid scintillation spectrometer is suitable. Source of ultraviolet light such as "Mineralight" obtained from Ultraviolet Products Inc., South Pasadena, California.

III. Reagents

^{35}S-labeled phenyl isothiocyanate of specific radioactivity about 50 mcuries/mmole. This is a liquid (bp 218°C) and should be handled in a fume hood. It may be obtained from the Radiochemical Centre, Amersham, England or from Nuclear-Chicago Corp., 333 East Howard Avenue, Des Plaines, Illinois and should be stored cold (−20°C).

N-Allyl piperidine. This may be obtained from K & K Laboratories, 121 Express Street, Plainview, New York. Pyridine, acetic acid, hydrochloric acid, formic acid, formamide, acetone, ethylene dichloride, ethanol, *o*-xylene, propionic acid, *n*-butyl acetate, *n*-heptane, aniline, unlabeled phenyl isothiocyanate, and light petroleum (bp 80–100°C) should all be analytical grade reagents.

PTH amino acids. A kit containing the phenyl thiohydantoin derivatives of the common amino acids may be obtained from the Sigma Chemical Co., St. Louis, Missouri, or these may be synthesized according to Edman (1950).

IV. Procedures

A. Formation of the ^{35}S PTH Derivatives of the N-Terminal Amino Acid(s)

The protein under investigation (1–2 mg is a convenient amount, but successful analyses have been carried out on as little as 50 μg of protein) is dissolved or suspended in water (0.1 ml) and an equal volume of *N*-allyl piperidine-pyridine-acetic acid buffer pH 9.0 is added. The buffer is prepared by mixing *N*-allyl piperidine (1 gm) with pyridine (39 ml) and adjusting the mixture to pH 9.0 with 1 *N* acetic acid (about 3.5 ml). ^{35}S phenyl isothiocyanate (5 μl) is then added to the solution of protein in buffer, and the mixture is incubated for 1 hour at 40°C with occasional shaking. This incubation and the subsequent series of reactions and extractions are best done in a Quickfit glass-stoppered tube, described in Section II. The ^{35}S phenylthiocarbamyl protein so obtained is freed from excess ^{35}S phenyl isothiocyanate by three extractions with benzene (4 ml) (the tube may be centrifuged in a bench centrifuge after each extraction to separate the upper benzene and lower aqueous phases) and then from phenylthiourea and diphenylthiourea, by-products of the coupling reaction, by successive extractions with ethanol (3×4 ml) and acetone (3×4 ml). The first ethanol extraction should precipitate the phenylthiocarbamyl protein. If precipitation is incomplete the addition of a drop of 0.1 *M* NaCl will assist the protein to flocculate.

The phenylthiocarbamyl protein is then dissolved in 98% formic acid (0.2 ml) and 6 *N* hydrochloric acid is added (0.2 ml). Care should be taken to ensure that protein sticking to the sides of the tube and on the bottom of the stopper is also dissolved in the formic acid. After standing for 5 minutes at 20°C, acetone (4.0 ml) is added and the protein residue, which should form a flocculant precipitate, is removed by centrifugation. The acetone supernatant containing the N-terminal amino acid of the protein, probably in the form of the ^{35}S 2-anilino-5-thiazolinone derivative, is evaporated in a current of nitrogen and the thiazolinone is extracted from the dry residue with acetone (2.0 ml).

This ensures that any ^{35}S phenylthiocarbamyl protein which escaped precipitation in the previous step is not carried through to the final reaction. (The ^{35}S phenyl isothiocyanate will, of course, combine with lysine residues in the protein as well as with its N-terminal amino acid and the remainder of the protein will be highly radioactive.) The acetone extract containing the thiazolinone is evaporated in a current of nitrogen, and the residue is redissolved in a drop of acetone, and 0.1 *N* hydrochloric acid (0.2 ml) is added. This mixture is left at room temperature overnight to convert the thiazolinone of the N-terminal amino acid to the corresponding phenylthiohydantoin and this is then taken to dryness in a current of nitrogen. The residue of ^{35}S PTH amino acid(s) is dissolved in glacial acetic acid (0.3 ml) and divided into three samples (0.1 ml each), which are again evaporated to dryness in a current of nitrogen.

B. Chromatography and Identification of the ^{35}S PTH Amino Acids

The radioactive PTH amino acid(s) so obtained are dissolved in solutions containing mixtures of unlabeled marker amino acid phenylthiohydantoins and chromatographed on 2.5 cm wide strips of Whatman No. 1 filter paper in three different solvent systems, D, E, and F of Edman and Sjöquist (1956). Samples (about 1.0 mg) of unlabeled PTH amino acids appropriate to the solvent system used are dissolved in 1.0 ml of either ethylene chloride (for solvents D and E) or in glacial acetic acid (for solvent F). These should be freshly dissolved, since the PTH amino acids decompose slowly in solution. For solvent D a suitable mixture includes the phenylthiohydantoins of glycine, alanine, methionine, leucine, and proline. (Figure 1 gives the relative positions of PTH amino acids in the three solvents.) PTH-aspartic acid, PTH-glutamic acid, PTH-tyrosine, PTH-glycine, PTH-alanine, and PTH-leucine make a suitable mixture for solvent F and PTH-serine, PTH-glycine, PTH-alanine, and PTH-leucine are suitable for solvent E. The phenylthiohydantoins of aspartic and glutamic acids have a low solubility in ethylene chloride and these are best run in solvent F only. PTH-arginine and PTH-histidine are insoluble in ethylene chloride and do not move from the origin in solvent F; they are best identified following paper electrophoresis in 0.01 *M* sodium phosphate pH 8.0 for 1 hour at 10 V/cm (Edman and Begg, 1967). Samples (0.05 ml) of the mixed unlabeled marker PTH amino acids are then added to the dried radioactive unknown phenylthiohydantoins and warmed briefly to ensure that the latter dissolve completely. These

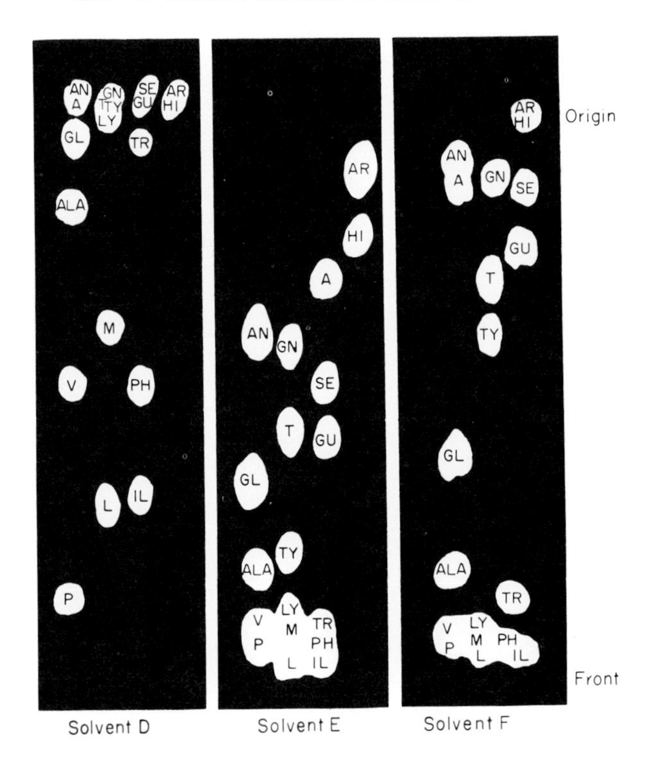

FIG. 1. Relative positions of various PTH amino acids after chromatography in solvents D, E, and F (Edman and Sjöquist, 1956). Abbreviations: A, aspartic acid; ALA, alanine; AN, asparagine; AR, arginine; GL, glycine; GN, glutamine; GU, glutamic acid; HI, histidine; IL, isoleucine; L, leucine; LY, lysine; M, methionine; P, proline; PH, phenylalanine; SE, serine; T, threonine; TR, tryptophan; TY, tyrosine; and V, valine.

mixtures are then applied as lines onto 2.5 cm wide strips of Whatman No. 1 filter paper (or filter paper impregnated with formamide for solvents D and E) using a piece of capillary tubing with a flame-polished tip. Several applications with drying in between will be needed to apply the whole of the 0.05 ml sample taken. The paper strips are best made by cutting slots in a sheet of filter paper as shown in Fig. 2. In this way it is possible to handle half a dozen strips at once and single, identifying marker PTH amino acids may be run on the wide strips at the sides if necessary.

1. Solvent System D; o-Xylene-Formamide

The paper strips are dipped into a solution of formamide in acetone (2:7 v/v), immediately placed horizontally on a sheet of dry filter paper

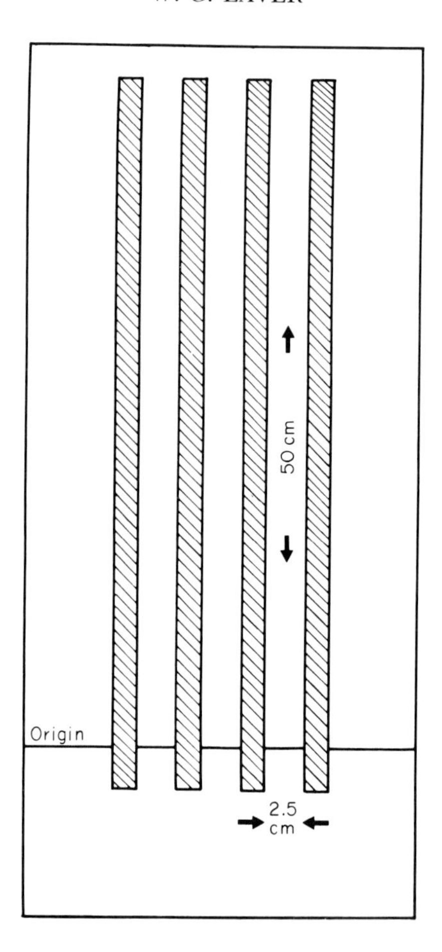

FIG. 2. Method of cutting filter paper strips for chromatography of PTH amino acids. The shaded portions are removed. More or fewer strips may be cut as required.

and blotted to remove excess solution. The strips are then waved briefly in the air for the acetone to evaporate. The PTH amino acids, dissolved in ethylene chloride, are then applied to the paper and descending elution of the chromatogram is immediately started using *o*-xylene. No time for equilibration is necessary and the solvent reaches the bottom of the paper in about 4 hours.

2. *Solvent System E; n-Butyl Acetate–Propionic Acid–Formamide*

The paper strips are impregnated with formamide as described for solvent D. The PTH amino acids, dissolved in ethylene chloride, are then applied. *n*-Butyl acetate (100 ml) is saturated with water (1.5 ml), propionic acid (3.0 ml) is added, and the mixture is saturated with formamide (12 ml) by shaking in a separating funnel. The upper phase only of this mixture is used. The sides and bottom of the chromatography jar are drenched with the solvent, and the paper strip is allowed to equilibrate for 30 minutes in the jar before descending chromatography is started.

3. Solvent System F; n-Heptane-Ethylene Chloride-Formic acid

n-Heptane (50 ml) is shaken in a separating funnel with 75% formic acid in water (100 ml) and ethylene chloride (100 ml). Two phases approximately equal in volume should separate. These solvents are very volatile and great care must be taken to ensure that the atmosphere inside the chromatography jar is always saturated with solvent vapor. This is best achieved by hanging sheets of filter paper inside the jar and soaking these in the upper phase of the solvent. The lower phase is used to drench the sides and bottom of the jar. The PTH amino acids, dissolved in glacial acetic acid, are applied to the paper strips which should be allowed to equilibrate in the jar for at least 30 minutes before descending chromatography with the upper phase of the solvent is started. The run takes 3–4 hours to complete.

After chromatography the paper strips are dried in an oven at 50°C and the positions of the unlabeled reference PTH amino acids are marked out under ultraviolet light. They are seen as dark bands on a light background. (The amounts of the ^{35}S-labeled PTH amino acids are far too small to be detected in this way.) Each strip is then scanned for radioactivity. This may be done by counting successive 1 cm sections with an end-window counter (manually or automatically) or by cutting the strip into 1 cm sections and counting each section in a liquid scintillation spectrometer. Coincidence between a radioactive peak and a marker phenylthiohydantoin indicates that the corresponding amino acid was N-terminal in the protein, and the radioactivity within the peak gives a measure of the amount of N-terminal residue recovered. Spots may be eluted from a chromatogram run in one solvent, mixed with more marker PTH amino acids and rerun in another solvent. The spots should be extracted with hot glacial acetic acid as soon as possible after drying the chromatogram; otherwise decomposition occurs and some radioactivity fails to elute from the paper.

C. Specific Activity of the ^{35}S Phenyl Isothiocyanate

In order to assess the yields of N-terminal amino acids obtained and to correct for ^{35}S decay, it is necessary to know the specific radioactivity of the ^{35}S phenyl isothiocyanate used in each experiment. If the paper strips are counted in a liquid scintillation counter this may be done quite simply. The ^{35}S phenyl isothiocyanate (1 μl) is diluted with nonradioactive phenyl isothiocyanate (10 ml) and a sample of this mixture (1 μl) is dissolved in scintillator fluid and counted in the same way and at the same time as the experimental samples (1 μl of phenyl isothiocyanate at 20°C contains 8.375 μmoles). If the paper strips are counted with an end-window counter, a nonvolatile derivative of the ^{35}S phenyl isothiocyanate must first be prepared. A sample of ^{35}S phenyl isothiocyanate (1 μl) is diluted with unlabeled phenyl isothiocyanate (1.0 ml) and the mixture is dissolved in light petroleum bp 80–100°C (40 ml). Aniline (0.767 ml) is then added and the mixture is allowed to stand overnight at 20°C. The crystals of ^{35}S *sym*-diphenylthiourea (M.W. 228) which separate out are filtered off, recrystallized twice from ethanol–water, and dried (mp 151–153°C). Some of the crystals are weighed out, dissolved in ethanol and a measured volume of the solution is spotted onto a strip of filter paper, dried and counted at the same time and in the same way as the chromatogram strips.

V. Interpretation of Results and Scope of the Procedure

The identification of an unknown ^{35}S PTH amino acid relies on exact coincidence being obtained between the radioactive material and a chemically identifiable reference PTH amino acid when mixtures of these are chromatographed in three different solvent systems. Occasionally radioactive peaks are observed which do not coincide with any known PTH amino acid; these probably represent by-products of the reactions. Similarly, some radioactivity always remains at the origin during chromatography. This probably results from decomposition of the ^{35}S PTH amino acids.

Figure 3 demonstrates the application of this method to the N-terminal amino acid analysis of horse hemoglobin, a protein which has been shown to possess four N-terminal valine residues per 68,000 g (Braunitzer, 1958). This figure illustrates both the sensitivity of the method (1.96 mg of hemoglobin yielded 656,000 counts/minute in the PTH-valine spot) and the way in which PTH amino acids which are poorly resolved by chromatography (in this case PTH-valine and PTH-phenylalanine) may be unequivocally identified. Thus it is clear that the radioactive peak obtained from horse hemoglobin (and containing insufficient material to be visible on the paper under ultraviolet light) coincides exactly with the unlabeled marker PTH-valine spot and inexactly with that of PTH-phenylalanine.

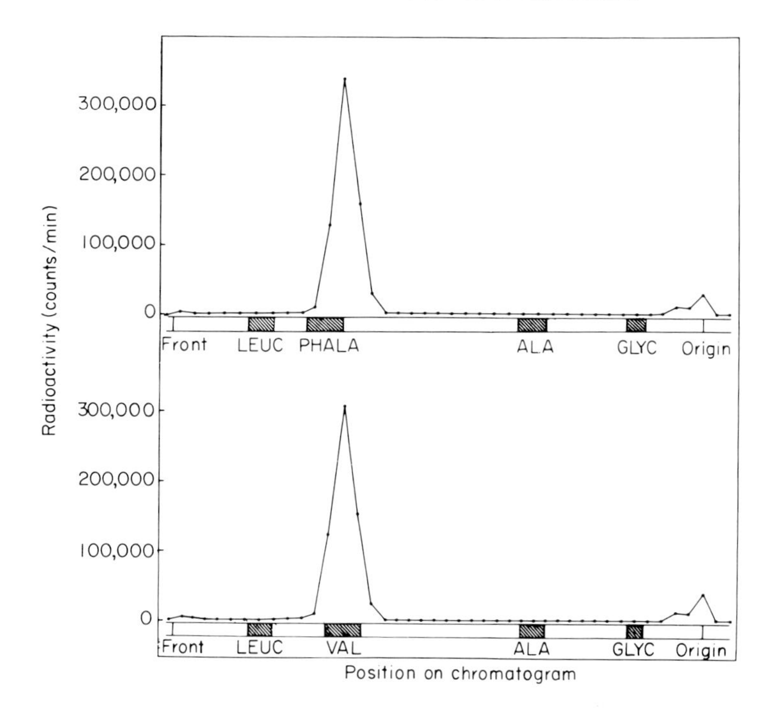

FIG. 3. Distribution of radioactivity on chromatograms (solvent D) of mixtures of the ^{35}S-labeled N-terminal amino acid phenylthiohydantoin (PTH-valine) from 1.96 mg of horse hemoglobin and various unlabeled marker PTH amino acids. The positions of the unlabeled PTH amino acids on the chromatogram are shown. In one case the mixture included PTH-phenylalanine, and in the other, PTH-valine. These two PTH amino acids are poorly resolved in solvent D, but it can be seen that the radioactivity coincides exactly with the PTH-valine spot and inexactly with that of PTH-phenylalanine. The radioactive peak contained 656,000 counts/minute, corresponding to 3.31×10^{-2} μmoles of PTH-valine, or 30% of the theoretical yield (the phenyl isothiocyanate used in this experiment gave 1.98×10^7 counts/minute μmole when counted under the same conditions as the experimental strips).

Terminal amino acid analysis is particularly useful for establishing the existence and molecular size of subunits in protein macromolecules such as viruses and was used classically for this purpose by Harris and Knight (1952) on tobacco mosaic virus. However, reliable assessments of molecular size depend on the ability to estimate accurately the quantity of terminal amino acid present in the protein. One of the disadvantages of the ^{35}S phenyl isothiocyanate method is that yields of N-terminal PTH amino acids from known proteins have been found to be only about 30–40% of theoretical and it is not known where the main losses occur. This difficulty can be overcome to some extent, once the N-terminal amino acid of the unknown protein has been identified, by mixing proteins with known amounts of (different) N-terminal amino acids with the unknown protein before analysis. The yield of N-terminal PTH amino acid from the unknown protein can then be compared directly with the yields from the standard proteins and corrected accordingly for losses. The assumption is made that both known and unknown proteins react to the same extent with phenyl isothiocyanate, but it should be borne in mind that this might not always be the case.

N-terminal amino acid analyses are also useful for following the fractionation of protein mixtures, for example, the fractionation of the structural proteins of animal viruses, where the proteins may have no biological activity originally or where this is destroyed by the separation procedure. Thus the N-terminal amino acid acts as a "label" by which any particular polypeptide chain may be identified. It is possible, of course, for two different polypeptide chains to have the same N-terminal amino acid (or no free N-terminal amino acid at all) and these limitations must be recognized.

VI. Alternative Methods of N-Terminal Amino Acid Analysis

The most widely used alternative to the phenyl isothiocyanate method for the N-terminal amino acid analysis of proteins is the classical DNP method of Sanger (Fraenkel-Conrat *et al.*, 1955, give a good description of this method). Other alternatives include the radioactive *p*-iodophenylsulfonyl chloride method of Udenfriend and Velick (1951) and the 1-dimethylaminonaphthalene-5-sulfonyl ("dansyl") method developed by Gray and Hartley (1963). Of these methods the phenyl isothiocyanate method of Edman is the most useful since this may be used also for sequence determination, whereas in the others the analysis is restricted to the N-terminal amino acid only. The use of radioactively labeled ^{35}S phenyl isothiocyanate offers a number of advantages over use of the unlabeled reagent. Thus the sensitivity of the method is enormously increased and very small amounts of ^{35}S-labeled PTH amino acids can be identified and measured quantitatively with ease and precision, while at the same time, the reagents used do not have to be rigorously purified to exclude traces of ultraviolet absorbing or sulfur (^{32}S) containing contaminants. Furthermore, the radioactive phenylthiohydantoins can be chromatographed in the same lane as the unlabeled reference PTH amino acids, and exact coincidence or otherwise can be established between the R_f of a radioactive peak and that of a reference PTH amino acid. This provides much stronger evidence for the identity of an unknown PTH amino acid than when comparisons have to be made between materials run in different lanes.

REFERENCES

Braunitzer, G. (1958). *Z. Physiol. Chem.* **312**, 72.

Edman, P. (1950). *Acta Chem. Scand.* **4**, 277.

Edman, P. (1956). *Acta Chem. Scand.* **10**, 761.

Edman, P., and Begg, G. (1967). *European J. Biochem.* **1**, 80.

Edman, P., and Sjöquist, J. (1956). *Acta Chem. Scand.* **10**, 1507.

Fraenkel-Conrat, H., Harris, J. I., and Levy, A. L. (1955). *Methods Biochem. Anal.* **2**, 359.

Gray, W. R., and Hartley, B. S. (1963). *Biochem. J.* **89**, 379.

Harris, J. I., and Knight, C. A. (1952). *Nature* **170**, 613.

Udenfriend, S., and Velick, S. F. (1951). *J. Biol. Chem.* **190**, 733.

36. Adsorption Chromatography for Isolation of Viral Proteins: The Use of Substituted Celluloses and Calcium Phosphate

Harold S. Ginsberg

Department of Microbiology
School of Medicine
University of Pennsylvania
Philadelphia, Pennsylvania

I. Introduction

The development of methods and equipment for separation and purification of macromolecules subsequently led to successful purification and characterization of virions and their components in the past decade. Adsorption chromatography has played a particularly important role in the isolation and purification of viral proteins. In a general sense adsorption chromatography is based upon the differential attachment of proteins to solid surfaces by ionic, hydrogen, or hydrophobic bonding. However, in practice most systems that have been applied to the purification of proteins have depended upon the ionic bonding of proteins to adsorbents having the properties of ion exchangers. The adsorbents developed have included substituted celluloses, calcium phosphate gels, ion exchange resins such as Dowex-50 and Amberlite XE-64, and cross-linked dextrans. The substituted cellulose ion exchangers (Peterson and Sober, 1962) and calcium phosphate gels (Tiselius, 1954) have been most extensively employed. The techniques for their use form the basis of this article.

II. Substituted Celluloses

The attachment of a limited number of ionizable groups to cellulose establishes multiple electrostatic bonds between charged groups on the absorbent (i.e., substituted cellulose) and sites bearing opposite charges on the surface of the protein. Because the net charges of proteins differ, unique species of proteins may be differentially eluted from the adsorbent by reducing the number of charges on the protein. This is accomplished by changing the electrolyte concentration or pH of the buffer passed through the adsorbent. Several types of ionic groups have been added to cellulose to make both anionic and cationic exchangers. Diethylaminoethyl cellulose (DEAE), a weak anion exchanger, and carboxymethyl cellulose (CMC), a weak cationic exchanger, have been most widely used for isolation of viral proteins, and their use will be described.

A. Selection of Substituted Cellulose

Diethylaminoethyl is effective for the separation of acidic and slightly basic proteins which include the majority of viral proteins that have been studied. Carboxymethyl cellulose is used for chromatography of basic proteins. For neutral proteins which are stable under acidic and basic conditions a choice may be made between the two forms. Hence to select the most effective substituted cellulose adsorbent the isoelectric points of the proteins to be studied should be known. The charge characteristics can be simply estimated by paper electrophoresis or by a batchwise adsorption and desorption on the two forms of ionic exchangers.

B. Preparation of Exchanger

Standardized lots of DEAE and CMC with good adsorptive qualities can now be obtained from a number of manufacturers.* The majority of preparations require treatment before use in order to achieve maximum adsorption and desorption of the protein and a convenient flow rate. Hydrogen bonds between the dried polysaccharide chains must be broken to permit maximum swelling of the adsorbent and maximum accessibility of the charged groups. This is accomplished by the following procedure.

*Brown Co., Berlin, New Hampshire; Bio-rad Laboratories, Richmond, California; Eastman Chemicals, Rochester, New York; Gallard-Schlesinger Chemical Mfg. Corp., Carle Place, New York; and Whatman Scientific Division of Reeve Angel, Clifton, New Jersey.

(1) Pour the exchanger slowly into a beaker containing 15 volumes (dry weight of exchanger/milliliter fluid) of 0.5 *N* HCl for DEAE or 0.5 *N* NaOH for CMC. Stir gently while adding the cellulose. Allow to stand for 30 minutes.

(2) Decant the supernatant fluid and wash with the same acid or base until the effluent is pH 4 for DEAE or pH 8 for CMC.

(3) Repeat the procedure described in step 1, but reverse the fluid used; i.e., 0.5 *N* NaOH for DEAE and 0.5 *N* HCl for CMC. Leave for 30 minutes.

(4) Repeat step 3 and then wash adsorbent until it is near neutral.

The above procedure is necessary for all preparations of substituted celluloses except for the Whatman grade DE 52 (DEAE) or CM 52 (CMC) which are preswollen and delivered as a powder containing approximately 75% water.

The pretreated DEAE or CMC must next be equilibrated with a suitable buffer and the fines must be removed to insure an adequate flow rate. Ideally for the anionic exchanger DEAE a cationic buffer such as tris HCl should be employed. However, many viral proteins are preferably chromatographed with buffers from pH 6.5–7.5, and therefore phosphate buffers are most commonly used. For example, we have used a 0.01 *M* phosphate buffer at pH 7.2 for separation of the adenovirus structural proteins. For CMC, anionic buffers containing phosphate, acetate, or borate should be utilized.

To remove fines and equilibrate the exchanger the following steps should be followed:

(1) Stir the exchanger into 20 volumes of the selected buffer and allow it to settle for 20 minutes. Decant the supernatant fluid and repeat until the fluid is clear.

(2) Add 20 volumes of buffer to the exchanger, mix gently, and leave for 20 minutes.

(3) Decant the supernatant fluid and repeat until the pH of the fluid remains that of the buffer employed.

(4) Add the prepared and equilibrated adsorbent to the starting buffer in a proportion of 5–10% (original dry weight/volume buffer).

C. Preparation of Column

1. Size

The bed volume of the column should be directly related to the quantity of protein in the sample to be chromatographed. For example, Whatman DEAE (DE 32 or DE 52) has a protein capacity of 850 mg protein/gram of DEAE. One gram of either preparation of DEAE will make a bed volume ($\Pi r^2 \times$ height) of about 6 ml at pH 7.5. To obtain the best separation it is necessary that the column height be sufficient. Hence, with small quantities of protein columns of 8–10 mm internal diameter should be used. Good recovery of the adsorbed protein requires that the bed volume not be excessive.

2. *Packing of the Column*

Make certain that the selected column is absolutely vertical. The slurry of exchanger and buffer is then poured into the column. For short columns the entire bed may be prepared with a single addition; for long columns the bed is formed in layers. One to 2 cm of the exchanger should be allowed to settle before opening the stopcock. Beds may be packed with the aid of 3–5 psi of pressure. Add a disc of fiber-glass paper to the top of the bed, and wash the column with a volume of the starting buffer at least equivalent to the bed volume of the adsorbent.

D. Chromatography of Protein

1. *Introduction of Sample*

Allow the buffer to sink into the adsorbent until it reaches the upper level of the exchanger bed (*never permit the top of the exchanger to become dry*). The protein to be chromatographed should be dissolved in or equilibrated with the starting buffer (dialysis or passage through an equilibrated G-25 Sephadex column). The sample, in as small a volume as possible, should be pipetted carefully onto the exchanger without disturbing its surface. If the surface of the adsorbent is made irregular by a misdirected stream of the sample, a thin layer encompassing the irregularity should be stirred thoroughly as soon as sufficient sample is added. The sample is allowed to enter the exchanger by use of a peristaltic pump. To wash adherent protein from the glass walls, and to introduce the sample into the exchanger in a relatively small band, the top of the column is washed three times with 2–3 ml of starting buffer. The column is then washed with a quantity of starting buffer equal to the bed volume of the adsorbent.

2. *Elution of Protein*

Desorption of the protein from the exchanger may be accomplished by increasing salt concentration or by changing pH. Increasing the molarity of the salt appears to be the more effective procedure for separation of viral proteins, and the method described will utilize this process. Increasing salt concentrations can be added to the column in small stepwise increments or with a smoothly increasing gradient. The former procedure is more rapid and can be utilized to afford some concentration of the desired protein. However, good separation is often difficult with stepwise elutions if the sample contains a complex mixture of viral and host proteins. Addition of the salt in a gradient permits a controlled gradual and smooth increase in the electrolyte concentration. Gradient elution therefore often yields higher resolution of the different species of protein than is obtained with stepwise elution.

The shape of the salt gradient may be varied depending on the elution characteristics of the protein studied. A simple linear gradient, however, appears to be preferred for separation of most viral proteins. A linear gradient can be simply produced by using two identical cylindrical vessels connected by a siphon or a connection at the bottoms of the vessels so that the hydrostatic equilibrium between the two vessels can be maintained. To one vessel is added buffer containing the highest salt concentration to be attained. To the other is added an equal weight (for most practical purposes an equal volume) of the starting buffer. The fluid in the latter vessel is continuously stirred with a magnetic mixer; the concentration of the electrolyte in the fluid withdrawn will then increase linearly as long as the hydrostatic equilibrium is maintained between the two vessels.

The composition of the buffer, the molarity of the salt, and the volumes of fluid used to generate the linear gradient are dependent upon the characteristics and the quantities of the proteins to be separated. As an example of conditions which have been utilized, the separation of adenovirus capsid proteins on a DEAE column may be cited: Whatman DE 52 (preswollen) DEAE cellulose equilibrated with 0.01 *M* phosphate buffer, pH 7.2, was packed in a column 1.1 by 9.0 cm for a sample of 35-50 mg of protein; the gradient was prepared with 100 ml of 0.01 *M* phosphate buffer in the mixing vessel and 100 ml of 0.5 *M* NaCl in 0.01 *M* phosphate buffer, pH 7.2, in the connecting vessel; the flow rate of the column was adjusted with a peristaltic pump at a rate of approximately 35 ml/hour.

E. Batchwise Separations

Substituted cellulose exchangers prepared as described above can also be used in a flask or beaker for adsorption and desorption of proteins. A measured amount of equilibrated exchanger is mixed with the sample for 20-30 minutes. The exchanger and liquid phase can be separated by centrifugation or the solid phase may be permitted to settle by gravity. The exchanger is washed once with the buffer used for equilibration, and elution of protein is carried out by the stepwise addition of buffer with increasing salt concentrations at a constant pH. The increments of increasing salt are dependent upon the complexity of the mixture of proteins and their charge characteristics.

This procedure is rapid and simple, and recovery of concentrated material is usually good. However, if the sample contains a complex mixture of proteins, the separation of the macromolecules is generally inferior to that obtained with column techniques.

III. Calcium Phosphate Gel

A. PRINCIPLES

Batchwise adsorption of enzymes and a few viruses to calcium phosphate gel has been employed for a long time. However, the adsorbent material used was not suitable for column chromatography because of its extensive resistance to the flow of aqueous solutions, and the separations obtained by the batch techniques were not highly satisfactory. These difficulties were overcome when Tiselius (1954) and his colleagues (1956) developed a method to prepare an active form of calcium phosphate gel, hydroxylapatite [$Ca_5(PO_4)_3OH$], which has good ion exchange properties and permits a reasonable flow rate of common buffer solutions (Levin, 1962).

Many different species of proteins, acidic and basic, can be adsorbed reversibly to hydroxylapatite; hence, this exchanger has wide applicability to the separation of proteins. Nucleic acids, which are also adsorbed, are usually held to the adsorbent much more avidly than proteins, thus affording a convenient separation between these macromolecules. Binding seems to involve ionic forces, but desorption is more predictably effected by phosphate ions than by salt concentration. Neutral salts such as NaCl, which are most commonly used for elution of proteins from other ionic exchangers, practically do not influence their elution from hydroxylapatite. The pH of the solution does have a pronounced influence on the adsorption of most proteins; adsorption is much greater at a low pH than at a high one. The presence of both positive and negative charges on calcium phosphate gel contributes to the unique properties of this exchanger, and also enhances its value when it is used in succession with other ionic exchangers and with electrophoresis.

B. Preparation of Calcium Phosphate

Satisfactory stable preparations of the hydroxylapatite form can now be obtained commercially* obviating the somewhat tedious task of preparing it by the method of Tiselius and colleagues (1956). The hydroxylapatite is stored in 0.001 *M* phosphate buffer, pH 6.5, and before use it is equilibrated by washing with the desired buffer (e.g., 0.001 *M* phosphate buffer, pH 7.2).

C. Preparation of Column

The chromatograph tube should be fitted with a dropping funnel to which a thin slurry of prepared hydroxylapatite is added. The characteristics of the tube are otherwise similar to those used for chromatography with substituted cellulose exchangers. The appropriate size of the adsorbent bed can be calculated on the basis of the quantity of protein to be added: 1 ml of bed volume has a capacity for 2–4 mg of protein under the conditions described. If a total of 50 mg is to be separated and the chromatographic tube has a diameter of 1.2 cm, the height of the adsorbent bed would be a minimum of 11 cm or a maximum of 22 cm. The chromatographic tube is filled to one-half its volume with 0.001 *M* phosphate buffer, pH 7.2, to which the adsorbent is slowly added and allowed to settle by gravity. After a layer of 2–3 cm of hydroxylapatite has accumulated, the tap at the bottom of the tube is opened to permit a slow exit of the buffer. The slurry of adsorbent is added at the same rate as the outflow of buffer until the settling hydroxylapatite forms a column of the desired height. The tap is then closed and the bed is allowed to settle for several hours at room temperature. Pressure should not be employed to pack this column. The column is washed with 3–5 volumes of starting buffer before application of the protein mixture; a peristaltic pump may be used to keep a constant flow rate of 35–50 ml/hour.

D. Chromatography of Protein

The sample is introduced as described above for the separation of a mixture of proteins on columns of substituted cellulose. The protein is applied in 0.001–0.005 *M* phosphate buffer, pH 7.2. Elution of the protein from the hydroxylapatite is accomplished by gradually increasing the phosphate concentration utilizing either a smooth gradient or a

*Bio-rad Laboratories, Richmond, California and Gallard-Schlesinger Chemical Mfg. Carle Place, New York.

stepwise incremental increase in molarity. Excellent separation of adenovirus capsid proteins is obtained with a linear gradient of phosphate ions from 0.01–0.5 *M* at pH 7.2. However, it is reported that a stepwise increase in molarity of phosphate in increments of 0.03 *M* may produce a better separation of some proteins. If stepwise elution is employed each elution step should be carried out with a volume of one to one and one-half times the bed volume.

E. Alternative Procedure

The brushite form [$CaHPO_4 \cdot H_2O$] of calcium phosphate prepared by the method of Tiselius *et al.* (1956) may also be employed using methods identical to those described for the hydroxylapatite columns. Brushite has the advantage that it can be easily made by mixing equal volumes of 0.5 *M* disodium phosphate and 0.5 *M* calcium chloride. The solutions are run from two dropping funnels at equal rates (12–15 ml/minute) into a flask fitted with a mechanical or magnetic stirrer for gentle mixing to keep the precipitate effectively suspended without fracturing the crystals formed. The precipitate is allowed to settle, washed four times with liter volumes of distilled water, and equilibrated with 0.001 *M* phosphate buffer at the desired pH (6.8–7.2).

The brushite form has the disadvantage that it is relatively unstable and is not uniform from preparation to preparation. However, good separations of mixtures of proteins can be obtained with a recovery of 50–80%.

IV. Critique

Adsorption chromatography with substituted celluloses and calcium phosphate gels has been utilized for many years. But the difficulties experienced in preparing exchangers with uniform characteristics for adsorption and desorption virtually precluded their use by most not versed in the nuances of protein chemistry and chromatography. The present commercial availability of satisfactory preparations of DEAE cellulose, CM cellulose, and calcium phosphate gel (hydroxylapatite form) has obviated these technical problems and made their uses practicable for separation and purification of viral proteins.

The substituted celluloses afford good separation of proteins with different isoelectric points, but the recovery may be poor unless careful attention is paid to the relationship of the protein concentration to the bed volume of the adsorbent. Optimum recovery, 50–60% is best realized when the charge groups of the exchanger are near saturation. On the other hand, the hydroxylapatite currently available, which is satisfactory for separation of both acidic and basic proteins, usually permits recovery of 80–100% of the protein applied.

Thus, the two types of adsorbents described permit good separation of many viral proteins and when employed in series yield proteins of reasonable purity.

REFERENCES

Levin, Ö. (1962). *Methods Enzymol.* **5**, 27–32.
Peterson, E. A., and Sober, H. A. (1956). *J. Am. Chem. Soc.* **78**, 751.
Peterson, E. A., and Sober, H. A. (1962). *Methods Enzymol.* **5**, 3–27.
Tiselius, A. (1954). *Arkiv Kemi* **7**, 443.
Tiselius, A., Hjertén, S., and Levin, Ö. (1956). *Arch. Biochem. Biophys.* **65**, 132.

37. Interferon: Production, Assay, and Characterization

Samuel Baron

U.S. Department of Health, Education and Welfare
National Institutes of Health
Laboratory of Viral Diseases
Bethesda, Maryland

I. General Considerations

The interferon system is thought to be composed of two distinct, induced proteins. Production of the interferon protein is most generally induced in cells exposed to virus but may sometimes be induced by rickettsia, bacteria, mold extracts, nucleic acids, or spontaneously. The interferon protein itself is not thought to be antiviral. Instead it reacts with cells to induce a hypothesized antiviral protein which alters cellular ribosomes so that viral RNA does not associate or function with the altered ribosomes. This section will consider the production, assay, and characterization of interferon and certain aspects of the proposed antiviral protein which confers antiviral activity to the cell. For discussion and references on mechanisms and phenomena mentioned here, the reader is referred to the recent book on interferon (Finter, 1966) and to a recent review (Wagner *et al.*, 1968).

II. Production of Interferon

Interferon, because of its host cell species specificity of action, is usually produced in cells of the same animal species in which it will be used. Although it is not yet possible to use a single method for inducing cells to produce interferon, several viruses have been identified which efficiently induce in most experimental animal species *in vivo* and in cell culture. Representative methods for producing interferons are outlined in Table I. Since interferon is rapidly released from producing cells, only extracellular fluids need be harvested.

To inactivate residual inducing virus from interferon preparations, the pH of the harvested fluids is reduced to 2.0 by dropwise addition of concentrated HCl. Control of pH is most simply achieved by sterilely transferring a drop of acidified fluid to low range pH indicator paper (pH range 1.0–2.5) or by adding a final concentration of 1:100,000 thymol blue to tissue culture fluids and observing for a color change from yellow to orange as pH 2.0 is reached. The acidified fluid is then transferred to a fresh container to insure that all the virus has been exposed to the low pH. It is then held at 4°C for 24 hours for all the viruses listed in Table I except for Newcastle disease virus which requires 5 days for inactivation. After this holding time, the pH is returned to 7.0 by dropwise addition of concentrated NaOH.

An alternative method for inactivating virus is used in the presence of certain types of interferon which are reported to be unstable at pH 2 (Gresser and Naficz, 1964) or in the presence of viruses resistant to acid inactivation (picornoviruses, adenoviruses, reoviruses, and papova viruses). In these cases virus is usually eliminated by a combination of ultracentrifugation and neutralization with hyperimmune antiserum.

Although substantial purification of interferons may be achieved with available methods, they will not be included in this limited presentation.

The stability of interferons varies especially in relation to the protein content of the suspending fluid. Mouse and rat interferons harvested in serum and also chicken interferon in allantoic fluid or culture medium are stable indefinitely at −20°C and for weeks at 4°C. Mouse and rat serum interferons and chicken interferon may also be repeatedly frozen and thawed without loss of activity (Baron and Buckler, 1963a; Billiau, 1966). It has not yet been determined whether all species of serum interferons are equally stable. Mouse, human, and rat interferons harvested in culture medium often lose activity when stored at −20°C for several weeks unless additional serum (Baron *et al.*, 1967a) or albumin (Merigan *et al.*, 1966) is added to the medium. Although the protein concentration needed for stability has not been determined quantitatively, present information suggests that a 10% final concentration of fetal bovine serum provides sufficient protein. Human tissue culture-produced interferon is reported to be stabilized at 4°C, at −20°C, and for lyophilization by a final concentration of 0.05% bovine serum albumin (Merigan *et al.*, 1966; Merigan, 1967).

III. Assay of Interferon

In general all assays of interferons are based on inhibition of replication of virus or viral components in interferon-treated cells as compared with untreated cells. The choice of an assay virus is determined by its convenience and its sensitivity to interferon. The choice of cell culture is determined by its convenience, by its sensitivity to the antiviral action of interferon, and by the host cell species specificity of interferon. Since the titer of interferon can vary up to ±2-fold in repeated assays, many laboratories correct titers in each assay against a laboratory reference pool of interferon originally compared with the reference interferons obtained from the Research Reference Reagents Branch of the National Institute of Allergy and Infectious Diseases, Bethesda, Maryland or from the Biological Standards Laboratory, Mill Hill, London, England.

The types of interferon assays include inhibition of formation of viral (a) hemagglutinin, (b) hemadsorption, (c) plaque formation, (d) cytopathogenic effect, (e) infectivity, (f) RNA (Goldsby, 1967), (g) induced disease in animals, and (h) disruption of cellular metabolism (Finter, 1966). The most widely used assay is viral plaque reduction (Wagner, 1961). In general, cell monolayers in a 60 mm petri dish are first reacted with 2–4 ml of serial 2-fold dilutions of interferon in a 5% CO_2 incubator at 37°C for a minimum of 3 hours. The monolayers are then rinsed three times with 2 ml of balanced salt solution (Buckler and Baron, 1966) and challenged with 50 plaque-forming units of a sensitive plaque-forming virus such as vesicular stomatitis virus, Indiana strain, in a volume of 0.2 ml. After further incubation for 1 hour the cells are overlayed with 5 ml of nutrient agar and reincubated. A convenient nutrient agar has a minimal essential Eagle's medium base plus final concentrations of 0.9% Noble's agar, 5% fetal bovine serum, 5% tryptose phosphate broth, and antibiotics. After 24 hours a second overlay of 2.5 ml of nutrient agar containing 1/10,000 neutral red is applied. Viral plaques are counted after overnight incubation. One unit of interferon is contained in the greatest dilution of interferon which inhibits 50% of the plaques as compared with cultures not treated with interferon. Therefore the titer of interferon is the reciprocal of the dilution which gives the 1 unit effect.

The type and size of culture vessel used for assay may be varied provided that appropriate volumes are used. Although vesicular sto-

TABLE I
OUTLINE OF METHODS FOR PRODUCTION OF INTERFERONS

Animal species	Interferon-producing system	Stimulating virus	Virus dose	Method of inoculation	Time of incubation (hours)	Substance harvested	Reference	Remarks
Chicken	11-day-old embryonated eggs	Influenza A, strain WS or B, strain Lee	$10^{4.0}$ EID_{50}[a] in 0.2 ml	Intra-allantoically	72	Allantoic fluid	Wagner (1960); Cantell *et al* (1965)	
Chicken	Primary embryo cell cultures	Arbovirus A, strain Chikungunya	$10^{6.0}$ pfu[b] in 0.2 ml	0.2 ml virus/ $10^{6.3}$ cells[c] for 1 hour, wash and feed w/Eagle's medium	24	Culture medium	Ruiz-Gomez and Isaacs (1963); Gifford (1963)	
Chicken	Primary embryo cell cultures	Arbovirus A, strain Semliki forest (Kumba) virus	$10^{7.0}$ pfu in 0.2 ml	0.2 ml virus/ $10^{6.3}$ cells[c] for 1 hour, wash and feed w/Eagle's medium	24	Culture medium	Ruiz-Gomez and Isaacs (1963); Taylor (1965)	
Mouse	Adult Swiss, random bred	Newcastle disease virus, strain Herts	$\geqq 10^{8.0}$ pfu in 0.2 ml	Intravenously	5	Serum	Baron and Buckler (1963b)	
Mouse	Adult Swiss, random bred	Newcastle disease virus, strain B1	$\geqq 10^{8.0}$ pfu in 0.2 ml	Intravenously	12	Serum	Youngner *et al.* (1966a)	
Mouse	Adult Swiss, random bred	West Nile virus	300 MLD_{50}[e] in 0.03 ml	Intracerebrally	72	Brain	Finter (1964)	
Mouse	L cells, strain CCL-1	Newcastle disease virus, strain B1 or strain Herts	$10^{6.3}$ pfu in 0.2 ml	0.2 ml virus/ $10^{6.3}$ cells for 1 hour, wash and feed w/Eagle's medium	24	Culture medium	Cantell and Paucker (1963); Youngner *et al* (1966b)	Add protein stabilizer at time of harvest[f]
Rabbit	Adult rabbits	Arbovirus A, strain Sindbis	10^{10} pfu in 5 ml	Intravenously	8	Serum	Kono and Ho (1965)	
Rabbit	Primary kidney cell cultures	Newcastle disease virus, strain CG	$10^{8.2}$ pfu in 0.5 ml	0.5 ml virus/ $10^{6.3}$ cells for 30 minutes, wash and feed w/Eagle's medium and 2% fetal bovine serum	6	Culture medium	Smith and Wagner (1967)	

Hamster	Adult Syrian hamster	Newcastle disease virus, strain Herts	$\geq 10^{9.0}$ pfu in 1.0 ml	Intravenously	8	Serum	Baron *et al.* (1966a)	
Rat	Adult Wistar, strain R	Arbovirus A, strain Sindbis or Newcastle disease virus, strain B_1	$10^{9.0}$ pfu in 1.0 ml	Intravenously	6	Serum	Van Rossum and De Somer (1966)	
Monkey	Primary kidney cell cultures	Influenza A, strain Kunz	50 HA[g] units in 0.2 ml	0.2 ml virus/ $10^{6.3}$ cells for 1 hour, wash and feed w/Eagle's medium	72	Culture medium	Scientific Committee (1962)	Add protein stabilizer[f]
Man	Human fibroblast cell cultures	Newcastle disease virus, strain Herts	$10^{5.0}$–$10^{6.0}$ pfu in 0.2 ml	0.2 ml virus/ $10^{6.3}$ cells for 1 hour, wash and feed w/Eagle's medium and 10% fetal bovine serum	48	Culture medium	Baron and Isaacs (1962); Merigan *et al.* (1966)	
Man	Human leukocytes	Sendai virus	1000 HA units in 1 ml	1.0 ml virus/ $10^{7.0}$ cell suspension in 9.0 ml Eagle's medium and 10% fetal bovine serum	24	Culture medium	Gresser (1961); Falcoff *et al.* (1966); Strander and Cantell (1967)	
Man	Human amnionic membrane	Sendai virus, inactivated[h]	1700 HA units in 1 ml	1.0 ml virus/ 1.0 gm tissue for 2 hours, wash and suspend in 8 ml of Eagle's medium and 2% fetal bovine serum	48	Culture medium	Fournier *et al.* (1967)	Membrane agitated during incubation. Add protein stabilizer.[f]

[a] EID_{50} stands for egg infectious doses, 50%.
[b] pfu stands for plaque-forming units.
[c] Approximate number of cells in 50 mm culture dish.
[e] MLD_{50} stands for mouse lethal dose, 50%, as determined by intracerebral titration.
[f] Tentative recommendation is final concentration of 10% fetal bovine serum of 0.05% bovine serum albumin.
[g] HA stands for hemagglutinin.
[h] Inactivation by 5100 ergs/mm^2 ultraviolet light.

matitis virus (VSV) is generally useful for interferon assays because of its infectivity for most cell cultures and its sensitivity to the antiviral action of interferons, other challenge viruses may have special usefulness. Chikungunya, O'nyong-nyong, and Semliki forest viruses are more sensitive to chicken interferon than is VSV. Semliki forest virus and Western equine encephalitis virus are more sensitive to mouse interferon; rubella virus is more sensitive to monkey interferon. Many strains of vaccinia virus may be used in the plaque reduction assay with a fluid overlay (Lindenmann and Gifford, 1963), but it is important to wash away nonspecific inhibitors before virus challenge (Buckler and Baron, 1966).

Homologous cell cultures are usually necessary to assay interferon from each species. Some homologous cell cultures manifest low sensitivity to interferon, and these frequently include primary or continuous cultures derived from very young embryos and certain substrains of continuous cell lines. The following cell cultures are satisfactory for assay of homologous interferons: primary and secondary cultures from one-half to three-fourths term chick embryos, mouse embryos, rabbit embryos, hamster embryos, and rat embryos; CCL-1 strain of mouse L cells [more sensitive to interferon than are primary Swiss mouse embryo cultures in a plaque reduction assay (Finter, 1966)]; primary or secondary monkey or rabbit kidney or monkey testes cultures; primary or diploid human fibroblasts derived from near term embryos, newborn infants or adults [e.g., primary and secondary adult thyroid cell cultures (Isaacs *et al.*, 1961) or foreskin fibroblasts (Merigan *et al.*, 1966), AH-1 (adult diploid-type cells from Mr. George Gardiner at the National Institutes of Health media section)]. The WI-38 human diploid cells are less sensitive to human interferon as compared with the above-mentioned human cell cultures. The AF-57 human diploid-type cells (obtainable from Dr. B. W. Uhlendorf, National Institutes of Health, Bethesda, Maryland) are sensitive to interferon although they are derived from amniotic fluid cells of a 6 week embryo.

Certain studies of the interferon-induced antiviral activity (proposed antiviral protein) require measurement of degree of antiviral activity very close to the time of virus challenge. The plaque reduction assay is unsuitable for this purpose because 2 days are usually required for the several cycles of virus replication to occur between removal of interferon and plaque formation. Determination of antiviral activity close to the time of virus challenge can be achieved by determining the interferon-induced reduction in yield of virus during a single step growth cycle initiated by a multiplicity of infection greater than one (Baron *et al.*, 1967a). Specifically, three replicate tube cultures are reacted at 37°C with 1 ml of each 0.5 $\log_{10}$

(3.2-fold) serial dilution of interferon in Eagle's minimal essential medium (MEM) containing 2% fetal bovine serum. After a minimum of 6 hours, but generally after overnight incubation, the cultures are rinsed two times with 2 ml of balanced salt solution and challenged with 0.2 ml of vesicular stomatitis virus containing an input of at least 20 pfu/cell. The tube cultures are reincubated for 1 hour, rinsed four times, refed 1 ml of MEM + 2% fetal bovine serum and held at 37°C for 20 hours. The three culture fluids per dilution are pooled, stored at −60°C in a mechanical freezer and subsequently assayed for plaque titer on mouse L cells, primary mouse embryo cells or primary chick embryo cells. The greatest dilution which inhibits 0.5 $\log_{10}$ of virus yield contains 1 unit of interferon. The preparation, treatment, rinsing, infection, and feeding of the tube cultures is greatly simplified if the cells are cultured in 1 ml of medium in 16 mm by 150 mm tubes held in a vertical position in a spring rack (A. H. Thomas Co., No. 9497-c) and loosely covered with aluminum foil in a 5% CO_2 incubator. With this system up to 64 tube cultures can be decanted, rinsed, flamed, fed, etc., simultaneously. A similar spring rack system simplifies the plaque assays (Baron *et al.*, 1966b).

IV. Characterization

To avoid misidentification of viral inhibition as interferon-mediated when instead it might be a result of the many natural inhibitors of virus it is necessary to (a) compare the properties of the inhibitor under study with that of interferon and (b) compare the characteristics of the viral inhibition under study with that of the interferon-induced inhibition (antiviral protein). This section will consider those properties which are sufficient to distinguish the interferon system from other inhibitors of virus. A sufficient characterization of interferon should include demonstration of (a) cellular and not viral origin of interferon including the requirement of intact cellular RNA and/or protein synthesis for its production, (b) inactivation of interferon by proteolytic enzymes such as trypsin, (c) host cell species specificity of interferon's action, (d) cell-mediated antiviral activity of interferon including the requirement of intact cellular RNA and/or protein synthesis for development of antiviral effect, (e) lack of viral specificity of antiviral action, and (f) decreased antiviral activity against viruses which have been predetermined to be less sensitive to the action of interferon in the same cell system. Specific characterization methods are discussed below.

A. Cellular Origin of Interferon

To rule out the possibility that the inhibitor is an interfering viral particle two methods are useful. Sedimentation at 100,000 *g* for 4 hours in the presence of 0.06% gelatin (Baron, 1957) is sufficient to enmesh most of any intact interfering virus in a gelatin pellet and thereby cause this type of inhibitory activity in the supernatant to decrease by a factor of at least 10. In contrast the titer of interferon in the supernatant would be unchanged. The second method is to incubate the viral inhibitor with antibody directed against the virus which induced production of the inhibitor. A satisfactory procedure is to mix a 1/10 dilution of hyperimmune serum with an equal volume of at least 10 units of inhibitor. After reaction for 1 hour in a 37°C water bath the inhibitory titer is determined in comparison with inhibitor reacted with normal serum rather than immune serum. A 3-fold or greater decrease of inhibitory activity signifies that the viral inhibitor is antigenically related to virus and therefore is most likely not interferon.

Production of interferon requires intact cellular RNA and protein syntheses. The one apparent exception is endotoxin-released interferon *in vivo*. Interruption of cellular RNA synthesis with actinomycin D should prevent at least 80% of interferon production, which is induced by an actinomycin D-resistant RNA virus (Heller, 1963). The dose of actinomycin D is generally 0.5–1.0 μg/ml except for African green monkey kidney cell cultures which require 100 μg/ml (Wong *et al.*, 1967). Similarly fluorophenylalanine or puromycin interruption of functional cellular protein synthesis should prevent at least 80% of interferon production (Isaacs, 1963; Buchan and Burke, 1966). The dose of D,L-*p*-fluorophenylalanine (FPA) is 100 μg/ml in phenylalanine-free medium or 1600 μg/ml in Eagle's medium. The characterization is simply done by applying the metabolic inhibitors to cell cultures over a 4 hour period of known interferon production and then comparing the interferon content of the medium in the presence of metabolic inhibitors with the content in their absence. The diluting fluid for the interferon assay should contain 50 μg/ml phenylalanine (as in MEM).

B. Effect of Proteolytic Enzymes

Inactivation by trypsin is an important property of interferon, but other protein inhibitors may also be inactivated. The procedure is to mix at least 10 units of the viral inhibitor with a final concentration of 100 μg/ml of recrystallized trypsin. After digestion for 1 hour in a 37°C water bath, an equal concentration of soybean trypsin inhibitor is added and the inhibitor assayed in comparison with control inhibitor treated similarly except that trypsin is replaced with diluent fluid. It may also be necessary to show that the trypsin is active under these conditions by inactivating a known preparation of interferon. Trypsin digestion under these conditions inactivates at least 80% of interferon activity. Since serum contains trypsin inhibitors, it is important, if possible, to dilute many serum preparations of serum interferon at least 1:40 before mixing with trypsin.

C. Host Cell Species Specificity of Action

Host cell species specificity is an important distinguishing characteristic of interferon. This is determined by comparing the antiviral titer of the inhibitor on homologous cells with the titer on heterologous cells as described under assay of interferon. Whereas interferon may induce little or no resistance in most heterologous cell systems (Buckler and Baron, 1966), most other inhibitors act equally well in the presence of heterologous cells (Ginsberg, 1960). More than 10-fold difference in titers on cells of related animal species is consistent with interferon. With few exceptions there is no interferon activity on unrelated heterologous cells.

D. Cell-Mediated Antiviral Action

Interferon does not directly inactivate virus, whereas most other inhibitors act by binding to virus. For this characterization 10 or more units of the inhibitor are mixed with at least 10^3 infectious doses of virus and held at 37°C. Samples which are taken at 0 time and at 10 minute intervals for 1 hour are immediately diluted beyond antiviral activity and assayed for virus. The same constituents with medium replacing the inhibitor serve as a control. Most but not all (Ginsberg, 1960) noninterferon inhibitors will progressively inactivate virus, but interferon will not decrease infectivity more rapidly than inactivation attributable to thermal or medium effects as determined with appropriate controls.

Induction of cellular resistance by interferon requires continued cellular RNA and protein syntheses. To test this property at least 20 units of the viral inhibitor are reacted at 37°C with cells in the presence of 100 μg/ml D,L-*p*-fluorophenylalanine in phenylalanine-free medium or 1600 μg/ml FPA in Eagle's medium to inhibit synthesis of functional protein. After 4 hours the cultures are washed three times with balanced salt solution to remove interferon and FPA, challenged with a high multiplicity of vesicular stomatitis virus in a yield reduction assay of antiviral activity in the presence of complete medium. Virus controls are done with and without FPA. If the inhibitor is interferon, the virus yield after treatment with interferon and FPA should be at least 8-fold greater than after treatment with interferon alone. Cycloheximide is not as desirable as FPA for inhibition of protein synthesis because in mouse embryo cells it may allow translation of the messenger RNA for the antiviral protein after removal of cycloheximide (Dianzani *et al.*, 1967). An experiment to determine the necessity for RNA synthesis is performed as above except that 1.0 μg/ml of actinomycin D is used in place of FPA for most types of cells except African green monkey kidney cultures which require 100 μg/ml of actinomycin D (Wong *et al.*, 1967). It is desirable to include biochemical controls to show that FPA specifically inhibits incorporation of phenylalanine into protein and that actinomycin D specifically inhibits RNA synthesis.

E. Lack of Viral Specificity of Antiviral Action

A relatively specific property of the interferon type of resistance is its broad antiviral activity. This is demonstrated by performing viral inhibitor assays with several unrelated viruses as challenge viruses. Suitable viruses are vesicular stomatitis (Indiana strain), vaccinia, Semliki forest, Sindbis, and encephalomyocarditis viruses. However, not all of these viruses will replicate in all cell systems (Andrewes, 1964).

F. Greatest Activity Against Interferon-Sensitive Viruses

Another distinguishing property of interferon-related resistance is its decreased antiviral activity against viruses which are less sensitive to the action of interferon (Isaacs *et al.*, 1961). This characterization is performed by comparing inhibitory titers against vesicular stomatitis virus with the more interferon-resistant polioviruses for primate cells, Newcastle disease virus for chicken cells, and certain strains of Herpes simplex virus for rodent cells.

G. Other Properties

Stability at pH 2 is characteristic of most interferon preparations, whereas many interfering viruses and other inhibitors are inactivated by this acidity as considered under interferon production.

The apparent molecular weights of interferons vary from 20,000 to 160,000 (Hallum *et al.*, 1965; Merigan *et al.*, 1965; Fournier *et al.*, 1967). The wide distribution of apparent molecular weights makes this an indistinct property of interferon although an inhibitory substance outside this range would be suspect of not being interferon.

The final distinctive property of interferon-induced resistance is the recently reported alterations in ribosomes of interferon-treated cells so that binding and translation of viral messenger RNA is inhibited (see references in Baron and Levy, 1966). This could be used for further characterization of an inhibitor by demonstrating that ribosomes from interferon-treated cells react normally with cell messenger RNA but do not react with viral RNA. For details of those procedures the reader is referred to the original reports (Marcus *et al.*, 1966; Carter and Levy, 1967) since this specialized method is not yet adapted to routine use.

REFERENCES

Andrewes, C. H. (1964). "Viruses of Vertebrates." Williams & Wilkins, Baltimore, Maryland.
Baron, S. (1957). *Proc. Soc. Exptl. Biol. Med.* **95**, 760.
Baron, S., and Buckler, C. E. (1963a). Unpublished observations.
Baron, S., and Buckler, C. E. (1963b). *Science* **141**, 1061.
Baron, S., and Isaacs, A. (1962). *Brit. Med. J.* **I**, 18.
Baron, S., and Levy, H. B. (1966). *Ann. Rev. Microbiol.* **20**, 291.
Baron, S., Buckler, C. E., McCloskey, R. V., and Kirschstein, R. L. (1966a). *J. Immunol.* **96**, 12.
Baron, S., Buckler, C. E., and Takemoto, K. K. (1966b). *Appl. Microbiol.* **14**, 1042.
Baron, S., Buckler, C. E., and Billiau, A. (1967a). Unpublished observations.
Baron, S., Buckler, C. E., Levy, H. B., and Friedman, R. M. (1967b). *Proc. Soc. Exptl. Biol. Med.* **125**, 1320.
Billiau, A. (1966). Unpublished observations.
Buchan, A., and Burke, D. C. (1966). *Biochem. J.* **98**, 530.
Buckler, C. E., and Baron, S. (1966). *J. Bacteriol.* **91**, 231.
Cantell, K., and Paucker, K. (1963). *Virology* **21**, 11.
Cantell, K., Valle, M., Schakir, R., Saukkonen, J. J., and Vroma, E. (1965). *Ann. Med. Exptl. Biol. Fenniae (Helsinki)* **43**, 125.
Carter, W. A., and Levy, H. B. (1967). *Science* **155**, 1254.
Dianzani, F., Buckler, C. E., and Baron, S. (1967). *Bacteriol. Proc.* p. 157.
Falcoff, E., Falcoff, R., Fournier, F., and Chany, C. (1966). *Ann. Inst. Pasteur* **111**, 562.
Finter, N. B. (1964). *Nature* **204**, 1114.
Finter, N. B., ed. (1966). "Interferons." North-Holland Publ., Amsterdam.
Fournier, F., Falcoff, E., and Chany, C. (1967). *J. Immunol.* **99**, 1036.
Gifford, G. E. (1963). *Nature* **200**, 91.
Ginsberg, H. S. (1960). *Bacteriol. Rev.* **24**, 141.
Goldsby, R. A. (1967). Personal communication.

Gresser, I. (1961). *Proc. Soc. Exptl. Biol. Med.* **108**, 799.
Gresser, I., and Naficz, K. (1964). *Proc. Soc. Exptl. Biol. Med.* **117**, 285.
Hallum, J. V., Youngner, J. S., and Stinebring, W. R. (1965). *Virology* **27**, 429.
Heller, E. (1963). *Virology* **21**, 652.
Isaacs, A. (1963). *Advan. Virus Res.* **10**, 1.
Isaacs, A., Porterfield, J. S., and Baron, S. (1961). *Virology* **14**, 450.
Kono, Y., and Ho, M. (1965). *Virology* **25**, 1965.
Lindenmann, J., and Gifford, G. E. (1963). *Virology* **19**, 302.
Marcus, R. I., and Salb, J. M. (1966). *Virology* **30**, 502.
Merigan, T. C. (1967). Personal communication.
Merigan, T. C., Winget, C. A., and Dixon, C. B. (1965). *J. Mol. Biol.* **13**, 679.
Merigan, T. C., Gregory, D. F., and Petralli, J. K. (1966). *Virology* **29**, 515.
Ruiz-Gomez, J., and Isaacs, A. (1963). *Virology* **19**, 8.
Scientific Committee on Interferon. (1962). *Lancet* **I**, 873.
Smith, T. J., and Wagner, R. R. (1967). *J. Exptl. Med.* **125**, 559.
Strander, H., and Cantell, K. (1967). *Ann. Med. Exptl. Biol. Fenniae (Helsinki)* **45**, 20.
Taylor, J. (1965). *Virology* **25**, 340.
Van Rossum, W., and De Somer, P. (1966). *Life Sci.* **5**, 105.
Wagner, R. R. (1960). *Bacteriol. Rev.* **24**, 151.
Wagner, R. R. (1961). *Virology* **13**, 323.
Wagner, R. R., Levy, A. H., and Smith, T. J. (1968). *In* "Methods in Virology" (K. Maramorosch and H. Koprowski, eds.), Vol. 4, pp 1-52. Academic Press, New York.
Wong, K. T., Baron, S., Levy, H. B., and Ward, T. G. (1967). *Proc. Soc. Exptl. Biol. Med.* **125**, 65.
Youngner, J. S., Scott, A. W., Hallum, J. V., and Stinebring, W. R. (1966a). *J. Bacteriol.* **92**, 862.
Youngner, J. S., Taube, S. E., and Stinebring, W. R. (1966b). *Proc. Soc. Exptl. Biol. Med.* **123**, 795.

VII. RNA Analyses

38. Isolation and Sucrose Gradient Analysis of RNA

Klaus Scherrer

Swiss Institute for Experimental Cancer Research
1005 Lausanne, Switzerland

I. Introduction

The hot phenol extraction has become a standard method for preparation of RNA from animal and bacterial cells. This procedure has made possible the detection in animal cells of the DNA-like RNA with molecular weights of up to eight million daltons, and of the precursors to rRNA* (Scherrer and Darnell, 1962; Scherrer *et al.*, 1963; Scherrer and Marcaud, 1965). Recently it permitted Salser *et al.* (1967) to isolate the biologically active messenger RNA which is capable of directing the synthesis of phage T4 lysozyme in a cell-free ribosome system. Thus, the biological activity of a natural messenger and the intactness of RNA molecules, which have recently been shown to be as long as 8 μ (Granboulan and Scherrer, 1969) are good criteria for the conclusion that the method permits the extraction of RNA in its physiological form.

The work of Schuster *et al.* (1956) and of Gierer and Schramm (1956), which is based on a paper by Westphal *et al.* (1952), had shown that phenol extraction could produce pure infectious viral RNA. Wecker (1958) reported that he was more successful in isolating infectious WEE virus RNA with hot phenol than with a cold extraction procedure. His results and chemical considerations convinced us that

**Abbreviations:* rRNA, ribosomal RNA; pre-rRNA, precursors to rRNA; and mRNA, messenger RNA. See Section II, B for further definitions.

heat would not damage RNA. This encouraged us to develop a method based on a hot phenol treatment which would allow high yields of undegraded cellular RNA (Section VI, A). It was necessary to find the conditions for eliminating DNA without using DNase treatment since this may damage high molecular weight RNA molecules. These goals have been achieved by the hot phenol extraction method described here.

However, it should be noted that there exist absolute contraindications to the utilization of heat in RNA extraction because of the thermosensitivity of the rRNA in some organisms (e.g., many species of diptera). In such cases the extraction is carried out with the same procedure at room temperature.

There is no attempt to describe herein other RNA extraction procedures. Only a concise description and some comments on the methods we are using for RNA extraction and analysis will be given. Since the first publication of this procedure (Scherrer and Darnell, 1962), we have described some modifications in a more recent paper (Scherrer *et al.*, 1966).

II. Material

A. Equipment

1. Extraction Flasks

Originally we used glass-stoppered (24/40) Pyrex tubes of 27 mm outer diameter and 150 mm length. These tubes can be used on a Vortex shaker and in some swing-out rotors. Because of their small volume and difficulty in handling them in the heat bath, we switched to longer tubes of the same type. Presently glass-stoppered (29/32) Erlenmeyer flasks appropriate for the gyrotory shaker are used.

2. Syringes

Withdrawal of phenol below the aqueous phase: 10 or 20 ml syringes with No. 14, 6 inch needle. Withdrawal of aqueous phase: 10 ml syringe with about 10 cm of a small diameter silicone rubber tubing attached.

3. Heating bath

We use a thermostat-regulated gyrotory shaker (type G-76, New Brunswick Instr. Inc., New Jersey) which allows efficient shaking and heat transfer in glass-stoppered Erlenmeyer flasks. For hand shaking any water bath that is deep enough is appropriate.

4. *Cooling bath*

We use a mixture of ice and methanol (2:1) which gives a temperature of about −15°C. The use of a cryostat at about −25°C (liquid:methanol/water) is very convenient.

5. *Shaker*

During extraction by hand we shake intermittently on a Vortex rotory shaker (Scientific Ind. Inc., Springfield, Massachusetts).

6. *Centrifuges*

(a) For extraction procedure the swing-out rotors of the International Centrifuge PR-2 (International Equipment Co., Boston, Massachusetts), the HG-4 rotor of the Sorvall RC-3 centrifuge or the angle rotor SS-1 (Sorvall, Norwalk, Connecticut), or any similar instrument are appropriate.

(b) For gradient centrifugation the commercially available models allowing speeds up to 50,000 rpm, temperature and vacuum control, and the use of large swing-out rotors are appropriate.

7. *Peristaltic Pump*

Perpex, 3 channel model (W. Meyer Inc., Luzern, Switzerland; distributed by LKB, Stockholm, Sweden) or Polystaltic pump (Buchler, Fort Lee, New Jersey).

8. *Gradient Mixer*

The gradient mixer consists of two chambers (reservoir and mixing chamber) of the appropriate volume which are interconnected by a small hole. The mixer can easily be made by any machine workshop. Two cylindrical chambers are cut into a block of Lucite (Plexiglas) at a distance allowing the placement of a stopcock which closes the connecting line. The height of the chambers should be 2.5–3-fold the diameter. The bottom of each chamber forms an inverted circular pyramid of about one-tenth the height of the chamber. A horizontal hole is drilled from the outside of the mixer through the lowest point of the mixing chamber to the bottom of the reservoir. This connecting hole is fitted with a Teflon stopcock which allows one to open and close the connection by a 90° rotation. The stopcock should be held by a screw since experience has proved that it loosens easily otherwise. The outlet hole is joined by two secondary ones which are drilled at the same level at an angle into the central channel. This allows one to attach three outlet tubes simultaneously by means of hypodermic needles which are pressed into the holes.

The mixer should be constructed in such a way that it can be placed on a magnetic stirrer since this is the most convenient way of mixing the gradient.

9. *Flow Cell, Spectrophotometer, and Recorder*

Any recording UV monitor may be used provided that the flow cell placed in the light path holds a small enough volume (less than 1% of the gradient volume) to give maximal resolution. We use the Zeiss flow cell (20 μl for 10 mm light path) in the microattachment to the PMQ II spectrophotometer (Zeiss Inc., Oberkochen, Germany) which is linked through an electronic Transmission-Extinction converter to a linear recorder or directly to a logarithmic recorder. Other widely used instruments are those of Gilford (Gilford Inc., Oberlin, Ohio), ISCO (Inst. Spec. Co., Lincoln, Nebraska), and LKB (LKB, Stockholm, Sweden).

B. Chemicals and Enzymes

(1) Phenol: We use liquified phenol (88–90%) without any additive. In the United States commercially available preparations proved to be satisfactory without further treatment.

Crystalline phenol has been distilled prior to use, since even highly purified preparations were not satisfactory. The distillation should be carried out under high vacuum. We distill at 95°C and less than 10 Torr in a rotary evaporator (Buechi, 9230 Flawil, Switzerland), keeping the phenol stock and the condenser at 45°C. This temperature allows one to load the distillation flask in operation without breaking the high vacuum and avoids the crystallization of phenol in the condenser. The distilled phenol is stored at low temperature.

(2) Acetate, trichloracetate, sucrose, EDTA, tris, NaCl, $MgCl_2$, and $MnCl_2$ are highest purity preparations (e.g., Merck, Darmstadt, Germany).

(3) Ethanol: 96% without any additives.

(4) Detergents

(a) Sodium dodecyl sulfate (SDS): any high grade, recrystallized, optical absorbancy free preparation.

(b) Sarkosyl NL-97 (Geigy Inc., Basel, Switzerland).

(c) Triisopropyl naphthalene disulfonate (TND) (Eastman Kodak, Rochester, New York).

(5) RNase inhibitor: polyvinyl sulfate (PVS) (Eastman Kodak, Rochester, New York).

(6) Bentonite: Any pharmacopoeia grade preparation, purified according to Singer and Fraenkel-Conrat (1961).

(7) Macaloid: Prepared analogous to Bentonite, purchased from Baroid Div., National Lead Co., Houston, Texas.

(8) Deoxyribonuclease: RNase-free preparation of Worthington, Freehold, New Jersey. Every batch has to be tested to show that it does not degrade rRNA molecules.

(9) Pronase: from Calbiochem, Los Angeles, California.

C. MISCELLANEOUS

(1) Glass fiber filters: Whatman GF/B of 25 mm diam. (Whatman Inc.).

(2) Material for scintillation counting from any company. NCS from Nuclear Chicago, Des Plaines, Illinois. 1 *M* Hyamine in methanol from Packard Instr. Inc., Downers Grove, Illinois.

D. SOLUTIONS AND BUFFERS

(1) Pretreatment of cells
- (a) Washing solution: Earle's saline (Earle, 1943).
- (b) Freezing solution (final concentration): Sucrose 0.25 *M*; tris 0.01 *M*; KCl 0.01 *M*; Mn^{++}, Mg^{++} 0.001 *M*.

(2) Extraction
- (a) Phenol liquified: Distilled phenol-water (9:1) or distilled phenol-extraction buffer (9:1).
- (b) Extraction buffer (final concentration): (A) CH_3COONa 0.01 *M*, pH 5.2; (B) Same as A with addition of NaCl 0.05 *M*; Mn^{++}, Mg^{++} 0.001 *M*.
- (c) Detergent solutions: SDS, 25% in H_2O; Sarkosyl, 20% in H_2O; TND, 10% in H_2O.

(3) Solution buffers (final concentration).
- (a) CH_3COONa 0.01 *M*, pH 5.2; NaCl 0.01 *M*.
- (b) Tris 0.01 *M*, pH 7.0; NaCl 0.01 *M*.

(4) DNase treatment
- (a) Tris 0.01 *M*, pH 7.0; NaCl 0.01 *M*; Mn^{++} 0.001 *M* (final concentration) or extraction buffer B.
- (b) DNase (RNase free) 1 mg/ml in CH_3COONa 0.1 *M*, pH 5.2.
- (c) EDTA 0.5 *M*, pH 7.2.

(5) Purification with adsorbing agents: 2.5% suspension of Bentonite or Macaloid in 0.01 *M* CH_3COONa, pH 5.2.

(6) Sucrose gradient solutions
Light solution: 5, 15, or 20% (w/w) sucrose in buffer. Heavy solution: 20, 30, or 40% (w/w) sucrose in buffer.

Buffers

(a) Acetate: CH_3COONa 0.01 *M*, pH 5.0; NaCl 0.05 *M*.
(b) EDTA: EDTA 0.01 *M*, pH 7.0; NaCl 0.05 *M*.
(c) Tris: Tris 0.01 *M*, pH 7.0; EDTA 0.001 *M*; NaCl 0.05 *M*.
(d) SDS: Same buffers containing 0.2% SDS.

The gradient solutions are treated with 1/50 volume of a 2.5% suspension of Macaloid in order to remove trace amounts of RNase. The Macaloid is removed by 30 minutes sedimentation at 5000 rpm.

(7) Assay of radioactivity

(a) Bray's solution: Naphthalene, 60 gm; PPO, 4 gm; POPOP, 0.2 gm; ethylene glycol, 20 ml; methanol, 100 ml. Dilute all with *p*-dioxane up to 1 liter (Bray, 1960).
(b) P-1: 0.5% PPO (2,5-diphenyloxazole); 0.03% DimPOPOP (1,4-bis-2(4-methyl-5-phenyloxazolyl)-benzene in toluene.
(c) P-5: Same as (b) but added by 0.5% of Hyamine solution (I *M* in methanol) or 0.5% of NCS.

III. Extraction Procedure

1. *Preparation of Animal Cells for Extraction*

The cells are washed with Earle's saline and sedimented at low speed (600–1000 rpm). If they cannot be processed immediately, they should be resuspended in a small volume of isotonic sucrose buffer and kept at −20°C, −70°C, or better still, in liquid nitrogen. Some types of cells cannot be frozen without breakdown of giant RNA molecules (Section VI, B).

2. *Step 1*

The pellet of washed or frozen cells (Section VI, B) is suspended as rapidly as possible in the appropriate (Section VI, C) extraction buffer using a volume of buffer equal to *100 times* the volume of the packed cells (Section VI, D). As soon as the suspension is complete, concentrated detergent (Section VI, E) is added to 1% final concentration and the contents are mixed. An equal volume of liquified phenol, preheated at 65°C, is added and the solution is vigorously shaken by hand until the viscosity of the solution drops substantially (10–20 seconds). *The time required from the first contact of the cells with the hypotonic extraction buffer until the addition of the hot phenol should not exceed 30 seconds* (Section VI, F).

The extraction mixture is shaken vigorously at 65°C (Section VI, G) for 3 minutes either in the gyrotory shaker or by hand in the water bath, placing it on the Vortex mixer every 30 seconds. Then the solution is quenched in a cold bath (kept at −15 to −25°C) until the viscosity of the solution rises and some phenol crystals appear (Section VI, G). Quick shaking brings the crystals back into a homogeneous suspension. At this time an aliquot may be taken to determine the total radioactivity (Section VI, H). The phases are separated in appropriate tubes (Section VI, I) by a 5 minutes' centrifugation at 5000 rpm or by centrifugation for 1 minute at 12,000 rpm. If the mixture was cold enough before centrifugation both phases should be clear afterward.

Now the phenol layer is removed completely from below by penetrating the aqueous phase with a long, large diameter hypodermic needle mounted on a large volume syringe (Section VI, J). Only clear phenol is removed, avoiding interphase, an eventual pellet (Section VI, K) and the aqueous phase.

After resuspension of the interphase (Section VI, L) on the Vortex mixer, the aqueous layer is transferred back to the extraction flask. More preheated liquified phenol is added corresponding to about 75 times (Section VI, M) the volume of the original cell pellet. The mixture is shaken in the 65°C bath for another 3 minutes. After centrifugation, removal of phenol and resuspension of the interphase, another 2 minutes' extraction at 65°C is performed. This time an amount of liquified phenol is used which should correspond to 40–50 times the original cell volume (Section VI, M).

At this stage the interphase should have almost completely disappeared after the separation of phases. If a substantial interphase remains a fourth extraction may be carried out. This time buffer-saturated phenol has to be used in order to avoid a further reduction in the volume of the aqueous phase (Section VI, M) and the heating has to be limited to 2 minutes. *The total heating time should never exceed 8–10 minutes during the whole extraction procedure* (Section VI, N).

After the last hot extraction and the separation of phases, the aqueous layer is gently sucked off the top. For this purpose we use a syringe with a silicone rubber tubing attached which is made to glide down the wall of the tube. The syringe allows one to remove the total volume by precise, irreversible suction, without disturbing the layers by repetitive immersion.

A heavy interphase persisting after four extractions should be checked for its content of RNA. If appreciable amounts remain the RNA can be liberated by pronase or an 80–90°C heat treatment (Section VI, O).

The aqueous layer is reextracted with half its volume of buffer-saturated phenol for 5 minutes at room temperature. After centrifugation the aqueous layer is removed and transferred to polypropylene centrifuge tubes.

The RNA solution is now adjusted with a concentrated NaCl solution to a final molarity of 0.1. Two volumes of −20°C ethanol are added. The solution is mixed (we blow air through the solution with a long-tipped, cotton-plugged Pasteur pipette) and the RNA is left to precipitate at −20°C for at least 2 hours.

3. *Step 2*

The bulk of the RNA precipitate is brought to the bottom of the centrifuge tube by spinning for 30 minutes at 5000 rpm in a swinging bucket rotor. To remove all RNA we centrifuge a second time for 20 minutes in an angle rotor at 12,000 rpm.

The ethanol is gently poured into another tube (this allows one to control an eventual loss of pelleted material) and the liquid is drained without reversing the tube for 1–2 minutes onto a paper towel.

After addition of polyvinyl sulfate (Section VI, P) to 5 μg/ml the pellet is rapidly redissolved on a Vortex mixer with cold extraction buffer corresponding to about 10 times the original cell volume. Immediately after solution the buffer is adjusted to 0.1 *M* in NaCl and the RNA is reprecipitated at −20°C by the addition of 2 volumes of ethanol.

If a quantitative recovery of 2–6 S RNA is necessary or if the RNA concentration is extremely low the ethanol precipitations (Section VI, Q) may be replaced by repetitive extraction with peroxide free (Section VI, R) ether to remove the phenol.

4. *Step 3*

After pelleting of the RNA and draining the tube, the remaining ethanol is evaporated by short exposure to high vacuum. It is preferable that the RNA retains some moisture; once the ethanol odor is gone we stop the drying. Care must be taken to break the vacuum gradually in order to avoid losing the dry RNA.

The RNA is now dissolved after addition of PVS (5 μg/ml) in a minimum amount (final RNA conc. 1–2 mg/ml) of the appropriate buffer. Concentration and purity of the preparation are controlled by diluting it 50–100-fold in water and measuring the absorbancy at 230, 260, and 280 mμ. A clean preparation should give a 260:230 mμ ratio higher than 2.3 and a 260:280 mμ ratio of above 2.0. One milligram/milliliter of RNA corresponds to 24.0 optical density units at 260 mμ in a 10 mm light path.

The method followed so far should reduce the contaminating cellular DNA (Section VI, S) and protein to about 0.1%. In the case of certain cells (e.g., physarum) the preparation may also contain appreciable amounts of polysaccharides. We have never had this problem (compare Section VI, Q). The RNA may be further purified by the methods described below.

IV. Purification of RNA

A. Elimination of Nuclease and Other Protein Contaminations

Since traces of RNase are dangerous during DNase treatment (see Section IV, B) the RNA preparation should first be treated with Bentonite. The RNA solution is adjusted to a concentration of less than 0.5 mg/ml in 0.01 *M* acetate (pH 5) and 0.05 *M* sodium chloride; 0.01-0.05 vol. of a 2.5% suspension of Bentonite or Macaloid is added and mixed with the RNA for 15 minutes at 4°C. The Bentonite is eliminated by a 20 minutes centrifugation at 30,000 rpm. (This high speed is necessary to eliminate completely the fine particles which always contaminate large size Bentonite preparations. Macaloid can be removed at 5000 rpm.) The supernatant is carefully pipetted off, adjusted to 0.1 *M* in NaCl and precipitated with ethanol. If a DNase treatment follows the supernatant can be treated directly.

An alternative to this treatment is an incubation with pronase (Huppert and Semmel, 1964), which digests most proteins. The enzyme is dissolved at 1 mg/ml in 0.01 *M* Tris or acetate and preincubated for 2 hours at 37°C to destroy contaminating RNase. It is then added at a concentration of 50 μg/ml to the RNA and incubated at 20°C for 1 hour. Thereafter the pronase is eliminated with phenol according to Section III but the extraction is carried out at room temperature.

B. Elimination of DNA

The small DNA contamination remaining in RNA prepared as described above is unimportant for gradient, MAK column, or electrophoretic analysis. However, it disturbs hybridization experiments and has to be removed by treatment with pancreatic DNase I.

The RNA preparation which should be free of PVS can be treated at pH 7 in tris-NaCl or at pH 5 in acetate-NaCl buffer, both containing manganese at 10^{-3} *M*. DNase (RNase-free) is added at 10 μg/ml and incubated at 0°C for 60 minutes. The reaction is stopped by the addition of EDTA (0.5 *M*) to 2×10^{-3} *M*. If the RNA is analyzed directly by gradients or electrophoresis the DNase is dissolved by the addition of 1% SDS before the loading of the solution. If the RNA is destined to serve in hybridization experiments the DNase has to be eliminated by phenol extraction. The solution is diluted to a concentration of not more than 0.5 mg/ml of RNA, adjusted to 0.01 *M* acetate, pH 5, and extracted three times according to Section III but at room temperature.

These methods permit one to eliminate DNA quantitatively. Since most of the DNA is left behind during the extraction of RNA the amount of oligodeoxyribonucleotides produced by the DNase is negligible and does not necessitate a special elimination procedure.

V. Sedimentation Analysis of RNA

A. Choice of Sucrose Concentration, Gradient Buffer, Type of Rotor, and Centrifugation Time

1. Sucrose concentration

The choice of the sucrose concentration in the gradient is essentially determined by the density of the sample to be loaded and by the desired resolution. A secondary consideration may concern the time of centrifugation which at 25,000 rpm in 15–30% gradients is almost twice that in 5–20%. In our hands 15–30% sucrose gradients do not allow a higher resolution of RNA molecules with molecular weights above one million daltons than 5–20% gradients. Actually, probably because of the shorter centrifugation time (diffusion), we obtain a better resolution of 28 S rRNA and 32 S pre-rRNA with 5–20% gradients. Practically, we use this concentration for the sedimentation analysis of relatively small amounts of RNA and 15–30% gradients for preparative purposes since the sample density is in this case generally higher than that of 5% sucrose. The steeper 10–40% gradients are convenient if components with a wide spectrum of sedimentation constants are to be separated. Thus, it is possible to separate polysomes, ribosomes, and ribosomal subunits in a single run.

Other supporting media such as glycerol have been proposed for gradient centrifugation. They allow physicochemical studies in completely nonaqueous media. In aqueous media, however, we could not find any advantage of glycerol over sucrose (if the latter is free of RNase).

2. Buffer and Salts

Almost any type of buffer may be used for sucrose gradients. Originally, we used 0.01 *M* sodium acetate (pH 5.1) in order to limit RNase activity. Since the nuclease is no longer a problem, we use 0.01 *M* EDTA, pH 7.0, which eliminates all danger of RNA aggregation due to bi- or trivalent metal ions. Since EDTA at high concentration precipitates in 66% ethanol, we use tris 0.01 *M* (pH 7.0) and reduce the EDTA concentration to 10^{-3} *M* in cases where we want to precipitate gradient fractions with alcohol.

The salt concentration may vary from 0.01 *M* to 0.15 *M* sodium chloride. Since 0.5 *M* definitely causes aggregations of RNA we maintain a safety margin and work at 0.05 *M* in spite of a slight reduction of the speed of sedimentation of RNA at this salt concentration.

Bivalent ions as magnesium or manganese cause aggregates of RNA, especially of the giant molecules from animal cells. At 10^{-4} *M* no aggregation occurs. This concentration has been used in order to work at a defined magnesium concentration (magnesium is always present in RNA preparations) and to inhibit RNase. Its use has been found unnecessary by us.

Sodium dodecyl sulfate may be added to the gradient at a concentration of 0.2% if the RNA still contains some protein. In the presence of SDS the temperature has to be kept above 12°C.

3. Rotor Type

The amount of RNA to be separated and the desired resolution define the choice of the rotor. A secondary consideration may concern the time of centrifugation. With 5 ml gradients it is difficult to obtain the same resolution as with 12, 15, or 25 ml gradients. For analytical purposes the six bucket rotors rotating at 40,000 rpm are very convenient. They hold 12–14 ml and may be loaded with 50 μg RNA in 0.5 ml. Up to 250 μg of RNA in 1.0 ml may be loaded if a high resolution is not needed. Seventeen milliliter buckets exist on rotors spinning at 25,000 rpm. However, at this speed we get better resolution in 25 ml gradients (rotors with six buckets are also available). These gradients may be loaded with 200 μg in 1.0 ml for analytical purposes or with preparative amounts of 1.0 mg in 2.0 ml. For large-scale preparations the 60 ml buckets of the rotors spinning at 25,000 rpm are convenient. High resolution can be obtained with 0.5–1.0 mg of RNA in 1.0–2.0 ml. Sacrificing resolution one may load 4.0 mg in 5.0 ml of liquid.

4. *Time of Centrifugation*

Determinant are the molecular weights of the RNA species to be fractionated. As a general rule one may state that the 28 S (23 S) and 18 S (16 S) rRNA molecules are well separated if the larger component (molecular weight about one million daltons) has sedimented as far as two-thirds into the gradient. For the analysis of RNA species with molecular weights of more than one million (RNA precursors in animal cells, polycistronic mRNA) the 28 rRNA should not be sedimented further than one-third into the gradient.

B. Preparation of Gradients

Linear sucrose gradients are prepared by mixing a concentrated (20, 30, and 40%) sucrose solution in the appropriate buffer with a more diluted one (5, 15, and 20%) in the gradient mixer. The centrifuge tubes are filled to leave enough space for the sample and a 5 mm upper margin.

It is convenient to mix three gradients simultaneously using the three vein Perpex peristaltic pump which allows perfect equality of flow in all veins. The three parallel outlets of the mixing chamber are connected with heavy wall silicone rubber tubings which are inserted into the three channels of the pump. About 2 cm of stiff Teflon or nylon tubing are inserted into the ends of the silicone tubing and are clamped to the edge of the centrifuge tube. The reservoir chamber is filled with the light solution which is brought into the connecting hole by turning the stopcock quickly for 180°. Spilled over light solution is pipetted back into the reservoir chamber. Thereafter, an equal volume of concentrated solution is filled into the mixing chamber. A stirrer is inserted (magnetic stirring is most convenient) and put into action. The stirring has to be fast enough to immediately mix the two solutions, but not so fast that the solution from the reservoir is sucked in. The pump is started and the three veins are filled. This draws enough heavy solution from the mixing chamber to avoid a backflow of the denser solution into the reservoir chamber. The stopcock is opened under continued pumping. One has to control (by the Schlieren formation) the flow of the light solution into the mixing chamber.

The sucrose solution which is made lighter linearly is layered gradually into the centrifuge tube. No absolute prescription is valid for the speed of filling the tube. We currently use pumping speeds that allow us to make up one or three gradients simultaneously in 15 minutes independent of the volume of the gradient.

The gradients are mixed in the cold room, starting with cold solutions (Section VI, T). Sodium dodecyl sulfate containing gradients must be mixed at room temperature.

C. Gradient Centrifugation

The centrifuge is precooled to 2°C, or to 15°C if SDS is incorporated into the gradient.

RNA in the smallest possible volume of liquid is loaded onto the gradient which is already placed in the rotor bucket. In order not to disturb the surface of the gradient a long pipette is used which touches with its tip the gradient surface but not the wall of the tube. The trembling of the hand can be eliminated by pressing the upper part of the pipette against the rotor body standing nearby.

A thin film of high vacuum grease is smeared on the edge of the caps which are screwed firmly onto the buckets. After fixation of the buckets, making sure that the pinholes or hooks are connected on both sides, the rotor is placed in the centrifuge and centrifugation can be started.

D. Collection of Gradients

After the completion of the run the gradients are kept in the cold until collected.

Any method of fractionation may be successful from simple hand collection through a hole punched into the bottom of the gradient tube to the use of a complicated apparatus including optical density monitor and fraction collector. We will describe only one version of collection which we found to be convenient, precise, and reproducible.

The gradient tube is either left in its bucket or transferred into a well-fitting plastic or steel cylinder which is surrounded by a tray holding an ice-water cooling mixture. We withdraw the gradient through a long stainless steel tube of 0.5–1.0 mm inner diameter (for gradients of 12 ml and more), which is lowered carefully through the gradient to the bottom (Section VI, U). Two V-shaped cuts on opposite sides at the end of the tube allow the fluid to enter. During insertion the tube is held firmly along its axis in a well-fitting hole pierced through a round metal bar which is fixed above the gradient tube. (An appropriate size hypodermic needle punched through a rubber stopper may also be employed.) This device allows one to penetrate the gradient without disturbing the layers of RNA by vibrations of the steel tube.

The stainless steel tube is connected to a Tygon or silicone rubber tubing of not more than 1 mm inner diameter which is attached to a flow through cell placed in a recording spectrophotometer. Absorbancy is monitored at 260 mμ. This cell should hold less than 1% of the gradient volume in order to give a sufficient resolution.

The flow cell is connected by another piece of tubing which leads through a peristaltic pump to the collection end. A short piece of Teflon tubing which determines the drop size by its diameter completes the collection line. During collection the Teflon end should be held vertically since the drop size varies with varying inclination. We collect the gradients at a maximal speed which still allows the counting of the drops.

The gradient may be split into any number of fractions. To get a good resolution of minor RNA species (as the rRNA precursor molecules in animal cells) about 50 fractions should be taken. To resolve 28 S and 18 S rRNA about 20 fractions are sufficient.

E. Assay of RNA Concentration and Radioactivity

If the gradient has been collected without UV monitoring the individual fractions may be read at 260 mμ in a spectrophotometer. Fractions of 0.5 ml may be read directly in a semi micro quartz cuvette of 10 mm light path and 4 mm width using a special screen which limits the height of the light beam; 0.2 ml fractions may be read in a microcuvette of 10 mm light path and 2 mm width.

To assay radioactivity the gradient effluent may be collected directly into scintillation vials and counted after addition of 10 ml of a scintillator fluid miscible with water. However, this has a double disadvantage: (1) a high quenching effect resulting from water and the water miscible scintillator fluid, and (2) the inclusion of acid-soluble radioactivity.

Since mononucleotides and ^{32}P can easily diffuse down one-third of a gradient during the run, we prefer to assay RNA by acid precipitation.

The following method has been developed in our laboratory for the assay of TCA precipitable radioactivity in RNA. It has the advantage of allowing a high counting efficiency and an almost complete suppression of self-absorption (Scherrer *et al.*, 1966). To each gradient fraction 1-3 drops of a solution (1 mg/ml) of cheap commercial RNA or DNA (no protein) is added, and the fraction is precipitated by addition of an equal volume of 10% cold TCA. After 20 minutes on ice each fraction is filtered on a Whatman GF/B glass-fiber filter under slow suction (about 2 ml in 5 seconds). Tube and filter are rinsed twice with cold 5% TCA and once with ethanol. The filter is then dried and placed with 10 ml of P-5 scintillator fluid containing some solubilizing agent such as Hyamine or NCS in toluene (Section VI, V) in a scintillation vial made of plastic or at least having a plastic cap (translucency). The glass filter is then disintegrated by vertical shaking of the vial and dispersed throughout the vial forming an almost stable gel. This eliminates the geometry effect on counting, liberates the RNA from the inside of the filter, and allows the solubilization of nucleic acids. This technique allows a high counting efficiency and completely eliminates effects of self-absorption of RNA or DNA in amounts of up to 0.5 mg/filter.

In an alternative procedure the RNA precipitated with TCA is filtered on nitrocellulose filters and counted in a scintillation vial with 0.5–1.0 ml of P-1, a scintillation fluid without solubilizer (cellulose reacts with Hyamine and produces a yellow quenching color). ^{14}C or ^{32}P containing RNA may be counted in a gas-flow counter after gluing the nitrocellulose filters (glass filters are not suitable since the precipitate penetrates under the surface) to an aluminum planchet.

VI. Comments

A. The Rationale of Heat Treatment

The combined effects of heat and of a strong detergent immediately dissolve the nucleoprotein complexes of chromatin and ribosomes and dissociate glycoproteid and lipid which can be resistant to cold phenol (compare Westphal *et al.*, 1952, and Wecker, 1958). The formation of artificial associations of RNA, DNA, and protein during the initial denaturation by phenol is reduced at high temperature. The heat treatment furthermore degrades the DNA which passes into the phenol phase at pH 5 leaving behind the RNA. Thus, the heat treatment has the double advantage of increasing the efficiency of the phenol extraction and of eliminating DNA.

B. Freezing of Cells

In many animal cells (as erythroblasts or liver tissue) freezing activates the endogenous nucleases probably by the destruction of lysosomes. This effect can be limited by freezing the cells rapidly in isotonic solutions and by passing directly from the frozen state into a hot phenol-buffer mixture. Hard tissues and organs are best frozen at −70°C and pulverized in a mortar with Dry Ice. The powder is rapidly suspended in SDS containing extraction buffer and the hot phenol can be added immediately.

C. Choice of Extraction Buffer

We use acetate buffer to extract cells which contain little RNase (e.g., HeLa cells). We were more successful extracting RNase containing erythroblasts by the use of a buffer containing manganese and magnesium which inhibit to some extent the endogenous nucleases. However, it is more difficult to get a complete extraction from the interphase with this buffer. The pH 5 buffer is essential for the elimination of DNA.

D. Volume of Extraction Buffer

It is crucial for a complete extraction of RNA to dissolve the cells in 100 times their volume of extraction buffer. At higher concentrations the dissolved cells form artificial agglomerates of denatured protein, DNA, and RNA which can be broken up only at temperatures above 80°C. Furthermore, RNA precipitates to the interphase at high concentration (more than 0.5 mg/ml) and is lost. *The use of too small a volume of extraction buffer is the most frequent cause of unsuccessful phenol extraction.*

E. Detergents

The most frequently used detergent is SDS. It has the disadvantage of precipitating in the cold and in the presence of potassium ions. Sarkosyl does not precipitate in the cold but forms insoluble magnesium and manganese salts. Tri-isopropylnaphthalene disulfonate has been reported to inhibit RNase (Parish, 1967). It also forms insoluble manganese and magnesium salts. Sarkosyl and TND strongly absorb UV light at 260 mμ. We use almost exclusively SDS.

F. Suspension and Dissolution of Cells

During this phase the danger of breakdown of high molecular weight RNA is highest since the hypotonic buffer destroys lysosomes and activates nucleases. Rapid work is therefore essential at this moment. Detergents such as SDS do not inhibit completely endogenous nucleases.

G. TEMPERATURE

In order to eliminate the DNA the mixture has to reach 60°C during extraction and must be cooled to 0°C before phase separation. The crystallization of phenol after cooling of the extraction mixture is a sign that a low enough temperature has been reached. Crystals redissolve during centrifugation.

H. ALIQUOTS

Aliquots to determine the extraction yield are taken at this moment (rather than before the addition of phenol) in order not to prolong the time between the suspension of cells and the addition of phenol. In order to precipitate the RNA, TCA is added to 10% and ethanol to 80% (EtOH takes care of the phenol).

I. THE CENTRIFUGE TUBES

The centrifuge tubes are preferentially of polypropylene since cellulose nitrate is attacked by phenol.

J. REMOVAL OF PHENOL

Removal of phenol with a syringe may be inconvenient if too large volumes are present. In these cases we connect a long (6 inch) hypodermic needle or a stainless steel tube of 1-2 mm inner diameter to a suction flask and suck off the phenol with a water pump.

K. PELLET

The pellet on the bottom of the centrifuge tube may consist either of interphase material which has to be kept with the aqueous phase or of crystallized phenol. The latter can easily be dissolved by warming up the bottom of the tube with the hand or by quick immersion in the hot water bath.

L. INTERPHASE

The interphase has to be completely resuspended before the next phenol extraction. If it is very heavy some SDS may be added before resuspension.

M. Volume

The volume of 90% phenol added is reduced on subsequent extractions. Otherwise it will concentrate the volume of the aqueous phase more than is desired and a loss of RNA may result. The use of unsaturated 90% phenol has the advantage of reducing the buffer volume which has to be large at the beginning (see Section VI, D) and can be reduced by 50% during the extraction.

N. Heat Stability of RNA

Phosphodiester bonds are relatively stable to heat, but hydrolysis of RNA will inevitably occur on prolonged heating. Gordon *et al.* (1963) gave the heat inactivation kinetics in 0.12 *M* NaCl at pH 7 of the infectivity of tobacco mosaic virus RNA: 65°C gives 10% inactivation in 10 minutes, 40% in 20 minutes; 80°C inactivates 75% in 10 minutes, 95% in 20 minutes. In the absence of salt (10^{-4} *M* EDTA) the inactivation is four times faster.

O. Release of RNA Remaining in Interphase

Release of remaining RNA from the interphase may be achieved by extracting for another 15 minutes at 80–90°C (Arion *et al.*, 1967) with fresh phenol and extraction buffer containing 1% of SDS. The RNA released by this treatment is however largely degraded.

Alternatively one may precipitate the interphase with 2 volumes of ethanol, spin out the pellet, and dry it by an exposure to high vacuum. The interphase is redissolved in extraction buffer A and treated with 50 μg/ml of preincubated pronase for 2 hours at 20°C. The pronase is thereafter removed by three phenol extractions at room temperature and the RNA is precipitated.

P. Polyvinyl Sulfate

Polyvinyl sulfate is a polymer with detergent properties which serves as an inactivator of RNase acting through binding of basic proteins (Bernfield *et al.*, 1960). It is not specific for nucleases and binds to many cellular proteins. Polyvinyl sulfate is useful at low concentrations to protect already purified RNA. Used at high concentration it has the disadvantage of precipitating in ethanol together with RNA.

Q. Ethanol Precipitation

The ethanol precipitation not only concentrates the RNA and removes phenol and other small molecules but it also removes polysaccharides to some extent. RNA precipitates at lower ethanol concentrations than polysaccharides (Westphal *et al.*, 1952). Therefore, the alcohol concentration should not exceed 66% for precipitation. The recovery of 2–6 S RNA is not quantitative on ethanol precipitation.

R. Removal of Peroxides from Ether

The removal of peroxide from ether (always present) can be achieved by shaking the ether with a saturated solution of ferrous sulfate until no further brown coloration (sign for peroxides) develops. Thereafter the ether is washed with 10^{-3} *M* EDTA.

S. Elimination of DNA

The elimination of DNA depends on the combined effects of degradation by heat and of a low pH and temperature during the separation of phases. (The hydrophylic properties of DNA relative to those of RNA may be reduced at low pH. The additional hydrophylic groups in RNA may play a role if the phosphate groups which determine at pH 7 the solubility by salt formation are partially in acidic form.) The DNA has to be degraded by heat treatment at 60°C in order to pass into the phenol phase or interphase. At temperatures above 2°C during phase separation the DNA remains to some extent in the aqueous phase.

T. Cooling Gradients

Cooling gradients mixed at room temperature requires about 10 hours in a refrigerator (to reach 4°C). Cooling on ice may produce some convection along the tube wall. It is therefore better to mix the gradients from cold solution in a cold room immediately before the centrifugation.

U. Gradient Collection

The rationale for penetrating the gradient with a collecting needle from above (instead of punching it from below through the bottom of the tube) is twofold: (1) the gradient can be left in the bucket or may be cooled during collection; (2) it is important that the liquid is sucked up from the lowest point of the gradient tube. A needle punched from below always leaves a cushion of heavy solution at the bottom of the tube. This may disturb the recording of absorbancy in a high resolution spectrophotometer cell since Schlieren patterns are produced by remixing with concentrated sucrose.

V. Scintillation Counting

Toluene-soluble solubilizers such as NCS or Hyamine dissolve negatively charged macromolecules in toluene. This effect suppresses the self-absorption of tritium radiation which reduces the counting efficiency if more than 50 μg of material are placed on a filter.

REFERENCES

Arion, V. J., Mantieva, V. L., and Georgiev, G. P. (1967). *Biochim. Biophys. Acta* **138**, 436.
Bernfield, P., Nisselbaum, J. S., Berkeley, B. J., and Hanson, R. W. (1960). *J. Biol. Chem.* **235**, 2852.
Bray, G. A. (1960). *Anal. Biochem.* **1**, 279.
Earle, W. R. (1943). *J. Natl. Cancer Inst.* **4**, 165.
Gierer, A., and Schramm, G. (1956). *Nature* **177**, 702.
Gordon, M. P., Huff, J. W., and Holland, J. J. (1963). *Virology* **19**, 416.
Granboulan, N., and Scherrer, K. (1969). *European J. Biochem.* **8**, in press.
Huppert, J., and Semmel, M. (1964). *Biochim. Biophys. Acta* **108**, 501.
Parish, J. H. (1967). Personal communication.
Salser, W., Gesteland, R. F., and Bolle, A. (1967). *Nature* **215**, 588.
Scherrer, K., and Darnell, J. E. (1962). *Biochem. Biophys. Res. Commun.* **7**, 486.
Scherrer, K., and Marcaud, L. (1965). *Bull. Soc. Chim. Biol.* **47**, 1697.
Scherrer, K., Latham, H., and Darnell, J. E. (1963). *Proc. Natl. Acad. Sci. U.S.* **49**, 240.
Scherrer, K., Marcaud, L., Zajdela, F., Breckenridge, B., and Gros, F. (1966). *Bull. Soc. Chim. Biol.* **48**, 1037.
Schuster, H., Schramm, G., and Zillig, W. (1956). *Z. Naturforsch.* **11b**, 339.
Singer, B., and Fraenkel-Conrat, H. (1961). *Virology* **14**, 54.
Wecker, E. (1958). *Virology* **7**, 241.
Westphal, O., Luderitz, O., and Bister, F. (1952). *Z. Naturforsch.* **7b**, 148.

39. Fractionation of Nucleic Acids on Columns Built with Methyl Esterified Albumin Kieselguhr

Gebhard Koch,[*] *J. Michael Bishop, and Henryk Kubinski*

Institut für Mikrobiologie
Medizinische Hochschule
Hannover, Germany

Department of Microbiology
University of California School of Medicine
San Francisco, California

Department of Neurosurgery
University of Wisconsin
Madison, Wisconsin

I. Introduction

Mandell and Hershey (1960) described a fractionating column for analysis of phage and bacterial nucleic acids. The column is composed of diatomaceous earth on which methyl esterified bovine serum albumin is adsorbed (Lerman, 1955). The method was applied in Hershey's laboratory in studies on T2 and T4 phage DNA and on λ DNA (Hershey and Burgi, 1960; Rubenstein *et al.*, 1961). Owing to their different content of glucose, T2 and T4 DNA are eluted by different salt concentrations. In general the order of elution of nucleic acids by a gradient of increasing concentrations of sodium chloride is correlated with the molecular weight and the secondary structure of nucleic acids. Smaller nucleic acid molecules leave the column first, the larger ones later. Double-stranded nucleic acids are less firmly bound to the column than their single-stranded counterparts.

A properly prepared column works equally well over a wide con-

[*]Visiting scientist of the Roche Institute of Molecular Biology, Nutley, New Jersey.

centration range of nucleic acids. Analytical and preparative fractionations of nucleic acids are, therefore, feasible.

Chromatography of nucleic acids on methyl esterified albumin kieselguhr (MAK) columns has offered great advantages in studies on the biological and physicochemical characterization of viral nucleic acids and in investigations on the metabolism of virus-infected cells.

Many laboratories still follow the procedure as outlined by Mandell and Hershey. We will refer to some suggested modifications and mainly describe the technique as used in our laboratory (Kubinski *et al.*, 1962; Koch and Kubinski, 1964; Bishop and Koch, 1967).

II. Materials

A. Reagents

(1) Kieselguhr: Grade Hyflo Supercel from Johns-Manville Products Corp., New York, New York. Other grades and sources of kieselguhr can be used (i.e., Kieselguhr Merck, Darmstadt, Germany). They consist of finer particles. Higher pressures are needed to obtain sufficient flow rates. This may cause some disadvantages (Fresdorf, 1967).

(2) Bovine serum albumin Fraction V "for microbiological use" purchased from the Armour Laboratories, Chicago, Illinois, or from the Nutritional Biochemical Corp., Cleveland, Ohio.

The esterified albumin is prepared as outlined by Mandell and Hershey (1960):

"Suspend 5 gm albumin in 500 ml absolute methyl alcohol and add 4.2 ml of 12 *N* hydrochloric acid. The protein dissolves and eventually precipitates again. Allow the mixture to stand in the dark for '5 days at 37°C (Hayashi *et al.*, 1963)' with occasional shaking. Collect the precipitate in 250-ml centrifuge bottles, and wash twice with methyl alcohol and twice with anhydrous ether in the centrifuge. Evaporate most of the ether in air and then *in vacuo* over KOH. Reduce the material to a powder and store it over KOH. Failure to remove promptly the residual acid reduces the basicity of the final product. The material is readily soluble in water and is stable either in solution or in the dry form. . . The protein is used in the form of a 1% solution in water."

(3) Phosphate-buffered salt solutions: Prepare solutions with different molarity of sodium chloride (0.1, 0.4, 0.6, 1.0, and 1.6 *M*) all with 0.05 *M* sodium phosphate, pH 6.8 (pH adjusted in the final salt solution). Add small amounts of chloroform to prevent bacterial con-

tamination. Evaporate the solution before use by vacuum or by boiling and cooling.

(4) Filter paper powder: Whatman standard of Schleicher & Schüll 2043 or paper discs of appropriate diameter.

B. Equipment

(1) Columns: The fractionation procedure can be easily adapted to columns of different sizes. We routinely use columns with 1 or 2 cm diam, but smaller and larger columns were successfully used also. The simplest way to prepare a column is to use a straight glass tubing and two tight-fitting silicone stoppers with narrow glass tubing for the inlet and outlet. A tight-fitting porose polyethylene disc serves as a base for the column. Columns with built-in sintered glass discs are also feasible but more laborious to clean.

(2) Ultrathermostat: Haake, Colora, or other types. For analysis of RNA preparations the column should be kept at 35°C (Kubinski *et al.*, 1962) or 30–35°C (Yoshikawa *et al.*, 1964, 1965) by passing water from a thermostat bath through a column jacket. The chromatographic behavior of native DNA appears to be independent of temperature.

(3) Fraction collector: any type.

(4) Glass or plastic tubes: Wassermann tubes or larger ones depending on the amount of nucleic acids to be analyzed or fractionated in one run. One or two drops of chloroform added to each tube prevent contamination and bacterial growth and thereby degradation of nucleic acids. Small amounts of chloroform do not interfere with the biological assay.

(5) Device for control of flow rate: A peristaltic pump with changeable speed (Sigmamotor or Buchler) or air or nitrogen pressure can be used to control flow rate.

(6) Ultraviolet adsorbance or transmittance: A continuous recording device to monitor optical density (LKB-Uvicord, Beckman, Gilford, or Cary) of the column effluent is helpful in detecting minor components and less time-consuming than the determination of the optical density of individual fractions.

(7) Radioactivity: Radioactivity in individual fractions can be determined by standard procedures. To obtain a continuous recording pass the column effluent through a coil (0.5 ml volume) of narrow gage polyethylene tubing placed under an end window Geiger-Müller tube connected to a rate meter (Nuclear Chicago, Tracerlab) with an attached recorder or through a tube with plastic scintillator connected to a Packard rate meter.

(8) Refractometer: An Abbé refractometer is used to measure the refractive index of individual fractions. The refractive indices are converted to NaCl concentrations with the use of an empirically derived standard curve.

C. Preparation of Nucleic Acids

The preparation of nucleic acids by the phenol method and by other methods is described in Chapters 38-46 of this volume. While low level contamination of the nucleic acid preparation with protein does not interfere with the fractionation procedure, a high level of protein contaminant does have to be avoided. DNA from osmotically shocked phage preparations can be analyzed by this technique only if trace quantities are used.

D. Titration of Infectious RNA

A suitable method for the titration of biological activity of viral RNA is described in Chapters 14 and 18. No loss of RNA infectivity occurs by chromatography on MAK columns. Removal of nucleic acid degradative enzymes by binding to the plain celite layer has a stabilizing effect on the biological activity of the nucleic acids.

III. Preparation and Operation of the Column

A. Preparation of the Column

Kieselguhr is heated to 600°C for 60 minutes to destroy organic residue. This step is not essential, but its omission can lead to slight disturbances in the optical recording of the column eluate. Overheating of celite makes the material unsuitable for chromatographic purposes.

The finer kieselguhr particles reduce the flow rate of the column. They can be removed, however, by repeated suspension of celite and decantation of the supernatant after the coarse particles have settled. This procedure also removes burned organic material.

It is advisable to fill the outlet of the column with buffer before starting to build the column. Care should be taken that air does not enter the kieselguhr-albumin layers at any time during the preparation. To prepare a 1 cm column suspend 5 gm of kieselguhr in 50 ml of buffered 0.4 *M* NaCl (20 gm in 200 ml for a 2 cm diam column). Boil (to expel air from celite) and cool or gently evacuate in a beaker and withdraw 5 ml of the suspension into a separate beaker. Use 5 ml of the suspension to form the first layer in the column above a preformed paper powder layer. The paper powder must be soaked in the 0.4 *M* salt solution and should be free of air. The paper powder prevents celite from entering into the sintered glass disc or the porose polyethylene disc of the column and does not adsorb measurable amounts of RNA.

Excess saline to a level approximately 2 mm above the settled celite surface is sucked off the column by a peristaltic pump or driven out by applying air pressure of 3–5 psi. Add to the remaining 40 ml of kieselguhr suspension 1 ml of 1% esterified albumin solution, stir, and form the column by placing 5 or 10 ml portions of the suspension into the tube. The coarse celite particles settle first so that the individual celite layers become visible. Carefully avoid disturbing the surface of the preceding celite layer and sticking and drying of celite on the column wall. Excess saline is expelled as described above. Rinse all remaining celite from the column wall after each application step with the same air-free salt solution. Be especially careful after the last albumin celite application. Form the top of the column with 5 ml of plain kieselguhr suspension which was withdrawn at the beginning. The upper layer of the column formed with plain celite will adsorb trace amounts of protein in the nucleic acid solution and serves as a mechanical barrier preventing disturbance of the first albumin-containing layer during washing, loading, and the subsequent elution of the nucleic acids from the column.

Wash the column with 50–100 ml of 0.4 *M* NaCl containing buffered solutions or with solutions of other salt concentrations (0.6 or 0.65 *M*). It is advisable to use the same salt concentration for washing and for the succeeding loading of the column. The rate at which the column is washed is not critical. A pressure of up to 5 psi can be applied. When the washing fluid is sucked out it is important to prevent formation of air bubbles.

The column may be used immediately or after being kept at room temperature for several days. The column can also be reused under certain circumstances described below.

B. Operation

(1) Loading: The anionic nucleic acids are bound to the cationic albumin by salt linkages. The binding forces are dependent on the salt concentration in the column or the nucleic acid solution. In order to

prevent a strong binding of all applied nucleic acids in a narrow upper zone of the column (which may shrink and lead to channeling) two facts have to be observed:

(a) The nucleic acid concentration in the loading solution should not exceed 0.5 mg/ml (12 OD units/ml).

(b) For any given nucleic acid a narrow concentration range of about 0.04 *M* NaCl can be determined in which the nucleic acid is still adsorbed to a MAK column but not yet eluted. It is advisable when loading to use a salt concentration which is 0.05–0.1 *M* lower than the salt concentration by which the first nucleic acid species to be analyzed is eluted.

The capacity of a MAK column for binding of nucleic acids is limited. The optical density of the effluent rises abruptly if the columns are overloaded. The high molecular weight nucleic acids or the single-stranded nucleic acids which are more firmly bound will start to displace nucleic acids with lower molecular weights or with double-stranded structure.

The flow rate during loading is not critical. Relatively fast flow rates are tolerated and called for in cases where contamination of the nucleic acid preparations with nucleases are expected.

(2) Washing: After loading wash the column with 50–100 ml of the salt solution used for loading the column or with the starting salt solution used for the elution of nucleic acids. Fast flow rates can be used.

(3) Elution by salt gradient: The salt gradient is developed by placing 100 ml of 0.4 *M* or 0.6 *M* saline in a mixing vessel in which the molarity is slowly increased by continuous input of 1.0 or 1.6 *M* salt solution. The input of saline in the mixing vessel equals the output of saline from the mixing vessel into the column. The salt gradient is almost linear until the salt concentration in the mixing vessel has increased by two-thirds of the difference between the starting salt concentration and the concentration of the input saline.

(4) The effect of temperature on the elution pattern of nucleic acids: The chromatographic behavior of double-stranded DNA does not change with a variation of the temperature within the range +10–35°C. The elution of mammalian and viral RNA, however, is strongly dependent on the temperature during chromatography. In a series of experiments we found 35°C as optimal temperature for the fractionation of RNA isolated from poliovirus-infected cells (Kubinski *et al.*, 1962). The yield of RNA is lowered at all other temperatures and especially at temperatures below 35°C. The temperature during chromatography also determines the degree of separation of 16 S and 28 S ribosomal RNA and 35 S viral RNA. The separation of the two ribosomal RNAs

from mammalian cells is very poor in contrast to the fair separation of the ribosomal RNAs from bacteria. Yoshikawa *et al.* (1964, 1965) obtained similar results on the effect of temperature on the chromatographic separation of mammalian ribosomal RNA and high molecular weight cellular messenger RNA. One hundred percent recovery of both single-stranded and double-stranded pneumococcal DNA from MAK columns by gradient elution at +5–6°C was reported recently by Roger (1968). Chromatography at elevated temperatures (10–40°C) resulted in a lower recovery of DNA.

(5) The effect of the flow rate on the yield of RNA: The chromatographic properties of the MAK column vary somewhat when different batches of methyl esterified serum albumin are used. The optimal flow rate is dependent on the steepness of the gradient which is determined by the amount of solution in the mixing vessel (80–100 ml for a 1 cm column, 300 ml for a 2 cm column) and the difference in the molarity of the solution in the mixing vessel and the spender vessel. An optimal flow rate for the elution of RNA at 35°C lies between 10 and 30 ml/hour for a 1 cm diam column and between 20 and 50 ml/hour for a 2 cm column with the stated volume in the mixing vessel and a 1 *M* difference in the salt solutions in spender and mixing vessel.

(6) Stepwise elution: Some laboratories prefer to use a stepwise increase in the salt solution for the elution of nucleic acids rather than a linear gradient. The trailing of one nucleic acid into the later eluting nucleic acid fraction is minimized thereby. The separation of transfer RNAs is improved with stepwise elution (Sueoka and Cheng, 1962). The recovery of heat denatured pneumococcal transforming DNA from MAK columns at room temperature is also improved by stepwise elution (Roger *et al.*, 1966).

(7) Influence of divalent cations and chelating agents on the chromatographic behavior of mammalian RNA: Addition of 10^{-2}–10^{-3} *M* Mg^{++} to the load volume or to the gradient or to both shows no influence on the chromatographic behavior of RNA from mammalian cells. The same was found for the presence of chelating agents (ethylenediaminetetraacetate) in the 10^{-2}–10^{-3} *M* range.

(8) Reuse of columns: The columns can be reused. Small amounts of nucleic acids retained by the column during the first chromatography are eluted in a second or third run. The repeated use of one column is indicated, therefore, only under certain circumstances, i.e., for the successive chromatography of samples from the same or related material or when a slight contamination of the effluent by heterologous material can be neglected. The columns are washed between successive runs with the salt solution which is indicated for the load-

ing of the next nucleic acid preparation. Repeated exposure of the column to high salt concentrations leads to the elution of small amounts of methylated albumin from the column. Nucleic acids are less firmly bound and will elute earlier from used columns than from fresh columns.

IV. Chromatographic Fractionation of Nucleic Acids

A. Analytical Procedure

Methyl esterified albumin kieselguhr column chromatography is a useful tool to analyze nucleic acids of different origins with regard to their size and physical structure. Soluble RNA, DNA single and double stranded, ribosomal RNA, single- and double-stranded viral and virus specific RNAs can be separated from each other by gradient elution in a single chromatographic run. As pointed out by Mandell and Hershey (1960) better results are obtained, however, by two separate chromatographic runs carried out as follows: The nucleic acids isolated from cells are first passed into a column in 0.66 *M* sodium chloride. All high molecular weights are bound and fractionated by gradient elution. The effluent, containing low molecular weight materials and soluble RNA can be fractionated on the same column or a fresh column after adjusting to a lower salt molarity (0.4 *M* or even 0.1 *M*).

We will describe below the application of MAK column chromatography for the analysis of RNA from purified poliovirus preparations and for the RNA isolated from poliovirus-infected cells.

1. RNA from Purified Poliovirus Preparations

Analysis of RNA isolated from purified poliovirus preparations by ultracentrifugation has revealed a heterogeneity with regard to molecular weight (Holland *et al.*, 1960). Since it is rather difficult to remove all traces of ribonuclease from purified poliovirus preparations it is uncertain to what extent a partial degradation of RNA has occurred after or during the isolation procedure. To minimize this degradation RNA is loaded on a MAK column in 0.65 *M* saline immediately after isolation. Under these experimental conditions all RNA with a molecular weight below 500,000 will not adsorb to the column. Most viral RNA preparations contain low molecular weight nonadsorbing RNA (Table I). No infectivity can be detected in the low molecular weight RNA fraction. In some viral RNA preparations the adsorbed RNA is

TABLE I

DISTRIBUTION OF INFECTIOUS AND NONINFECTIOUS RNA IN DIFFERENT VIRAL RNA PREPARATIONS

Experiment No.	RNA in %		
	Not adsorbed noninfectious	Adsorbed noninfectious	Adsorbed infectious
1	19	0	81
2	1	0	99
3	21	0	79
4	62	13	25
5	11	7	82
6	8	27	64

further fractionated into a noninfectious and an infectious fraction. The relative amounts of RNA in these three fractions for six viral RNA preparations are given in Table I. The elution profiles from two viral RNA preparations are shown in Fig. 1.

2. RNA from Poliovirus-Infected Cells

While the replication of poliovirus in HeLa cells is not inhibited and not affected by the presence of up to 5 μg actinomycin/ml the synthesis of all high molecular weight cellular RNA is prevented. It is possible to label with radioisotopes exclusively virus specific RNAs. HeLa cells were infected with poliovirus in the presence of actinomycin and carrier free ^{32}P was added to the medium. Five hours after infection the RNA was isolated by phenol extraction at 60°C, precipitated twice with alcohol to remove phenol, and a 17 mg portion of this RNA was loaded in 50 ml of 0.6 *M* NaCl onto a MAK column 2 cm in diameter. The column was washed with 100 ml of 0.6 *M* NaCl and the RNA eluted by a gradient of increasing concentration of NaCl. The elution diagram is illustrated in Fig. 2. Two major types of labeled RNA are observed. The bulk of labeled RNA elutes at a salt concentration of approximately 1 *M* NaCl and represents the single-stranded infectious viral RNA. Host cell ribosomal RNA accounts for the optical density peaks which elute earlier than the single-stranded viral RNA. As mentioned previously the poor separation of the 16 S from the 28 S is typical for mammalian ribosomal RNA.

A second major peak of radioactive-labeled RNA is eluted at 0.8 *M* NaCl. This RNA fraction consists of double-stranded poliovirus specific RNA. The earlier eluting optical density peaks at 0.75 *M* NaCl represent a small proportion of the soluble cellular RNA (4 S). A third small peak of labeled RNA precedes or overlaps the intial portion of

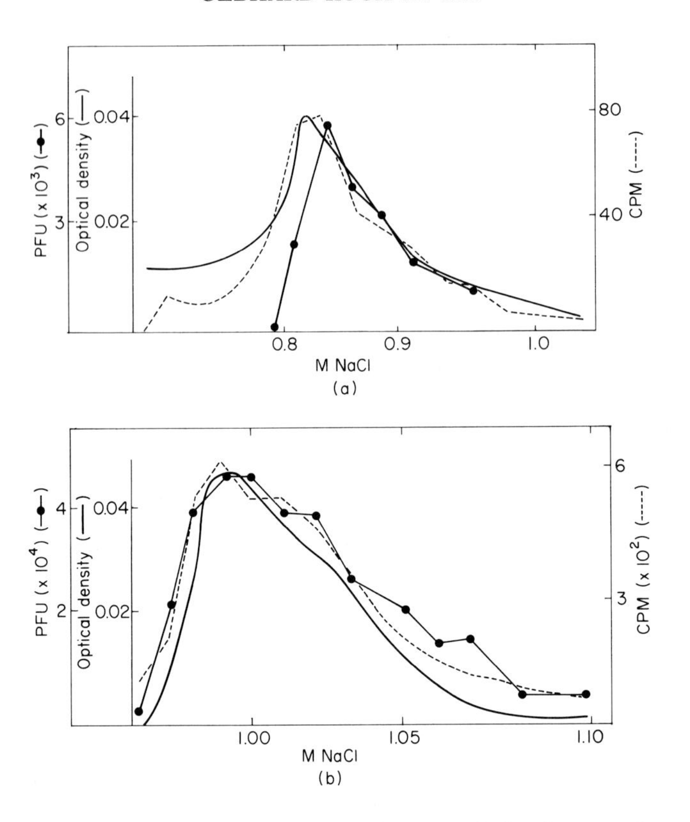

FIG. 1. Chromatography of RNA isolated from purified poliovirus. Concentrated suspended amnion cells, strain Fernandes (2.5×10^9 cells at 6×10^6 cells/ml) were infected with 10 pfu/cell of poliovirus, strain Mahoney, and incubated in serum-free, phosphate-free Eagle medium for 20 hours at 36°C. A pH of 7.2 was maintained by dropwise addition of 0.1 *M* NaOH controlled by a pH stat. Carrier-free ^{32}P orthophosphate was present at 10 μC/ml. Virus was purified following the method of Levintow and Darnell (1960). The RNA was isolated from the virus preparation by phenol extraction. Two hundred micrograms of viral RNA were loaded in 5 ml of 0.65 *M* NaCl on a 2 cm MAK column and fractionated by gradient elution (Koch and Kubinski, 1962). Samples from each fraction were diluted appropriately and the infectivity determined by the 1 *M* sodium chloride technique (Koch *et al.*, 1960). The elution diagrams of the RNA obtained in two separate experiments are shown in (a) and (b).

16 S ribosomal RNA. This RNA species is also virus specific and has been characterized as a multistranded poliovirus induced RNA. The multistranded RNA is obtained in higher quantities when the isolation of RNA is carried out at 20°C rather than at 60°C as in the experiment shown in Fig. 2. The multistranded RNA is strongly bound to the MAK column and the recovery of this RNA is extremely poor. Like

high molecular weight mammalian messenger RNA the multistranded RNA remaining on the column can be eluted only at high pH values. The eluting RNA is contaminated with methyl esterified serum albumin.

3. *Viral and Cellular DNA*

The high shear sensitivity of DNA was pointed out in the original paper by Mandell and Hershey. The higher the molecular weight of the nucleic acid, the later the nucleic acid will elute from the column. It is important therefore to avoid mechanical breakage of the DNA during isolation and chromatography. Some viral DNAs are considerably smaller than DNA extracted from the host cell. These DNAs can therefore be separated from cellular DNA on MAK columns. Dulbecco *et al.* (1965) used MAK chromatography to analyze the effect of polyoma virus infection on DNA synthesis in contact inhibited monolayer cultures of mouse kidney cells. The authors showed that polyoma virus infection leads to a marked increase in DNA synthesis. While part of the newly synthesized DNA elutes from MAK columns together with infectious viral DNA, the bulk of the newly synthesized

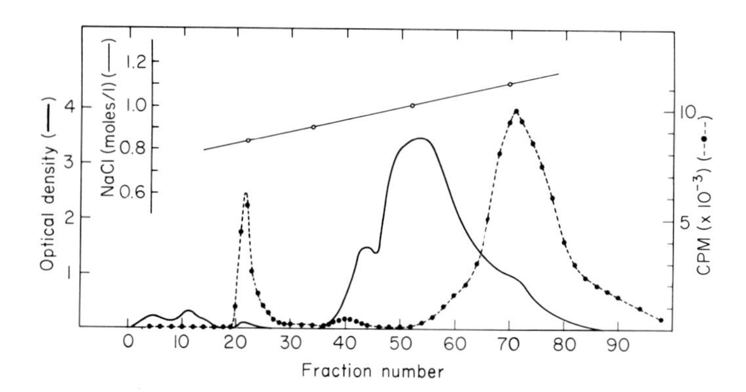

FIG. 2. Chromatography of RNA isolated from poliovirus-infected cells. Concentrated suspended HeLa cells (7.5×10^8 at 6×10^6 cells/ml) preincubated for 1 hour with actinomycin at 5 μg/ml were infected with 100 pfu/cell of poliovirus and incubated for 5 hours at 36°C in the presence of ^{32}P orthophosphate (25 μC/ml). The cells were centrifuged and resuspended in phosphate-buffered saline and the RNA isolated by phenol extraction, and precipitated by addition of 2 volumes of precooled alcohol at −20°C. After a single wash with a 2:1 mixture of ethanol saline at −20°C the precipitate was redissolved in buffered saline and the RNA (17 mg) passed into a 2 cm column in 50 ml of 0.6 *M* NaCl and fractionated by gradient elution (Bishop and Koch, 1967). Samples from each fraction were diluted appropriately for determination of infectivity using an agar cell suspension assay (Koch *et al.*, 1966).

DNA is eluted like cellular DNA. The authors suggested that the ability of the virus to stimulate the synthesis of cellular DNA may be related to its tumorigenic property.

Heat-denatured DNAs are difficult to process on MAK columns at room temperature (Mandell and Hershey, 1960). The partially renatured heat denatured DNA is so strongly bound to MAK columns that the elution of the DNA may require high pH values in the gradient produced by 1.5 *M* NH_4OH (Lacks, 1962). Circular viral DNA, however, reanneals completely and can be chromatographed successfully on MAK columns and quantitatively separated from cellular DNA (see Section IV, B) (Sheinin, 1966; Ben-Porat *et al.*, 1966).

Roger has reported recently (1968) that heat-denatured single-stranded pneumococcal transforming DNA can be chromatographed on MAK columns at low temperatures +5-6°C. The two complementary DNA strands are well separated and quantitatively eluted from the column by a salt gradient. This technique might prove to be useful for the separation of the complementary strands of viral DNA.

B. Preparative Procedure

A great advantage of the MAK column is its usefulness for preparative purposes. The analytical procedure has to be modified in certain aspects. Instead of fractionation of nucleic acids by gradient elution we make use of the finding that the adsorption of RNA on MAK columns is even more dependent on a narrow concentration range of salt than the elution of the RNA. Therefore, a considerably cleaner separation of RNA can be achieved by differentiating between nucleic acids on the basis of their adsorption properties instead of their elution properties. During gradient elution the early eluting nucleic acids always trail somewhat into the following nucleic acid fractions. In the following paragraphs we give a short description for preparative procedures.

1. Preparation of Single-Stranded Poliovirus RNA

Most investigators use purified poliovirus as a source for the preparation of poliovirus RNA. The purification of poliovirus, however, is a laborious process and not all the RNA isolated from purified poliovirus is high molecular weight RNA. An additional purification step for the RNA isolated from virus is called for (see Section IV, A).

As an alternative we propose MAK column fractionation of RNA isolated from poliovirus-infected tissue culture cells. It is possible to obtain high molecular weight single-stranded poliovirus in a one step purification procedure as follows:

First, 3–5 × 10^6 cells/ml are preincubated with actinomycin 5μg/ml for 30–60 minutes, and infected with 30 pfu of poliovirus per cell. The RNA is isolated by extraction of the cells with phenol at 60°C 5–6 hours after infection and processed as described in Section IV, A, 2. Two hundred milligrams of RNA can be fractionated on one 20 gm kieselguhr column in a single run. The RNA is loaded on an MAK column at a salt concentration 0.04 *M* below the eluting concentration of poliovirus RNA. This eluting concentration is determined in a previous analytical run with the same batch of serum albumin. The RNA is recovered from the column with a salt gradient or by one step elution with a salt concentration 0.1 *M* higher than the loading concentration. An elution diagram obtained in such an experiment is shown in Fig. 3. The radioactivity, the optical density, and the biological activity of the eluting RNA coincide suggesting that the RNA adsorbed and eluted from the column is a homogeneous RNA fraction with regard to molecular weight. This was further verified by analysis with the ultracentrifuge. Depending on nutritional conditions, time of incubation of the infected cells, and treatment with

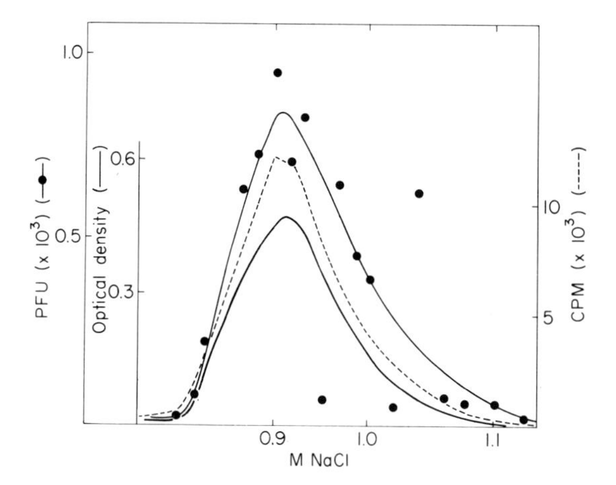

FIG. 3. Preparative chromatography of single-stranded viral RNA isolated from poliovirus-infected amnion cells; 8 × 10^9 cells at 6 × 10^6 cells/ml were infected with poliovirus and incubated for 18 hours as described in Fig. 1. Twenty-five milligrams of the isolated RNA in 200 ml of 0.78 *M* NaCl were passed into an MAK column. Three percent of the RNA was bound and recovered from the column by gradient elution (Koch and Kubinski, 1964). Infectivity was determined as described in Fig. 1.

actinomycin, the viral RNA obtained in this way may be contaminated with cellular RNA that is DNA-like in nucleotide composition and has the same molecular weight as viral RNA. The degree of contamination of the single-stranded viral RNA by cellular RNA can be calculated on the basis of the nucleotide composition determined on the basis of the optical density of the separated nucleotides and the content of radioactivity in the four nucleotide fractions.

2. Preparation of Double-Stranded Poliovirus-Induced RNA

The preparative procedure outlined above for single-stranded viral RNA can be adapted for the preparation of double-stranded virus specific RNA. The RNA isolated from infected cells is precipitated with ethanol (final concentration 70%) and then dissolved in 0.02 *M* sodium phosphate, pH 7.2, at a concentration of 2 mg/ml. An equal volume of 2 *M* NaCl is added and the solution frozen at −20°C, then thawed at approximately +1°C. A flocculent precipitate contains most of the cellular RNA (all ribosomal and messenger RNA) and the single and multistranded viral RNA. The 1 *M* NaCl precipitate is removed by centrifugation and the supernatant containing soluble cellular RNA, double-stranded viral RNA, and trace amounts of single-stranded RNA is adjusted to a salt molarity of approximately 0.6 *M* NaCl and loaded on a MAK column. Most of the soluble RNA passes through the column. The double-stranded RNA is eluted from the column by a salt gradient. A representative elution diagram is shown in Fig. 4. As in the case of single-stranded RNA, biological activity, radioactivity, and optical density coincide in one peak. A minor portion of cellular soluble RNA is adsorbed under the chromatographic conditions used in this experiment and is eluted as a heterogeneous peak in advance of the double-stranded RNA. The double-stranded RNA peak was shown to sediment homogeneously in the analytical ultracentrifuge and in zonal centrifugation in a sucrose gradient. The nucleotide composition is consistent with a double-stranded RNA.

3. Preparation of Viral DNA

The time course of the synthesis of polyoma DNA (Sheinin, 1966) and of pseudorabies DNA (Ben-Porat, *et al.*, 1966) has been followed by MAK chromatography. The DNA of infected cells was isolated at different times after infection, denatured by heat, and loaded onto a MAK column at room temperature. The viral DNA reanneals and elutes from the column, whereas the heat-denatured cellular DNA remains denatured and therefore is not eluted. The DNA isolated from extensively purified polyoma virus shows nucleotide sequence homology to mouse synthetic RNA (mouse ^{3}H-RNA). Fractionation of

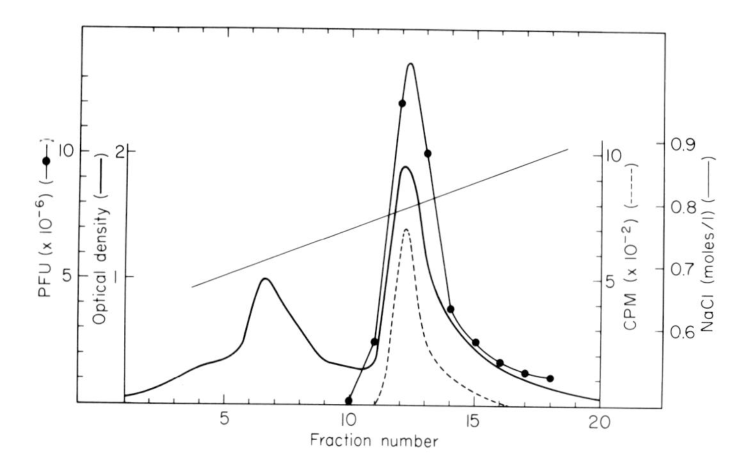

FIG. 4. Preparative chromatography of double-stranded RNA from poliovirus-infected HeLa cells. The RNA (500 mg) extracted from 1.8×10^{10} cells 5 hours after infection (incubated as described under Fig. 2) was precipitated with 1 *M* NaCl. The supernatant containing 100 mg of RNA was adjusted to 0.6 M NaCl and passed into a 2 cm column with a small quantity of purified ^{32}P-labeled double-stranded RNA to serve as a marker (Bishop and Koch, 1967). Infectivity was assayed as described in Fig. 2.

heat-treated polyoma DNA by MAK column chromatography produced an infectious DNA component with little or no detectable homology to mouse ^{3}H-RNA (Winocour, 1967). The author proposed that the observed homology to mouse ^{3}H-RNA may result from the encapsidation of cellular DNA fragments during the maturation stage of virus development. The preparation of polyoma DNA by MAK column chromatography from DNA which was isolated from infected cells and heat denatured may therefore yield DNA preparations which are more virus specific than DNA isolated from purified polyoma virus preparations.

V. Discussion

A. PRINCIPLES OF OPERATION

The chromatographic fractionation of nucleic acids on columns of methyl esterified bovine serum albumin bound to kieselguhr as developed and described by Mandell and Hershey (1960) provides a very useful tool for studies on viral and cellular nucleic acids.

The anionic nucleic acids are bound to the cationic albumin by salt linkages. The binding forces are dependent on the salt concentration. The nucleic acids are eluted from the column by a gradient of increasing concentration of sodium chloride, the order of elution of the nucleic acids is correlated to their molecular weight. The smallest molecules leave the column first, the larger ones later. Double-stranded nucleic acids are considerably less firmly bound than their single-stranded components. The chemical composition of nucleic acids (nucleotide composition, glucose content) has some influence on the elution properties. The chromatographically separated individual nucleic acid fractions are homogeneous with regard to molecular weight in the analytical ultracentrifuge.

The analytical results obtained with the MAK column as judged by separation of individual nucleic acid fractions, position of appearance in the elution diagram, and the height of their peaks are highly reproducible.

A properly prepared column works equally well over three logarithms of nucleic acid concentration, namely, 0.01 to more than 10 mg for a 2 cm column.

The columns can be reused. Small amounts of nucleic acids retained by the column during the first chromatography are eluted in a second or third run. The repeated use of one column is indicated, therefore, only under certain circumstances, i.e., for the successive chromatography of samples from the same or related material or when a slight contamination of the effluent by heterologous material can be neglected.

Individual batches of methyl esterified serum albumin may differ in their capacity to bind nucleic acids and in other adsorption characteristics which have to be determined, therefore, in a preliminary run.

B. Recovery of Nucleic Acids

The recovery of nucleic acids from the column is 80% or better. The recovery increases by repeated use of a column. The capacity of a column to bind nucleic acids is limited and decreases by repeated use. The recovery is furthermore dependent on the difference between the salt concentrations used for loading and eluting of nucleic acids. The smaller the difference in salt concentrations between the loading solution and the concentration necessary for elution, the better the recovery.

Certain nucleic acids are poorly or not at all recovered from a MAK column by a salt gradient, i.e., heat-denatured high molecular weight DNA (Mandell and Hershey, 1960), DNA with radiation damage

(Mandell and Hershey, 1960), high molecular weight double-stranded DNA with single-stranded regions like phage DNA concatenates (Smith and Burton, 1966), high molecular weight mammalian messenger RNA (Ellem and Sheridan, 1964), and virus specific multistranded RNA (Koch and Bishop, 1966). These nucleic acids can be eluted from the column at high pH values, they are then contaminated with methylated albumin.

The biological activity of viral nucleic acids separated and purified by column chromatography is not only retained but often enhanced (Kubinski *et al.*, 1962; Winocour, 1967).

C. Limitations of the Method

The most severe limitation of the method is the partial or complete retention of certain nucleic acids listed above. Gradient elution causes some trailing of the earlier eluting nucleic acids in the later eluting fractions, stepwise elution minimizes this trailing. Nucleic acids eluted at high salt molarities may be contaminated with trace amounts of methylated albumin. However, the plain celite layer on top of the column removes nucleases or other contaminating proteins.

REFERENCES

Ben-Porat, T., Coto, C., and Kaplan, A. S. (1966). *Virology* **30**, 74.

Bishop, J. M., and Koch, G. (1967). *J. Biol. Chem.* **242**, 1736.

Dulbecco, R., Hartwell, L. H., and Vogt, M. (1965). *Proc. Natl. Acad. Sci. U.S.* **53**, 403.

Ellem, K. A. O., and Sheridan, J. W. (1964). *Biochem. Biophys. Res. Commun.* **16**, 505.

Fresdorf, W. (1967). M.D. Dissertation, University of Hamburg.

Hayashi, M., Hayashi, M. N., and Spiegelman, S. (1963). *Proc. Natl. Acad. Sci. U.S.* **50**, 664.

Hershey, A. D., and Burgi, E. (1960). *J. Mol. Biol.* **2**, 14.

Holland, J. J., Hoyer, B. H., McLaren, L. C., and Syverton, J. T. (1960). *J. Exptl. Med.* **112**, 821.

Koch, G., and Bishop, J. M. (1966). Unpublished data.

Koch, G., and Kubinski, H. (1962). Z. *Naturforsch.* **17b**, 656.

Koch, G., and Kubinski, H. (1964). Z. *Naturforsch.* **19b**, 683.

Koch, G., Koenig, S., and Alexander, H. E. (1960). *Virology* **10**, 329.

Koch, G., Quintrell, N., and Bishop, J. M. (1966). *Biochem. Biophys. Res. Commun.* **24**, 304.

Kubinski, H., Koch, G., and Drees, O. (1962). *Biochim. Biophys. Acta* **61**, 332.

Lacks, S. (1962). *J. Mol. Biol.* **5**, 119.

Lerman, L. S. (1955). *Biochim. Biophys. Acta* **18**, 132.

Levintow, L., and Darnell, J. E. (1960). *J. Biol. Chem.* **235**, 70.

Mandell, J. D., and Hershey, A. D. (1960). *Anal. Biochem.* **1**, 66.
Roger, M. (1968). *Proc. Natl. Acad. Sci. U.S.* **59**, 200.
Roger, M., Beckmann, O., and Hotchkiss, R. D. (1966). *J. Mol. Biol.* **18**, 156.
Rubenstein, J., Thomas, C. A., and Hershey, A. D. (1961). *Proc. Natl. Acad. Sci. U.S.* **47**, 1113.
Sheinin, R. (1966). *Virology* **28**, 621.
Smith, M., and Burton, K. (1966). *Biochem. J.* **98**, 229.
Sueoka, N., and Cheng, T. Y. (1962). *J. Mol. Biol.* **4**, 161.
Winocour, E. (1967). *Virology* **31**, 15.
Yoshikawa, M., Fukuda, T., and Kawada, Y. (1964). *Biochem. Biophys. Res. Commun.* **15**, 22.
Yoshikawa, M., Fukuda, T., and Kawada, Y. (1965). *Biochim. Biophys. Acta* **103**, 383.

40. Procedures for the Purification of Intermediate Forms of Viral RNA from RNA Virus-Infected Cells*

R. L. Erikson

Department of Pathology
University of Colorado Medical School
Denver, Colorado

I. Introduction

In addition to the form which enters the virion at least two forms of virus specific RNA are found in cells infected with viruses that contain single-stranded RNA. Several techniques for purification of these double-stranded RNAs from such virus-infected cells have been published. In most cases the purification includes steps such as ribonuclease (RNase) treatment (Billeter and Weissmann, 1966) or precipitation with high salt (Ammann *et al.*, 1964; Baltimore, 1966) to remove the large amount of host cell ribosomal RNA present. The double-stranded replicative form (RF) obtained by these procedures is completely resistant to low concentrations (0.1 μg/ml) of RNase. However, a second form of virus specific RNA, the replicative intermediate (RI) is discarded or degraded during such manipulations (Erikson, 1966).

Purification procedures will be described that are suitable for handling the large amounts of RNA obtained from infected cells, but which yield both forms of virus specific RNA free of host RNA and the viral RNA that is originally in the preparation.

*Research supported by Grant AI 06844 from the U.S. Public Health Service and Grant E-389A from the American Cancer Society.

II. Experimental Requirements and Methods

A. Materials and Equipment

1. *Enzymes and Reagents*

Deoxyribonuclease I, electrophoretically purified (Worthington Biochemical Corp., No. DPFF); Ribonuclease A (Worthington Biochemical Corp., No. RAF); Phenol (Mallinckrodt 88% phenol liquified; phenol without further treatment is saturated with buffer immediately prior to use. Discolored phenol should be discarded.). Phosphoric-^{32}P acid (New England Nuclear, in 0.02 *N* HCl which is neutralized just prior to use); tritium-labeled nucleosides (Nuclear Chicago or Schwarz BioResearch, Inc.); sodium dodecyl sulfate (Sigma Chem. Corp.); all media for growth of bacteria were obtained from Difco. Medium for growth of animal cells was obtained from Hyland Laboratories.

2. *Columns*

In this laboratory we now routinely use 1.5 by 90 cm columns (Pharmacia Fine Chemicals, K15/90) for agarose columns. Other columns are obtained from the same source. Any column that has a small mixing space below the bed would be suitable.

3. *Pump*

Although all agarose columns are run with gravity flow it is desirable to control the flow rate of a cellulose column. For this purpose a Sigma Motor Inc. model T8 peristaltic pump equipped to provide flow rates of 0.05–60 ml/minute is used. It is suggested that polyurethane tubing should also be obtained from Sigma Motor for use with this pump.

4. *Column Materials*

Beaded agarose 2% and 4% were obtained from Pharmacia Fine Chemicals (Sepharose 2B and 4B). Cellulose was CF11 from Whatman.

5. *Glassware*

All glassware used in this laboratory is dry-heat sterilized at 375°F overnight or autoclaved for 30 minutes at 20 pounds pressure. In order to concentrate or store RNA, it is precipitated with ethanol at −20°C. Corex centrifuge tubes, 25 ml, with a screw cap (Corning No. 8446), are convenient for this purpose. Fractions from columns are collected in sterilized tubes (Bellco No. 1711, 12 by 75 mm).

6. *Fraction Collector*

An inexpensive and suitable fraction collector [the model AT equipped with a timer module and a lift off reel (No. 116) equipped for 90 12 by 75 mm tubes] is supplied by the Instrumentation Specialties Co., Inc., Lincoln, Nebraska.

B. Preparation of Infected Cell Nucleic Acids

All buffer solutions used in this laboratory are autoclaved for 30 minutes at 20 pounds pressure. The RNA bacteriophage R17 (Paranchych and Graham, 1962) and various suitable hosts have been used such as *E. coli* C3000 or *E. coli* $RNase^{-}_{10}$ (Gesteland, 1966) which was obtained through the courtesy of Dr. R. Roblin. RNA phage-infected *E. coli* were prepared as described previously (Erikson *et al.*, 1966). The cells were washed once in 0.15 *M* NaCl, 0.05 *M* Tris, pH 7.2, 10^{-3} *M* EDTA (STE) and resuspended at $1\text{-}2 \times 10^{10}$ cells/ml and lysed by the addition of sodium dodecyl sulfate (SDS) to a final concentration of 1%. The cells were then extracted with vigorous mixing on a vortex-type mixer at room temperature two times with an equal volume of cold STE-saturated phenol, and the two phenol layers were washed serially with another equal volume of STE. The STE (containing RNA and DNA) was combined and precipitated with two volumes of ethanol twice to remove the traces of phenol in the aqueous phase. Nucleic acids prepared this way from 400 ml *E. coli* (6×10^8/ml) may be handled in about 2 ml of solution.

III. Purification of Intermediates

A. Fractionation of RNA

1. *Precipitation with NaCl*

To ensure efficient fractionation at this step care must be taken to have a nucleic acid solution of OD_{260} about 100. This nucleic acid solution is made 2 *M* by the addition of an equal volume of 4 *M* NaCl and after 6–10 hours at 4°C the precipitate that is formed contains viral, ribosomal, and replicative intermediate RNA (Erikson, 1966). This precipitate is dissolved and again precipitated with NaCl to reduce the traces of DNA and replicative form RNA. The supernatants are combined, diluted by 50% to reduce the NaCl concentration, and the nucleic acids (DNA, replicative form RNA and sRNA) are precipitated with 2 volumes of ethanol. The NaCl precipitate is reprecipitated once with ethanol from STE.

2. *DNase Treatment*

Each of the above fractions is dissolved in 0.15 *M* NaCl, 0.05 *M* tris, pH 7.3, and 5×10^{-3} *M* $MgCl_2$ and treated at 37°C for 25 minutes with 25 μg DNase I/ml. Cold phenol is added and DNase is removed with three phenol extractions followed by serial washing of the phenol layers and precipitation with ethanol. The nucleic acid preparations still contain DNA fragments which are small enough, however, to be retarded on agarose columns.

B. The Use of Agarose Columns

Beaded agarose was introduced to provide a means for the fractionation according to size of molecules with molecular weights greater than 2×10^5 (Bengtsson and Philipson, 1964; Hjertén, 1962) and was then utilized for the purification of RI from infected cells (Erikson and Gordon, 1966). Either 2B or 4B Sepharose is used to pack columns under gravity flow until the column height is approximately 80 cm. Such a column should have a flow rate of 8–10 ml/hour with the reservoir placed 5-10 cm above the top of the bed. After the column is packed the top of the bed is protected with a paper disc, and the column should be washed with 300 ml of STE or until the OD_{260} is less than 0.05. At least 5 mg of RNA may be layered on such a column in 0.5 ml ($OD_{260} = 125$ units). We routinely use the conversion factor of OD_{260} $1 = 40$ μg RNA/ml. The sample is allowed to pass into the column, washed twice with 1–2 ml STE, the reservoir attached, and the RNA filtered through the column with STE while 0.5–1 ml fractions are collected. The RI and RF are found in the void volume of the column (Fig. 1). A simple means to determine the void volume of the column is by determination of the elution volume of intact phage T7 DNA (Faras and Erikson, 1969). Greater than 90% recovery of ribosomal RNA and intermediate forms of viral RNA is always found, as measured by optical density or RNase-resistant radioactive RNA recovered. Since the columns are used at room temperature and bac-

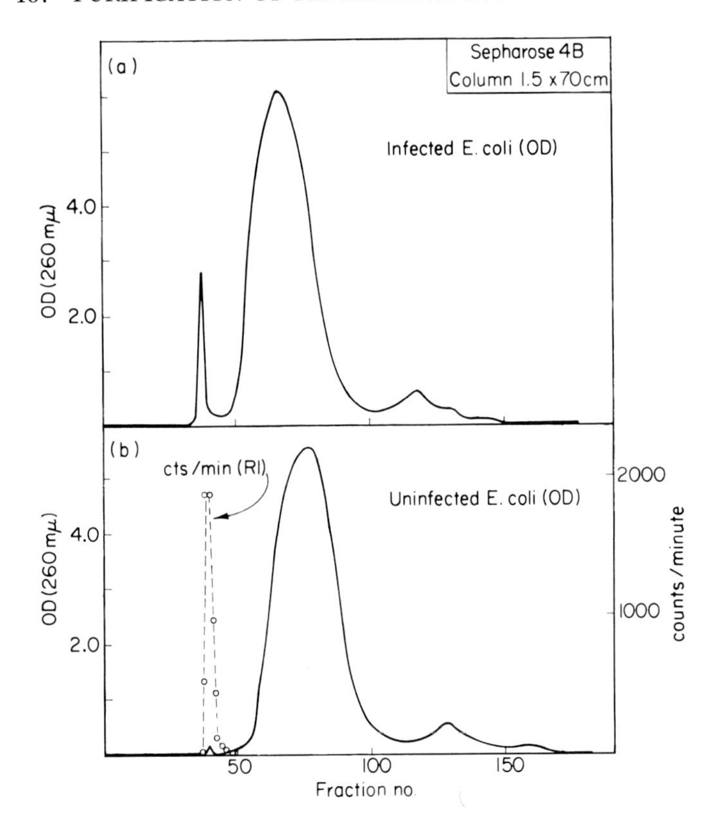

FIG. 1. (a) Elution of infected cell RNA from an agarose column compared to (b) the elution of uninfected cell RNA. In the column illustrated in the bottom panel ^{32}P-labeled RI, which does not contribute significantly to the OD, has been added to the cellular RNA to mark the void volume. In both cases, the RNA was prepared by NaCl precipitation as described in the text. If the NaCl supernatant is examined, analogous results are found with RF in the void volume.

terial growth will occur in a column containing STE, it is recommended that a column either be discarded after use or that buffer plus 0.02% Na azide be washed into the column and the column be stored until further use.

A comparison of the optical density profile obtained after filtration of the NaCl precipitate from infected and uninfected cells is shown in Fig. 1. Less than 0.3% of the uninfected cell RNA applied to the column appears in the void volume. In contrast, all of the RI from the infected cells that was applied appeared in the void volume. Therefore clean separation of RI or RF from ribosomal and viral RNA or sRNA and DNA fragments can be obtained by one passage through a column. An important aspect of the fractionation is that there are no losses of any types of intermediates.

Separation, in this case, is based mainly on molecular configuration. The more rigid RI or RF molecule is excluded from the gel while in this buffer the more tightly coiled, single-stranded molecules penetrate the gel. The small amount of RNA in the void volume of the column used to examine uninfected cell RNA has been shown to be ribosomal RNA aggregates which can be dissociated by heating at temperatures below the melting temperature of RI and RF which is 89° in 10^{-3} *M* EDTA, 10^{-2} *M* Tris, pH 7.3.

C. The Use of Cellulose Columns

Fractionation of RNA on cellulose columns was described by Barber (1966) and subsequently utilized for the purification of RF and RI (Franklin, 1966). The column (0.9 by 25 cm) is packed and washed with 0.05 *M* Tris, pH 7.3, 0.1 *M* NaCl, and 10^{-3} *M* EDTA (TSE) until the OD_{260} is less than 0.05. The reader should note the NaCl concentration because changes in NaCl concentration result in changes in the characteristics of the column. After the column is equilibrated with the starting buffer (35% ethanol:65% TSE, v/v) the nucleic acids are applied to the column in the same medium. In Fig. 2a a reconstruction experiment is presented in which purified RI, viral RNA, and ribosomal RNA were applied to the column and eluted in a stepwise manner as described previously (Franklin, 1966). This elution consists of 42 ml of the starting medium, 40 ml of 15% ethanol:85% TSE and finally 50 ml of TSE. The flow rate was controlled at 12 ml/hour by a peristaltic pump and 2 ml fractions were collected. DNA elutes at the first step, viral RNA and ribosomal RNA at the second, and RI or RF at the third.

The recovery of RNA from cellulose columns is about 75%. As shown in Fig. 2a, 7% of the viral RNA eluted with the RI in the first passage through the column as does about the same fraction of ribosomal RNA. For comparison, a mixture of purified RI, viral RNA, and ribosomal RNA was filtered through an agarose column and the results are shown in Fig. 2b. The results confirm those shown in Fig. 1 that less than 0.3% of the single-stranded RNA appears in the fractions that contain RI.

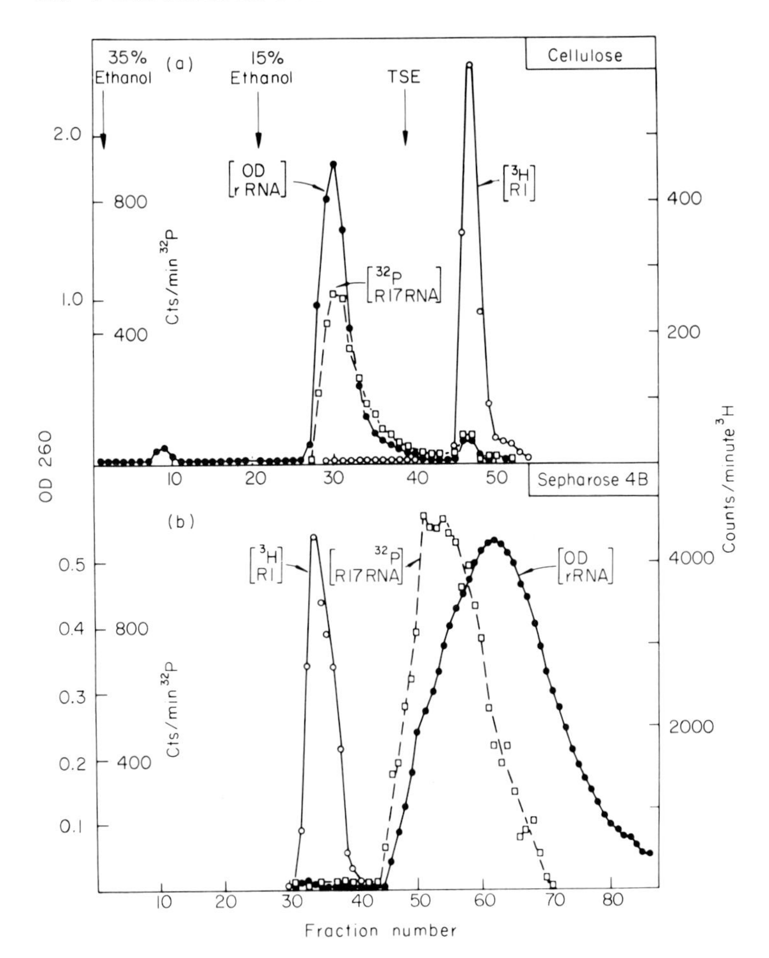

FIG. 2. Elution of a mixture of previously purified RI, R17, and ribosomal RNA from (a) cellulose column and (b) agarose column. The cellulose column was eluted in a stepwise manner as described in the text. Each change of buffer is shown by the position of the arrows. In the bottom panel the elution of a similar mixture from an agarose column is illustrated. The final fractions from the column are not illustrated. rRNA refers to ribosomal RNA.

IV. Comments

A. THE QUESTION OF EXTENT OF PURIFICATION

The extent to which a molecule is purified by any given procedure may be examined by reconstruction experiments such as those shown in Fig. 2a and b. In experiments of this type care must be taken to use enough of each type of molecule so that small percentages of contamination may be easily detected. It is obvious that a few hundred counts of viral RNA are not adequate to determine the contamination of RI if levels of a few percent are to be detected. Contamination levels acceptable for certain types of experiments are frequently unacceptable for other experiments and recycling may be necessary. Therefore, other techniques for the purpose of replicative intermediate purification or for use with RNA from virus-infected cells other than those described in this paper should be critically examined prior to use.

B. Properties of the Purified RI and RF

The biological and biophysical properties of the purified molecules have been extensively described previously (Erikson and Gordon, 1966; Erikson, *et al.*, 1966; Erikson and Erikson, 1967; Franklin, 1966, 1967a,b) and need not be pursued here.

C. The Purification of RNA Intermediates in Other Virus Infections

The agarose filtration technique described here should be suitable for use with RNA viruses if the molecules of single-stranded viral RNA present in the infected cells are small enough to be retarded by an agarose column. The available information on the elution of single-stranded nucleic acids from agarose columns is summarized in Table I. No information is available concerning the elution from cellulose columns of RNA other than *E. coli* and R17 RNA and therefore preliminary experiments must be done on the viral RNA to be studied.

The column procedures described here are particularly well suited for use when large amounts of RNA from infected cells must be examined for small quantities of virus specific RNA forms. Techniques that are well suited for microgram separations such as polyacrylamide gel electrophoresis (Bishop *et al.*, 1967) have not been demonstrated to be suitable for use with large amounts of RNA, although presumably they could be adapted for column-type operation.

ACKNOWLEDGMENTS

The author wishes to thank Dr. W. K. Roberts for a gift of mouse encephalitis virus and for suggestions on methods for its growth and the isolation of its RNA.

TABLE I
V_e/V_o FOR SEVERAL NUCLEIC ACIDS[a]

Nucleic acid	S value (in 0.1 M NaCl)	Molecular weight ($\times 10^{-6}$)	V_e/V_o percent agarose 2	4
Bacteriophage R17 RNA	27	1.0	2.2	1.6
Ribosomal RNA (*E. coli*)	16 and 23	0.56 and 1.1	2.4	1.8
Ribosomal RNA (mammalian)	16 and 28	0.56 and 1.6	2.5	1.8
Soluble RNA	4	0.027	3.2	3.0
T7 DNA (denatured)	65	13.0	1.0	1.0
Mouse encephalitis virus RNA	35	2.0	1.8	1.0
R17 replicative intermediate RNA	14-30	>2.0	1.0	1.0
R17 replicative form RNA	14	2.0	1.0	1.0
Avian myeloblastosis virus RNA	60.0	10.0	1.7	1.0

[a] V_e indicates the volume of buffer required to elute a given sample, and V_0 the volume of buffer in which a molecule appears that has been completely excluded from the column. Buffer=0.15 *M* NaCl, 10^{-3} *M* EDTA plus 0.05 *M* tris pH 7.2.

REFERENCES

Ammann, J., Delius, H., and Hofschneider, P. H. (1964). *J. Mol. Biol.* **10**, 557.
Baltimore, D. (1966). *J. Mol. Biol.* **18**, 421.
Barber, R. (1966). *Biochim. Biophys. Acta* **114**, 422.
Bengtsson, S., and Philipson, L. (1964). *Biochim. Biophys. Acta* **79**, 399.
Billeter, M. A., and Weissmann, C. (1966). *In* "Procedures in Nucleic Acid Research" (G. L. Cantoni and D. B. Davies, eds.), pp. 498-512. Harper, New York.
Bishop, D. H. L., Claybrook, J. R., and Spiegelman, S. (1967). *J. Mol. Biol.* **26**, 373.
Erikson, R. L. (1966). *J. Mol. Biol.* **18**, 372.
Erikson, R. L., and Erikson, E. (1967). *J. Virol.* **1**, 523.
Erikson, R. L., and Gordon, J. A. (1966). *Biochem. Biophys. Res. Commun.* **23**, 422.
Erikson, R. L., Erikson, E., and Gordon, J. A. (1966). *J. Mol. Biol.* **22**, 257.
Faras, A., and Erikson, R. L. (1969). Submitted for publication.
Franklin, R. M. (1966). *Proc. Natl. Acad. Sci. U.S.* **55**, 1504.
Franklin, R. M. (1967a). *J. Virol.* **1**, 64.
Franklin, R. M. (1967b). *J. Virol.* **1**, 514.
Gesteland, R. F. (1966). *J. Mol. Biol.* **16**, 67.
Hjertén, S. (1962). *Arch. Biochem. Biophys.* **99**, 466.
Paranchych, W., and Graham, A. F. (1962). *J. Cellular Comp. Physiol.* **60**, 199.

41. Cs_2SO_4 Banding of RNA*

R. L. Erikson

Department of Pathology
University of Colorado Medical School
Denver, Colorado

I. Introduction

RNA has been demonstrated to have a buoyant density of about 1.6 gm cm^{-3} in a Cs_2SO_4 equilibrium density gradient (Hearst and Vinograd, 1961). In contrast, RNA sediments to the bottom of the gradient at densities that can be achieved with CsCl solutions at room temperature and, therefore, in order to increase the CsCl concentration, RNA must be banded at higher temperatures in CsCl equilibrium density gradients (Kelly *et al.*, 1965; Bruner and Vinograd, 1965). Centrifugation of RNA at or below room temperature in Cs_2SO_4 eliminates some technical problems of handling the gradients and eliminates the degradation of RNA that occurs because of prolonged centrifugation at high temperatures in CsCl. However, some types of RNA precipitate in Cs_2SO_4 density gradients and no practical solution to this problem has been presented.

In this communication the use and application of Cs_2SO_4 for equilibrium density gradient centrifugation of RNA will be described. A more complete treatment of this subject with particular attention to DNA has been presented (Szybalski, 1968).

II. Materials and Equipment

(1) Cs_2SO_4: Cs_2SO_4, optical grade, may be purchased from S. H. Cohen Associates, Yonkers, New York. A saturated solution is pre-

*Research supported by Grant AI 06844 from the U.S. Public Health Service and Grant E-389A from the American Cancer Society.

pared in a sterile solution of EDTA-tris (EDTA 10^{-3} M + tris 10^{-2} M, pH 7.2).

(2) RNA preparation: RNA should be prepared from purified viruses as described previously (Erikson *et al.*, 1964) and RNA from infected or uninfected cells may be prepared as described elsewhere in this volume. (Chapters 40 and 38).

(3) Analytical centrifugation: Analytical density gradient centrifugation should be carried out in a cell equipped with a 2° or 4° 12 mm Kel-F centerpiece, and a minus 1° upper wedge window. Sets of cells with wedge windows for multicell operation are available from Spinco. For details of multicell operation see Szybalski (1968).

(4) Preparative centrifugation: Density gradient centrifugation in a preparative ultracentrifuge may be carried out using cellulose nitrate or polyallomer tubes in a SW39 or SW50 Spinco rotor.

(5) Desalting the RNA after centrifugation: The most convenient means of removing the Cs_2SO_4 from the band of purified RNA is by passing the pooled fractions through a G-25 column equilibrated with the desired buffer. Normally 3–4 ml of RNA in Cs_2SO_4 can be equilibrated with a new buffer by one passage through a column 1.5 by 30–40 cm.

III. Procedure

It is convenient to prepare a saturated Cs_2SO_4 solution which is then mixed in a 3:2 ratio with a solution of RNA in EDTA-tris. The mixture should then be adjusted to a density of about 1.62 gm cm^{-3}. Determination of the refractive index is a convenient means to check on the density. The refractive index can be related to the density of the solution with the following formula (Hearst and Vinograd, 1961):

$$\eta_{D}^{25} = 0.0730\,\rho^{25} + 1.2646$$

Usually 50 μg of RNA may be centrifuged in 3 ml of Cs_2SO_4 solution in the preparative ultracentrifuge with the remainder of the tube filled with liquid petrolatum to prevent it from collapsing during the run. The use of radioactively labeled RNA aids in the detection of small amounts of RNA that may form minor bands in the gradient. Preparative gradients should be run for about 72 hours at 30,000 rpm at 5°C. The time should be increased if the tube is filled with Cs_2SO_4 solution.

The usual means of fractionating the contents of the tube may be employed after the RNA has been centrifuged to equilibrium. Simple and convenient means for fractionation have been described (Fenwick, 1963; Szybalski, 1960). In order to determine which fractions contain RNA the optical density can be determined or an aliquot of each fraction can be precipitated with 5% trichloroacetic acid and counted if radioactively labeled RNA is used.

Recovery of RNA from concentrated Cs_2SO_4 is not possible by ethanol precipitation because of the precipitation of the salt. The RNA is most easily recovered by filtration of a 3–4 ml sample through a 1.5 by 30–40 cm column of G-25 Sephadex equilibrated with the buffer desired.

Analytical ultracentrifugation requires 0.8 ml of Cs_2SO_4 solution adjusted to the proper density and containing the RNA to be examined. One microgram of RNA per band expected should be used if centrifugation is carried out with a cell containing a 12 mm centerpiece. Centrifugation at 44,000 rpm should result in a nearly equilibrium position for the RNA after 24 hours. Forty-eight hours would be required to attain equilibrium when centrifugation is carried out at 30,000 rpm.

IV. Applications and Comments

One of the most striking demonstrations of the use of Cs_2SO_4 was presented by Shatkin (1965) who demonstrated that Cs_2SO_4-purified reovirus RNA would not act as a template for DNA-dependent RNA polymerase. It had been previously believed that reovirus RNA served as a template for this polymerase; however, these results had apparently been obtained with reovirus RNA contaminated with L cell DNA which must have been the actual template. Shatkin's use of Cs_2SO_4 is straightforward since DNA bands above RNA in the gradients at approximately 1.42 gm cm^{-3}. Therefore, if the tube is unloaded from the bottom there is little chance of contaminating the RNA with DNA. These experiments suggest that RNA to be used in experiments such as induction of antibody response or other biological functions in cells should first be purified by Cs_2SO_4 equilibrium density gradient centrifugation.

Cs_2SO_4 equilibrium density gradients have been used to demonstrate the similarity of MS2 phage replicative form RNA formed *in vivo* and by RNA replicase *in vitro* (Weissmann *et al.*, 1964).

Viral replicative intermediate RNA was first purified by Cs_2SO_4 equilibrium density gradient centrifugation (Erikson, 1966). However, only small amounts of radioactively labeled replicative intermediate can be obtained by this procedure because of the small amount of

RNA that can be centrifuged, most of which is host ribosomal RNA. In addition, the precipitation of ribosomal RNA and the trapping of some virus specific RNA introduce other problems.

Most ribosomal RNAs and some viral RNAs including those of tobacco mosaic virus and avian myeloblastosis virus precipitate in Cs_2SO_4. However, most coliphage RNAs, and double-stranded RNA forms, including phage replicative intermediate RNA which has single-stranded tails in addition to a double-stranded core, do not precipitate (Lozeron and Szybalski, 1966; Erikson, 1966). A greater degree of secondary structure is probably the reason that some types of RNA do not precipitate. The suppression of this precipitation with formaldehyde has been reported (Lozeron and Szybalski, 1966) but this is not a practical solution of the problem when other properties of the RNA, such as biological activity, are to be determined. Nor is the effect of formaldehyde on buoyant density fully resolved.

In conclusion, the technique of Cs_2SO_4 banding of RNA is indicated when the RNA sample may be contaminated with DNA, viruses, or proteins. As with DNA, double-stranded RNA may be separated from single-stranded RNA in Cs_2SO_4 gradients although special attention must be directed to the question of single-stranded RNA precipitation.

REFERENCES

Bruner, R., and Vinograd, J. (1965). *Biochim. Biophys. Acta* **108**, 18.
Erikson, R. L. (1966). *J. Mol. Biol.* **18**, 372.
Erikson, R. L. (1966). Unpublished data.
Erikson, R. L., Fenwick, M. L., and Franklin, R. M. (1964). *J. Mol. Biol.* **10**, 519.
Fenwick, M. L. (1963). *Virology* **19**, 234.
Hearst, J., and Vinograd, J. (1961). *Proc. Natl. Acad. Sci. U.S.* **47**, 1005.
Kelly, R. B., Gould, J. L., and Sinsheimer, R. L. (1965). *J. Mol. Biol.* **11**, 562.
Lozeron, H. A., and Szybalski, W. (1966). *Biochem. Biophys. Res. Commun.* **23**, 612.
Shatkin, A. J. (1965). *Proc. Natl. Acad. Sci. U.S.* **54**, 1721.
Szybalski, W. (1960). *Experientia* **16**, 164.
Szybalski, W. (1968). *Methods Enzymol.* **12**, 330.
Weissmann, C., Borst, P., Burdon, R. H., Billeter, M. A., and Ochoa, S. (1964). *Proc. Natl. Acad. Sci. U.S.* **51**, 682.

42. Determination of the Base Composition of Newly Synthesized RNA

Edwin D. Sebring

Laboratory of Biology of Viruses
National Institute of Allergy and Infectious Diseases
National Institutes of Health
Bethesda, Maryland

The base composition of newly synthesized RNA can be determined by exposing cells to medium containing orthophosphate-^{32}P and measuring the distribution of radioactivity among the four nucleotides of isolated RNA. By using this procedure, Volkin and Astrachan (1956) have demonstrated that the composition of newly synthesized RNA in bacteria infected with T-even bacteriophages is similar to phage DNA, and differs from cellular RNA.

The individual nucleotides have been separated from alkaline digests of RNA by several procedures, such as ion exchange chromatography (Midley, 1962), paper electrophoresis (Smith and Thomas, 1960), thin-layer chromatography (Keck and Hagen, 1964), and various combinations of these. We have found high voltage paper electrophoresis in a pyridine acetate buffer to be well suited for the precise determination of a large number of samples (Sebring and Salzman, 1964).

The distribution of orthophosphate-^{32}P in RNA is determined in the following manner. The labeled RNA is mixed with 0.5 mg of carrier ribosomal RNA and is precipitated by adding an equal volume of 5%

perchloric acid (PCA). The RNA is collected by centrifugation and washed with 2 ml of 2.5% PCA. After *carefully* aspirating off all of the wash solution, the RNA is dissolved in 0.25 ml of 0.3 *N* KOH and hydrolyzed at 37°C for 16–18 hours. The digest is then acidified to pH 2–4 by adding 20 μl of 2.5 *N* PCA. After cooling at 0°C for 15 minutes, the precipitate of $KClO_4$ is removed by centrifugation, and the supernatant fluid is applied to Whatman No. 1 chromatography paper in a 5-6 cm wide band, 8–10 cm from one end. Up to five digests can be applied to a 46 by 56 cm sheet of paper. The paper is placed on a sheet of polyethylene with the area containing the digests supported by a glass rod. The paper is then wetted by spraying with pyridine acetate buffer pH 3.5 (1 ml of pyridine, 10 ml of glacial acetic acid, 0.558 gm of EDTA, water to 300 ml) in such a manner that the bands containing the nucleotides are not wet directly but rather by capillary action. The area above the bands is then blotted with tissue paper to remove excess buffer, and the paper is placed in a Gilson Model D Electrophorater containing the same buffer which is overlaid with Varsol. The nucleotides are separated by electrophoresis at 3000 V for 70 minutes. After air drying, the ultraviolet absorbing pyridine is removed by exposing the paper for 20 minutes to steam at atmospheric pressure in an autoclave. The individual nucleotide bands are then located under ultraviolet light. An example of the separation is shown in Fig. 1.

For the determination of the radioactivity associated with each nucleotide, the bands are cut out, folded once, and placed in liquid scintillation vials. Scintillation fluid (4 gm of PPO and 0.2 gm of POPOP/liter of toluene) is added and the samples are counted in a liquid scintillation spectrophotometer. The count rate is not affected by the area or the position of the paper as long as the paper is completely immersed in scintillation fluid.

When 17 different samples of RNA were analyzed in duplicate, the standard deviation was ±1.0%, and the maximum deviation was 3.3%.

In order to obtain reproducible results, especially with RNA that has been labeled for a short time period, it is important that the RNA preparation be free of radioactive low molecular weight contaminants. Repeated precipitation of RNA with 65% ethanol is not sufficient to remove all radioactive contaminants. RNA can be obtained in a suitable form for nucleotide analysis by passing the RNA sample in 1–2 ml of 0.1 *N* NaCl-0.01 *N* sodium acetate, pH 5.1, over a 2 by 25 cm column of Sephadex G-25, equilibrated with the same buffer. Samples of RNA eluted from methylated albumin kieselguhr (MAK) columns are also suitable for analysis.

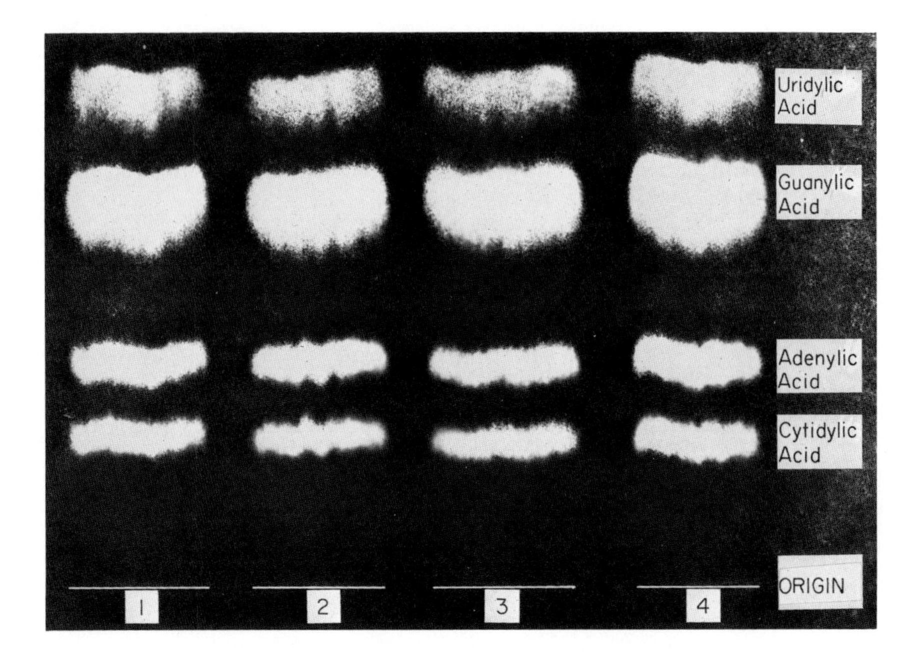

FIG. 1. A photograph made under ultraviolet light after separation of the ribonucleotides in four RNA samples. Details are given in the text.

REFERENCES

Keck, K., and Hagen, U. (1964). *Biochim. Biophys. Acta* **87**, 685.

Midgley, J. E. M. (1962). *Biochim. Biophys. Acta* **61**, 513.

Sebring, E. D., and Salzman, N. P. (1964). *Anal. Biochem.* **8**, 126–129.

Smith, I., and Thomas, M. J. (1960). *In* "Chromatographic and Electrophoretic Techniques" (I. Smith, ed.), Vol. II, p. 31. Wiley (Interscience), New York.

Volkin, E., and Astrachan, L. (1956). *Virology* **2**, 149.

43. Use of DNA-RNA and DNA-DNA Hybridization on Nitrocellulose Membranes in Virus Research*

Maurice Green, Kei Fujinaga, and Magdalena Piña

Institute for Molecular Virology
Saint Louis University School of Medicine
Saint Louis, Missouri

I. Introduction

The application of nucleic acid hybridization techniques of high sensitivity and specificity to virology has proved very useful in studying numerous basic problems. Before the development of hybridization methodology, direct studies on viral nucleic acid synthesis and viral gene transcription were quite limited, especially for most animal virus-cell systems in which virus specific macromolecules represent less than a few percent of the mass of the infected cell. Information about viral nucleic acid synthesis was obtained mainly in systems where intracellular viral nucleic acids could be distinguished from host cell nucleic acid by their unique properties such as unusual bases, high buoyant density, infectivity or ability to be synthesized in the presence of actinomycin D. Now quantitative measurements on the

*This work was supported by U.S. Public Health Service Grant AI-01725, contract PH-43-64-928 from the National Institute of Allergy and Infectious Diseases, and contract PH-43-67-692 from the National Cancer Institute. One of the authors (M.G.) is a Research Career Awardee (5-K6-AI-4739) of the National Institutes of Health.

synthesis of viral nucleic acid and viral mRNA molecules can be performed with almost any system if the purified viral genome is available as a reagent for hybridization measurements.

Hybridization (or annealing) refers to the specific interaction between two polynucleotide strands by detailed complementary base pairing. This reaction provides one of the few methods available for studying base sequence homology among nucleic acids which carry genetic information in cells and viruses. Three types of hybridization reactions are in use: DNA-RNA, DNA-DNA, and RNA-RNA hybridization.

In this section, we present (1) a detailed description of DNA-RNA and DNA-DNA hybridization procedures with documentation of the main parameters of the hybridization reactions, and (2) a brief description of applications to problems in animal virology. The DNA-RNA procedure is based on the method of Gillespie and Spiegelman (1965) in which one of the reactants, denatured DNA, is immobilized on a nitrocellulose membrane filter. The modifications of the Gillespie and Spiegelman method, introduced by Warnaar and Cohen (1966), is used for DNA-DNA hybridization. These procedures were established by the above authors using bacterial and bacteriophage nucleic acids. We have applied these methods, with appropriate modifications, to animal virus and mammalian cell nucleic acids. With these techniques, we have studied viral nucleic acid synthesis in virus-infected and transformed animal cells and also base sequence homology among viral DNAs and among viral specific RNAs (Thomas and Green, 1966; Piña and Green, 1968; Fujinaga and Green, 1966, 1967a,b, 1968). These techniques were found to be sensitive, specific, reproducible, and convenient for carrying out large numbers of hybridization reactions at the same time.

II. Materials

A. Reagents

(1) 20 × SSC,* 3.0 *M* NaCl plus 0.3 *M* trisodium citrate: Used after dilution to 0.1 × SSC as a solvent for RNA and DNA. Used after dilution to 2 × SSC for washing filters and to 2 × SSC or 4 × SSC for the hybridization solution.

*Abbreviations: SSC, standard saline citrate = 0.15 *M* NaCl-0.015 *M* trisodium citrate; SDS, sodium dodecyl sulfate; and Ad, adenovirus.

(2) 1.0 *N* NaOH: Used to denature DNA.

(3) 1.0 *N* HCl: Used to neutralize solutions of alkali-denatured DNA.

(4) SDS, 5% (Fisher Scientific Co. U.S.P.): SDS was recrystallized from hot ethanol. Used in the hybridization solution (final concentration 0.1%) to reduce radioactive background levels and to inhibit the action of contaminating nucleases on radioactive RNA.

(5) Ribonuclease (Sigma Chemical Corp.): Bovine pancreatic RNase A, 5 × crystallized: Stock solution, 1 mg/ml in water, heated at 90°C for 10 minutes to inactivate any contaminating DNase. Diluted 1 to 50 in 2 × SSC to give a solution of 20 μg/ml for removing unpaired RNA fragments from DNA-RNA hybrids.

(6) 0.003 *M* tris buffer, pH 9.2: Stock solution of 2 *M* tris(hydroxymethyl)aminomethane when diluted to 0.003 *M* has a pH of 9.2 at 25°C.

B. Equipment

1. pH meter, for Alkali Denaturation of DNA

The Metrohm E-300 pH meter equipped with a combination universal electrode with low sodium error (type U) requires no correction at pH 12.8. Any pH meter with a suitable electrode and corrections for sodium ion error should be satisfactory.

2. Vacuum Filtration Apparatus for Immobilizing DNA on Membrane Filters and Washing Filters

For large numbers of hybridization reactions it is convenient to use a vacuum filtration apparatus which holds multiple membrane filters. We routinely use a 30 unit filtration setup, fabricated by our machine shop, which consists of a vacuum tight stainless steel pan with a removable plastic top lid holding 30 stainless steel grids. The nitrocellulose membrane filters are placed on top of the grids and carefully covered with stainless steel cylinders. After applying a vacuum, 10 ml amounts of buffer or DNA solution are added to each cylinder and rapidly passed through the filter. Filtration setups are commercially available from several sources.

3. Sonic Oscillator for Fragmentation of DNA

A Raytheon DF-101, 10 kc sonic oscillator is used for fragmentation of labeled viral and cellular DNA.

III. DNA-RNA Hybridization Procedure

The procedure is based on that described by Gillespie and Spiegelman (1965) in which radioactive bacterial RNA in solution is hybridized with denatured bacterial DNA immobilized on a nitrocellulose membrane filter. The conditions described here are for the optimal detection of complementary RNA in solutions using high ratios of immobilized DNA to RNA in solution.

A. Immobilization of Denatured Viral DNA on Nitrocellulose Membrane Filters

Native viral or cellular DNA in 0.1 × SSC is made up to 20 ml with 0.1 × SSC (viral DNA at 3 μg/ml or less), stirred with a magnetic bar, and denatured by the slow addition of 1.0 *N* NaOH until pH 12.8 is reached (about 2.3 ml of alkali). After standing at room temperature for 10 minutes, 1 *N* HCl is added carefully to bring the pH to 6.8–7.2. Five milliters of 20 × SSC and a volume of 4 × SSC are added so that 10 ml of solution contain the desired amount of DNA for each filter. Schleicher and Schuell type B-6, 25 mm membrane filters are soaked in 4 × SSC for at least 20 minutes and washed with 10 ml of 4 × SSC by suction filtration. Ten milliliter amounts of the denatured viral DNA are passed through each filter under suction and the filters are washed with five 10 ml amounts of 4 × SSC. The filters are placed in individual glass scintillation vials (28 mm diam), dried at room temperature for at least 4 hours, and at 80°C for 4 hours *in vacuo*. The DNA filters are stored in a vacuum desiccator at 4°C and used within one month.

B. Hybridization Reaction

To each DNA filter is added 1.0 ml of radioactive RNA in 4 × SSC containing 0.1% SDS. Usually duplicate DNA-containing filters and one empty filter are incubated with each RNA preparation. It is desirable to check the level of nonspecific binding of labeled RNA preparations also by using filters containing heterologous DNA such as bacterial or bacteriophage DNA. Vials are tightly capped with polyethylene screw caps to prevent evaporation and incubated at 66°C for 14–16 hours, or longer periods if necessary, with occasional stirring (vials should be retightened after about 30 minutes of incubation). Each filter is carefully removed from the vial and rinsed through two beakers containing 300 ml each of 2 × SSC (the 2 × SSC is changed every 10 filters). The filters are mounted on a vacuum filtration apparatus, washed with five 10 ml amounts of 2 × SSC, inverted, and rewashed with five 10 ml amounts of 2 × SSC. The filters are then transferred to new scintillation vials, incubated in 5 ml of 2 × SSC containing 20 μg/ml of RNase at room temperature for 1 hour, and washed again as described above. The filters are dried at 80°C for 1 hour and counted in 10 ml of scintillation fluid (4 gm of 2,5-bis[2-(5-*tert*-butylbenzoxazolyl)]-2-thiophene per liter of toluene) using a Packard or Beckman scintillation spectrometer.

C. Characteristics of the DNA-RNA Hybridization Reaction

1. *Efficiency of Immobilization of DNA on Membrane Filters*

Viral DNA (Ad 2 and 7) and mammalian cell DNA (Ad 12 hamster tumor cells) are efficiently immobilized (95–100%) on membrane filters (Table I) under the conditions described above.

2. *Time Course of Hybridization*

Gillespie and Spiegelman (1965) reported that maximum hybridization of bacterial DNA and RNA occurs at 2–10 hours, depending upon the ratio of DNA to RNA. As shown in Fig. 1, the reactions between Ad 12 DNA (3 μg) and labeled RNA from Ad 12 transformed cells is

TABLE I
Efficiency of Immobilization of DNA on Membrane Filters[a]

DNA from	Label	μg DNA/ filter	Counts/minute added/filter	Counts/minute immobilized/filter[b]	Percent immobilized
Ad 2[c]	^{32}P	5	375	354	94
Ad 7[c]	^{32}P	5	418	412	99
Ad 12 hamster tumor cell[d]	^{3}H	50	1288	1295	100
Ad 12 hamster tumor cell[e]	^{3}H	50	1114	1086	97

[a] From Fujinaga and Green (1969).
[b] Determined in duplicate.
[c] Viral DNA extracted from purified adenovirus by the method of Green and Piña (1963, 1964).
[d] DNA prepared from Ad 12 hamster tumor cell line by the method of Marmur (1961) and further purified by CsCl density-gradient centrifugation.
[e] DNA prepared from an Ad 12 hamster tumor cell line by the method of Winocour (1965).

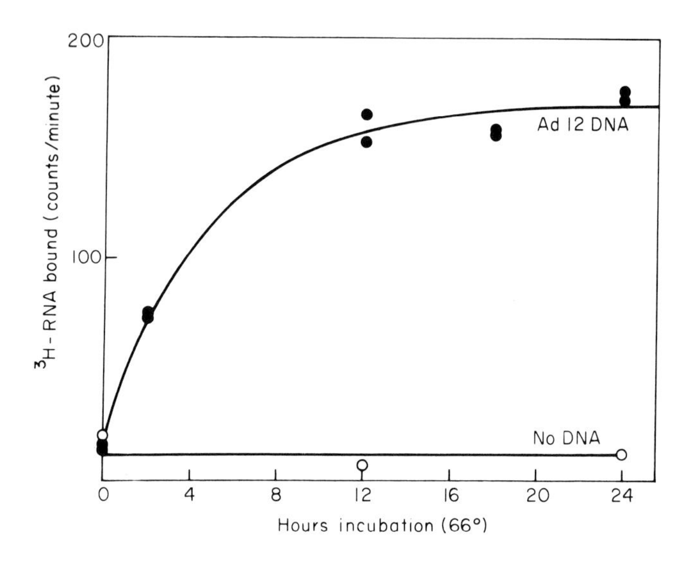

FIG. 1. Time course of DNA-RNA hybrid formation. DNA filters, containing 3 μg of Ad 12 DNA, were incubated with 1 ml of ^{3}H-RNA (62,000 counts/minute) from polyribosomes of Ad 12 transformed hamster embryo cells labeled with uridine-^{3}H (4 μC/ml, 20 C/m*M*) for 180 minutes (Green and Fujinaga, 1966).

complete within 12 hours; thus 14–16 hours are routinely used for this type of analysis in which high ratios of DNA to RNA are used for the optimal detection of complementary RNA in solution.

The time required for maximum hybridization is a function of not only the amount but also the number of different nucleotide sequences represented per microgram of DNA and RNA reactants, and therefore should be determined for each DNA–RNA system.

3. *Ratio of DNA to RNA*

The optimal ratio of DNA to RNA and amount of each reactant depend upon the purpose of the hybridization experiment. For example, to measure the amount of complementary RNA present in an RNA preparation, sufficient DNA must be present to bind all available complementary RNA. To determine this level, membranes containing increasing amounts of DNA are incubated with a fixed amount of labeled RNA. As shown in Fig. 2, maximum detection of complementary RNA is obtained with less than 2 μg of Ad 12 DNA using an input of 80,000 counts/minute of labeled polyribosomal RNA from Ad 12 transformed cells. Therefore, 3 μg of DNA are used in this experimental system for the optimal detection of complementary RNA. At this level, binding of complementary RNA is a linear function of input RNA up to at least 300,000 counts/minute. The amount of DNA required for different DNA-RNA reaction systems will depend upon the size of the DNA genome, and the specific activity, number, and distribution of different complementary RNA molecules in the RNA preparation. Each system therefore must be separately calibrated.

4. *Efficiency of Hybridization*

As shown in Table II, 70–80% of adenovirus specific RNA, after purification by several cycles of hybrid formation and elution, hybridizes with homologous DNA. Thus, hybrid formation is a very efficient means for detecting and quantitating complementary RNA.

5. *Purity of DNA and RNA*

DNA and RNA of high purity are required for hybridization analysis, but the absolute degree of purity needed depends upon the

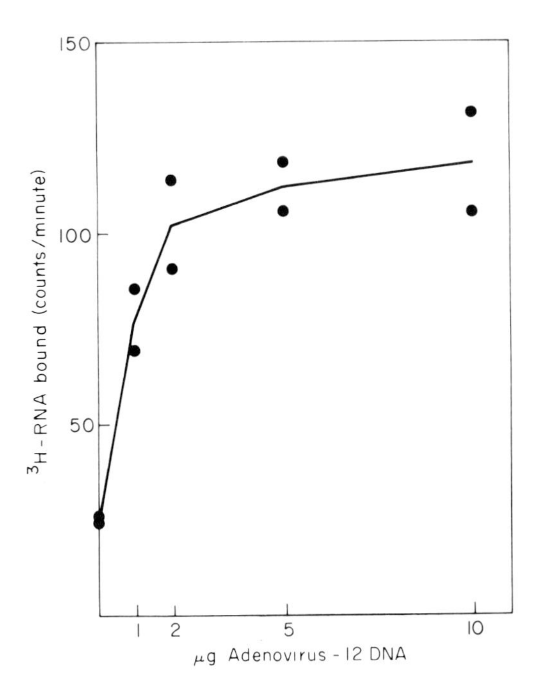

FIG. 2. Effect of amount of immobilized DNA on the extent of DNA-RNA hybrid formation. DNA filters were incubated with 1 ml of ^{3}H-RNA (80,000 counts/minute) from polyribosomes of Ad 12 tumor cells labeled with uridine-^{3}H (2 μC/ml, 20 C/mM) for 120 minutes (Fujinaga and Green, 1966).

TABLE II
HYBRIDIZATION EFFICIENCY OF PURIFIED VIRUS SPECIFIC RNA WITH HOMOLOGOUS DNA[a]

RNA			DNA	Bound radioactivity[b]	
Source	Purification cycle[c]	Input (counts/minute)	(3 μg/filter)	(counts/minute)	(%)
Ad 12[d]	1	552	Ad 12 DNA	371	67
	2	272	Ad 12 DNA	211	78
	3	174	Ad 12 DNA	131	75
	4	173	Ad 12 DNA	133	77
Ad 12[d]	1	435	Ad 12 DNA	222	51
	2	155	Ad 12 DNA	117	76
Ad 7[e]	1	394	Ad 7 DNA	213	54
	2	132	Ad 7 DNA	102	77
	3	143	Ad 7 DNA	103	72
Ad 16[f]	1	523	Ad 16 DNA	284	54
	2	205	Ad 16 DNA	147	72

[a] Taken from Fujinaga and Green (1968).

[b] Average of duplicate hybridization reactions corrected for nonspecific binding to DNA-free filters.

[c] Number of purification steps by hybrid formation and elution.

[d] Nuclear RNA from Ad 12 transformed hamster embryo cells labeled for 180 minutes with orthophosphate-^{32}P.

[e] Nuclear RNA from Ad 7 hamster tumor cells labeled for 180 minutes with orthophosphate-^{32}P.

[f] Nuclear RNA from Ad 16 hamster tumor cells labeled for 180 minutes with orthophosphate-^{32}P.

particular experiment. To detect small amounts of virus specific RNA in the presence of large amounts of cell RNA, it is essential that the viral DNA preparation is free of contaminating cell DNA. Viral DNA prepared from highly purified virus by standard procedures is expected to be free of cell DNA, but the recent demonstration of small amounts of cell DNA within the polyoma virion (Winocour, 1967; Michel *et al.*, 1967) emphasizes the need for testing viral DNA preparations for traces of cell DNA. An important and highly sensitive control is to establish that viral DNA preparations do not bind labeled RNA from uninfected cells.

We have found that uridine-^{3}H-labeled cell RNA prepared by the hot phenol-SDS procedure (Warner *et al.*, 1966) is satisfactory for hybridization without further purification provided that 0.1% SDS is included in the hybridization solution. ^{32}P-labeled RNA requires further purification to reduce nonspecific binding. RNA prepared from nuclei (Penman, 1966) and from cytoplasmic organelles (Girard *et al.*, 1965) as described by Fujinaga and Green (1966, 1967a) is satisfactory for hybridization analysis. An important control is that labeled RNA does not bind appreciably to empty filters or to filters containing heterologous DNA. Binding to empty filters is generally below one part in 10^4 of labeled input RNA, and can be reduced to 2–5 parts in 10^5 by several further extractions of RNA with cold phenol.

IV. DNA-DNA Hybridization Procedure

The procedure described by Warnaar and Cohen (1966) for bacteriophage T4 DNA using Millipore H.A. and type M.F. 30 filters has been modified for the analysis of animal virus DNA and mammalian cell DNA as follows: DNA was immobilized on Schleicher and Schuell B-6 membrane filters and hybridization was carried out in 2 × SSC containing 0.1% SDS. The use of SDS reduces background levels to negligible values; without SDS, background levels were extremely high on Schleicher and Schuell filters. The conditions described here are for the optimal detection of complementary DNA in solution using high ratios of immobilized DNA to solution DNA.

A. Immobilization of DNA on Membrane Filters

See Section III, A.

B. Hybridization Reaction

(See Section III, B for further details on techniques.) Radioactive viral or cell DNA in 2–5 ml of 0.1 × SSC in a 13 by 100 mm nitrocellulose tube is fragmented by sonication for 10 minutes at full power in a Raytheon sonic oscillator. Under these conditions, DNA is reduced in size to fragments of about 6×10^5 daltons. DNA fragments are denatured by heating for 10 minutes in a boiling water bath and quenching in an ice water bath. One-tenth volume of 20 × SSC plus sufficient 2 × SSC are added to give the desired final concentration of DNA. One milliliter of radioactive denatured DNA fragments and 20 μl of 5% SDS are added to each DNA filter; the incubation is carried out at 60°C for 24 hours. Filters are then rinsed through two beakers containing 300 ml each of 0.003 *M* tris buffer, pH 9.2, and washed on each side with ten 10 ml amounts of the same buffer by suction filtration. Filters are dried and radioactivity counted as described in Section III, B.

C. Characteristics of the DNA-DNA Hybridization Reaction

1. *Time Course of Hybridization*

Warnaar and Cohen (1966) found that 24 hours were required to obtain maximum hybrid formation using several different levels of immobilized DNA. As shown in Table III, 24 hours of incubation gave maximum formation of Ad 2 DNA-DNA and KB cell DNA-DNA hybrids; no increase in hybridization efficiency was found at 48 hours of incubation. Times other than 24 and 48 hours were not investigated.

2. *Ratio of Immobilized DNA to Solution DNA and Efficiency of the Hybridization Reaction*

The optimal ratio of immobilized DNA to DNA in solution depends upon the needs of the particular experiment and the particular DNA-DNA system being studied. The following animal virus DNA and mammalian cell DNA systems were examined: (1) The binding of Ad 2 ^{3}H-DNA in solution at different concentrations to 3 μg of immobilized Ad 2 DNA, and (2) the binding of KB ^{3}H-DNA in solution at different concentrations to 10 μg of immobilized KB DNA. As shown in Table IV, a 7:1 ratio of immobilized DNA to DNA in solution gave maximum binding of Ad 2 DNA; no further increase in binding was observed at ratios of 20:1 and 60:1. A 14:1 ratio gave maximum binding of KB DNA; no further increase was observed at ratios of 29:1 and 57:1. Under these conditions the efficiency of hybridization was

TABLE III
Incubation Time and DNA-DNA Hybrid Formation[a]

Input DNA	Immobilized DNA (μg/filter)	Time at 60°C	Bound DNA: Counts/minute	Bound DNA: % of input
Ad 2 DNA, 567 counts/minute	Ad 2 (3 μg)	24	487, 474[b]	85
0.15 μg	Ad 2 (3 μg)	48	506, 485	87
	None	24	1, 1	–
KB DNA[c], 2460 counts/minute	KB (10 μg)	24	505	21
0.35 μg	KB (10 μg)	48	489, 520	21
	None	24	0, 1	–

[a] Piña and Green (1969).

[b] Duplicate determination.

[c] KB DNA prepared by lyses of cells labeled for 3 hours with thymidine-^{3}H (0.3μC/ml, 6 C/m*M*) in buffer containing 0.5% SDS (Dulbecco *et al.*, 1965), digestion with pronase (2 mg/ml) for 3 hours at 37°C, phenol treatment, and CsCl density-gradient centrifugation.

TABLE IV
EFFICIENCY OF HYBRIDIZATION AT DIFFERENT RATIOS OF IMMOBILIZED DNA TO DNA IN SOLUTION[a]

Input DNA	Immobilized DNA (μg/filter)	DNA immobilized/input	Bound DNA	
			Counts/minute	% of input
Ad 2 DNA, 1700 counts/minute 0.44 μg	Ad 2 (3 μg)	6.8	1365	81
Ad 2 DNA, 567 counts/minute 0.15 μg	Ad 2 (3 μg)	20.0	487, 474[b]	85
Ad 2 DNA, 189 counts/minute 0.05 μg	Ad 2 (3 μg)	60.0	153, 160	83
KB DNA, 4920 counts/minute, 0.7 μg	KB (10 μg)	14.3	1154, 1192	24
KB DNA, 2460 counts/minute, 0.35 μg	KB (10 μg)	28.5	489, 520	21
KB DNA, 1230 counts/minute, 0.18 μg	KB (10 μg)	57	356, 318	27

[a] From Piña and Green (1969).
[b] Duplicate determination.

81–85% for viral DNA and 21–27% for cell DNA. No significant binding to empty filters or filters containing heterologous DNA occurs with inputs of 1200 counts/minute; larger inputs are needed to determine the precise background level.

V. Application of DNA–RNA and DNA–DNA Hybridization Analysis to Problems in Animal Virology

Polynucleotide interactions by complementary base pairing play important roles in normal cell function and provide the high specificity involved in DNA replication, transcription, and translation *in vivo*. The precise limits of the specificity of the analytical counterpart of these interactions, the *in vitro* nucleic acid hybridization reaction, are not known. For example, we do not know how many nucleotide pairs can be mismatched before hybrid formation is reduced. Furthermore, "hybrids" formed between complex mammalian nucleic acids, containing 10^3–10^6 times more genetic information than bacterial and viral nucleic acids, are much less specific and their nature is poorly understood at present. In contrast, hybrid formation with the relatively simple viral and bacterial nucleic acids appears to be highly specific and quantitative measurements agree well with genetic data (see discussion by McCarthy, 1966).

A. DNA-RNA Hybridization

Hybrid formation between viral DNA and labeled RNA from infected or transformed cells provides a specific means for the identification, quantitation, and characterization of virus specific RNA. The following are examples of such studies:

(1) The kinetics of synthesis of "early" and "late" virus specific mRNA (Benjamin, 1966; Thomas and Green, 1966; Oda and Joklik, 1967).

(2) The intracellular location and transport of viral mRNA (Joklik and Becker, 1965; Thomas and Green, 1966).

(3) The detection and characterization of virus specific RNA in cells transformed by DNA viruses (Fujinaga and Green, 1966, 1967a,b, 1968; Benjamin, 1966).

(4) The detection and quantitation of viral DNA in transformed cells by hybrid formation between cell DNA and radioactive viral complementary RNA prepared by the action of RNA polymerase on a viral DNA template *in vitro* (Westphal and Dulbecco, 1968; Green and Piña, 1969).

In (1) to (4), high ratios of DNA to RNA are used for the optimal detection of viral specific RNA. In (5) and (6) below, high ratios of RNA to DNA are used.

(5) The determination of the fraction of the DNA genome which codes for complementary RNA by "saturating" DNA sites with excess RNA. The amount of bacterial DNA which codes for ribosomal RNA (Yankofsky and Spiegelman, 1963) and transfer RNA (Giacomoni and Spiegelman, 1962; Goodman and Rich, 1962) has been determined in this manner.

(6) The analysis of relationships between virus specific RNA formed at different times after infection (Benjamin, 1966; Oda and Joklik, 1967) by hybridization-competition between unlabeled RNA and labeled RNA for sites on viral DNA.

B. DNA-DNA Hybridization

Hybridization between immobilized viral DNA and labeled viral DNA or labeled infected cell DNA can yield the following types of information:

(1) The genetic relatedness between DNA viruses as studied in detail with the human adenoviruses (Lacy and Green, 1964, 1965, 1967; Green and Piña, 1969).

(2) The amount of replicating viral DNA present at different times after infection as studied with human adenoviruses (Piña and Green, 1969).

(3) Hybridization-competition between unlabeled DNA fragments and labeled DNA fragments for sites on immobilized DNA to determine the relationship between two DNA species.

(4) Estimation of the fraction of the adenovirus genome involved in the transcription of a RNA population (Mak and Green, 1968) by a "sandwich" type of experiment in which immobilized DNA is first saturated with unlabeled homologous RNA and then annealed with labeled homologous DNA.

REFERENCES

Benjamin, T. L. (1966). *J. Mol. Biol.* **16**, 359.
Dulbecco, R., Hartwell, L. H., and Vogt, M. (1965). *Proc. Natl. Acad. Sci. U.S.* **53**, 403.
Fujinaga, K., and Green, M. (1966). *Proc. Natl. Acad. Sci. U.S.* **55**, 1567.
Fujinaga, K., and Green, M. (1967a). *Proc. Natl. Acad. Sci. U.S.* **57**, 806.
Fujinaga, K., and Green, M. (1967b). *J. Virol.* **1**, 576.
Fujinaga, K., and Green, M. (1968). *J. Mol. Biol.* **31**, 63.
Fujinaga, K., and Green, M. (1969). Unpublished data.
Giacomoni, D., and Spiegelman, S. (1962). *Science* **138**, 1328.
Gillespie, D., and Spiegelman, S. (1965). *J. Mol. Biol.* **12**, 829.
Girard, M., Latham, E., Penman, S., and Darnell, J. E. (1965). *J. Mol. Biol.* **11**, 187.
Goodman, H. M., and Rich, A. (1962). *Proc. Natl. Acad. Sci. U.S.* **48**, 2101.
Green, M., and Fujinaga, K. (1966). *In* "Subviral Carcinogenesis" (Y. Ito, ed.), pp. 82-95. Nissha Printing Co., Kyoto, Japan.
Green, M., and Piña, M. (1963). *Virology* **20**, 199.
Green, M., and Piña, M. (1964). *Proc. Natl. Acad. Sci. U.S.* **51**, 1251.
Green, M., and Piña, M. (1969). Unpublished data.
Joklik, W. K., and Becker, Y. (1965). *J. Mol. Biol.* **13**, 511.
Lacy, S., Sr., and Green, M. (1964). *Proc. Natl. Acad. Sci. U.S.* **52**, 1053.

Lacy, S., Sr., and Green, M. (1965). *Science* **150**, 1296.
Lacy, S., Sr., and Green, M. (1967). *J. Gen. Virol.* **1**, 413.
McCarthy, B. J. (1966). *In* "Subviral Carcinogenesis" (Y. Ito, ed.), pp. 41-61. Nissha Printing Co., Kyoto, Japan.
Mak, S., and Green, M. (1968). *J. Virol.* **2**, 1055.
Marmur, J. (1961). *J. Mol. Biol.* **3**, 208.
Michel, M. R., Hirt, B., and Weil, R. (1967). *Proc. Natl. Acad. Sci. U.S.* **58**, 1381.
Oda, K., and Joklik, W. K. (1967). *J. Mol. Biol.* **27**, 395.
Penman, S. (1966). *J. Mol. Biol.* **17**, 117.
Piña, M., and Green, M. (1968). *Virology* **36**, 321.
Piña, M., and Green, M. *Virology* (in press).
Thomas, D. C., and Green, M. (1966) *Proc. Natl. Acad. Sci. U.S.* **56**, 243.
Warnaar, S. O., and Cohen, J. A. (1966). *Biochem. Biophys. Res. Commun.* **24**, 554.
Warner, J. R., Soeiro, R., Birnboim, H. C., Girard, M., and Darnell, J. E. (1966). *J. Mol. Biol.* **19**, 349.
Westphal, H., and Dulbecco, R. (1968). *Proc. Natl. Acad. Sci. U.S.* **59**, 1158.
Winocour, E. (1965). *Virology* **27**, 520.
Winocour, E. (1967). *Virology* **31**, 15.
Yankofsky, S. A., and Spiegelman, S. (1963). *Proc. Natl. Acad. Sci. U.S.* **49**, 538.

VIII. DNA Analyses

44. Extraction of High Molecular Weight Viral DNA

Charles C. Randall and Lanelle G. Gafford

Department of Microbiology
University of Mississippi School of Medicine
Jackson, Mississippi

I. Introduction

The extraction of DNA is a commonplace procedure in many laboratories but the techniques vary somewhat depending on the nature of the material extracted. A classical paper of general interest is that of Marmur (1961) which deals with the isolation of DNA from microorganisms and discusses some of the technical problems involved. The problem of extracting DNA from cells following viral infection may be complicated by the necessity of separating viral and host cell DNA which are usually extracted together. Though it is not within the scope of this contribution to discuss methods of separation of these macromolecules, a useful procedure for such purposes is that employing a methylated albumin-kieselguhr complex.

The purpose of this communication is primarily to outline a technique which has been refined in this laboratory to obtain high molecular weight DNA from purified fowlpox virus (Gafford and Randall, 1967). The procedure may be extended to purification of cellular DNA, preferably obtained from isolated nuclei. Basically the method is a combination of the techniques of Watson and Littlefield (1960) and Marmur (1961), with some modifications originated in this laboratory.

II. Reagents

All chemicals should be reagent grade unless otherwise specified.

Standard saline citrate, pH 7: (SSC) 0.15 *M* NaCl, 0.02 *M* trisodium citrate, 0.0005 *M* EDTA (ethylenedinitrilo) tetraacetic acid disodium salt, Eastman Organic Chemicals, Rochester, New York. The saline maintains the ionic strength of the extractive mixture and the other components chelate divalent ions (Marmur, 1961).

Dilute SSC: 0.1 × SSC. Precipitated DNA dissolves more readily in dilute salt solutions.

Concentrated SSC: 10× SSC is used to reconstitute dilute SSC after the DNA has been dissolved.

Sodium lauryl sulfate (SLS): 10% in ethanol:water (45:55), U.S.P. grade, Fisher Scientific Co., Fair Lawn, New Jersey. If other brands are used it may be necessary to recrystallize the SLS from ethanol (Crestfield *et al.*, 1955). The SLS lyses the virus and promotes the extrusion of the DNA from the nucleocapsid.

5 *M* NaCl: The addition of the NaCl causes precipitation of the protein and excess SLS (Watson and Littlefield, 1960).

n-Butyl alcohol (butanol).

Chloroform.

The chloroform-butanol mixture is used to deproteinize the material further.

Ethyl alcohol, 95% and 80%: 95% ethanol is used to precipitate the DNA and 80% ethanol for rinsing, since the DNA dissolves more readily if it has not been exposed to more concentrated alcohol solutions (Freese and Freese, 1963).

III. Procedure

A sample of purified virus is suspended in 8 volumes of SSC and 2 volumes of 10% SLS are added. The suspension is mixed by stirring very gently with a glass rod and allowed to stand at room temperature for 30-60 minutes. At this time the suspension should be very viscous, but it may not show extensive clearing. Sufficient 5 *M* NaCl is added to give a final concentration of 1 *M* NaCl, the suspension is mixed by gently inverting several times, and is stored at 4°C overnight. Upon removal from the refrigerator the material will be a solid gel, and it should be allowed to stand at room temperature until it again becomes fluid (30-45 minutes). The mixture is then centrifuged at 15,000 g for

30 minutes in a Servall RC2, and the supernatant removed. The extract should retain essentially all of its viscosity at this point and it will most probably still contain an appreciable quantity of protein. To remove the residual protein, add an equal volume of chloroform and one-third volume of butanol and extract for 5 minutes in a 40 ml screw cap heavy duty centrifuge tube by gently inverting several times per minute. Actual shaking of the tube must be avoided. Separation of the layers is effected by 15 minutes' centrifugation at 900 g. The top phase which contains the DNA is removed very slowly with a 2 or 5 ml widemouth pipette (Kimble 37034-B) and a propipette with great care being taken not to disturb the film of protein at the interface. The chloroform–butanol extraction is repeated if necessary until the top phase is crystal-clear. After the final extraction the DNA-containing supernatant is transferred to a large diameter tube (50 ml round bottom centrifuge tube is ideal), and two volumes of 95% ethanol are added. The DNA precipitates as the layers are mixed gently with a stirring rod (diameter, 5–8 mm) and can be easily wound on the rod which is then rinsed by transferring to a tube containing 80% ethanol and allowing it to stand for about 5 minutes. The rod containing the DNA is then placed in a tube containing dilute SSC and allowed to stand until the DNA detaches. This may take from 30 minutes to 2 hours depending on the quantity of DNA present and the size of the molecules. The process should not be hastened by stirring since this will shear the molecules. After all the DNA is released from the rod, sufficient 10 × SSC is added to bring the solution up to the standard concentration. The DNA should be stored at 4°C until complete solution is obtained. This may require 1 week or longer if one is working with high molecular weight material.

The pellet from the initial centrifugation may contain an appreciable amount of DNA and if maximal yields are desired the pellet may be resuspended in a few milliliters of SSC, centrifuged, and the supernatant extracted with chloroform–butanol as above.

IV. Discussion

The most important feature of this isolation procedure and one which cannot be overemphasized is the extremely gentle handling techniques that must be employed once the SLS has been added to the virus suspension. The preparation should never be shaken and stirring is kept to a minimum. The suspension should always be pipetted slowly, and a wide-mouth pipette is mandatory. The procedure is carried out at high DNA concentrations to avoid degradation, and the DNA is redissolved in as small a volume as is practical. The volume of dilute SSC used to redissolve the precipitated DNA should never exceed one-half the initial volume used to suspend the virus, and frequently it is desirable to employ an even smaller volume.

The technique described has been used in this laboratory to obtain high molecular weight DNA from both fowlpox virus and equine abortion virus (equine herpes). It is also applicable to extraction of DNA from both primary and established cell cultures. When used in conjunction with MAK column chromatography, DNA preparations of uniform molecular size may be obtained.

It is possible that with some viruses or cells the prescribed procedures may not be sufficient to release DNA from gels or tightly bound proteins. The use of enzymes such as pronase and RNase to obtain pure DNA is well documented by Flanagan (1967).

REFERENCES

Crestfield, A. M., Smith, K. C., and Allen, F. W. (1955). *J. Biol. Chem.* **216**, 185.
Flanagan, J. F. (1967). *J. Virol.* **1**, 583.
Freese, E. B., and Freese, E. (1963). *Biochemistry* **2**, 707.
Gafford, L. G., and Randall, C. C. (1967). *J. Mol. Biol.* **26**, 303.
Marmur, J. (1961). *J. Mol. Biol.* **3**, 208.
Watson, J. D., and Littlefield, J. W. (1960). *J. Mol. Biol.* **2**, 161.

45. Isopycnic Banding of Viral DNA in Cesium Chloride

Albert S. Kaplan

Department of Microbiology, Research Laboratories
Albert Einstein Medical Center
Philadelphia, Pennsylvania

1. Introduction

The technique of CsCl density gradient centrifugation developed by Meselson *et al.* (1957) has proved to be a powerful tool for the physicochemical analysis of macromolecules and viruses. According to this technique, a solution of CsCl is rotated in an ultracentrifuge until a sedimentation-diffusion equilibrium is produced. The CsCl will sediment in the direction of the field, and back-diffusion will occur as a result of the nonuniform concentration. Since the concentration of the CsCl increases with distance from the center of rotation, a density gradient is obtained. If DNA is present in the initial solution, it will be forced into a unique position in the density gradient and will form a band, the density of the solution at this point corresponding to the buoyant density of the DNA. Various macromolecules with different buoyant densities may thus be separated and density differences of less than 0.001 gm/cm^3 may be detected. The distribution of the molecules of DNA in the band is Gaussian, the variance of this distribution being inversely proportional to the molecular weight (Meselson *et al.*, 1957). For a theoretical consideration of this subject, see the review by Vinograd and Hearst (1962).

Density gradients of CsCl may be produced by centrifugation or may be preformed by a layering technique. Although formation of a gradient by centrifugation requires a considerably longer time, it has the advantage that the gradient formed by this method can be calculated. In a preformed gradient the exact value of the gradient at the end of an experiment is uncertain. In most cases, isopycnic banding of DNA has been carried out with gradients formed by centrifugation.

Density gradient centrifugation with CsCl is performed in analytical or in preparative ultracentrifuges, depending upon the goal of the experiment. Accurate determinations of the buoyant density of DNA molecules are carried out best in the analytical centrifuge. By this method, one can also estimate the molecular weight of the DNA. The preparative ultracentrifuge possesses the advantage that one can collect a series of fractions that may be tested for biological activity, radioactivity, etc.

II. Materials and Methods

A. Reagents and Their Preparation

(1) Saline-citrate: 1.5×10^{-1} *M* NaCl + 1.5×10^{-2} *M* sodium citrate, buffered at pH 7.3. [Saline-citrate is used to dissolve DNA, because citrate chelates divalent ions, thus inhibiting the activity of deoxyribonuclease (DNase).]

(2) SDS: Commercially available sodium dodecyl sulfate should be repurified before use as follows: To each gram of SDS, add 1 ml H_2O and dissolve. (This may require warming in a water bath at about 45°C.) When the SDS is dissolved completely, add 6 volumes of ethanol (95%) and refrigerate at 4°C overnight. The precipitate is collected by centrifugation, washed twice with ethyl ether, dried thoroughly, and pulverized. A stock solution (30%) of SDS is prepared in water.

(3) DNA: This is isolated and purified as described elsewhere in this volume. It is not always necessary, however, to purify viral DNA prior to its banding in CsCl. If the buoyant density of viral DNA differs sufficiently from that of cellular DNA so that it will appear as a separate band in the density gradient, cells lysed with SDS (3%) can be used for some purposes.

(4) CsCl: Purified optical grade CsCl may be obtained from the following sources: Harshaw Chemical Co., Cleveland, Ohio; Stanley H. Cohen Co., Yonkers, New York; Gallard-Schlesinger Chemical Mfg. Co., Carle Place, Long Island, New York; American Fluoride Co., New York, New York.

Solutions are prepared by dissolving CsCl in 2×10^{-2} *M* tris [tris(hydroxymethyl)aminomethane], pH 8.5. A convenient formula for preparing CsCl solutions of a given density at 25°C is as follows:

Weight percent = 137.48 − 138.11 ($1/\rho$), where ρ = density (Vinograd and Hearst, 1962).

In practice, it is best to prepare a concentrated stock solution by dissolving 130 gm of CsCl in 70 ml of tris buffer (Schildkraut *et al.*, 1962). The DNA to be tested is added to this solution which is diluted to give the appropriate density.

The density of the CsCl solution may be determined from its refractive index by the following equation (Ifft *et al.*, 1961):

$$\rho^{25°} = 10.8601\ \eta_{\mathrm{D}}^{25°} - 13.4974$$

The determination of the refractive index is rapid, but much evaporation of the sample occurs as it is being read. Under ideal conditions, the density obtained in this manner is accurate to three significant figures.

The density of a solution may also be determined from its weight. Calibrated lambda pipettes (20–50 λ) standardized against water are used. The density is determined from the difference in weight, and the values obtained are accurate to three significant figures.

B. Equipment

1. *Centrifuges and accessories*

a. Analytical. The Spinco model E ultracentrifuge is equipped with an ultraviolet light absorption optical system. The material is centrifuged in an An-D rotor with two holes, one for the cell and one for the counterbalance. The cells consist of 12 mm Kel-F or charcoal-filled Epon centerpieces with a 4° sector, a lower standard plane quartz window, and an upper 1° negative wedge quartz window. The wedge window is used to compensate for the deviation of the light caused by the refractive index gradient of CsCl. More than one sample may be analyzed at the same time by using four-holed rotors now available for four cell operation (see Szybalski, 1969).

The formation of ultraviolet absorbing bands is recorded on film (Kodak Commercial Film, 2½ by 3½ inch) after equilibrium is reached. The best time interval for exposure (1, 2, 4, 6 . . . minutes) should be tested; an exposure time within the linear range should be selected. The film is developed in Kodak D-11 developer according to the following schedule at 20°: (1) developer (full strength), 5 minutes; (2) Kodak indicator stop, 20 seconds; (3) Kodak acid-fix, 6 minutes; (4) Kodak hypo-cleaning agent, 2 minutes; (5) water wash, 5 minutes; (6) Photo-Flo solution, dip; (7) distilled water, dip; and (8) dry in dust-free area.

The Joyce-Loebl double beam recording microdensitometer (Joyce, Loebl & Co., Inc., Burlington, Massachusetts 01803) is widely used for densitometer film tracings. Films are positioned in this instrument with the emulsion side up and magnified five times in the horizontal direction on the tracing. To change the vertical magnification, different density wedges must be used (see manufacturer's operational directions for details). The Analytrol equipped with a film densitometer attachment (Beckman Instruments, Spinco Division) may also be used.

b. Preparative. Preparative ultracentrifuges supplied with swinging bucket rotors are used whenever isolation of the DNA is required for analytical purposes. Generally, these rotors consist of three tube holders which take plastic tubes, approximately ½ by 2 inches, that have a capacity of 5 ml. These tubes generally are made of cellulose nitrate. However, cellulose nitrate tubes should not be used for banding of denatured DNA, which will adhere to the walls of these tubes. In this case, polyallomer tubes (Beckman) should be used. [Density gradient centrifugation with CsCl may also be performed in angle-head rotors (Fisher *et al.*, 1964).]

III. Experimental Procedures

A. Analytical

1. Preparation of Sample

A solution containing 1–2 μg of sample DNA and about 0.5 μg of standard DNA of known buoyant density is added to the stock solution of CsCl (see above) (0.84 ml of stock CsCl and 0.23 ml of DNA in saline-citrate). A small amount of the DNA-CsCl solution should be removed for the determination of density by one of the two methods described above. This solution should have a density of about 1.71 gm/ml ($\eta_D^{25°} = \sim 1.4000$). The density of the solution can be increased by adding solid CsCl or decreased by adding water so that the DNA will band at about the center of the gradient. As standard references, the DNA of a number of bacteria may be used, such as *Pseudomonas aeruginosa*, $\rho = 1.727$ gm/cm^3 or *Escherichia coli*, $\rho = 1.710$ gm/cm^3. For other DNA standards, see Schildkraut *et al.* (1962). A reference DNA should be selected that will band outside the region of the density gradient in which the sample DNA may be expected to band. For greater accuracy, two reference standards that will appear above and below the sample DNA in the gradient may be used.

2. *Ultracentrifuge Runs*

Approximately 0.75 ml of the DNA-CsCl solution is placed in the centrifuge cell by means of a 1 ml syringe and a 22 gauge needle with the beveled tip made level to avoid scratching the plastic centerpiece of the cell.

When molecular weight is to be determined, it is essential to avoid shearing the DNA molecules. In this instance, therefore, the sample is introduced very slowly into the cell through an enlarged loading port via an 18 gauge needle or a pipette.

Centrifugation of the DNA for the determination of its buoyant density is usually carried out at 44,770 rpm at 25°C. At this speed, CsCl with a density of approximately 1.70 gm/cm^3 will reach equilibrium in about 12 hours, and the DNA between 20 and 24 hours. (Equilibrium in the density gradient is reached when the position and shape of the bands do not change.)

For band-width molecular weight determination, the centrifuge is run at lower speeds for longer periods of time (generally, 31,410 rpm for 4 days). Equilibrium is tested by checking the width of the band on photographs taken at 12–24 hour intervals; a constant band-width indicates equilibrium. (For estimations of the time required to reach equilibrium, see Vinograd and Hearst, 1962.) A problem encountered during long centrifugation times is the possibility that oil will splatter and foul the optics.

B. PREPARATIVE

1. *Preparation of Sample*

In general, samples of DNA for equilibrium sedimentation centrifugation in the preparative centrifuge are made in the same way as for the analytical centrifuge. For some purposes purification of DNA is, however, not essential, and whole lysates of infected cells can be used for isopycnic centrifugation. In order to obtain good separation of the DNA from the protein, a dilute solution of infected cells (approximately 4×10^6 cells containing 80 μg DNA) in saline citrate is lysed with SDS and a sufficient amount of solid CsCl is added to yield a solution with the desired density.

When the preparative centrifuge is used, the position of the unknown DNA relative to marker DNA can be determined by labeling the two DNA preparations with different labels (for example, ^3H and ^{14}C).

2. *Ultracentrifuge Runs*

Four and one-half milliliters of the DNA-CsCl solution (for example, 4.36 gm CsCl + 3.5 ml DNA solution, $\rho \sim 1.69$) are placed in plastic centrifuge tubes. (If a smaller amount is used, the volume is made up with mineral oil to avoid collapse of the tubes.) The filled tubes are placed in the rotor buckets and the tops tightened. If the tops are not sufficiently tight, the vacuum may cause a loss of solution. All the rotor tubes should be properly balanced.

The rotor is run at 35,000–37,000 rpm for periods of time ranging from about 48 to 72 hours. At the end of the run, the plastic tubes are removed from their holders and are mounted on a ring stand supplied with rubber sleeves. The plastic tubes are closed with a small rubber stopper and connected to any container by means of which one can apply variable air pressure so that the rate of drop formation may be controlled. The plastic tubes are pierced at the bottom with a fine hypodermic needle or a pin and samples are collected dropwise into tubes. (A fractionating apparatus is available commercially from Beckman Instruments, Spinco Division, Brochure PL-286.) If the samples are to be used for density determinations, the tubes should be covered immediately with parafilm to prevent evaporation. If the fractions are not to be used for this purpose, they may be collected in a buffer solution and then monitored for other parameters, such as infectivity, absorbance, or radioactivity.

IV. Practical Applications

A. Determination of Density

1. *Analytical*

The buoyant density of DNA can be calculated from its position in the density gradient (Vinograd and Hearst, 1962). It is easier, however, to centrifuge the unknown DNA with a reference DNA with a known buoyant density. The distances of the peaks of DNA (traced from the absorption photograph) are measured from the center of rotation and the density of the unknown DNA is calculated as follows (Sueoka, 1961; Vinograd and Hearst, 1962):

$$\rho = \rho_0 + 4.2\ \omega^2\ (r^2 - r_0^2) \times 10^{-10}\ \text{gm/cm}^3$$

where

ρ = density of the unknown DNA,
ρ_0 = density of the standard DNA,
ω = speed of rotation in radians/second,
r = distance of unknown DNA from the center of rotation, and
r_0 = distance of standard DNA from the center of rotation.

At 44,770 rpm,

$$\rho = \rho_0 + 0.0092\ (r^2 - r_0^2)\ \text{gm/cm}^3$$

For example, the buoyant density of the DNA of rabbit kidney cells was determined by banding it with reference *Pseudomonas aeruginosa* DNA at a speed of 44,770 rpm. The reference DNA banded at 6.485 cm from the center of rotation and rabbit kidney cell DNA at 6.289 cm. Thus,

$$\rho = 1.727 + 0.0092\ (39.552 - 41.815)$$
$$\rho = 1.706\ \text{gm/cm}^3$$

2. *Preparative*

If fractions collected as described above consist of individual drops, alternate fractions may be used to measure the refractive index and the density gradient may thus be determined. If the fractions consist of several drops, a portion of the fractions is removed for the measurement of refractive index and the remainder is used for the measurement of other parameters. A plot of density versus fraction number will yield a straight line. The density of the DNA is determined graphically by plotting radioactivity, infectivity, or absorbance versus fraction number on the same chart.

B. Calculation of Guanine-Cytosine (GC) Content of DNA from Its Buoyant Density in CsCl

The GC content of DNA is related in a linear fashion to its buoyant density; the greater the GC content, the greater the density (Sueoka *et al.*, 1959; Rolfe and Meselson, 1959; Schildkraut *et al.*, 1962). This relationship holds true for double-stranded DNA not containing odd bases. The base composition of DNA can thus be rapidly and accurately determined by this method. Several equations have been derived that may be used to calculate the GC content of DNA from its density. According to Rolfe and Meselson (1959), this equation is:

$$\rho = 0.100\ (\text{GC}) + 1.658\ \text{gm/cm}^3 \qquad (1)$$

according to Sueoka (1961):

$$\rho = 0.103\ (\text{GC}) + 1.662\ \text{gm/cm}^3 \qquad (2)$$

according to Schildkraut *et al.* (1962):

$$\rho = 0.098\ (\text{GC}) + 1.660\ \text{gm/cm}^3 \qquad (3)$$

The buoyant density of pseudorabies virus DNA, for example, is 1.732 gm/cm^3 (Kaplan and Ben-Porat, 1964). Thus, according to Eq. (1), the mole fraction of GC in this DNA is 0.740, Eq. (2), 0.679, and Eq. (3), 0.735. The mole fraction of GC in pseudorabies virus DNA obtained by chemical analysis is 0.733 (Ben-Porat and Kaplan, 1962).

C. Structural Alterations

A change in the native, rigid structure of DNA may be detected by isopycnic centrifugation in CsCl. Thus, denaturation of linear DNA by a variety of methods (Marmur *et al.*, 1963; Vinograd *et al.*, 1963) will cause a collapse of the extended native DNA molecule and separation of the two strands. This procedure results in an increase in buoyant density of 0.014–0.045 gm/cm^3 which is easily observed by density gradient centrifugation (Meselson and Stahl, 1958; Sueoka *et al.*, 1959; Schildkraut *et al.*, 1962; Vinograd *et al.*, 1963).

Denaturation by heat is a simple, widely used method to effect structural collapse of DNA. The higher the GC content, the higher the denaturation temperature (T_m) of the DNA (Marmur and Doty, 1959, 1962). The T_m of DNA is also dependent on ionic strength, and denaturation of DNA with high GC content is best achieved by lowering the ionic strength of the solvent. Generally, the DNA is dissolved in sodium-citrate in small, well-stoppered tubes, placed into boiling water for 10 minutes, and then plunged into an ice water bath.

An increase in buoyant density after denaturation may be used as one criterion to show that the DNA being studied is double-stranded; the buoyant density of single-stranded DNA does not change after heating. However, the cyclic helical forms of viral DNA characteristic of the so-called papova viruses renature with a high efficiency after heating (Weil, 1963; Dulbecco and Vogt, 1963; Weil and Vinograd, 1963; Crawford and Black, 1964; Crawford, 1965). To prevent renaturation, this type of DNA is heated in the presence of formaldehyde (Freifelder and Davison, 1963). Circular DNA may also be effectively denatured by means of alkaline CsCl (Vinograd *et al.*, 1963).

D. Molecular Weight

The equations derived by Meselson *et al.* (1957) show that the molecular weight can be determined from the distribution of the molecules of DNA in the band formed at equilibrium in the density gradient. Calculation of molecular weight by equilibrium sedimentation and a discussion of advantages of this method are given by Thomas and Berns (1961) and Thomas and Pinkerton (1962).

REFERENCES

Ben-Porat, T., and Kaplan, A. S. (1962). *Virology* **16**, 261-266.
Crawford, L. V. (1965). *J. Mol. Biol.* **13**, 362-372.
Crawford, L. V., and Black, P. H. (1964). *Virology* **24**, 388-392.
Dulbecco, R., and Vogt, M. (1963). *Proc. Natl. Acad. Sci. U.S.* **50**, 236-243.
Fisher, W. D., Cline, G. B., and Anderson, N. G. (1964). *Anal. Biochem.* **9**, 477-482.
Freifelder, D., and Davison, P. F. (1963). *Biophys. J.* **3**, 49-63.
Ifft, J. B., Voet, D. H., and Vinograd, J. (1961). *J. Phys. Chem.* **65**, 1138-1145.
Kaplan, A. S., and Ben-Porat, T. (1964). *Virology* **23**, 90-95.
Marmur, J., and Doty, P. (1959). *Nature* **183**, 1427-1429.
Marmur, J., and Doty, P. (1962). *J. Mol. Biol.* **5**, 109-118.
Marmur, J., Rownd, R., and Schildkraut, C. L. (1963). *Progr. Nucleic Acid Res.* **1**, 231-300.
Meselson, M., and Stahl, F. W. (1958). *Proc. Natl. Acad. Sci. U.S.* **44**, 671-682.
Meselson, M., Stahl, F. W., and Vinograd, J. (1957). *Proc. Natl. Acad. Sci. U.S.* **43**, 581-588.
Rolfe, R., and Meselson, M. (1959). *Proc. Natl. Acad. Sci. U.S.* **45**, 1039-1043.
Schildkraut, C. L., Marmur, J., and Doty, P. (1962). *J. Mol. Biol.* **4**, 430-443.
Sueoka, N. (1961). *J. Mol. Biol.* **3**, 31-40.
Sueoka, N., Marmur, J., and Doty, P. (1959). *Nature* **183**, 1429-1431.
Szybalski, W. (1969). *Methods Enzymol.* **12**, Part B, 330-360.
Thomas, C. A., Jr., and Berns, K. I. (1961). *J. Mol. Biol.* **3**, 277-288.
Thomas, C. A., Jr., and Pinkerton, T. C. (1962). *J. Mol. Biol.* **5**, 356-372.
Vinograd, J., and Hearst, J. E. (1962). *Progr. Chem. Org. Nat. Prod.* **20**, 418-422.
Vinograd, J., Morris, J., Davidson, N., and Dove, W. F., Jr. (1963). *Proc. Natl. Acad. Sci. U.S.* **49**, 12-17.
Weil, R. (1963). *Proc. Natl. Acad. Sci. U.S.* **49**, 480-487.
Weil, R., and Vinograd, J. (1963). *Proc. Natl. Acad. Sci. U.S.* **50**, 730-738.

46. Base Composition Analysis of DNA

*Aaron J. Shatkin**

Laboratory of Biology of Viruses
National Institute of Allergy and Infectious Diseases
National Institutes of Health
Bethesda, Maryland

I. Introduction

Determination of the base composition of purified DNA consists of two essential steps: (1) digestion of the DNA by chemical or enzymatic means and (2) separation and quantitation of the degradation products. In the standard chemical procedure the acid-labile glycosidic bonds in DNA are hydrolyzed with hot perchloric or formic acid (Wyatt, 1955; Bendich, 1957). The resulting free bases are separated by paper chromatography and measured spectrophotometrically. The enzymatic procedures are especially useful for the analysis of small amounts of ^{32}P-labeled DNA. Liberation of 3′-mononucleotides is achieved by digestion with micrococcal nuclease followed by calf spleen phosphodiesterase (Josse *et al.*, 1961); 5′-mononucleotides are released by the combined action of pancreatic DNase and snake venom phosphodiesterase (Lehman *et al.*, 1958). The nucleotides are well resolved by paper electrophoresis (Smith, 1955) or ion exchange chromatography (Cohn, 1955). Both the chemical and enzymatic procedures are described below.

II. Enzymatic Digestion

A. Formation of 3′-Mononucleotides

1. Solutions

(a) Purified ^{32}P-labeled DNA of specific activity 5–10 × 10^4 dis-

*Present address: Roche Institute of Molecular Biology, Nutley, New Jersey.

integrations/min/μmole dissolved at a concentration of 10 μmoles/ml in 0.01 *M* tris(hydroxymethylaminomethane) buffer, pH 8.6.

(b) Micrococcal nuclease (Worthington Corp.): 30 units/ml in 0.1 *M* potassium phosphate buffer, pH 7.3.

(c) Calf spleen phosphodiesterase (Worthington Corp.): 15–20 units/ml in H_2O.

(d) Tris buffer, 0.4 *M*, pH 8.6, containing 0.2 *M* $CaCl_2$.

(e) Salmon sperm DNA (Calbiochem) or calf thymus DNA (Worthington Corp.): 15 mg/ml in 0.01 *M* tris buffer, pH 8.6. The highly viscous solution is digested with micrococcal nuclease (0.1 unit/ml, 0.001 *M* $CaCl_2$, 37°C, 1 hour) to facilitate its use.

(f) Potassium phosphate buffer: 0.5 *M*, pH 7.0.

(g) Pyridine acetate-EDTA buffer, pH 3.5: Prepared by mixing 33.3 ml glacial acetic acid, 3.3 ml pyridine, and 3.72 gm of disodium versenate (EDTA) and diluting to 1 liter with H_2O.

2. *Procedure*

a. Digestion. In a 3 ml centrifuge tube mix 30 μl ^{32}P-labeled DNA sample, 5 μl of $CaCl_2$-tris buffer, and 5 μl of micrococcal nuclease. To a second tube add 0.10 ml of sperm or thymus DNA and 5 μl of $CaCl_2$-tris buffer. Incubate for 2 hours at 37°C. Next add to each of the tubes 20 μl of potassium phosphate buffer to decrease the pH to 7, and 10 μl of spleen phosphodiesterase. Incubate 1 hour at 37°C. Add another 10 μl of spleen phosphodiesterase, reincubate, and repeat (total of 3 hours and 30 μl).

b. Separation of nucleotides. At the end of the incubation period add 0.5 ml pyridine acetate-EDTA buffer to the sperm or thymus DNA digest, mix, and add 0.32 ml of this unlabeled DNA-buffer solution to the ^{32}P-labeled DNA digest. Two 0.1 ml aliquots of the radioactive mixture are applied to Whatman No. 1 filter paper (22 by 18 inch sheets) in approximately 5 by 1 cm bands. The paper is wet by spraying with pyridine acetate-EDTA buffer and placed in a high voltage electrophoresis apparatus (Gilson Medical Electronics) containing the same buffer. After electrophoresis for 75 minutes at 3000 V, the paper is dried in warm air in a hood and exposed to steam in an unsealed autoclave for 15 minutes to volatilize the pyridine. The nucleotide spots are located under ultraviolet light and appear in the following order: cytidylic acid, adenylic acid, guanylic acid, and thymidylic acid. The spots are cut out, folded, and placed directly in 20 ml glass counting vials with 15 ml Liquifluor-toluene (Nuclear-Chicago). The composition expressed as moles percent is calculated by dividing the number of counts in a single nucleotide spot by the sum of the counts in the four spots.

3. Notes

(a) The calf spleen phosphodiesterase may contain phosphomonoesterase activity which is removed by chromatography on Dowex 50 resin (Keller, 1964).

(b) After mixing the initial small volumes, the tubes should be centrifuged briefly to ensure that no materials adhere to the walls.

(c) The presence of K^+ during the digestion competitively inhibits phosphomonoesterase activity (Hilmoe, 1968).

(d) For high resolution of the nucleotides the current during electrophoresis should be about 120 mA.

(e) As a control for recovery of radioactivity, 0.1 ml aliquots of the ^{32}P-labeled DNA digest are applied to Whatman No. 1 paper and counted directly. The number of counts is compared to the total present in the four nucleotide spots. The recoveries are usually 95%.

(f) Replicate assays agree within 1%.

(g) The procedure can be used to analyze nonradioactive DNA in amounts of about 0.25 mg. The separated bases are eluted from the paper and measured by ultraviolet absorption spectrophotometry as described below.

(h) Nearest neighbor base sequence frequencies are determined by digestion of ^{32}P-labeled DNA to 3′-mononucleotides (Josse and Swartz, 1963).

B. FORMATION OF 5′-MONONUCLEOTIDES

1. Solutions

(a) ^{32}P-labeled DNA as in Section II, A.
(b) Pancreatic DNase (DNase I, Worthington, Corp.), 3 μg/ml in 0.01 M tris buffer, pH 6.9.
(c) Snake venom phosphodiesterase (Worthington Corp.), 5 mg/ml in H_2O.
(d) Tris buffer, 0.5 *M*, pH 6.9, containing 0.05 *M* $MgCl_2$.
(e) NaOH, 1.4 *M*.
(f) Nucleotide solution, 1 mg/ml in H_2O of each of the following: 5′-thymidylic acid, 5′-deoxyguanylic acid, 5′-deoxycytidylic acid, and 5′-deoxyadenylic acid (Calbiochem).
(g) Pyridine acetate-EDTA buffer, pH 3.5.

2. Procedure

a. Digestion. In a 3 ml tube mix 30 μl ^{32}P-labeled DNA, 20 μl $MgCl_2$-tris buffer, and 10 μl DNase. Incubate for 2 hours at room temperature. Adjust to pH 8.6 by adding 5 μl 1.4 *M* NaOH. Add 2 μl of venom phosphodiesterase and incubate for another 2 hours.

b. Separation of Nucleotides. Add 0.1 ml of pyridine acetate-EDTA buffer and 0.25 ml of nucleotide solution to the incubation mixture and analyze 0.1 ml aliquots as described in Section II, A.

3. Notes

(a) Monoesterase activity can be removed from the venom preparation by the chromatographic method of Keller (1964).
(b) The recovery and reproducibility is also 95 and 1%, respectively.
(c) Both of the above procedures are modifications by C. Patch and N. P. Salzman from the published work of Josse *et al.* (1961) and Lehman *et al.* (1958).

III. Chemical Digestion

A. Solutions

(1) $HClO_4$, 70% (Mallinckrodt analytical reagent grade) or 88% formic acid (Merck & Co.)
(2) HCl: concentrated, 1 *N*, and 0.1 *N*.
(3) Isopropanol/HCl solvent for chromatography, freshly prepared by mixing 65 ml of distilled isopropanol and 16.7 ml of concentrated HCl and diluting to 100 ml with H_2O.

B. Procedure

1. Digestion

a. With $HClO_4$ (Marshak and Vogel, 1951). Purified, dry DNA is mixed with 70% $HClO_4$ (15 μl for each mg) and heated in a glass-stoppered tube for 1 hour at 100°C. The mixture is cooled and diluted to a concentration of approximately 10 mg/ml with H_2O. After grinding with a glass rod to obtain a uniform suspension, the black sediment is removed by centrifugation.

b. With formic acid (Vischer and Chargaff, 1948). DNA (0.5–1 mg) is mixed with 0.5 ml 88% formic acid in a Pyrex glass bomb tube. The tube is sealed and heated at 175°C for 30 minutes in an oven (Wyatt and

Cohen, 1953). Pressure develops during heating from the decomposition of formic acid to carbon monoxide. It is released from the cooled, secured tube by melting a small hole in the tip with a flame. The hydrolysate is then evaporated to dryness at a temperature of less than 75°C and under reduced pressure in a stream of N_2. It is dissolved in 25 μl of 1 *N* HCl. No insoluble residue is present.

2. *Separation of Bases*

To Whatman No. 1 paper (20 inch sheets) apply a small volume of hydrolysate (10 μl containing 5–30 μg of each base) about 7 cm from the end of the paper. Chromatograph in the isopropanol-HCl solvent. In an ascending system the solvent front is close to the top of the paper, and the bases are well separated after 48 hours at room temperature. The paper is dried and the spots are located under ultraviolet light. They are in the order: origin, guanine, adenine, cytosine, thymine, front. The spots are cut out and the bases are eluted from the fragmented paper by shaking for 2 hours at room temperature in 5 ml of 0.1 *N* HCl. Alternatively, the bases may be eluted by cutting the paper to a point and allowing the acid to diffuse across it. The base is carried with the solvent which is collected dropwise at the point. This method minimizes the elution volume and is preferred for collecting and concentrating minor components. The spectrum of each eluate is read against an acid extract of a piece of Whatman No. 1 paper of similar size. The quantity of base present in the eluates is calculated according to the formula: μmoles base = optical density at maximum absorption × volume of eluate × $1/\epsilon$, where ϵ is the molecular extinction coefficient. The values for $1/\epsilon$ in μmoles/OD unit are: adenine 0.0795, guanine 0.0901, uracil 0.123, thymine 0.126, cytosine 0.100, 5-methylcytosine 0.102, and 5-hydroxymethylcytosine 0.103 (Bendich, 1957).

C. Notes

(1) The procedures described result in recoveries of greater than 95% for most DNAs and an accuracy of 4% or better. Small losses of thymine have been noted when the volume of 70% $HClO_4$ used for hydrolysis is greater than 15 μl/mg DNA. $HClO_4$ but not formic acid also destroys 5-hydroxymethylcytosine.

(2) It is important to minimize the void volume in the sealed tube to prevent oxidizing conditions during the formic acid digestion. For this purpose, a tube of internal diameter 6 mm is sealed about 20 mm above the fluid level.

(3) A preferred method for calculating the quantity of base is the differential extinction procedure. Read the optical density of the eluate at the maximum absorption and at a higher wavelength, approximately 300 mμ. The difference is then compared to that obtained with a standard solution of the base read at the same two wavelengths. This method eliminates the variable contribution of the ultraviolet absorbing material present in filter paper (Vischer and Chargaff, 1948).

REFERENCES

Bendich, A. (1957). *Methods Enzymol.* **3**, 715-723.

Cohn, W. E. (1955). *In* "The Nucleic Acids" (E. Chargaff and J. N. Davidson, eds.), Vol. 1, pp. 211-265. Academic Press, New York.

Hilmoe, R. J. (1968). Personal communication.

Josse, J., and Swartz, M. (1963). *Methods Enzymol.* **6**, 739-751.

Josse, J., Kaiser, A. D., and Kornberg, A. (1961). *J. Biol. Chem.* **236**, 864.

Keller, E. B. (1964). *Biochem. Biophys. Res. Commun.* **17**, 412.

Lehman, I. R., Bessman, M. J., Simms, E. S., and Kornberg, A. (1958). *J. Biol. Chem.* **233**, 163.

Marshak, A., and Vogel, H. J. (1951). *J. Biol. Chem.* **189**, 597.

Smith, J. D. (1955). *In* "The Nucleic Acids" (E. Chargaff and J. N. Davidson, eds.), Vol. 1, pp. 267-284. Academic Press, New York.

Vischer, E., and Chargaff, E. (1948). *J. Biol. Chem.* **176**, 715.

Wyatt, G. R. (1955). *In* "The Nucleic Acids" (E. Chargaff and J. N. Davidson, eds.), Vol. 1, pp. 243-265. Academic Press, New York.

Wyatt, G. R., and Cohen, S. S. (1953). *Biochem. J.* **55**, 774.

IX. Electron Microscopic Procedures

47. Electron Microscopic Procedures in Virology

A. F. Howatson

The Ontario Cancer Institute
Toronto, Canada

I. Introduction

Viruses were among the first biological objects to be examined in electron microscope when it first became a practical instrument for biological research in the late 1930's. The first virus to be observed in the electron microscope was tobacco mosaic virus (Kausche *et al.*, 1939). The early studies were concerned with simple viral morphology, but since then improvements in the instrument and the development of many new specimen preparation techniques have greatly widened the scope of electron microscopy in virology. The aim of this chapter is to describe the applications of electron microscopy in virology, giving as much detail as is possible in the limited space available. For more extensive discussions and details the reader is referred to original articles and reviews mentioned in the text. Many articles in the following books will also be found valuable: "Techniques for Electron Microscopy" (Kay, 1961), "Electron Microscopy" (Mercer and Birbeck, 1961), "Traité de Microscopie Electronique" (Magnan, 1961), "The Interpretation of Ultrastructure" (Harris, 1962), "Modern Developments in Electron Microscopy" (Siegel 1964), "Histological Techniques for Electron Microscopy" (Pease, 1964), "Quantitative Electron Microscopy" (Bahr and Zeitler, 1965), "Electron Microscopy of Cells and Tissues" (Sjöstrand, 1967), and "Methods in Virology," Vol. III (Maramorosch and Koprowski, 1967).

II. Thin Sectioning

A. Introduction

Preparation of thin sections of virus-infected cells and tissues is an indispensable technique for the study of those aspects of virus-cell interaction that are accessible to direct examination by electron microscopy. It is also a necessary step in the localization at the subcellular level of virus-associated materials by the techniques of radioautography and antibody labeling and for cytochemical studies. Thin sectioning is also of value in elucidating the structure of viruses, the information obtained often complementing that provided by the negative staining procedure, though at a somewhat lower level of resolution.

Since the first reasonably satisfactory fixative (buffered osmium tetroxide) and embedding medium (methacrylate) were introduced almost two decades ago, numerous improvements in technique have been made and various new procedures for special purposes have been introduced. For most purposes optimum preservation of fine structure in animal cells and viruses is the prime consideration and procedures for ensuring this are now fairly well standardized. Double fixation, first in glutaraldehyde and then in osmium tetroxide is now widely adopted and gives, in general, better preservation than fixation in osmium tetroxide alone. Some cellular and viral structures, e.g., cytoplasmic microtubules and the internal component of paramyxoviruses which are difficult or impossible to detect in sections after osmium fixation, are well preserved after double fixation.

Other advantages of using glutaraldehyde are (1) it penetrates tissues rapidly, (2) tissue blocks can be left in the fixative for long periods without deterioration and can be processed at any convenient time, and (3) some enzymatic activity can be preserved.

B. Glutaraldehyde Fixation

The use of glutaraldehyde as a fixative arose out of studies by Sabatini *et al.* (1963, 1964) on the properties of aldehydes in general as tissue preservatives.

Glutaraldehyde is obtainable commercially in the form of a 25% solution (Union Carbide Co., New York, New York; Eastman Kodak Co., Chemical Division, Rochester, New York; or K & K Laboratories, 177-10 93rd Avenue, Jamaica, New York).

Acidic breakdown products should be removed by adding activated charcoal to the bottle which is stored in the refrigerator and protected from light. The charcoal is removed by filtering before use.

The fixative is generally used at concentrations between 1 and 6% and buffered at a neutral pH with either cacodylate or phosphate buffer.

Three percent glutaraldehyde fixative in cacodylate buffer may be prepared as follows:

Stock solution A: 0.2 *M* sodium cacodylate
4.28 gm $Na(CH_3)_2\ AsO_2 \cdot 3H_2O$ in 100 ml distilled water
Stock solution B: 0.2 *M* HCl

Add sufficient stock B to 50 ml of A to give required pH, e.g., pH 7.2 requires about 4.2 ml of B, and dilute to 200 ml with distilled water. To prepare fixative, add 12 ml of 25% glutaraldehyde to 88 ml of buffer. Adjust pH if necessary. For rinsing, sucrose may be added to the buffer (7.3 gm/100 ml).

Alternatively, phosphate buffer as recommended by Millonig (1961) may be used. This buffer resembles body fluids more closely than cacodylate buffer. It is made up as follows:

Stock solutions: A. 2.26% $NaH_2PO_4 \cdot H_20$
B. 2.52% NaOH
C. 5.4% glucose
D. 1% $CaCl_2$

41.5 ml of A added to 8.5 ml of B should have a pH of 7.3. To 45 ml of this solution may be added 5 ml of Stock C to increase tonicity and 0.25 ml of stock D. The calcium chloride is thought to aid in preservation of certain cell structures including membranes.

C. Osmium Fixation

Osmium tetroxide in buffered solution, either alone or more frequently in recent years, following glutaraldehyde fixation, has since the earliest days of thin sectioning been recognized as an effective preservative of cell fine structure. A 1% solution of osmium tetroxide is usually employed. A number of different buffers can be used including the phosphate buffer of Millonig previously described. Another commonly used buffer is the veronal-acetate buffer originally recommended by Palade (1952). This is made up as follows:

Solution A:	Sodium veronal (sodium barbitone)	2.88 gm
	Sodium acetate (anhydrous)	1.15 gm
	Distilled water to make 100 ml	
Solution B:	0.1 *N* HCl	

The buffer is made by mixing 10 ml of solution A to 10 ml of B and adding 5 ml of distilled water; pH should be about 7.4.

Two percent osmium tetroxide solution is made by breaking an ampoule containing 1 gm of crystalline OsO_4 under distilled water and making up the volume to 50 ml. The ampoule should be washed free of organic matter (paper, glue, etc.) before use.

The fixative is made by mixing equal volumes of buffer and osmium tetroxide solution.

D. Fixation Procedure

Details of fixation procedure depend on the type of specimen under study. Most frequently in virus work the specimen consists of cells grown in monolayers or in suspension. Cells in suspension or cells scraped from monolayers can be spun down in a clinical centrifuge tube at a speed sufficient to form a solid pellet. The supernatant is decanted and 1 or 2 ml of fixative added. If the pellet is large it should be broken into smaller pieces at this stage. In the ensuing procedure the pellet or pellet fragments are treated in the same way as tissue blocks.

The above fixation procedure may not be satisfactory for a number of reasons. Damage to cells in monolayers may occur if they are scraped off or released by trypsination before fixation; also, the configuration of the cells and their relationship to one another may be lost. Surface structures such as budding virus may be disturbed or destroyed by centrifugation or by too tight packing of the cells. These effects are minimized if cells are fixed *in situ*, i.e., in monolayers or in suspension. The difficulty then is that the pellets formed are not compact and tend to disperse especially in the later stages of embedding. This can be avoided by agar infiltration as described in the next section.

E. Agar Infiltration

The object of agar infiltration is to allow loosely bound specimen material such as packed cells to be processed for thin sectioning in the same way as tissue blocks. A suitable procedure is as follows: The cells are fixed *in situ* (glutaraldehyde or osmium tetroxide alone or both in succession may be used) and spun down to form a pellet. Washing of the cells in buffer to remove fixative may be done by centrifuging and resuspending several times. Four percent agar in water is melted by heating in a bath of boiling water for some 10 minutes and then cooled to about 45°C. A small drop of the melted agar about equal in volume to that of the pelleted cells is mixed with the cells and allowed to infiltrate for at least 10 minutes at 45°C. Too large a volume of agar will dilute the cell suspension so that in thin sections the cells are too far apart for convenient viewing. After infiltration of the pellet with agar the tubes are allowed to cool after which the pellet can be loosened and removed from the bottom of the tube and if necessary cut into smaller pieces for dehydration and embedding.

F. Dehydration and Embedding

Since the commonly used embedding media are not miscible with water, this must be removed and replaced by a solvent which will mix with the medium. This is accomplished by immersing the specimen in increasing concentrations of alcohol or acetone in water, finishing with several changes of the pure organic liquid before starting infiltration with the embedding medium.

Methacrylate is now largely of historical interest and has been superseded for most purposes by epoxy or polyester resins of which the most widely used is epon. Some workers prefer a mixture of epon and araldite which is said to be easier to section (Mollenhauer, 1964). Another epoxy resin that has been used successfully is Maraglas. The polyester resin Vestopol W, originally introduced for embedding bacteria, can be used equally well for embedding animal cells and has its strong advocates. However, for general purposes epon remains the most popular embedding material.

The following schedule for preparing epon embedding medium (Luft, 1961) gives satisfactory results. Two mixtures are employed and the hardness of the resulting blocks can be varied by altering the proportions.

Mixture A:	Epon 812	62 ml
	DDSA (dodecenyl succinic anhydride)	100 ml
Mixture B:	Epon 813	100 ml
	MNA (methyl nadic anhydride)	89 ml

The selected proportions of mixtures A and B are blended and, immediately before use the accelerator, 1.5% v/v of DMP-30 (2,4,6-dimethylamine-methyl-phenol), is added. To obtain consistent results it is imperative that the mixing be done very thoroughly. Electrically driven Teflon mixers are suitable for this purpose. A one-to-one mixture of A and B gives a block of suitable hardness for most purposes. It is convenient to make up the complete mixture, minus accelerator, and store it under refrigeration until required. To prevent condensation of water in the resin the container should be warmed to room temperature before opening. If softer or harder blocks are required the proportion of mixture A to mixture B is increased or decreased respectively. The chemicals may be obtained from the following sources:

Epon 812: Shell Chemical Corp., San Francisco, California.
Dodecenyl succinic anhydride: R. P. Cargille Laboratories Inc., 117 Liberty Street, New York, New York.
MNA methyl nadic anhydride: National A, Division Allied Chemical and Dye Corp., New York.
DMP-30: Rohm and Haas Co., Philadelphia, Pennsylvania.

Embedding kits and chemicals are also obtainable from suppliers of accessories for electron microscopy (Ladd Research Industries Inc., P.O. Box 901, Burlington, Vermont, E. F. Fullam Inc., P.O. Box 444, Schenectady, New York).

After impregnation with the medium, tissue blocks or cell pellets are placed in capsules mounted on a suitable rack. The capsules are filled with the resin mixture and hardened for 48 hours or more at 65°C. The original schedule called for two or three stages of curing at increasing temperatures, but this does not appear to be necessary.

Gelatine capsules (size 00) may be used, but the more recently introduced polyethylene capsules (Beem capsules) shaped to minimize block trimming prior to sectioning are convenient and satisfactory. Flat embedding molds are also available (Ladd Research Industries, Inc.).

G. Processing Schedule

The following is a typical schedule for fixation, dehydration, and embedding of tissue blocks or firmly pelleted cells:

(1) Fix in 3% buffered glutaraldehyde for 1 hour or longer (no maximum time).

(2) Wash three times in buffer with sucrose added (3 × 10 minutes).
(3) Fix for 1–2 hours (not longer) in 1% buffered osmium tetroxide.
(4) Rinse twice in 30% acetone
(5) Dehydrate in 30, 50, 70, and 90% acetone, 10 minutes in each concentration.
(6) Two changes of 100% acetone.
(7) Epon (with accelerator) and acetone (1–1 ratio) 30 minutes at 37°C.
(8) Epon (with accelerator) 1 hour at 37°C.
(9) Label capsules, fill two-thirds with fresh epon, place tissue or pellet on surface. It will gradually sink to the bottom of the capsule.
(10) Leave in oven overnight at 37°C, then overnight at 65°C (or straight into 65°C oven).

If ethanol dehydration is preferred, it is customary to infiltrate with propylene oxide after the dehydration step and before introducing the embedding medium.

More rapid processing than the above is feasible if this should be necessary. Coulter (1967) has recently described a procedure that, by using very small samples, rapid dehydration, vacuum infiltration of the resin, and polymerization at 95°C allows the processing time to be cut to a few hours. He also recommends a somewhat different ratio of anhydride to epoxy than that proposed by Luft.

For bacterial cells the fixation and embedding procedures outlined above may not be satisfactory, especially if good preservation of the nuclear region is required. Kellenberger and Ryter (1964) have discussed fixation of bacterial cells and recommend a procedure for optimum preservation. More recently, prefixation with glutaraldehyde has been introduced before fixation with osmium tetroxide (Kellenberger *et al.*, 1967).

H. Sectioning

Several types of satisfactory microtomes for thin sectioning are now available and most of the technical problems of cutting sections suitable for electron microscopy have now been overcome (Porter, 1964; Sjöstrand, 1967). The quality of the sections is limited by that of the cutting edge. Good diamond knives are preferred because of their convenience and reliability, but sections of high quality can also be produced by glass knives. Sections are picked up on specimen grids, the Athene type of copper grid being preferred because of its flat surface to which the sections adhere readily. If necessary the grids may be degreased before use by rinsing in acetone and drying on filter paper. Sections may be supported on filmed or unfilmed grids. Unfilmed grids are preferable since there is no loss of contrast because of the supporting film, but stability of the sections in the electron beam may be a problem. Unfilmed grids with small holes (300 mesh) can be used satisfactorily but at the expense of reducing the viewing area of the sections compared with that available with a more open mesh.

I. Staining

Staining of thin sections with heavy metal salts is almost always necessary to provide sufficient contrast. The two most useful stains are uranyl acetate and lead citrate either singly or in succession. The staining is in general nonspecific, but uranyl acetate does have an affinity for nucleoproteins.

Uranyl acetate staining: Grids on which the sections are mounted are floated on a drop of a saturated aqueous solution of uranyl acetate, placed in a plastic petri dish or on a sheet of dental wax. The uranyl acetate solution may be warmed to 60°C on a hot plate before use. Under these conditions, staining requires about 15 minutes after which the grids are washed thoroughly with distilled water, drained, and dried. Alternatively, a 1% solution of uranyl acetate in a mixture of equal parts ethanol and water may be used at room temperature.

Lead staining: Lead citrate is now generally the lead salt of choice since precipitation of crystals on the sections, so troublesome with other lead stains, is less of a problem.

The stain is prepared as follows (Reynolds, 1963): 1.33 gm of lead nitrate $Pb(NO_3)_2$ and 1.76 gm of sodium citrate $Na_2(C_6H_5O_7)2H_2O$ are added to 30 ml of distilled water in a 50 ml flask and shaken vigorously for 1 minute and then intermittently. After 30 minutes, 8 ml of 1 *N* NaOH freshly made from carbonate-free 10 *N* NaOH is added, the volume made up to 50 ml with distilled water and thoroughly mixed. The solution should have a pH of about 12 and should be completely clear. If not, the turbidity may be removed by centrifugation. The stain should be stable for several months. Sections are stained as before by floating grids with the section side down on a drop of the stain for about 15 minutes at room temperature. After staining the grids are washed in alternate streams of distilled water and 0.02 *N* NaOH.

Toluidine blue staining: It is often useful before selecting an area for thin sectioning to obtain an over-all view of the embedded material by cutting relatively large and thick sections that can be examined in the light microscope. Such sections (0.5–2.0 μ in thickness) can be examined by phase contrast microscopy or by ordinary light microscopy after staining. Toluidine blue is a nonspecific stain that works well on epon-embedded materials. It is used as follows:

One milliliter of a 1% solution of toluidine blue in water is mixed immediately before use with 20 ml of a 2.5% solution of sodium carbonate and filtered. The sections floating on a drop of water on a microscope slide are heated slowly until the water evaporates and they flatten and attach to the glass. A drop of stain is placed on the section and left for 10–20 minutes at 45–50°C. After rinsing and drying a cover slip is mounted over the sections using oil or a permanent mounting medium.

III. Special Procedures

The standard thin sectioning procedures outlined above give valuable information about viruses and virus-cell interaction. However, there are major gaps in the information provided by direct electron microscope observation especially in relation to the important biochemical events that occur in the infected cell in the eclipse phase. A number of special procedures have been devised in an attempt to bridge the gap and extend the information obtainable from the study of thin sections. These have been developed for the most part from procedures that have been used successfully at the light microscope level and are aimed at exploiting the superior resolving power of the electron microscope to improve the precision with which viral components and virus-associated cell alterations can be identified and located. Only a very brief discussion of the techniques is possible here. For more detailed information the reader is referred to the articles cited and to the books listed in the introduction to this chapter.

A. Radioautography

The principles, aims, and applications of radioautography in electron microscopy and light microscopy are similar, but the technical requirements for electron microscopy are more exacting. Thin sections of cells or tissues in which a radioactive material has been incorporated are cut in the usual way and then covered with a very thin layer of a special fine grain photographic emulsion (e.g., Ilford L4 or

Gevaert NUC 307). After a suitable exposure time (roughly 10 times as long as required for light microscopy), the emulsion is developed, and the sections are stained and examined in the electron microscope. The location and concentration of the tagged material is shown in relation to cell structures by the position and areal density of developed grains. The best resolution obtainable is about 0.1 μ.

B. Antibody Labeling

Conjugation of antibody with a substance (usually ferritin) easily recognizable by electron microscopy allows virus and virus specific proteins to be identified and localized by specific antigen-antibody reactions. Unfortunately, nonspecific adsorption of the ferritin-antibody complex to the embedding material does not allow direct application of the complex to thin sections. Instead, the ferritin-conjugated antibody is applied to unfixed or lightly fixed cells which are then thoroughly washed to remove nonadsorbed antibody; the cells are then fixed, embedded, and sectioned. The method works well for antigens located at the cell surface, e.g., budding viruses. In order to tag intracellular virus it is necessary to render the cell permeable to the antibody-ferritin conjugate. This can be done by freezing and thawing the cells (Rifkind *et al.*, 1964) or by treating them with a dilute solution of digitonin (Dales *et al.*, 1965), at the expense of some degree of disruption of the cell architecture. In this way it has been possible to label intracellular antigens of several viruses.

C. Cytochemical Procedures

The Gomori technique for identification of phosphatases can readily be adapted to electron microscopy since the product formed, lead phosphate, is electron dense. By this means, adenosine triphosphate (ATP) has been identified at the surface of several viruses. Another application has been to reveal the presence of acid phosphatase in cytoplasmic vacuoles containing ingested vaccinia virus particles (Dales and Kajioka, 1964).

The identification of viral materials by specific enzyme digestion at the electron microscope level has proved to be possible though subject to difficulties. Some positive results have been reported with nucleases on methacrylate-embedded sections (Thomas and Williams, 1961; Epstein, 1962). The major effort in this field, however, has been by Bernhard and his colleagues who have concentrated on searching for fixation procedures and embedding media that would allow good preservation of cell structure without loss of susceptibility to enzyme action.

In a recent paper, Leduc and Bernhard (1967) described an improved method for embedding tissues in glycol-methacrylate, a water-soluble embedding medium. The method is particularly useful for subsequent enzymatic extraction from thin sections.

Most of the enzyme digestion work on viruses has been concerned with identifying the type of nucleic acid and its location within the virus particles.

IV. Negative Staining

The value of negative staining as a technique for enhancing contrast and revealing details of virus structure was first clearly appreciated and demonstrated by Horne and his colleagues in their studies on adenovirus and T2 bacteriophage published in 1959 (Brenner and Horne, 1959; Horne *et al.*, 1959). The method is now widely used in virology and continues to provide structural information not obtainable by any other means. The negative staining procedure is essentially simple: it consists of mixing a suspension of the material under study, e.g., a suspension of virus particles, with a solution of a heavy metal salt and allowing the mixture to dry down from a thin layer deposited on a suitably filmed grid. The salt forms a dense, almost structureless background against which the specimen material stands out as relatively translucent. The stain usually penetrates components of virus particles to different degrees providing sufficient contrast to allow the substructure to be visualized. The first negative stain to be widely used was sodium or potassium phosphotungstate (PTA), and this is still the most useful stain for general purposes. However, PTA denatures many proteins even on short exposure and it may be necessary with any given specimen to try a number of different stains at a variety of pH values in order to obtain optimal preservation or to supplement the information obtained from PTA staining. Some of the more commonly used heavy metal salts are uranyl acetate and formate, sodium silicotungstate, and ammonium molybdate.

There are many variations in the methods used in mixing specimen and stain and in applying the mixture to the film-coated grid. Most of these give comparable results and the method chosen will depend on personal preference or prejudice. The following points, however, are important:

(1) Uniform spreading of the specimen material on the grid is es-

sential. The best substrate in general is a Formvar film coated with a moderately thick layer of evaporated carbon. Since they provide better support than more open mesh, 400 mesh grids are recommended. Trouble in spreading may result from the carbon layer being too thick or contaminated with oil from the vacuum pump. The surface may be rendered more hydrophilic by exposing the grids to a glow discharge in a vacuum unit or to ultraviolet light, the best conditions and times of exposure being determined by trial. However, such treatment is not usually necessary. Spreading is greatly facilitated by the presence of "soluble" protein in the specimen. Highly purified virus preparations may cause trouble, but spreading can be facilitated by addition of a suitable protein (usually bovine serum albumin at a concentration of 0.01-0.05%) at the expense of a somewhat increased background granularity because of the protein. The addition of sucrose (0.4%) to the staining solution may give a more uniform layer on drying but contrast is reduced.

(2) Prolonged exposure of the specimen material to the stain should be avoided. Most of the salts used can induce structural and chemical alterations in the specimen material. Some salts, e.g., uranyl salts have a positive staining effect if the specimen is exposed to the stain for some time. This may cause some confusion in interpretation.

(3) Double condenser illumination is desirable since the small beam diameter confines exposure of the specimen to the area being viewed.

A typical staining procedure is as follows: A small drop of the specimen fluid is applied to the grid with a Pasteur pipette or with a platinum loop and allowed to remain for ½-1 minute. A larger drop of 3% PTA solution (pH 6.5) is then applied and left for a few seconds. The bulk of the fluid is removed by touching it with the torn edge of a piece of filter paper. The thin layer of fluid remaining should dry quickly and uniformly from the periphery inward.

The presence of small quantities of buffer salts or other nonvolatile substances is not troublesome, but if the specimen contains appreciable amounts of nonvolatile salts or sucrose it becomes necessary to wash off the bulk of this by applying and then removing, once or several times, a drop of water or of a solution of a volatile salt such as ammonium acetate (2%) before the negative staining step. Alternatively, the grid with the specimen material adhering to it may be inverted and floated on a large drop of the staining solution. After allowing a minute or so for diffusion of the salts, the grid is removed, blotted free of excess liquid, and dried as before.

Another procedure is to mix the specimen and stain on a glass slide and then apply a drop of the mixture to the grid. The bulk of the fluid is removed after a short interval as before.

The concentration of material in the specimen is not critical, but obviously too much material or too large aggregates should be avoided. The concentration of stain may require adjustment according to the type of specimen and the method of preparation.

It is worth noting that PTA and other negative stains are not necessarily virocidal. Suitable precautions should be taken with pathogenic material. It is, in any event, desirable to thoroughly clean by flaming or otherwise, the forceps used to handle grids after each specimen is prepared. Specimen fluid from the grid often runs by capillary action between the blades of the forceps where it can lodge after drying and subsequently be transferred to a different specimen.

An advantage of negative staining in examining viruses is that much more background material can be tolerated than is possible with other techniques, e.g., metal shadowing. Some cellular components may not be visible at all; for example, with PTA staining, nucleic acids are not seen and ribosomes, unless previously fixed, are degraded and invisible. Most viruses, however, are well preserved and, especially if they have a well-defined characteristic structure, can readily be identified even in the presence of much contaminating material. It is possible to obtain useful information about the association of virus and cell in completely unpurified material by methods that allow thinly spread areas of infected cells to be examined after negative staining (Almeida and Howatson, 1963; Parsons, 1963).

Fixation of the specimen before negative staining is sometimes useful in preserving virus structures, but it may affect penetration of the stain with loss of structural detail. Furthermore, background materials, ribosomes, etc., become much more obvious after fixation.

V. Visualization of Nucleic Acid Molecules

A specimen preparation method which allows information about the conformation of nucleic acid molecules to be obtained by electron microscopy was introduced by Kleinschmidt and Zahn (1959). It has found wide application in the study of viral nucleic acids.

A solution of 1 *M* ammonium acetate containing the nucleic acid at a concentration of about 2 μg/ml and a protein (usually cytochrome C, 100 μg/ml) is spread on the surface of a solution of 0.2 *M* ammonium acetate in a shallow trough. The solutions should be made up freshly and the receiving surface must be clean. The nucleic acid solution is allowed to run down gently over a clean microscope slide dipped into the trough. The spreading of the protein, as it forms a monolayer in which the nucleic acid molecules are trapped, may be followed by scattering a little talc powder on the surface. Specimens are collected by touching the surface with filmed grids. They are then touched briefly to a surface of absolute alcohol and then isopentane and allowed to dry. To enhance contrast and allow the threadlike nucleic acid molecules to be visualized clearly over their entire lengths, the grid is shadowed while being rotated in the evaporating unit. Alternatively, the grids can be positively stained by floating them on a 10^{-5} *M* solution of uranyl acetate in 100% ethanol for 30 seconds. After washing in ethanol followed by isopentane and drying, the grids are ready for examination in the electron microscope.

VI. Particle Counting

The enumeration of virus particles, whether complete virions or other entities recognizable as viral, as distinct from infectious or other biological units, is almost exclusively the province of electron microscopy. The objective is to determine the number of the specified particles per unit volume of a given suspension. The problem is essentially that of depositing on a filmed specimen grid from a known or determinable volume of the virus suspension an array of particles clearly and individually identifiable, present in sufficient numbers to make counting feasible, and truly representative of the population of particles in the original suspension.

Several different counting methods are available. The choice of method will depend on a number of factors among which are the following:

(1) The concentration of the particles in the suspension.
(2) The stability of particles to the preparative procedures.
(3) The ease of identification, often in the presence of contaminating material.
(4) The accuracy of counting desired.

In the sedimentation method (see below) particles are deposited on the grid from a measured volume of fluid, but usually the volume is not actually measured but determined indirectly by the method introduced by Backus and Williams (1950) which involves a comparison of numbers of virus particles with reference polystyrene latex (PSL) particles added in known concentration to the virus suspension. Stock suspensions of PSL particles (Dow Chemical Co., Midland, Michigan) at known concentration can be prepared by determining the dry mass of latex in a measured volume, and the particle mass, obtained from the known density of PSL (1.05 gm/ml) and the mean particle diameter. The ratio of the masses gives the number of particles. It is in the measurement of the diameter that the main source of error arises. The mean diameter should be checked by comparison with a reference standard such as a diffraction grating replica since there is reason to believe that the figure given by the supplier may not be accurate (Pinteric and Taylor, 1962). The concentration of latex particles used in the final mixture will depend on the concentration of virus particles and should be chosen so that the numbers are of the same order of magnitude.

A. Single Drop Method

The simplest procedure for mounting particles from a liquid suspension is to apply a single drop to a filmed specimen grid and allow it to dry. Shadowing or negative staining can be used to enhance contrast and latex particles as a particle concentration reference. The main drawback is that only a small portion of the total area covered by the drop can be assessed for particle numbers, and there is no guarantee that, in the areas selected for counting, the ratio of virus particles to latex particles is representative of that of the original suspension. It has been shown that, in general, the concentration of particles in a dried-down drop is greater near the periphery and that smaller particles are relatively more concentrated in this region. Also, nonvolatile materials usually present in the suspending medium are likely to result in an unacceptably high background of nonviral material.

B. Lowered Drop Method

Pinteric and Taylor (1962) have devised a method of controlled drying of a large drop that avoids both of these difficulties and is suitable for partially purified virus suspensions which still contain proteins and salts. The former are useful since they aid in the spreading; the latter are removed by dialysis before drying.

The procedure is as follows:

(1) Several unfilmed grids (200 mesh, silver or gold grids are recommended since copper may react with the buffer) are placed on a piece

of sintered glass on the floor of a container having an outlet at the bottom (a Büchner funnel is suitable), and the container is filled with ammonium acetate–ammonium carbonate buffer.

(2) A film of Formvar is floated on the surface and several drops (each about 2–4 × 10^{-3} ml) of a mixture of virus and PSL suspension placed on the floating film. The drops are left for 30 minutes to allow dialysis through the Formvar film.

(3) The buffer is drained out, and as the surface level falls the film is guided so that two or three of the drops come to rest on grids.

(4) The grids, still resting on the sintered glass, are placed in a petri dish and allowed to dry down. To absorb CO_2 and prevent alteration in the pH of the drop as it dries, a small vessel containing pellets of NaOH is placed in the petri dish which is sealed with a rubber band.

When the drop and all the buffer in the sintered glass have evaporated (approximately 2 hours) the grids are shadowcast while still resting on the sintered glass. Alternatively, the grids can be negatively stained by soaking the sintered glass with the stain just before the drop dries. The object of using buffer-saturated sintered glass is to promote uniform drying of the drop and especially to prevent too rapid drying of the drop at the periphery. Under these drying conditions, the particles are randomly distributed and no edge effect is observed. When highly purified virus suspensions are used without added protein, however, the distribution of particles is not uniform. The addition of protein (0.01% serum albumin) eliminates this problem. The method is sensitive; for example, concentrations of poliovirus down to about 5 × 10^7 particles/ml can be conveniently measured.

C. Agar Filtration Method

In the agar filtration technique (Kellenberger and Arber, 1957) a few drops of the virus suspension mixed with a known concentration of latex particles are spread with a glass rod on an agar gel surface coated with a collodion film. The suspending fluid diffuses into the agar leaving the particulate material on the collodion surface. After exposure to the vapor of 40% formalin for 7 minutes, the gel is cut into pieces and the collodion membranes are floated off on the surface of a 2% lanthanum nitrate solution. The membranes are mounted on grids, metal shadowed, and particle counts made in the electron microscope. This method allows the particles under investigation to remain in a medium of constant composition until they are fixed. The relative precision of the counts is estimated to be 15% but the absolute value, as in all methods using latex reference particles, is dependent on the accuracy of the determination of the latex particle concentration.

D. Loop Drop Method

Watson (1962) has described a simple method for counting virus particles in relatively low concentrations. The use of negative staining allows viruses with characteristic structure to be recognized in unpurified preparations. The virus suspension is mixed with latex at a concentration of about 10^9 particles/ml and a ½% solution of PTA. Drops of the mixture are placed on Formvar-coated grids with a platinum loop and allowed to dry. Counts of latex and virus particles are made directly on the electron microscope screen by scanning the grid at a magnification of 40,000. The reliability of the method was checked by the spray drop method and by showing linearity of numbers with dilution factor.

A similar method has been used in the author's laboratory to obtain data on the relative numbers of viral entities of various types in lysates of *E. coli* infected with mutants of λ bacteriophage. In crude lysates enough protein is present to ensure excellent spreading on a carbon-Formvar substrate, and the salt concentration, after dilution with the negative stain, is not sufficiently great to be troublesome. An almost uniform background of negative stain covers the whole grid surface. Areas from well-separated squares are selected at random and photographed at a magnification of 15,000. Numbers of latex particles and viral entities are counted on the plates. Under defined spreading conditions the reproducibility of relative numbers obtained from different grids of the same lysates and from grids prepared from replicate lysates is good. Furthermore, the specimen is subjected to minimal preparation treatment so that the loss of unstable structures is minimized.

E. Sedimentation Method

The sedimentation method (Sharp, 1949, 1965) employs a relatively large, directly measurable, volume of the virus suspension. All the particles in suspension are sedimented by centrifugation on a layer of agar of 2% concentration and 2 mm thickness, and after removal of the supernatant fluid are exposed to vapor from 2% osmium tetroxide for 10 minutes. The agar absorbs soluble material from the residual supernatant fluid, but larger particulate material is left on the surface from which it can be removed in the form of a pseudo-replica by flooding the surface with collodion or Formvar solution and stripping the film off after drying. It is claimed that more than 99% of the particulate material is removed in the replica (Galasso, 1967).

A centrifuge rotor containing eight cells designed especially for this work is commercially available (Ivan Sorvall Inc., Norwalk, Connecticut). By using suitably shaped cells, a uniform distribution over the whole receiving area of the agar can be achieved, and counts of virus particles can be made over randomly selected regions. The method is not dependent on the use of reference latex particles and is very sensitive, giving useful particle count data from suspensions at concentrations as low as 10^6/ml.

The replica is usually shadowed before being examined in the electron microscope. As an alternative the pseudo-replica can be stripped in 0.5% PTA, allowing the advantages of negative staining to be realized (Rhim *et al.*, 1961; Smith and Melnick, 1962).

F. Spray Method

In the spray method introduced by Riedel and Ruska (1941) and refined by Backus and Williams (1950), the specimen material mixed with a known concentration of latex particles is deposited on a filmed specimen grid in the form of minute drops from a spray gun or throat spraying device. On drying, the contents are deposited over discrete circular areas of the grid. Serum albumin (0.1%) is usually added to facilitate spreading of the droplets and to outline the edge. The circles are small enough (2–20 μ) that the whole area can be observed and photographed after suitable contrast enhancement. Concentration of virus is determined by direct counts of the number of virus particles and reference particles present in each dried-down drop.

Since each droplet is a random sample of the bulk suspension (subject to statistical fluctuations) and the entire dried contents are visualized, the counts give a reliable measure of the particle population in the suspension. It is, of course, essential that the contents of the droplet are not disturbed by washing after being deposited and, consequently, the suspension must be free of buffer salts and other nonvolatile material. For viruses that are not stable in aqueous suspension, Backus and Williams recommend the use of a volatile ammonium carbonate–ammonium acetate buffer to maintain a suitable pH and ion concentration.

The method is only suitable for fairly high virus concentrations (10^9/ml or more). Metal shadowing has generally been used to enhance contrast. Negative staining can equally well be employed and offers several advantages. Among these are simplicity, better resolution and easier identification of viral structures, and greater tolerance of the presence of background material.

In spraying virus suspensions it should be remembered that formation of aerosols is a very effective way of spreading infection. If pathogenic materials are used, suitable precaution should be taken. Horne (1961) described a simple device that allows spraying to be done without releasing any specimen material to the surroundings.

REFERENCES

Almeida, J. D., and Howatson, A. F. (1963). *J. Cell Biol.* **16**, 616.

Backus, R. C., and Williams, R. C. (1950). *J. Appl. Phys.* **21**, 11.

Bahr, G. F., and Zeitler, E. H., eds. (1965). "Quantitative Electron Microscopy." Williams & Wilkins, Baltimore, Maryland.

Brenner, S., and Horne, R. W. (1959). *Biochim. Biophys. Acta* **34**, 103.

Coulter, H. D. (1967). *J. Ultrastruct. Res.* **20**, 346.

Dales, S., and Kajioka, R. (1964). *Virology* **24**, 278.

Dales, S., Gomatos, P. J., and Hsu, K. C. (1965). *Virology* **25**, 193.

Epstein, M. A. (1962). *J. Exptl. Med.* **115**, 1.

Galasso, G. J. (1967). *Proc. Soc. Exptl. Biol. Med.* **124**, 43.

Harris, R. J. C., ed. (1962). "The Interpretation of Ultrastructure." Academic Press, New York.

Horne, R. W. (1961). *In* "Techniques for Electron Microscopy" (D. Kay, ed.), p. 154. Thomas, Springfield, Illinois.

Horne, R. W., Brenner, S., Waterson, A. P., and Wildy, P. (1959). *J. Mol. Biol.* **1**, 84.

Kausche, G. A., Pfankuch, E., and Ruska, H. (1939). *Naturwissenschaften* **27**, 292.

Kay, D., ed. (1961). "Techniques for Electron Microscopy." Thomas, Springfield, Illinois.

Kellenberger, E., and Arber, W. (1957). *Virology* **3**, 245.

Kellenberger, E., and Ryter, A. (1964). *In* "Modern Developments in Electron Microscopy" (B. M. Siegel, ed.), pp. 335-393. Academic Press, New York.

Kellenberger, E., Eiserling, F. A., and Boy de la Tour, E. (1967). *J. Ultrastruct. Res.* **21**, 335.

Kleinschmidt, A. K., and Zahn, R. K. (1959). *Z. Naturforsch.* **14b**, 770.

Leduc, E. H., and Bernhard, W. (1967). *J. Ultrastruct. Res.* **19**, 196.

Luft, J. H. (1961). *J. Biophys. Biochem. Cytol.* **9**, 409.

Magnan, C., (1961). "Traité de Microscopie Électronique," Hermann, Paris.

Maramorosch, K., and Koprowski, H., eds. (1967). "Methods in Virology," Vol. 3. Academic Press, New York.

Mercer, E. H., and Birbeck, M. S. C. (1961). "Electron Microscopy," Thomas, Springfield, Illinois.

Millonig, G. (1961). *J. Appl. Phys.* **32**, 1967.

Mollenhauer, H. H. (1964). *Stain Technol.* **39**, 111.

Palade, G. E. (1952). *J. Exptl. Med.* **95**, 285.

Parsons, D. F. (1963). *J. Cell Biol.* **16**, 620.

Pease, D. C. (1964). "Histological Techniques for Electron Microscopy," 2nd ed. Academic Press, New York.

Pinteric, L., and Taylor, J. (1962). *Virology* **18**, 359.
Porter, K. R. (1964). *In* "Modern Developments in Electron Microscopy" (B. M. Siegel, ed.), pp. 119-145. Academic Press, New York.
Reynolds, E. S. (1963). *J. Cell Biol.* **17**, 208.
Rhim, J. S., Smith, K. O., and Melnick, J. L. (1961). *Virology* **15**, 428.
Riedel, C., and Ruska, H. (1941). *Kolloid-Z.* **96**, 86.
Rifkind, R. A., Hsu, K. C., and Morgan, C. (1964). *J. Histochem. Cytochem.* **12**, 131.
Sabatini, D. D., Bensch, K., and Barrnett, R. J. (1963). *J. Cell Biol.* **17**, 19.
Sabatini, D. D., Miller, F., and Barrnett, R. J. (1964). *J. Histochem. Cytochem.* **12**, 57.
Sharp, D. C. (1949). *Proc. Soc. Exptl. Biol. Med.* **70**, 54.
Sharp, D. G. (1965). *In* "Quantitative Electron Microscopy" (G. F. Bahr and E. H. Zeitler, eds.), pp. 93-125. Williams & Wilkins, Baltimore, Maryland.
Siegel, B. M., ed. (1964). "Modern Developments in Electron Microscopy." Academic Press, New York.
Sjöstrand, F. S. (1967). "Electron Microscopy of Cells and Tissues," Vol. 1, Academic Press. New York.
Smith, K. O., and Melnick, J. L. (1962). *Science* **137**, 543.
Thomas, R. S., and Williams, R. C. (1961). *J. Biophys. Biochem. Cytol.* **11**, 15.
Watson, D. H. (1962). *Biochim Biophys. Acta* **61**, 321.

Subject Index